Element	Symbol	Atomic Number	Atomic
Mendelevium	Md	101	[25
Mercury	Hg	80	20
Molybdenum	Mo	42	9
Neodymium	Nd	60	144
Neon	Ne	10	20
Neptunium	Np	93	[237]
Nickel	Ni	28	58.71
Niobium	Nb	41	92.906
Nitrogen	N	7	14.0067
Nobelium	No	102	[254]
Osmium	Os	76	190.2
Oxygen	O	8	15.9994
Palladium	Pd	46	106.4
Phosphorus	P	15	30.9738
Platinum	Pt	78	195.09
Plutonium	Pu	94	[242]
Polonium	Po	84	[210]
Potassium	K	19	39.102
Praseodymium	Pr	59	140.907
Promethium	Pm	61	[145]
Protoactinium	Pa	91	[231]
Radium	Ra	88	[226]
Radon	Rn	86	[222]
Rhenium	Re	75	186.2
Rhodium	Rh	45	102.905
Rubidium	Rb	37	85.47
Ruthenium	Ru	44	101.07
Samarium	Sm	62	150.35
Scandium	Sc	21	44.956
Selenium	Se	34	78.96
Silicon	Si	14	28.086
Silver	Ag	47	107.870
Sodium	Na	11	22.9898
Strontium	Sr	38	87.62
Sulfur	S	16	32.064
Tantalum	Ta	73	180.948
Technetium	Tc	43	[99]
Tellurium	Te	52	127.60
Terbium	Tb	65	158.924
Thallium	Tl	81	204.37
Thorium	Th	90	232.038
Thulium	Tm	69	168.934
Tin	Sn	50	118.69
Titanium	Ti	22	47.90
Tungsten	W	74	183.85
Uranium	U	92	238.03
Vanadium	V	23	50.942
Xenon	Xe	54	131.30
Ytterbium	Y	39	88.905
Zinc	Zn	30	65.37
Zirconium	Zr	40	91.22

Quantitative Chemical Analysis

Quantitative Chemical Analysis

SECOND EDITION

GILBERT H. AYRES

PROFESSOR OF CHEMISTRY
THE UNIVERSITY OF TEXAS AT AUSTIN

Harper & Row, Publishers

NEW YORK, EVANSTON, AND LONDON

CONTENTS

PART III. TITRIMETRIC METHODS

PART IV. SOME PHYSICOCHEMICAL METHODS

PART V. LABORATORY EXPERIMENTS

APPENDIXES

PREFACE

The fundamental principles of elementary quantitative analysis, both theory and practice, are covered in this textbook. Although the amount of material presented is adequate for a full year's work, the arrangement is such that the subject matter, for both class and laboratory, for a one-semester course can be selected easily.

In recent years great strides have been made in the development of new analytical techniques and sophisticated instrumentation. Obviously, it is impossible, even if it were desirable, to include these newer methods at any considerable depth in the time available for analytical chemistry in the curriculum, without crowding out much of the basic material. In the present edition some new topics have been added and some of the original topics have been expanded, while much of the material of traditional or classical quantitative analysis is still retained. It is the author's belief that quantitative analysis is, foremost, a course in *chemistry*, including principles, reactions, calculations, applications, and techniques. Considering recent trends in the subject-matter coverage in general chemistry, it is all the more important for the course in quantitative analysis to emphasize solutions chemistry, that is, the properties, reactions, equilibrium principles, and applications of ionogens. Furthermore, it is the author's opinion that a textbook for elementary quantitative analysis must give detailed treatment of fundamental principles and methods, with explanations and examples that can be assimilated by the student, without the need for supplementary study from reference books or journals.

A major change in the present edition is the use of the IUPAC (Stockholm) conventions of electrochemistry. A generalized treatment of acid-base equilibria in water solution is given, while the simplified classical approximations are still retained. The concept of ionic strength and activity is discussed and the applications illustrated. A fuller treatment of complex ion equilibria is given. The section on chromatography has been expanded, and a short section on thermogravimetry has been added. A much fuller discussion is given of the interaction of radiant energy and matter. Compensating for these increases in coverage, the descriptive material on the equal-arm balance has been shortened considerably, and the calibration of weights has been deleted. The discussion of specific gravimetric determinations has been condensed considerably.

In the experimental part some simple experiments on separations by liquid-liquid extraction, ion exchange, and thin layer chromatography have been added. In order to meet a growing demand for more "instrumental" methods, the section on spectrophotometry has been expanded to include analysis of a two-component system and also the determination of the composition of a complex by the method of continuous variations and by the mole ratio method; experiments involving potentiometric titration and polarographic analysis have been added.

Some of the problems from the first edition are retained, with answers given; many new problems (without answers) have been added.

The author gratefully acknowledges the comments of many users of the previous edition of this text. Thanks are expressed to his colleagues, Dr. S. H. Simonsen and Dr. A. J. Bard, for their wholehearted cooperation and valuable suggestions on teaching a beginning course in analytical chemistry based on this text. The author owes a special debt of gratitude to Dr. Bard for his suggestion of the organization of the chapter on electroanalysis and his generous help with the treatment of the topics included. My thanks go also to my wife, Katherine, for her forbearance during preparation of this edition and for sharing in the task of proofreading the manuscript.

GILBERT H. AYRES

Austin, Texas
December, 1967

Part I □ Fundamental Principles

1

THE SCOPE, AIMS, AND METHODS OF QUANTITATIVE ANALYSIS

Analytical chemistry deals with the detection of the kinds (qualitative analysis) and the measurement of the amounts (quantitative analysis) of substances present in samples of material. Analytical chemistry includes not only the manipulative techniques, but also the theoretical considerations upon which separations, detections, and measurements are based.

In many respects analytical chemistry is the foundation upon which other branches of chemistry build. Chemical reactions are studied on the basis of the qualitative and quantitative changes that occur; new compounds are identified by analysis; the law of definite proportions and the law of multiple proportions resulted from a study of the quantitative relations in the combination of elements to form compounds; Faraday's law is a statement of the quantitative relation between the amount of electricity and the chemical change associated with it; and so on for the other laws of chemistry.

Although analytical chemistry is not a new branch of science, there has been very rapid development of new methods of analysis since about the third or fourth decade of the present century. These developments have come largely through necessity owing to the rapid expansion of the industrial economy, as well as the extensive growth of research programs in many fields. Quantitative analysis is required in a wide variety of technical and commercial operations: agriculture, foods, drugs, mining, metallurgy, water supply, waste disposal, manufactured products of almost infinite variety, etc. There is scarcely a material related to modern living in which analytical chemistry did not play some part.

The analytical chemist must be well trained in the other branches of chemistry as well, and to an increasing extent also in mathematics and physics. Distinction

3

should be made between a "chemical analyst" and an "analytical chemist." The former is a "determinator," with little or no scientific knowledge, who follows prescribed directions in performing certain operations that will, if everything goes according to plan, produce a "result." The analytical chemist interprets results, modifies existing methods as circumstances warrant, and develops new methods. He must be inquisitive, and sometimes skeptical. He must be scrupulously honest, for upon the results of his work may depend the success of an industrial venture, or even the lives of many individuals. He must have patience, ingenuity, and perseverance. Analytical chemistry is a challenging field of endeavor, calling for the best efforts of a well-trained individual; career opportunities are attractive in industrial and in academic areas.

THE AIMS OF QUANTITATIVE ANALYSIS

The primary objective of a course in quantitative analysis is to teach the *chemistry* of the subject, which includes fundamental principles, chemical reactions, applications, techniques, and calculations. A thorough understanding of the principles, reactions, limitations, and sources of error is indispensable to intelligent, efficient performance of the laboratory work. The course in quantitative analysis extends the knowledge and training of the student into new areas. The principles and methods have a direct utility as part of the pre-professional training of students who will enter chemistry, engineering, medicine, pharmacy, metallurgy, geology, and many other fields. But even for students who will not enter these fields, there is an educational value in acquiring knowledge of the subject matter and in getting some further experience in scientific methods. An interested and apt student will develop neatness and orderliness of thought as well as action; he will develop patience, self-reliance, and integrity. The extent to which these objectives are realized is very largely dependent upon the student's attitude toward the subject and the work to be done; the rewards are well worth the effort.

METHODS OF QUANTITATIVE ANALYSIS

Quantitative analysis in its various aspects may be considered from several points of view, such as the materials analyzed, the methods employed, the scale (magnitude) of the desired constituent in the sample, and so on.

1. Inorganic and Organic Analysis. Usually the first course in quantitative analysis deals primarily with the analysis of inorganic materials, and the analysis of organic substances (carbon compounds) is reserved for later study. The fundamental principles are much the same, regardless of the inorganic or organic nature of the sample.

2. Partial or Complete Analysis. For many purposes it may be adequate to measure only one or a few components of the sample; for example, the analysis of a copper ore for copper content is a **partial** analysis. A **complete** analysis involves the measurement of all components of the sample that can be detected by sensitive qualitative tests.

3. Proximate and Ultimate Analysis. The **proximate** analysis of a sample consists in the measurement of substances that react alike to a certain treatment or reagent. For example, weight loss on ignition of a limestone includes all changes in weight that occur when the sample is heated strongly, such as volatilization of water, carbon dioxide, sulfur dioxide, and organic matter, as well as oxidation of sulfides to sulfates and of lower to higher oxides. The "R_2O_3" or "mixed oxides" analysis in limestone includes all substances precipitated by ammonia; the ignited precipitate may contain Fe_2O_3, Al_2O_3, TiO_2, $FePO_4$, MnO_2, and other substances. In an **ultimate** analysis, sometimes called elemental analysis, the content of each element is measured; for example, in the ultimate analysis of nitrobenzene, $C_6H_5NO_2$, the percentage of carbon, hydrogen, nitrogen, and oxygen is determined.

4. The Scale of Analysis. Analytical methods are sometimes classified on the basis of the size of sample ordinarily taken or the amount of material that is measured. The limits given below are not to be considered rigid, but only approximate.

a. Macro: 0.1 to 1 or 2 g of sample.

b. Semimicro: about 0.01 to 0.05 g (10 to 50 mg) of sample.

c. Micro: 1 to a few milligrams of sample. A micro balance, sensitive to about 0.001 mg, and diminutive laboratory ware are used. This scale of analysis is best called *milligram analysis*.

d. Ultramicro, or *microgram*, analysis determines an amount of material of the order of a few micrograms (0.001 mg = 1 μg, sometimes referred to as "gamma," γ). Microgram analysis can be applied either to the analysis of traces of substances in large samples or to the analysis of very small samples.

The size of sample taken for analysis will depend not only upon the scale of analysis to be used, but also upon the content of the constituent to be measured. For example, if macro-analysis methods were to be used, the determination of a major constituent (above about 1%) would ordinarily require samples in the range of 0.1 to 1 g, whereas the analysis for a minor constituent (about 1% down to 0.01%) would require a sample of 1 to 10 g. For minor constituent and trace analysis, it is often practical to take a macro sample, but make the final measurement by a semimicro or a micro method. For any given scale of analysis, major constituents are usually determined with greater accuracy than are minor constituents. The accuracy demanded will depend upon the importance and use attached to the results.

5. Methods of Analysis. Quantitative methods may be classified by the measurement method employed; an outline of several important methods is given in the following section. When alternative methods are available for measurement of a given substance, the choice of method requires consideration. Suppose, for example, that a substance can be determined by gravimetric, titrimetric, or colorimetric methods of reliability sufficient for the purpose at hand. Which method should be used? The choice involves a consideration of the number of samples to be run, the range of variation of the content of the desired constituent in the sample, the time required, and perhaps other factors. In general, titrimetric and colorimetric procedures are more rapid than gravimetric, once the standardization of titrant or the calibration of the colorimetric method has been made, provided there is little or no difference in removal of interferences (or other preparative treatment) before measurement can be made. If only a few samples are to be analyzed, perhaps the gravimetric method, usually more tedious, would be more economical of the analyst's time.

Classification of Methods

A classification, much used in the past, into the two categories, **noninstrumental** (e.g., titrimetric, gravimetric) and **instrumental** (e.g., colorimetric, potentiometric), is scarcely adequate. Burets, pipets, and volumetric flasks are instruments, regardless of their simplicity; the analytical balance, used in one way or another in nearly every analysis, is a precision instrument capable of measuring relative masses (weights) of one part per ten thousand to one part per hundred thousand or more. Another classification into **chemical** and **physical** methods leaves something to be desired; many of the so-called physical methods involve chemical preparative steps before the measurement is made; this class of methods is better called "physicochemical." The above comments indicate the inadequacy of trying to include widely divergent methods into only a few categories, with names that may lead to ambiguity.

Some of the more common methods, listed below, represent the variety of principles that can be used as a basis for measuring the amount of desired constituent present in a sample. In a beginning course in quantitative analysis, only a few of these methods are covered, the emphasis being on gravimetric precipitation and on titrimetric methods; most of the other methods are reserved for later study, after the student has acquired a background of physical chemistry.

1. Gravimetric Methods. The amount of substance sought is determined by the weight of the pure substance itself, or some definite compound containing the substance or chemically equivalent to it.

a. Precipitation. The desired constituent is determined as an insoluble product of a reaction; the method is chemical because *definite stoichiometric (weight) relations are involved.* An example is the determination of chloride by precipitation as silver chloride, the weight of which is determined.

b. Electrodeposition. Electrolysis causes the separation of a solid product on an electrode, as in the electrolytic determination of copper.

c. Volatilization. The method may be physical, as the loss in weight in oven drying, or chemical, as in the expulsion of carbon dioxide from carbonates by heating or by the action of an acid. The measurement may be direct, by determining the weight increase of an absorbent for the volatile constituent, or indirect, by determining the weight loss.

2. Volumetric Methods. The determination is made by measuring the volume of some phase quantitatively related to the desired constituent.

a. Titrimetric methods.[1] Measurement is made of the volume of a solution of known concentration that is required to interact exactly with the desired constituent, or with another substance chemically equivalent to it. *Definite reaction stoichiometry* is involved. Titrimetric methods may be further classified by the type of reaction involved (neutralization, precipitation, redox, etc.) and by methods of indicating the end point (color indicators, electrical methods).

b. Gasometric methods. Determination is made by measuring the volume of gas at known or at constant conditions of temperature and pressure. Gasometric methods may be further classified as (1) **evolution** methods, as in the Dumas method for nitrogen content of compounds by conversion to nitrogen gas, the volume of which is measured; or (2) **absorption** methods, in which the quantity measured is the decrease in gas volume when a component is absorbed in a suitable absorbent. Chemical reaction may or may not be involved. This method is sometimes called merely "gas analysis."

c. The volume of a liquid or of a solid contained in or formed from a sample may be measured. For example, water in some types of samples can be determined by distillation with an immiscible solvent; the volume of water in the distillate is measured. Sodium may be determined by precipitating the "triple acetate" (sodium magnesium uranyl acetate), which is settled into the narrow graduated stem of a centrifuge tube, and measuring the volume of the precipitate.

3. Systemic Property Methods (Physicochemical Methods). Measurement is made, on the *system* under observation, of some property that is quantitatively related to the amount of desired constituent in the sample from which the system is derived. Calibration, either directly or indirectly against standards, is required in these methods. Many of these methods are based upon either optical or electrical phenomena; two types of methods are mentioned below.

a. Optical methods. These are based upon the properties of radiant energy and its behavior upon interaction with the system being measured. Several kinds of optical properties can be measured for analytical purposes. Colorimetry and spectrophotometry are based on the fact that radiant energy is absorbed by the system in proportion to its content of absorbing material.

---

[1] The titrimetric method was originally called "volumetric" analysis, and the term is still used by some writers; volumetric is a generic term, whereas titrimetric is specific for a method involving a titration process.

b. Electrical methods. Although certain electrical properties of a system are quantitatively related to its composition, electrical methods are often applied to detect abrupt changes that occur in the system under observation as a result of chemical reaction. For example, rapid or abrupt changes in certain electrical properties usually occur at the end point of a titration.

2

THE ANALYTICAL
BALANCE AND ITS USE

The amount of a certain substance in the sample is usually expressed as a weight percent. Regardless of the method used for measurement of the desired constituent, the weight of the sample must be known; if the determination is finished gravimetrically, the weight of the product containing (or equivalent to) the desired constituent must be measured; in titrimetric finish methods, accurate weights of primary standards are required in the preparation of standard solutions. The analytical balance is the analyst's most important tool or instrument, and mass is one of the fundamental quantities. The analytical balance is unique in having a high ratio of capacity to sensitivity; it can weigh up to 200 g to the nearest 0.1 mg, a precision of one part in two million; few other instruments approach this degree of precision. The analytical balance is a somewhat delicate instrument that will not stand abuse, but with proper care it will render excellent and long service.

Mass and Weight. The **mass** of an object is a measure of the amount of material in that object, and is invariant. The **weight** of an object is a measure of the force exerted on it by the earth's gravitational attraction. Because the force of gravity varies with latitude on the earth's surface and with elevation, the weight of an object is variable. The mass of an object is measured by comparing its weight with that of a known mass. For a constant value of the force of gravity, masses are proportional to weights. An analytical balance determines *mass*, because gravity exerts the same force on the object and the weights. For convenience, the term *weight* is used as identical with mass; although not strictly correct, the practice is permissible if the distinction is understood and is used where necessary.

9

TYPES OF BALANCES

Construction

The equal-arm analytical balance consists essentially of a beam supported at its center by a bearing or fulcrum, so that it operates as a simple lever. From each end of the beam, at points equidistant from the central fulcrum, there is suspended a pan to carry the object and the weights. The object (placed on the left pan) has the same mass as the weights (placed on the right pan) when the beam is in a horizontal position, showing that the gravitational forces acting on the two arms of the lever are equal. The position of the beam with respect to the horizontal is shown by a pointer, attached to the beam and perpendicular to its length, in reference to a scale with a center mark directly below the central fulcrum.

An excellent discussion of the fundamentals of the analytical balance has been given by Evans.[1]

In principle of construction and operation, most balances do not differ essentially from that given above. Changes in certain mechanical features have been incorporated to permit more rapid weighing.

1. Equal-Arm Balance. The functional parts of an equal-arm rider balance are illustrated in Fig. 2-1. The entire balance mechanism is enclosed in a case to protect the balance when not in use, as well as to eliminate air currents when making a weighing; the front window may be raised and lowered to place objects and weights on the pans. Leveling of the balance is accomplished by screw legs on the case; spirit levels in the base show when it is level.

On the **chain-weight balance** the rider is eliminated, and small increments of weight are added by means of a small metal chain, one end of which is attached to the right-hand arm of the balance; the other end of the chain is attached to a device, operated by a wheel on the right end of the balance case, that can be moved to vary the effective weight of the chain loop operating on the balance arm. A scale and vernier registers the effective weight of the chain, the full value of which is 100 mg.

On the **notched-beam balance** the top of the beam is notched, at appropriate intervals along its length, to receive a dumbbell rider that adds weight in 0.1-g increments, up to 1 g. In combination with a 100-mg chain, this balance requires no separate fractional weights.

Another balance design adds fractional weights by means of a **keyboard** operated from the front of the case.

Readings of swings across the pointer scale, for determination of zero point and rest points, can be eliminated by incorporating a magnetic or air dash-pot **damping** device to retard oscillations so the pointer comes to rest in a short

[1] W. D. Evans, *J. Chem. Educ.*, **32**, 419–421 (1955).

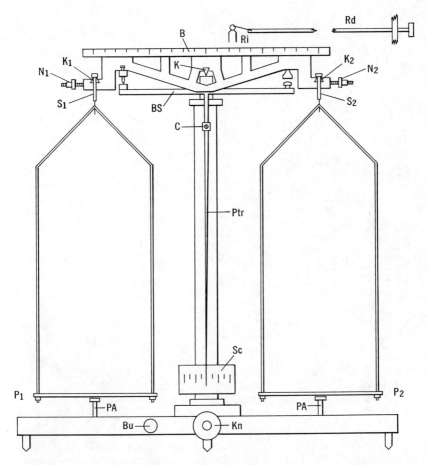

Fig. 2-1 Diagram of equal-arm rider balance. B, beam; K, central knife
edge; P_1, P_2, pans, supported by stirrups S_1, S_2, with bearings resting on
terminal knife edges K_1, K_2; N_1, N_2, nuts for adjusting horizontal
equilibrium; Kn, knob to control beam support BS; PA, pan arrests,
operated by button Bu; Ptr, pointer, which moves across scale Sc when
beam is in motion; C, "bob" to adjust center of gravity; Ri, rider, placed
on beam by operation of rod Rd.

time. When a damped balance is used, the operator should determine the minimum time required for the equilibrium position to be reached.

A chain-weight, notched-beam, magnetically damped balance is shown in
Fig. 2-2.

2. Single-Pan Balance. This balance design makes for very rapid weighing
by using the substitution principle. The balance pan and weights are suspended

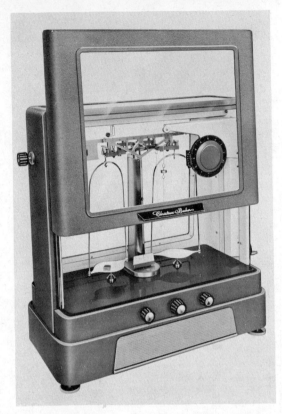

Fig. 2-2 Chainomatic, notched-beam, magnetically damped balance. (Courtesy of Christian Becker Division of The Torsion Balance Co.)

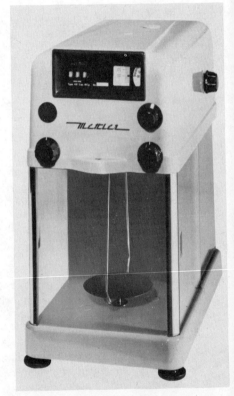

Fig. 2-3 Single-pan, constant-load analytical balance. (Courtesy of Mettler Instrument Corp.)

from the same end of the beam, which is counterpoised on the opposite end and is damped by an air dash-pot. To weigh an object on the pan, weights are *removed* from the beam, to restore its original position, by operating knobs on the panel until the next unit removed would be too much; the total of the weights is registered on a dial. The weight difference corresponding to the difference between this rest position and the zero point of the beam is indicated on an optical projection scale the full range of which corresponds to the smallest weight on the beam. (In the Mettler Type H5 or H6 balance, full optical scale represents 1000 mg.) By means of an index and vernier, the optical scale is read to 0.1 mg. Some models have a digital readout of the final adjustment. Use of a linear projection scale for indicating the final weight increments, regardless of the weight of the object, is possible because the beam always has the same

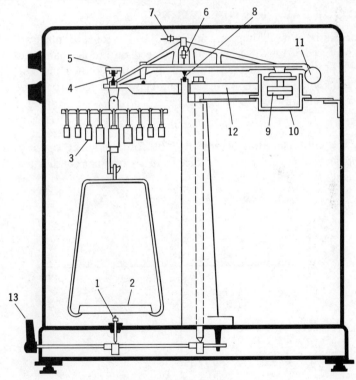

Fig. 2-4 Diagram of single-pan, constant-load balance. 1, pan brake; 2, pan; 3, set of weights; 4, sapphire knife edge; 5, stirrup for hangers and weights; 6, movable weight for adjustment of sensitivity; 7, movable weight for initial adjustment of zero point; 8, main knife edge (sapphire); 9, counterweight; 10, air damper; 11, engraved optical scale; 12, lifting device; 13, arrest lever. (Courtesy of Mettler Instrument Corp.)

total load, and therefore constant sensitivity. However, by operating always at maximum load, the balance is also operating at minimum sensitivity.

A balance of the type just described is pictured in Fig. 2-3, and is shown schematically in Fig. 2-4.

For small-scale work, a micro balance of about 10-g capacity, and reliability to one microgram or better, is required. For the calibration of volumetric flasks by weight, a balance should be available having a capacity of 2 kg; weights are taken to the nearest milligram, or sometimes only to the nearest 10 mg. Every laboratory should be equipped with some type of platform balance or a "trip scale," for rough weighing of chemicals; weighings to the nearest 0.1 g are adequate.

THEORY OF BALANCE OPERATION

The principle of weighing with an equal-arm balance is illustrated in Fig. 2-5. If an object of mass (weight) M_1 is placed on the left-hand pan, the displacement of the beam can be restored by adding known masses (weights), M_2, to the right-hand pan until the pointer returns to its original position. The forces acting on the two lever arms are

$$F_1 = M_1 g \quad \text{and} \quad F_2 = M_2 g$$

where g is the acceleration of gravity. The force moment is the product of force and lever arm; when the balance is in its original equilibrium position, the moments are equal, that is,

$$F_1 L_1 = F_2 L_2 \quad \text{or} \quad M_1 g L_1 = M_2 g L_2$$

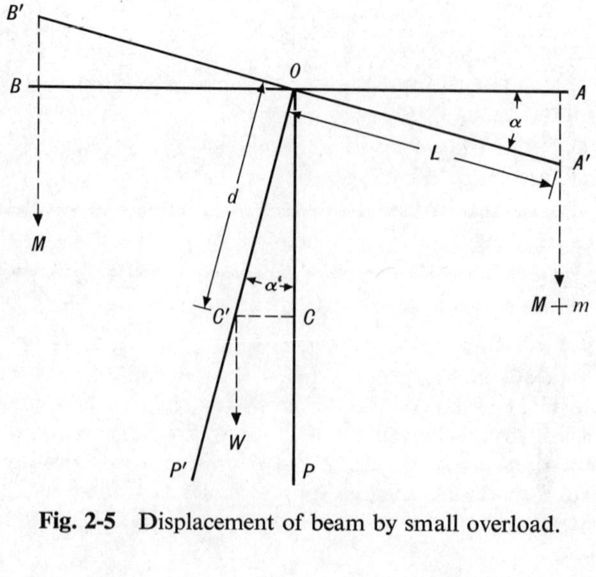

Fig. 2-5 Displacement of beam by small overload.

If $L_1 = L_2$ (balance arms of equal length), then $F_1 = F_2$ and $M_1 = M_2$, since g is constant. In fact, F_1 is the weight of the object, since weight is a measure of the gravitational force exerted on the object of mass M_1.

The **sensitivity** of a balance, which is the pointer deflection produced by a small excess weight on one pan, is dependent upon several features of construction or adjustment of the balance. Consider a balance in its horizontal equilibrium position, either with no load, or with equal loads, M, on each pan. If, now, a small overload m is added to the right arm, the beam and pointer will rotate through an angle α to a new equilibrium position. From the geometry of Fig. 2-5, it can be shown that

$$\tan \alpha = \frac{mL}{Wd} \cong \alpha$$

where m is the overload, L is the length of balance arm, W is the weight of the moving system, and d is the distance from the point of support to the center of gravity. When the angle α is small, the tangent of the angle may be taken equal to the angle itself, which is proportional to the distance measured by the displacement PP' of the pointer across the scale. This formula shows directly the influence of four factors on the sensitivity of a balance. The student should know this formula as an aid to understanding the performance of a balance; specific reference to it will be made in the next section.

REQUISITES OF AN ANALYTICAL BALANCE

The requisites of an analytical balance and the construction features upon which each requirement depends are given below.

1. The balance must be **accurate**; that is, it must give correct results in repeated weighings of the same object, and it must retain its original horizontal position when equal masses are placed on each pan. For the balance to be accurate, the following conditions of construction must be fulfilled.

a. The balance arms must be of equal length, within a few parts per million. When weighings are made by difference, no net error results from a slight inequality of the balance arms because the individual errors cancel. When absolute masses are needed, account must be taken of any balance arm inequality. (See Weighing by Transposition, p. 18.)

b. All three knife edges must lie in the same plane and must be parallel to one another.

2. The balance should be **sensitive**, that is, it should respond to very small differences in weight. The **sensitivity** of a balance is determined by the pointer displacement, in scale divisions, produced by a given small overload on one pan. The sensitivity of a balance depends upon the following factors, as shown by the formulation $\alpha = mL/Wd$ developed above.

a. The displacement of the pointer is directly proportional to the amount of the overload *m*, provided the overload is small. For ordinary analytical balances an overload of 1 mg is used for the determination of sensitivity.

b. The sensitivity is directly proportional to the length *L* of the balance arm. Other things being equal, long-arm balances are more sensitive than short-arm balances.

c. The sensitivity is inversely proportional to the weight *W* of the moving system (beam, pans, and load). The smaller this weight, the greater the sensitivity. Balance parts are therefore made, as far as possible, from lightweight metals such as aluminum or aluminum-magnesium alloys. In going from no load to capacity load (200 g) the sensitivity should not decrease by more than 40 to 50%.

d. The sensitivity is inversely proportional to the distance *d* of the center of gravity below the point of support; the shorter this distance, the greater the sensitivity.

e. Friction should be minimum; as friction increases, sensitivity decreases. Careful operation of the balance is required to prevent damage to the knife edges. The bearing surfaces must be kept free from dust; occasional cleaning with a camel's-hair brush should be done by a person knowing the proper procedure.

3. The balance should be **rapid**, so that the time consumed in taking readings of swings is not unduly great. The **period** of a balance is the time required for the pointer to move from one turning point to the opposite turning point.

4. The balance must be **stable**, so that, after the beam is set in motion, it will oscillate about and return to its original position. This condition is fulfilled if the center of gravity of the moving system is *below* the point of support.

Because several of these conditions are incompatible, a compromise between the maximum effects of the various features is required to construct a balance that is sufficiently sensitive and rapid for the work at hand. Most analytical balances have 10-in. beams (5-in. arms), a sensitivity of 20 to 40 scale points (2 to 4 divisions on the scale, read to the nearest 0.1 division), and a period of 5 to 10 seconds. The sensitivity of a given balance is largely fixed in its manufacture; the center of gravity can be changed slightly by changing the position of the small bob attached to the pointer. There is a practical limit, however, to which the sensitivity may be increased by raising the center of gravity, because the oscillation period becomes very long, the sensitivity change with load becomes greater, and the maximum overload that can be used with the method of swings is very small. The sensitivity of a balance will remain constant over long periods of time, provided the bearings are not damaged. The sensitivity of a balance must *never* be changed by a student using it; if it should become necessary to adjust the sensitivity, this shall be done *only* by an instructor, who knows how to do it properly and who will notify other students using the same balance so that its sensitivity can be redetermined by all users.

THE WEIGHING OPERATION

Every weighing operation[2] with an equal-arm balance involves a determination of the equilibrium position of the beam, as indicated by the pointer position on the scale, for the empty balance (zero point) and for the load being weighed (rest point), and application of the sensitivity of the balance for the load. Experiment 34-1 gives detailed directions with illustrative examples for the determination of the sensitivity of the equal-arm balance and for the weighing operation.

Rest Point Methods

Different methods have been used for the determination of what might be called a "practical" zero point and rest point, for use in the weighing operation. Some of these methods are outlined below.

1. Method of Swings. This method is illustrated in detail in Experiment 34-1. It is believed to be the most reliable for beginners, and is in fact used by many experienced analysts. It is the method always used for the calibration of weights.

2. Method of Deflection. Deflection is defined as "the other point of inflection (turning point) of an ideal swing having zero for one point of inflection." Swings are read as + and − on either side of scale zero (center). The deflection is the *algebraic sum* of the mean positive and mean negative readings.

3. Restoring the Rest Point (or the Deflection). By trial and error, the rider (or chain) is adjusted to give a rest point (or a deflection) that coincides with the zero point (or zero deflection). The method is a wasteful consumption of time. However, after calculating the final 0.1 mg by the method of swings and the sensitivity, the rider (or chain) may be placed at the calculated position and the rest point coincidence with the zero point determined by swings, as a check on the previous determination of the weight.

4. Method of Short Swings. The rider (or chain) is adjusted, by trial and error, until the pointer swings an equal distance on each side of the scale center. The procedure is time consuming.

Methods of Weighing

1. Direct Weighing. This method is satisfactory for ordinary analytical work, where weights of samples, precipitates, etc., are obtained by difference.

---

[2] Sound movies on the use of the equal-arm balance are available from the University of Minnesota and from the University of Wisconsin. A sound color film, "The Modern Balance," is available on loan from Mettler Instrument Corporation and many of its dealer representatives; the film may also be purchased for a nominal sum.

If the balance arms are unequal and absolute masses are required, the determined weight can be corrected by use of the balance arm ratio, determined by weighing by transposition as described in item 3 below.

2. Weighing by Substitution. The object is placed on either pan of the balance, and counterpoised by any suitable tare, such as spare weights, sand, and lead shot, on the opposite pan. The object is then removed, and weights are placed on that pan to counterpoise the tare exactly. The objects and the weights are then identical (neglecting air buoyancy effects), having been compared on the same balance arm against the tare. The procedure, known as Borda's method, is the simplest way to avoid errors due to inequality of the balance arms. It is one of the methods often used in the calibration of weights, and it is the basic principle of operation of the single-pan balance.

3. Weighing by Transposition (Double Weighing). If the balance arms are unequal, the true weight of an object can be obtained by weighing it first on one pan and then on the other pan.

If M = true mass of the object,
  W_1 = weights on left pan with object on right pan,
  W_2 = weights on right pan with object on left pan,
  L_1 = length of left balance arm,
  L_2 = length of right balance arm,

then, by the principle of moments,

$$ML_1 = W_2 L_2 \tag{2-1}$$

$$ML_2 = W_1 L_1 \tag{2-2}$$

Multiplying (2-1) by (2-2) gives

$$M^2 L_1 L_2 = W_1 W_2 L_1 L_2$$

from which

$$M = \sqrt{W_1 W_2}$$

If the balance arms are nearly equal, then W_1 and W_2 are nearly identical, and a satisfactory approximation is given by $M = \frac{1}{2}(W_1 + W_2)$, that is, the mass of the object is the average of the two weights.

The ratio of the balance arms can be calculated by dividing equation (2-1) by equation (2-2), which gives

$$L_1/L_2 = \sqrt{W_2/W_1}$$

The method of weighing by transposition, known as the method of Gauss, is capable of twice the precision of the method of substitution, and is often used in the calibration of weights.

4. Weighing with a Single-Pan Balance.   This method is described in Experiment 34-1.

WEIGHTS

The unit of mass in the metric system is the **gram**, which is 1/1000 of the mass of the standard kilogram represented by a platinum-iridium alloy kept at the International Bureau of Weights and Measures near Paris. The kilogram is the mass of 1000 cc of water at its temperature of maximum density.[3] Analytical weights are reference masses used to determine the weights of objects. For student use, the largest denomination in most sets is 100 or 50 g and the smallest is 10 or 5 mg; the smallest weight need be no smaller than the rider on the balance to be used.

Classes.   Different classes of weights are used for different purposes, depending upon the accuracy required. The National Bureau of Standards establishes tolerances for different classes of weights, as well as specifications of materials and design (N.B.S. Circular 547, Section 1, "Precision Laboratory Standards of Mass and Laboratory Weights," August 20, 1954). The classifications include:

Class M: reference standards, to be used only for calibration of other weights. The integral weights are of one-piece construction, and are usually plated with rhodium, platinum, or gold to prevent corrosion; fractional weights are of platinum, gold, or tantalum.

Class S: for analytical work of the highest precision, and for routine calibration of other weights.

Class S-1: for routine analytical work. Tolerances are from 2 to 5 times those for Class S, depending on the weight denomination.

Class P (formerly Class S-2): "rough" weights, for routine work requiring only moderate accuracy. Tolerances are twice those for Class S-1.

Calibration of Weights

When much importance is attached to the analytical work performed, the weights used should be calibrated, and the calibration should be repeated once or twice a year if the weights are used much. For the determination of fundamental chemical values, it is necessary to know the absolute masses of the various weights used. Most analytical results, however, are derived from weight ratios; it is therefore unnecessary to know the absolute masses of the weights, but it is necessary that the weights have the proper ratio to one another, or that the

---

[3] Originally the kilogram was established as the mass of 1000 cc of water at 4°C, thought to be its temperature of maximum density. More careful determination showed the temperature of maximum density to be 3.98°C. At this temperature, the volume of 1 kg of water is 1000.028 cc. For most purposes, the difference, only about 3 parts per hundred thousand, is of no significance.

magnitude of the deviations from the proper ratio is known. For example, in most analytical work it is not necessary that the " 10-g " weight have an absolute mass of 10.00000 g, but it should have a mass exactly ten times as large as the 1-g weight, five times as large as the 2-g weight, and so on. If this condition is not fulfilled, then the magnitude of any discrepancy from the proper ratio of the nominal values must be known so that corrections can be applied, to give corrected values that are in exactly the same ratio as the nominal values 1, 2, 3, 5, 10, etc.

The calibration procedure commonly used is known as the method of Richards,[4] and makes use of the substitution method of weighing. The details can be found in the original publication or in the first edition of this text.[5]

ERRORS IN WEIGHING

The principal sources of error, and methods of eliminating or correcting for them, are as follows:

1. Inequality of Balance Arms.   In the direct method of weighing, the error due to unequal balance arms can be corrected by applying the balance arm ratio, or the error can be eliminated by use of the substitution method or the transposition method of weighing.

2. Knife Edges Nonplanar or Nonparallel.   These conditions are inherent in the balance construction, and there is no simple means of correcting for them. Because most weighings are done by difference and the differences are usually small, errors due to nonplanar or nonparallel knife edges are insignificant.

3. Inaccurate Weights.   This source of error is eliminated by using calibrated weights.

4. Temperature Effects.   The object to be weighed must be at balance-room

---

[4] T. W. Richards, *J. Am. Chem. Soc.*, **22**, 144 (1900).

[5] In the author's opinion the calibration of a set of weights should not be assigned at the beginning of a first course in quantitative analysis. The reasons are as follows: (1) The calibration is very time-consuming and tedious for a person inexperienced in the use of the balance. (2) A good calibration requires a balance of higher sensitivity than may be available for student use in beginning courses. (3) The "corrections" found by the student are often so far in error that their use results in larger errors than if no corrections were applied. These errors originate from inexperience in reading the pointer scale, from faulty simple arithmetic in computing rest points, and in application of weight differences in the wrong direction. Any error made in the early stages of the calibration procedure snowballs to a relatively enormous value in the larger pieces of the set. It is a huge task for the instructor to check all the details of weight calibration for all students in a large class. In the author's classes, the mistakes made by the student are detected by careful scrutiny of the record made in the practice weighing in Experiment 34-1, and in the reported weight of the brass block, the accurate weight of which is known to the instructor.

If weights are not calibrated by the student, the integral weight sets used by the classes should be checked periodically against a standard set, and the weights readjusted if significant errors are found.

temperature. The balance should be placed where no direct sunlight strikes it at any time; it should not be located near a radiator nor the outlet of an air conditioner. Provided the material being weighed is stable, a creeping rest point of a balance usually indicates uneven temperature change of the beam.

5. Electrification. Glass surfaces may acquire static electric charges when wiped with a cloth. If weighed in this condition, charges may be induced on the surrounding surfaces and cause the beam to swing erratically. When relatively large glass vessels must be wiped before weighing, it is best to use a damp cloth, then allow the vessel to stand until the surface moisture evaporates to equilibrium with the air. Electrification effects are most pronounced in air of low humidity.

6. Substances Taken from the Atmosphere. Absorption of moisture and/or carbon dioxide from the air can give rise to large errors in weighing certain materials unless closed containers (weighing bottles, covered crucibles) are used. All solid surfaces will adsorb moisture, the amount depending principally upon the extent of the surface and upon the relative humidity. Because of their large specific surface, finely divided solids readily adsorb moisture, and should be weighed in closed containers. Samples that have been dried and precipitates that have been ignited are stored in a dry atmosphere (desiccator) before weighing. When the vessels are transferred from the desiccator to the balance, the surfaces may adsorb moisture from the air and produce weighing errors. The error is most conveniently eliminated by using another vessel, of the same size and shape, as a tare in all weighing operations; the vessel and the tare are exposed to the same conditions, and the errors due to adsorption of moisture cancel. The use of a tare has the additional advantage of canceling buoyancy errors (see item 7.)

7. Buoyancy Effects. Any solid body immersed in a fluid (liquid or gas) is buoyed up by a force equal to the weight of the fluid displaced (principle of Archimedes). If an object being weighed has a density different from that of the weights used to counterbalance it, the object and the weights occupy different volumes and displace different weights of air. The object therefore has a different apparent weight in air than if it were weighed in vacuum.

The effect of buoyancy is illustrated in Fig. 2-6. An object of density less than that of the weights is exactly counterbalanced in air. Each pan is buoyed up by a force equal to the weight of air displaced by the substance on it; these different buoyancy forces are represented by the lengths of the arrows under the pans in Fig 2-6(*a*). Now, suppose the balance to be enclosed in an airtight case and connected to a vacuum pump and the air exhausted. The buoyancy forces previously operating are no longer present, and the left pan moves down, as in Fig. 2-6(*b*). Additional weight would have to be placed on the right pan to restore the horizontal position of the beam. Thus, the weight of the object in

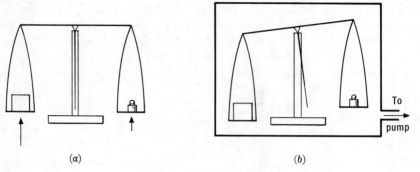

(a)   (b)

Fig. 2-6   Buoyancy effect.

vacuum is greater than its weight in air. If the object on the left pan is more dense than the weights, the converse situation prevails, and the vacuum weight of the object is less than its air weight.

The calculation of vacuum weight is made as follows.

Let W_v = weight of object in vacuum,

W_a = weight of object (and of weights) in air,

B_o = buoyancy of object,

B_w = buoyancy of weights,

D_o = density of object,

D_w = density of weights,

D_a = density of air.

Then

$$W_v = W_a + B_o - B_w$$

But

$$B_o = D_a W_a / D_o \quad \text{and} \quad B_w = D_a W_a / D_w$$

Hence

$$W_v = W_a + \frac{D_a W_a}{D_o} - \frac{D_a W_a}{D_w}$$

$$= W_a + D_a W_a \left(\frac{1}{D_o} - \frac{1}{D_w} \right)$$

$$= W_a \left[1 + D_a \left(\frac{1}{D_o} - \frac{1}{D_w} \right) \right]$$

Thus, when $D_o < D_w$, $1/D_o > 1/D_w$, the buoyancy term has a positive sign, and $W_v > W_a$.

The weight of 1 cc of air at 0°C and a pressure of 760 mm of mercury is 0.001293 g. At ordinary room temperatures and at altitudes less than about a thousand feet above sea level, a value of 0.0012 g/cc for the density of air is sufficiently accurate for most purposes.

An illustrative calculation will show how the reduction to vacuum weight is made.

Problem: What is the vacuum weight of water (density 1.00) which weighs 10.0000 g in air against brass weights (density 8.4)?

Solution:

$$W_v = 10.0000 + 10.0 \times 0.0012\left(\frac{1}{1.00} - \frac{1}{8.4}\right)$$

$$= 10.0000 + 0.012(1.00 - 0.12)$$

$$= 10.0000 + 0.012(0.88)$$

$$= 10.0000 + 0.0106 = 10.0106 \text{ g}$$

The buoyancy correction for 10 g of water is slightly more than 10 mg or about one part per thousand.

Most of the substances weighed in making a quantitative analysis are more dense than water; the samples taken and the precipitates weighed are usually of the order of only a few to several tenths of a gram, and the weights are taken by difference. In ordinary gravimetric work, therefore, buoyancy corrections are well below the limit of accuracy of the weighings.

When weights by difference are used, buoyancy errors can be eliminated by weighing against a tare identical with the container and preferably filled to about the same extent with the same substance as is being weighed.

In the calibration of volumetric flasks by the weight of water contained, buoyancy corrections must be applied in the calibration of flasks of capacity 25 ml or greater, because the buoyancy effects are greater than the calibration tolerance. From the previous example, it is noted that the buoyancy effect on 1000 g (approximately one liter) of water against brass weights is 1.06 g. Failure to take this correction into account would result in an error of more than 1 ml on a 1-liter volumetric flask; the calibration tolerance is only 0.30 ml.

In weighing substances in tightly closed containers (weighing bottles), it is very important that the air in the container is at the same temperature and pressure as the surrounding air. At temperatures near 25°C, a difference of 1°C between the temperature inside and outside a 25-ml stoppered container corresponds to an error of 0.1 mg in the weight. Vessels that have been tightly stoppered before reaching temperature equilibrium with the surroundings should be unstoppered momentarily to equalize the inside pressure of air with that outside.

PROBLEMS

In these problems it is assumed that the pointer scale is read by the method in which the center mark is designated 100, so that the space between adjacent marks has a value of 10 units, and that the weighing is made with the object on the left pan and weights on the right pan, unless otherwise stated. See Appendix VI for densities of substances involved in making buoyancy corrections.

2-1 Readings of swings with a 10-g load on each balance pan: 82, 145, 85, 141, 89; readings of swings with 1-mg overload: 113, 48, 110, 52, 106. Calculate, for a 10-g load, (*a*) the sensitivity, (*b*) the reciprocal sensitivity.

Ans. (*a*) 34 div/mg, (*b*) 0.029 mg/div.

2-2 A crucible is approximately counterpoised with weights totaling 21.43 g. Given the following data:

Swings with rider at 6-mg position: 143, 98, 139, 101, 136.
Swings with rider at 7-mg position: 59, 102, 61, 98, 65.

(*a*) Calculate the weight of the crucible to the nearest 0.1 mg.
(*b*) If the zero point of the balance were 100 (other data being as given above), what is the exact weight of the crucible?   *Ans.* (*a*) 21.4364 g, (*b*) 21.4365 g.

2-3 A crucible, weighed by the method of transposition, weighs 20.004 g when on the left balance pan and 20.000 g when on the right balance pan.

(*a*) What is the correct weight of the crucible?
(*b*) What is the ratio of the lengths of the left arm to the right arm of the balance?
(*c*) If the right arm of the balance is 12.700 cm long, what is the length of the left arm?   *Ans.* (*a*) 20.002 g, (*b*) 1.0001, (*c*) 12.701 cm.

2-4 The following substances are weighed in air against brass weights. Calculate their vacuum weight.

(*a*) 40.5172 g of aluminium   (*e*) 19.8765 g of brass
(*b*) 24.9986 g of mercury   (*f*) 43.4300 g of gold
(*c*) 25.0000 g of lead   (*g*) 22.4550 g of alcohol
(*d*) 12.7000 g of platinum   (*h*) 24.9300 g of water

Ans. (*a*) 40.5204 g, (*b*) 24.9988 g.

2-5 If the weights given in Problem 2-4 were taken in air against gold weights, what would be the vacuum weight of each?   *Ans.* (*a*) 40.5204 g, (*b*) 25.0008 g.

2-6 A 20.0000-g porcelain crucible is exactly counterbalanced in air by a gold crucible. In vacuum, which crucible is heavier, and by how much?

Ans. Porcelain heavier by 0.0088 g.

2-7 Two crucibles, one iron and the other gold, have the same weight, 25.2500 g, in vacuum. What is the air weight of the iron crucible against gold weights?

Ans. 25.2477 g.

2-8 A solid weighing 40.0000 g in air against brass weights has a weight of 40.0060 g in vacuum. What is the density of the solid?   *Ans.* 4.1.

2-9 If the vacuum weight of the solid in Problem 2-8 were 39.9969 g, what would be the density of the solid?   *Ans.* 18.4.

2-10 An equal-arm balance having 10 main divisions from the central fulcrum to the right knife edge was inadvertently provided with a 12-mg rider. Following the usual method of weighing, a crucible was found to weigh 18.5262 g. What was the correct weight of the crucible?   *Ans.* 18.5274 g.

2-11 The following are consecutive readings of the pointer for an empty balance in oscillation. Suggest a probable cause for the behavior of the balance as indicated by the readings.

(*a*) 140, 57, 140, 61, 140, 64, 140.

(*b*) 72, 132, 74, 129, 80, 134, 78.

2-12 Readings of swings with a 50-g load on each balance pan: 83, 135, 86, 131, 88; readings of swings with 1-mg overload: 108, 58, 105, 62, 101. Calculate (*a*) the sensitivity, and (*b*) the reciprocal sensitivity of the balance for this load.

2-13 A combustion boat weighs 15.141 g when on the left balance pan and 15.155 g when on the right balance pan.

(*a*) What is the correct weight of the combustion boat?

(*b*) What is the ratio of the lengths of the left arm to the right arm?

(*c*) If the left balance arm is 15.259 cm long, what is the length of the right arm?

2-14 An object having a true weight of 20.0000 g is weighed by transposition on a balance the left arm of which is 30 ppm (parts per million) longer than the right arm. What is the apparent weight of the object (*a*) when weighed on the left pan? (*b*) when weighed on the right pan?

2-15 Refer to the text, Fig. 2-5. As a very close approximation, tan α = ratio of linear displacement of the pointer (*PP'*) to the length of the pointer (*OP*). Given the following data for a certain balance: length of beam (distance between terminal knife edges), 25.40 cm; length of pointer, 20.50 cm; space between marks on pointer scale (= "10 divisions"), 1.50 mm; weight of beam, pans, pointer, etc. (moving system), 110.0 g; sensitivity of balance, 24 div/mg.

(*a*) Calculate the distance *d* of the center of gravity below the central fulcrum.

(*b*) If the distance *d* is changed to 0.120 mm, what is the sensitivity of the balance, in div/mg?

2-16 A 50-ml volumetric flask is balanced against a similar flask as a tare on the right pan, requiring use of 0.7500 g on the right pan for exact counterpoise. The flask is filled to the mark with water at 25°C (at 25°C, one milliliter of water in air against brass weights = 0.9960 g) and weighed against brass weights, requiring a total of 50.1600 g for exact counterpoise.

(*a*) Calculate the volume of the flask to the nearest 0.01 ml.

(*b*) Calculate the vacuum weight of exactly one milliliter of water at 25°C.

2-17 A porcelain crucible and a nickel crucible have exactly the same weight (10 g) in air. In vacuum, which crucible is the heavier and by how much?

2-18 Two crucibles, one iron and one platinum, have the same weight, 25.0000 g, in vacuum. What is the air weight of the iron crucible against platinum weights?

2-19 A nickel crucible that weighs 16.2500 g in vacuum has what air weight (*a*) against brass weights? (*b*) against platinum weights?

2-20 A quantity of liquid that weighs 20.0000 g in air against brass weights has a vacuum weight of 20.0310 g. Calculate the density of the liquid.

2-21 If the vacuum weight of the liquid in Problem 2-20 were 19.9993 g, what would be the density of the liquid?

2-22 A balance having 10 main divisions from the central fulcrum to the right knife edge was inadvertently provided with a 12-mg rider. Following the usual method of weighing, a crucible was found to weigh 14.614 g. What was the correct weight of the crucible?

2-23   A 2.0000-g sample of impure lead acetate (density of sample, 2.6 g/ml) is converted to 0.5000 g of pure lead oxide, PbO (density 9.5 g/ml), both weights being taken in air against brass weights. Calculate the percent PbO in the sample, (*a*) without making buoyancy corrections and (*b*) after making buoyancy corrections.

2-24   An object that weighs approximately 10 g in air against brass weights shows a decrease of 0.010% when weighed in vacuum. Calculate the density of the object.

2-25   A weighing bottle having a volume of 20.0 ml is dried in an oven at 110°C, and stoppered air-tight at this temperature; it is then cooled to 25°C and weighed. Calculate the buoyancy error, in sign and magnitude (mg), arising through failure to equalize the pressure in the weighing bottle before weighing.

2-26   A 10-ml volumetric flask is calibrated by weighing it first empty, then filled to the mark with mercury, both weighings in air against brass weights. The contained mercury (density 13.59) weighed 136.680 g.

(*a*) Neglecting buoyancy correction, what is the volume of the flask?

(*b*) What error in volume results from failure to make the buoyancy correction? Is the error significant for ordinary quantitative work?

3

IONIC REACTIONS

Most of the reactions of inorganic quantitative analysis involve electrolytes or ionogens, that is, acids, bases, and salts, which furnish ions in solution. The original Arrhenius theory of ionization, although not completely adequate for all purposes, nevertheless serves satisfactorily in the interpretation of equilibria in solutions of ionogens. A significant portion of the theory of analytical chemistry involves such equilibria, and a thorough understanding of ionic equilibria is indispensable.

IONIZATION THEORY

The main points of ionization theory are given below; the student will find it advantageous to review the subject, including the experimental basis for the assumptions of the theory, in a textbook on general chemistry.

1. Acids, bases, and salts dissolved in a suitable solvent, of which water is the most common and most important, are **dissociated** into units called **ions** (hence the name "ionogens"). Acids furnish hydrogen ions, H^+; bases furnish hydroxyl ions, OH^-; salts furnish positive ions other than H^+ and negative ions other than OH^-.

2. Ions are electrically charged, as a result of which the solution conducts electric current (hence the name "electrolyte"). Ions that, in electrolysis, migrate to the anode (positive electrode) are negatively charged and are called **anions**; those that migrate toward the cathode (negative electrode) are positively charged and are called **cations**. Ions may be simple, such as Ag^+, Cu^{++}, Cl^-, or compound, such as UO_2^{++}, SO_4^{--}, PO_4^{---}, or complex, such as $[Ag(NH_3)_2]^+$, $[Cd(CN)_4]^{--}$.

3. Ionization is a reversible, equilibrium process; this is implicit in the word "dissociated" used in item 1.

4. Different ionogens vary widely in degree or extent of ionization.

5. The degree or extent of ionization is increased as the solution becomes more dilute; all ionogens are considered to be completely ionized at infinite dilution.

6. Each ion has its own characteristic physical and chemical properties.

Modern Concept of Ionization

It is well known that fused salts, such as sodium chloride, and fused bases, such as sodium hydroxide, are good conductors of electric current; the ions must be already present in the solids. For example, solid sodium chloride consists of sodium ions Na^+ and chloride ions Cl^- held in a regular geometric pattern; when the solid is melted, the forces between the ions are weakened, and the ions can behave more or less independently, as indicated by electrolysis experiments. On the other hand, liquid hydrogen chloride does not exhibit acidic properties and is a nonconductor; but when it is dissolved in water, the solvent molecules cause the hydrogen—chlorine bond to be broken in such a way that the one electron of the hydrogen atom is acquired by the chlorine atom, resulting in the formation of the hydrogen ion H^+ and the chloride ion Cl^-. The aqueous solution is a good conductor of electric current and exhibits the properties commonly associated with strong acids. The Debye-Hückel theory assumes that strong ionogens in solutions up to moderate concentrations are completely ionized, and that any deviations from the laws of ideal solutions are due to the influence of oppositely charged ions (and of solvent molecules) that form an "atmosphere" around a given ion. With increasing dilution, the ionic atmosphere of oppositely charged ions becomes more and more diffuse, and its influence therefore becomes less pronounced.

There is, of course, adequate basis for believing that ions in solution are "solvated" ("hydrated," if water is the solvent). The "hydrogen ion" cannot exist in water solution as the simple proton H^+ but is associated with water molecules; the ion can be represented as $H(H_2O)_n^+$, where n may be large. The "hydrated proton" is often represented as H_3O^+ (called "hydronium ion"), implying that only one water molecule is associated with the proton. In some textbooks the hydrogen ion is written as H_3O^+ in all ionic equations in which it is a reactant or a product. If one were to be completely consistent, other ions should also be written as their solvates, such as $Cu(H_2O)_4^{++}$, $Al(H_2O)_6^{+++}$, and $SO_4(H_2O)^{--}$. In this text the viewpoint is taken that the use of the solvated ion formulas, including the hydronium ion, is an unnecessary complication in the writing of ionic equations, except where it may be desired to emphasize this concept for a particular reason, as in a discussion of coordination, or of the Brønsted-Lowry concept of acids and bases.

Modern Concepts of Acids and Bases

The original Arrhenius concept of acids and bases has been considerably extended and modified to include many substances that were not considered acids or bases in the original theory.

1. Brønsted-Lowry Concept. In this system, **an acid is a proton donor**, and **a base is a proton acceptor**. An acid-base reaction consists of the transfer of a proton from an acid to a base, and a new acid and a new base are formed. Solvent molecules are involved, either as acid or as base. A few examples in the water system are as follows:

$$
\begin{array}{llll}
Acid_1 & + Base_1 & \rightleftarrows Acid_2 & + Base_2 \\
H_2O & + H_2O & \rightleftarrows H_3O^+ & + OH^- \\
HCl & + H_2O & \rightleftarrows H_3O^+ & + Cl^- \\
HAc & + H_2O & \rightleftarrows H_3O^+ & + Ac^- \\
H_2O & + NH_3 & \rightleftarrows NH_4^+ & + OH^- \\
NH_4^+ & + H_2O & \rightleftarrows H_3O^+ & + NH_3 \\
HCO_3^- & + H_2O & \rightleftarrows H_3O^+ & + CO_3^{--} \\
H_3O^+ & + HCO_3^- & \rightleftarrows H_2CO_3 & + H_2O
\end{array}
$$

The pairs $Acid_1$-$Base_2$ or $Base_1$-$Acid_2$ are said to be "conjugates"; for example, acetate ion is the conjugate base of acetic acid and ammonia is the conjugate base of ammonium ion. It is noted that some substances, e.g., bicarbonate ion, HCO_3^-, can act either as proton donor or as proton acceptor; this is always true of the solvent itself.

2. Lewis Concept. In the Lewis concept, **a base is a substance having an unshared pair of electrons that can be donated**; **an acid is a substance that can accept an electron pair**. The base-acid reaction is therefore the donation of a pair of electrons by one atom to another; the product of the reaction is called the "adduct." By this theory, the Lewis acids are positive ions and molecules containing an unfilled octet of electrons; the Lewis bases are the negative ions, and molecules containing one or two unshared pairs of electrons. For example:

$$Acid + Base \;\rightleftarrows\; Adduct$$

$$H^+ + \left[:\!\overset{..}{\underset{..}{F}}\!: \right]^- \rightleftarrows \; H\!:\!\overset{..}{\underset{..}{F}}\!:$$

$$H^+ + :\overset{H}{\underset{..}{O}}\!:\!H \;\rightleftarrows\; \left[H\!:\!\overset{H}{\underset{..}{O}}\!:\!H \right]^+$$

$$H^+ + :\overset{H}{\underset{H}{N}}\!:\!H \;\rightleftarrows\; \left[H\!:\!\overset{H}{\underset{H}{N}}\!:\!H \right]^+$$

$$Acid + Base \quad \rightleftarrows \quad Adduct$$

$$
\begin{array}{ccc}
:\ddot{F}: & H & :\ddot{F}:H \\
:\ddot{F}:\ddot{B}+:\ddot{N}:H & \rightleftarrows & :\ddot{F}:\ddot{B}:\ddot{N}:H \\
:\ddot{F}: & \ddot{H} & :\ddot{F}:H
\end{array}
$$

The Lewis concept of acids and bases is useful in interpreting many inorganic and organic reactions.

WRITING AND BALANCING EQUATIONS

A chemical change is indicated by writing an equation representing the reaction that occurs. The requisites of an equation are as follows.

1. It must represent the chemical facts. Originally, this information was determined experimentally, by observing that certain substances when brought together under certain conditions always gave certain products, as determined by analysis. With a knowledge of the properties of the substances involved, the indicated reaction or skeleton equation can be written without making personal verification by experiment. Obviously, the reactants and the products must be represented by correct formulas.

2. It must show the same kind and number of atoms in the products as in the reactants; that is, it must be *balanced*—this is implicit in the term *equation*. The skeleton equation is balanced by the use of appropriate coefficients to show the number of molecules or formula weights of substances used and produced. The balanced equation shows the stoichiometry (weight relations) in the reaction that occurs.

3. If written in the ionic form, the balanced equation will show also an equality of ionic charges; that is, the algebraic sum of the charges on the reactants equals the algebraic sum of the charges on the products.

4. If the reaction involves oxidation-reduction (redox), the equation must also show an equality of electron transfer.

It was mentioned earlier that most of the reactions of inorganic analytical chemistry take place between ions in solution; equations for the reactions should therefore be written in the ionic form. An ionic equation has the advantage of showing only those substances actually involved in the reaction; it is both simpler and more significant than the corresponding "molecular" equation.

Rules for Writing Ionic Equations

1. Only those ions taking part in or resulting from reaction should appear in the equation. In the reaction of solutions of silver nitrate and hydrochloric acid, write $Ag^+ + Cl^- \rightarrow AgCl$. Do not include the hydrogen ion of the hydrochloric

acid, nor the nitrate ion of the silver nitrate, for they play no part in the reaction; the same essential change would be produced by *any* soluble silver salt and *any* soluble chloride. Soluble, highly ionized electrolytes appear in the equation only insofar as their ions are involved in the reaction. Consider, for example, the situation when solutions of potassium nitrate and sodium chloride are mixed. These salts are soluble and highly ionized, the ions being the reactive units. But the possible "products" of reaction are sodium nitrate and potassium chloride, also soluble and highly ionized. Endeavoring to write an equation for a "reaction" results in the following:

$$K^+ + NO_3^- + Na^+ + Cl^- \rightarrow Na^+ + NO_3^- + K^+ + Cl^-$$

The same kind and number of substances appear on both sides of the "equation"; no change has occurred, and the "equation" has no significance.

2. Write in the "molecular form" those substances which are very slightly soluble (as $AgCl$, $PbSO_4$, $Fe(OH)_3$), very slightly ionized (weak acids, bases, salts), or not ionized (NO_2, NO, CO). Applications of this rule are amply illustrated below. In order to follow this rule, it is necessary to know what substances are insoluble or weakly ionized. The solubility rules and the list of weakly ionized substances, given below, should be memorized.

3. Balance the equation for atoms and for ionic charges, and in the case of redox reactions, also for electron transfer.

Solubility Rules. The solubilities of different substances vary over wide limits. Solubilities, usually in grams per 100 g of solvent, may be found in tables in various handbooks. The following general rules cover the solubility, in water, of the common inorganic compounds.

1. Sodium, potassium, and ammonium salts are soluble. Nitrates, nitrites, chlorates, and acetates are soluble; silver nitrite is sparingly soluble.

2. Metal oxides and hydroxides are insoluble except those of the alkali metals (sodium and potassium, and also ammonium) and barium; oxides and hydroxides of strontium and calcium are sparingly soluble.

3. Sulfides are insoluble except those of the alkalies, the alkaline earths (calcium, strontium, barium), and magnesium.

4. Chlorides, bromides, and iodides are soluble except those of silver, mercury(I), and lead; mercury(II) iodide is also insoluble.

5. Fluorides are insoluble except those of the alkalies, and of silver, bismuth, iron(III), and tin(IV).

6. Sulfates are soluble except those of lead, barium, and strontium; the sulfates of calcium and silver are sparingly soluble.

7. Chromates are insoluble except those of the alkalies, calcium, magnesium, and zinc.

8. Carbonates, sulfites, phosphates, arsenates, arsenites, borates, and oxalates are insoluble except those of the alkalies. (Insoluble salts of these anions are soluble in acids.)

Weak Ionogens. The degree of ionization of a "weak" electrolyte is usually expressed in the form of its ionization constant; see Chap. 5. The following generalizations should be noted.

There is no relation between *solubility* and *degree of ionization* of an electrolyte. For example, silver chloride is very slightly soluble, but the amount of silver chloride that is in solution is highly ionized, although the *concentration* of its ions is small. Lead acetate is soluble in water, but it is weakly ionized, so the solution contains only a low concentration of lead ions and acetate ions.

An acid having more than one acidic hydrogen (a polyprotic acid) ionizes in steps; the first ionization is always more extensive than the second, and the second more than the third; each step has its own ionization constant. For example,

$$H_3PO_4 \rightleftharpoons H^+ + H_2PO_4^- \tag{3-1}$$

$$H_2PO_4^- \rightleftharpoons H^+ + HPO_4^{--} \tag{3-2}$$

$$HPO_4^{--} \rightleftharpoons H^+ + PO_4^{---} \tag{3-3}$$

Reaction (3-1) is more extensive than reaction (3-2), which is more extensive than reaction (3-3).

The following are some of the common weak ionogens.

1. *Acids.* Acetic, arsenious, arsenic, boric, carbonic (both steps), hydrocyanic, hydrofluoric, hydrosulfuric (H_2S, both steps), nitrous, oxalic (second step), phosphoric (second and third steps), silicic, sulfurous (second step).

2. *Bases.* Ammonium hydroxide, hydrazine, and most metal hydroxides except those of the alkali and alkaline earth metals and silver; the weak metal hydroxides are also insoluble. Weak organic bases include aniline, ethylamine, phenylhydrazine, and many others.

3. *Salts.* Most salts are highly ionized; notable exceptions are lead acetate, iron(III) thiocyanate, the halides of cadmium, and most salts of mercury.

4. *Complex ions.* Most complex ions are weakly ionized. The degree of ionization is usually indicated by the "instability constant" of the complex ion, which is entirely analogous to the ionization constant of a weak acid or a weak base; see Chap. 7.

Balancing Ionic Equations

1. Reactions Involving No Electron Transfer. The equation for this type of reaction is balanced very easily by inspection. Use appropriate coefficients so that the same number of each kind of atom appears on each side of the reaction arrow; this almost automatically results in a charge balance also.

EXAMPLE 1

$$CO_3^{--} + 2H^+ \rightarrow H_2O + CO_2$$

Charge on left: $-2 + 2 = 0$; charge on right: $0 + 0 = 0$.

EXAMPLE 2

$$[Ni(NH_3)_4]^{++} + 4CN^- \rightarrow [Ni(CN)_4]^{--} + 4NH_3$$

Charge on left: $+2 - 4 = -2$; charge on right: $-2 + 0 = -2$.

EXAMPLE 3

$$As_2O_3 + OH^- \rightarrow AsO_3^{---} + H_2O \quad \text{(incomplete)}$$

One mole of As_2O_3 will give two moles of AsO_3^{---}; the additional atoms of oxygen for the formation of $2AsO_3^{---}$ come from the hydroxyl ions; two hydroxyl ions can "lose" one atom of oxygen and leave one molecule of water; therefore, $6OH^-$ are required to furnish the three oxygen atoms needed, leaving three molecules of water. The balanced equation is

$$As_2O_3 + 6OH^- \rightarrow 2AsO_3^{---} + 3H_2O$$

Charge on left: $0 - 6 = -6$; charge on right: $-6 + 0 = -6$.
If the "skeleton" equation were given merely as

$$As_2O_3 + OH^- \rightarrow AsO_3^{---} + ? \quad \text{(incomplete)}$$

a balanced expression could be written

$$As_2O_3 + 3OH^- \rightarrow 2AsO_3^{---} + 3H^+$$

This is not a correct equation, however, because it does not represent the chemical facts; both OH^- and H^+ cannot coexist in high concentration—they react extensively to form water.

2. Reactions Involving Electron Transfer. Reactions in which electrons are transferred from one substance to another are **oxidation-reduction**, or **redox**, reactions. An oxidation results from the loss of one or more electrons from an atom or ion; a reduction results from the gain of one or more electrons by an atom or ion. The following indicated changes will illustrate these reactions.

Oxidation:
$$Fe^{++} - e \rightarrow Fe^{+++}$$
$$S^{--} - 2e \rightarrow S$$
$$MnO_4^{--} - e \rightarrow MnO_4^-$$

Reduction:
$$Fe^{+++} + e \rightarrow Fe^{++}$$
$$S + 2e \rightarrow S^{--}$$
$$MnO_4^- + e \rightarrow MnO_4^{--}$$

Electrons cannot be "lost" by one substance unless another substance capable of accepting them is present. A redox reaction is therefore a chemical change in which **electrons are transferred** from atoms or ions to other atoms or ions. In the balanced redox equation for the reaction, the total number of electrons lost by one atom or ion must equal the total number of electrons gained by some other atom or ion. The substance that loses electrons is the **reducing agent**, and in the reaction it is oxidized; the substance that gains electrons is the **oxidizing agent**, and in the reaction it is reduced. The **ion-electron method** of balancing equations for redox reactions has many advantages:

a. It is applicable to all redox reactions involving ionogens in solution.

b. It is free from any assumption as to the distribution of valence bonds among the atoms constituting the reactants and products.

c. It emphasizes the fact that the reactants are the *ions*, which have their own characteristic properties, both physical and chemical. For example, in oxidations with potassium permanganate solution, the oxidizing agent is *not* the $KMnO_4$ molecule, nor is it Mn^{+7} (as the valence change method would assume); the oxidizing agent is the permanganate ion, MnO_4^-, the concentration of which can be determined experimentally and can be controlled.

d. The ion-electron half reactions are not imaginary; they have a firm experimental basis. The reactions actually take place when solutions of the oxidant and of the reductant, in separate containers, are connected internally by a salt bridge and externally through electrodes and a wire; even though the solutions are not in physical contact, reaction occurs by the transfer of electrons from the reducing agent to the oxidizing agent.

e. The influence of hydrogen ion or hydroxyl ion is usually evident in the final ionic equation derived by the ion-electron method.

f. The final ionic equation includes only the substances that are involved in the reaction.

In balancing an equation for a redox reaction by the ion-electron method, the equation is resolved into two partial equations, one for the oxidation of the reductant, the other for the reduction of the oxidant. Each partial equation (half reaction) is first separately balanced, and then the two partial equations are combined by addition, using, when necessary, such coefficients of the entire partial equations as are required to leave no electrons in the final equation.

EXAMPLE 4

Reduction of iron(III) by tin(II) in solution. Write the skeleton partial equation for the oxidation of the reductant:

$$Sn^{++} \rightarrow Sn^{4+} \quad \text{(incomplete)}$$

This expression is balanced for atoms, but not for net charge. In order to equalize the charges, add two electrons on the right or subtract two electrons on the left of the reaction arrow:[1]

$$Sn^{++} - 2e \rightarrow Sn^{4+}$$

Charge on left: $+2 - (-2) = +4$; charge on right: $+4$. The ion-electron half-reaction

---

[1] Some writers and teachers prefer not to use negative signs in chemical equations; the half-reaction equation may be written

$$Sn^{++} \rightarrow Sn^{4+} + 2e$$

The author's preference, in the use of the ion-electron method for balancing redox equations, is to show the electrons on the left side of the reaction arrow; this emphasizes the concept of the *loss* of electrons by the reducing agent, and their *gain* by the oxidizing agent.

equation for the oxidation is now balanced. Next, write the skeleton partial equation for the reduction of the oxidant:

$$Fe^{+++} \rightarrow Fe^{++} \qquad \text{(incomplete)}$$

and balance it by the use of electrons:

$$Fe^{+++} + e \rightarrow Fe^{++}$$

It is noted at once that each Sn^{++} loses two electrons, but each Fe^{+++} gains only one electron; two Fe^{+++} are therefore required to take the electrons that are provided by one Sn^{++}. The final ionic equation for the reaction is derived as follows:

$$Sn^{++} - 2e \rightarrow Sn^{4+}$$
$$2(Fe^{+++} + e \rightarrow Fe^{++})$$

Adding: $\overline{Sn^{++} + 2Fe^{+++} \rightarrow Sn^{4+} + 2Fe^{++}}$

Charge on left: $+2 + 6 = +8$; charge on right: $+4 + 4 = +8$. The final ionic equation is balanced for atoms, for electron transfer, and for ionic charges. The ionic equation is not only more significant than the "molecular" equation

$$SnCl_2 + 2FeCl_3 \rightarrow SnCl_4 + 2FeCl_2$$

which is sometimes written, but it is also much simpler, because the anions in the solution play no role in the fundamental reaction that occurs. Suppose, for example that a solution of iron(III) sulfate, $Fe_2(SO_4)_3$, were to be reduced with tin(II) chloride; consternation usually results when the student tries to write the "molecular" equation!

EXAMPLE 5

Oxidation of iron(II) by permanganate in acid solution. Write the skeleton partial equation for the oxidation and balance it as illustrated above:

$$Fe^{++} - e \rightarrow Fe^{+++}$$

Write the skeleton partial equation for reduction of the oxidant:

$$MnO_4^- \rightarrow Mn^{++} \qquad \text{(incomplete)}$$

This expression is not balanced for kind and number of atoms, nor for charge. To balance it for atoms, keep in mind that ionic reactions take place in water solution, and that the latter may be neutral, alkaline, or acidic; hence, H_2O, OH^-, and H^+ are always available and can be employed in writing and balancing ionic partial equations. In fact, two of these three substances are nearly always involved in redox reactions in which the oxygen content of a molecule or ion changes. In this case the reaction takes place in acid solution, so it is reasonable to write H^+ as a reactant and accomplish the hydrogen and oxygen balance thus:

$$MnO_4^- + 8H^+ \rightarrow Mn^{++} + 4H_2O \qquad \text{(incomplete)}$$

This expression is now balanced for atoms, but not for charge; charge on left: $-1 + 8 = +7$; charge on right: $+2 + 0 = +2$. The charges on both sides are equalized by adding 5 electrons on the left side, to give:

$$MnO_4^- + 8H^+ + 5e \rightarrow Mn^{++} + 4H_2O \qquad \text{(balanced)}$$

It is now obvious from the two half reactions that $5Fe^{++}$ are required to furnish the electrons needed for the reduction of one MnO_4^-.

$$5(Fe^{++} - e \rightarrow Fe^{+++})$$
$$MnO_4^- + 8H^+ + 5e \rightarrow Mn^{++} + 4H_2O$$

Adding: $5Fe^{++} + MnO_4^- + 8H^+ \rightarrow 5Fe^{+++} + Mn^{++} + 4H_2O$

Charge on left: $+10 - 1 + 8 = +17$; charge on right: $+15 + 2 + 0 = +17$.

After adding two half-reaction equations, it is sometimes necessary to simplify the resultant equation by combining similar terms that appear on the same side of the equation, or by cancelling equal quantities of similar terms that appear on opposite sides. For example

$$5(NaBiO_3 + 6H^+ + 2e \rightarrow Na^+ + Bi^{+++} + 3H_2O)$$
$$2(Mn^{++} + 4H_2O - 5e \rightarrow MnO_4^- + 8H^+)$$

$5NaBiO_3 + 2Mn^{++} + 30H^+ + 8H_2O \rightarrow 5Na^+ + 5Bi^{+++} + 2MnO_4^- + 16H^+$
$$+ 15H_2O$$

The expression is simplified by cancellation of $16H^+$ and $8H_2O$ from each side of the equation, which then becomes

$$5NaBiO_3 + 2Mn^{++} + 14H^+ \rightarrow 5Na^+ + 5Bi^{+++} + 2MnO_4^- + 7H_2O$$

In using H_2O, H^+, and OH^- in balancing ion-electron partial equations, it should be remembered that all three of these substances do not appear in the same equation, for H^+ and OH^- in high concentration are incompatible, that is, they react extensively and the solution cannot contain a high concentration of both species. The only permissible pairs of these substances in the same partial equation are H_2O and H^+, or H_2O and OH^-. If one substance of a pair appears on one side of the equation, the other permissible substance of that pair will usually appear on the opposite side. The following principles and examples show the methods of using H_2O, H^+, and OH^- in ion-electron partial equations.

1. If the oxy-content of an ion or molecule decreases in the reaction (reduction),

a. In acid solution, two H^+ are required and one H_2O is formed for each atom of "surplus" oxygen of the oxidizing agent:

$$MnO_4^- + 8H^+ + 5e \rightarrow Mn^{++} + 4H_2O$$

b. In alkaline solution, one H_2O is required for each atom of "surplus" oxygen, and twice as many OH^- are formed:

$$MnO_4^- + 2H_2O + 3e \rightarrow MnO_2 + 4OH^-$$

Occasionally, in alkaline solution, some hydrogen atoms are required for the formation of a product; use one H_2O for each hydrogen atom required, and obtain one OH^- as a product. For example, in alkaline solution, nitrate ion may be reduced to ammonia:

$$NO_3^- + 6H_2O + 8e \rightarrow NH_3 + 9OH^-$$

Three H_2O are required for the three oxygen atoms of the nitrate ion, forming six OH^-, and three more H_2O are required to furnish the hydrogen atoms for NH_3, forming three more OH^- for a total of nine OH^-.

2. If the oxy-content of an ion or molecule increases in reaction (oxidation),

a. In acid solution, write on the left one H_2O for each atom of additional oxygen required, and on the right two H^+ for each molecule of H_2O used:

$$SO_3^{--} + H_2O - 2e \rightarrow SO_4^{--} + 2H^+$$

b. In alkaline solution, write on the left twice as many OH^- as the number of additional oxygen atoms required, and on the right one molecule of H_2O for every two OH^- used on the left:

$$SO_3^{--} + 2OH^- - 2e \rightarrow SO_4^{--} + H_2O$$
$$Mn^{++} + 4OH^- - 2e \rightarrow MnO_2 + 2H_2O$$

Ion-electron partial equations are added, as illustrated previously, to get the total ionic equation. If the medium is acidic, both partial equations must be used in the form defined and illustrated in 1*a* and 2*a*, respectively; thus:

$$2(MnO_4^- + 8H^+ + 5e \rightarrow Mn^{++} + 4H_2O)$$
$$\underline{5(SO_3^{--} + H_2O - 2e \rightarrow SO_4^{--} + 2H^+)}$$
$$2MnO_4^- + 5SO_3^{--} + 6H^+ \rightarrow 2Mn^{++} + 5SO_4^{--} + 3H_2O$$

If the medium is alkaline, then both partial equations are used in the form defined and illustrated in 1*b* and 2*b*, respectively; for example,

$$2(MnO_4^- + 2H_2O + 3e \rightarrow MnO_2 + 4OH^-)$$
$$\underline{3(Mn^{++} + 4OH^- - 2e \rightarrow MnO_2 + 2H_2O)}$$
$$2MnO_4^- + 3Mn^{++} + 4OH^- \rightarrow 5MnO_2 + 2H_2O$$

There are instances in which more than one substance is oxidized (or reduced) in the same reaction. The simplest cases are those in which the substances oxidized (or reduced) are part of the same molecule of weakly ionized or slightly soluble ionogen, and their ratio is therefore fixed. In the ion-electron partial equation the total oxidation (or reduction) must be considered. For example, nitric acid will oxidize As_2S_3 to $H_2AsO_4^-$ and SO_4^{--}; because the ratio of arsenic to sulfur is fixed by the formula As_2S_3, the total loss of electrons per molecule of As_2S_3 is fixed.

$$As_2S_3 + 20H_2O - 28e \rightarrow 2H_2AsO_4^- + 3SO_4^{--} + 36H^+$$
$$\underline{28(NO_3^- + 2H^+ + e \rightarrow NO_2 + H_2O)}$$
$$As_2S_3 + 28NO_3^- + 20H^+ \rightarrow 2H_2AsO_4^- + 3SO_4^{--} + 28NO_2 + 8H_2O$$

Occasionally a reaction occurs in which one (or more) atom of a compound is oxidized and another atom of the compound is reduced; in this case only the net electron loss or gain is considered in writing the ion-electron partial equation.

For example, an acid solution of permanganate converts copper(I) thiocyanate, $CuCNS$, to Cu^{++}, HCN, and SO_4^{--}. The partial equation for the oxidation of $CuCNS$ is balanced without making any assumptions about the valence or oxidation numbers of the atoms in $CuCNS$. Proceeding as before, write the reactants and the products:

$$CuCNS \rightarrow Cu^{++} + HCN + SO_4^{--} \qquad \text{(incomplete)}$$

Account for the increase in oxy-content, and balance for atoms:

$$CuCNS + 4H_2O \rightarrow Cu^{++} + HCN + SO_4^{--} + 7H^+ \qquad \text{(incomplete)}$$

Although the expression is balanced for atoms, it is not balanced for ionic charge; charge on left: $0 + 0 = 0$; charge on right: $+2 + 0 - 2 + 7 = +7$. The charges are equalized by adding $7e$ on the right, or by subtracting $7e$ from the left side; the balanced ion-electron partial equation is then

$$CuCNS + 4H_2O - 7e \rightarrow Cu^{++} + HCN + SO_4^{--} + 7H^+$$

This half-reaction equation can then be combined with the partial equation for the reduction of the oxidizing agent (MnO_4^-) to obtain the total ionic equation.

There are instances in which a single substance undergoes both oxidation and reduction simultaneously; a reaction of this kind is known as an **auto-redox** reaction, or **internal redox** reaction, or **disproportionation**.

EXAMPLE 6

$$\begin{array}{c} Hg_2Cl_2 + 2Cl^- - 2e \rightarrow 2HgCl_2 \\ Hg_2Cl_2 + 2e \rightarrow 2Hg + 2Cl^- \\ \hline 2Hg_2Cl_2 \rightarrow 2Hg + 2HgCl_2 \end{array}$$

Simplified: $$Hg_2Cl_2 \rightarrow Hg + HgCl_2$$

EXAMPLE 7

$$\begin{array}{c} 2NH_4^+ - 6e \rightarrow N_2 + 8H^+ \\ 2NO_2^- + 8H^+ + 6e \rightarrow N_2 + 4H_2O \\ \hline NH_4^+ + NO_2^- \rightarrow N_2 + 2H_2O \end{array}$$

Some substances are capable of gaining electrons from strong reducing agents and losing electrons to strong oxidizing agents; the following examples will illustrate:

$$H_2O_2 \text{ (oxidant)} + 2H^+ + Sn^{++} \rightarrow 2H_2O + Sn^{4+}$$
$$5H_2O_2 \text{ (reductant)} + 6H^+ + 2MnO_4^- \rightarrow 2Mn^{++} + 5O_2 + 8H_2O$$
$$NO_2^- \text{ (oxidant)} + 2H^+ + Fe^{++} \rightarrow NO + Fe^{+++} + H_2O$$
$$5NO_2^- \text{ (reductant)} + 6H^+ + 2MnO_4^- \rightarrow 5NO_3^- + 2Mn^{++} + 3H_2O$$

The examples given in this section illustrate an additional important advantage of writing ionic equations; for a given set of conditions, the ion-electron partial equation for a given oxidant (or reductant) represents a property of that substance, and is applicable to reactions with many reductants (or oxidants). For example, permanganate as an oxidant in acid solution always gains five electrons per ion in going to Mn^{++} as the reduction product; it is therefore unnecessary for the student to learn one equation for its reaction with Fe^{++}, another for its reaction with H_2O_2, and still another for its reaction with NO_2^-, and so on. Similarly, the partial equation for the oxidation of SO_3^{--} to SO_4^{--} in acid solution is always the same, whether the oxidizing agent be MnO_4^-, NO_3^-, $Cr_2O_7^{--}$, Br_2, OCl^-, Ce^{4+}, or any other oxidizing agent. Furthermore, there are complicated redox reactions the equations for which cannot be balanced easily by any method except the ion-electron method.

Extent of Reaction

Reactions between ionogens are reversible, and the extent of reaction is dependent upon the properties of the reaction components. Ionic reactions approach completeness when any change occurs that removes ions from solution; that is, ionic reactions are extensive in the direction in which ion concentrations decrease. This fact is exactly what would be expected by application of Le Chatelier's principle (see Chap. 4) in equilibrium systems. Ion concentrations are decreased in several ways.

1. Formation of an Insoluble Product. The student should know the solubility rules given on p. 31.
　a. Insoluble solid.

EXAMPLE 8

$$Ag^+ + Cl^- \rightarrow AgCl$$

A soluble silver salt and a soluble chloride react to form insoluble silver chloride; its formation removes Ag^+ and Cl^- from solution, and the reaction is so extensive as to be considered complete.

The transposition of one insoluble compound to another can occur if the second compound, in saturated solution, furnishes a lower concentration of the common ion than does the first.

EXAMPLE 9

$$Ag_2CrO_4 + 2Cl^- \rightarrow CrO_4^{--} + 2AgCl$$

In a solution containing a high concentration of chloride ion, the silver ion concentration in equilibrium with chloride ion is much smaller than the silver ion concentration in equilibrium with chromate ion; the reaction is therefore extensive.

　b. Insoluble gas.

EXAMPLE 10

$$NaCl \text{ (solid) } + H_2SO_4 \text{ (concentrated) } \rightarrow NaHSO_4 + HCl$$

The hydrogen chloride, which is very slightly soluble in concentrated sulfuric acid, leaves the reaction mixture as a gas, and the reaction is extensive. If much water were present in the reaction mixture, the reaction would be quite incomplete, because hydrogen chloride is very soluble in water and no ions would have been removed from solution.

2. Formation of a Slightly Ionized Product.   The student should be familiar with the list of weakly ionized substances, p. 32.

a. Water formed by metathesis ("double decomposition").

EXAMPLE 11

$$H^+ \text{ (strong acid)} + OH^- \text{ (strong base)} \rightarrow H_2O$$
$$2H^+ + MgO \text{ (insoluble base)} \rightarrow Mg^{++} + H_2O$$
$$HAc \text{ (weak acid)} + OH^- \rightarrow Ac^- + H_2O$$

b. Weak acid.

EXAMPLE 12

$$H^+ \text{ (strong acid)} + Ac^- \rightarrow HAc \text{ (weak acid)}$$
$$FeS + 2H^+ \rightarrow Fe^{++} + H_2S \text{ (very weak acid)}$$

c. Weak base.

EXAMPLE 13

$$NH_4^+ \text{ (ammonium salt)} + OH^- \rightarrow NH_4OH \text{ (weak base)}$$

d. Weakly ionized salt.   Although most salts are highly ionized, there are several exceptions; see p. 32.

EXAMPLE 14

$$Hg^{++} + 2Cl^- \rightarrow HgCl_2 \text{ (weak ionogen)}$$
$$Pb^{++} + 2Ac^- \rightarrow PbAc_2 \text{ (weak ionogen)}$$
$$PbSO_4 + 2Ac^- \rightarrow PbAc_2 + SO_4^{--}$$

Although lead sulfate is insoluble in water, it dissolves in a high concentration of acetate ion (e.g., sodium or ammonium acetate solution); reaction occurs because lead ions, although of low concentration in saturated lead sulfate solution, are removed by the formation of weakly ionized lead acetate. Stated in another way, the lead ion concentration in equilibrium with a high concentration of acetate ion is less than the lead ion concentration in equilibrium with sulfate ion in saturated lead sulfate solution.

e. Complex ion.   Complex ions are formed by the union of certain ions with other ions or with molecules.

EXAMPLE 15

$$Cd^{++} \text{ (ion)} + 4Cl^- \text{ (ion)} \rightarrow CdCl_4^{--} \text{ (complex ion)}$$
$$H^+ \text{ (ion)} + NH_3 \text{ (molecule)} \rightarrow NH_4^+ \text{ (complex ion)}$$
$$Ni^{++} + 4NH_3 \rightarrow Ni(NH_3)_4^{++}$$
$$SbCl_4^- \text{ (complex ion)} + 2Cl^- \rightarrow SbCl_6^{---} \text{ (complex ion)}$$
$$HgI_2 + 2I^- \rightarrow HgI_4^{--}$$

3. Change of Charge (Redox). Redox reactions are virtually complete if there is sufficient difference in the potentials of the half reactions of the oxidizing agent and the reducing agent. Many illustrations of redox reactions have been given earlier in this chapter. Potentials and equilibrium in redox systems are discussed in detail in Chap. 26.

Skill in the writing and balancing of equations comes only through a knowledge of the chemical properties of the substances involved, and much practice. The exercises given at the end of this chapter are designed to provide some practice in balancing equations; in general, the chemistry of the indicated reaction is given, by including the formulas of the substances formed when the reactants are brought together.

PRACTICE EQUATIONS

Skeleton equations or indicated reactions for a number of reactions of analytical importance are listed below. Write the balanced *ionic* equation for the reaction. If the skeleton equation is given in the molecular form, remember that the ionic equation uses only the ions actually involved in the essential reaction, namely, the reacting ions of soluble, highly ionized electrolytes; molecular formulas are to be used to indicate substances that are insoluble, or weakly ionized, or non-ionic. In all cases of redox reactions, balance by the ion-electron method, showing the separate ion-electron partial equations and the method of obtaining the final balanced ionic equation. These equations are useful for practice in classifying a reaction by type (neutralization, precipitation, complexation, redox). In connection with titrimetric methods (Chaps. 23 to 30), many of these reactions are useful for practice in deducing titrimetric equivalents.

1. $NH_4Cl + NaOH \rightarrow NH_4OH + NaCl$.
2. $Ba(C_2H_3O_2)_2 + HCl \rightarrow BaCl_2 + HC_2H_3O_2$.
3. $K_2Cr_2O_7 + KOH \rightarrow K_2CrO_4 + H_2O$.
4. $Na_2B_4O_7 + HCl + H_2O \rightarrow H_3BO_3 + NaCl$.
5. $Fe_2O_3 + HCl \rightarrow FeCl_3 + H_2O$.
6. $Na_2CO_3 + H_2SO_4 \rightarrow Na_2SO_4 + H_2CO_3$.
7. $Fe(NO_3)_3 + KOH \rightarrow Fe(OH)_3 + KNO_3$.
8. $TiCl_4 + NH_4OH \rightarrow NH_4Cl + Ti(OH)_4$.
9. $Bi(NO_3)_3 + (NH_4)_2S \rightarrow Bi_2S_3 + NH_4NO_3$.
10. $Ag_2SO_4 + BaCl_2 \rightarrow AgCl + BaSO_4$.
11. $Pb(NO_3)_2 + KI \rightarrow KNO_3 + PbI_2$.
12. $Hg_2(NO_3)_2 + KBr \rightarrow Hg_2Br_2 + KNO_3$.
13. $Hg(NO_3)_2 + KI \rightarrow KNO_3 + HgI_2$.
14. $MnSO_4 + NaF \rightarrow Na_2SO_4 + MnF_2$.
15. $Mg(ClO_4)_2 + K_2CO_3 \rightarrow MgCO_3 + KClO_4$.
16. $Ba(NO_3)_2 + Na_3PO_4 \rightarrow NaNO_3 + Ba_3(PO_4)_2$.

17. $CaCl_2 + Na_2C_2O_4 \rightarrow NaCl + CaC_2O_4$.
18. $Na_2SiO_3 + HCl \rightarrow H_2SiO_3 + NaCl$.
19. $K_2CrO_4 + AgNO_3 \rightarrow Ag_2CrO_4 + KNO_3$.
20. $KCNS + Ag_2SO_4 \rightarrow K_2SO_4 + AgCNS$.
21. $Ag_2CrO_4 + HCl \rightarrow H_2CrO_4 + AgCl$.
22. $CuI + KCNS \rightarrow KI + CuCNS$.
23. $PbSO_4 + NH_4C_2H_3O_2 \rightarrow Pb(C_2H_3O_2)_2 + (NH_4)_2SO_4$.
24. $PbCO_3 + HC_2H_3O_2 \rightarrow Pb(C_2H_3O_2)_2 + H_2CO_3$.
25. $Al(OH)_3 + NaOH$ (excess) $\rightarrow NaAlO_2 + H_2O$.
26. $Na_2ZnO_2 + HCl$ (excess) $\rightarrow ZnCl_2 + NaCl + H_2O$.
27. $HgCl_2 + KI$ (excess) $\rightarrow KCl + K_2HgI_4$.
28. $AgCl + NH_4OH$ (or NH_3) $\rightarrow Ag(NH_3)_2Cl +$?   .
29. $AgI + KCN \rightarrow KAg(CN)_2 + KI$.
30. $Ag(NH_3)_2Cl + HNO_3 \rightarrow NH_4\overset{\cdot}{N}O_3 + AgCl$.
31. $Fe_2(SO_4)_3 + NaF$ (excess) $\rightarrow Na_2SO_4 + Na_3FeF_6$.
32. $KCN + AgNO_3 \rightarrow KAg(CN)_2 + KNO_3$.
33. $KAg(CN)_2 + AgNO_3 \rightarrow AgCN + KNO_3$.
34. $AgI + Na_2S_2O_3 \rightarrow Na_3Ag(S_2O_3)_2 + NaI$.
35. $Ni(OH)_2 + KCN \rightarrow K_2Ni(CN)_4 + KOH$.
36. $FeS + HCl \rightarrow FeCl_2 + H_2S$.
37. $Sb_2S_3 + HCl \rightarrow SbCl_6^{---} + H_2S$.
38. $H_3PO_4 + (NH_4)_2MoO_4 + HNO_3 \rightarrow (NH_4)_3PO_4 \cdot 12MoO_3 + NH_4NO_3 + H_2O$.
39. $(NH_4)_3PO_4 \cdot 12MoO_3 + OH^- \rightarrow MoO_4^{--} + HPO_4^{--} + NH_4^+ + H_2O$.
40. $PbS + HNO_3 \rightarrow Pb(NO_3)_2 + NO_2 + S + H_2O$.
41. $HgS + HNO_3 + HCl \rightarrow HgCl_4^{--} + NO_2 + S + H_2O$.
42. $Cu + HNO_3 \rightarrow Cu(NO_3)_2 + NO + H_2O$.
43. $CuS + HNO_3 \rightarrow Cu(NO_3)_2 + NO_2 + S + H_2O$.
44. $Cu_2S + HNO_3 \rightarrow Cu(NO_3)_2 + NO_2 + S + H_2O$.
45. $Ag + HNO_3 \rightarrow AgNO_3 + NO_2 + H_2O$.
46. $Zn + HNO_3$ (very dilute) $\rightarrow Zn(NO_3)_2 + NH_4NO_3 + H_2O$.
47. $Pt + H^+ + NO_3^- + Cl^- \rightarrow PtCl_6^{--} + NO_2 + H_2O$.
48. $NO_2^- + H^+ \rightarrow NO_3^- + NO + H_2O$.
49. $NH_4^+ + NO_2^- \rightarrow N_2 + H_2O$.
50. $Bi(OH)_3 + SnO_2^{--} \rightarrow Bi + SnO_3^{--} + H_2O$.
51. $HgCl_2 + SnCl_2 \rightarrow Hg_2Cl_2 + SnCl_4$.
52. $Hg_2Cl_2 + SnCl_2 \rightarrow Hg + SnCl_4$.
53. $S + Na_2SO_3 \rightarrow Na_2S_2O_3$.
54. $FeCl_3 + Zn \rightarrow FeCl_2 + ZnCl_2$.
55. $VO_3^- + Zn + H^+ \rightarrow V^{++} + Zn^{++} + H_2O$.
56. $VO_4^{---} + Fe^{++} + H^+ \rightarrow VO^{++} + Fe^{+++} + H_2O$.
57. $Fe_2(SO_4)_3 + SO_2 + H_2O \rightarrow FeSO_4 + H_2SO_4$.
58. $FeSO_4 + KClO_3 + H_2SO_4 \rightarrow Fe_2(SO_4)_3 + K_2SO_4 + Cl_2 + H_2O$.

59. $Fe + H^+ + ClO_4^- \rightarrow Fe^{+++} + Cl_2 + H_2O$.

60. $[Cu(NH_3)_4]^{++} + CN^- + H_2O \rightarrow [Cu(CN)_3]^{--} + CNO^- + NH_4^+ + NH_3$.

61. $CuCNS + IO_3^- + Cl^- + \quad ? \quad \rightarrow Cu^{++} + SO_4^{--} + HCN + ICl + \quad ? \quad$.

62. $Ce(SO_4)_2 + Na_2C_2O_4 \rightarrow Ce_2(SO_4)_3 + Na_2SO_4 + CO_2$.

63. $FeSO_4 + (NH_4)_2S_2O_8 \rightarrow Fe_2(SO_4)_3 + (NH_4)_2SO_4$.

64. $VO_2^+ + V^{++} + H^+ \rightarrow VO^{++} + H_2O$.

65. $NaCrO_2 + Na_2O_2 + H_2O \rightarrow NaOH + Na_2CrO_4$.

66. $K_2Cr_2O_7 + FeCl_2 + HCl \rightarrow CrCl_3 + FeCl_3 + KCl + H_2O$.

67. $Cr + ClO_4^- + \quad ? \quad \rightarrow Cr_2O_7^{--} + Cl_2 + \quad ? \quad$.

68. $K_2Cr_2O_7 + KI + H_2SO_4 \rightarrow Cr_2(SO_4)_3 + K_2SO_4 + I_2 + H_2O$.

69. $HAsO_2 + MnO_4^- + \quad ? \quad \rightarrow H_3AsO_4 + Mn^{++} + \quad ? \quad$.

70. $MnO_2 + H_2C_2O_4 \rightarrow Mn^{++} + CO_2 + H_2O$.

71. $H_2O_2 + KMnO_4 + H_2SO_4 \rightarrow MnSO_4 + KHSO_4 + O_2 + H_2O$.

72. $MnO_2 + HCl \rightarrow MnCl_2 + Cl_2 + H_2O$.

73. $Mn^{++} + IO_4^- + \quad ? \quad \rightarrow MnO_4^- + IO_3^- + \quad ? \quad$.

74. $Cr^{+++} + MnO_4^- + \quad ? \quad \rightarrow Cr_2O_7^{--} + MnO_2 + \quad ? \quad$.

75. $HCNS + MnO_4^- + H^+ \rightarrow HCN + SO_4^{--} + Mn^{++} + H_2O$.

76. $KMnO_4 + MnSO_4 + \quad ? \quad \rightarrow MnO_2 + K_2SO_4 + \quad ? \quad$.

77. $K_3Co(NO_2)_6 + MnO_4^- + H^+ \rightarrow K^+ + Co^{++} + Mn^{++} + NO_3^- + H_2O$.

78. $U(SO_4)_2 + KMnO_4 + H_2O \rightarrow UO_2SO_4 + MnSO_4 + KHSO_4 + H^+$.

79. $CoCl_2 + KMnO_4 + HgO + H_2O \rightarrow Co(OH)_3 + MnO_2 + HgCl_2 + KCl$.

80. $K_2MnO_4 + HCl \rightarrow KMnO_4 + MnO_2 + KCl + H_2O$.

81. $MnO_4^- + I^- + Cl^- + H^+ \rightarrow Mn^{++} + ICl + H_2O$.

82. $Mn^{++} + MnO_4^- + H^+ + H_2P_2O_7^{--} \rightarrow Mn(H_2P_2O_7)_3^{---} + H_2O$.

83. $Br^- + MnO_4^- + H^+ + HCN \rightarrow BrCN + Mn^{++} + H_2O$.

84. $H_3AsO_4 + KI + HCl \rightarrow HAsO_2 + I_2 + KCl + H_2O$.

85. $H_2SO_3 + I_2 + H_2O \rightarrow H_2SO_4 + HI$.

86. $KI + KMnO_4 + H_2SO_4 \rightarrow I_2 + MnSO_4 + K_2SO_4 + H_2O$.

87. $NaClO + NaI + HCl \rightarrow NaCl + I_2 + H_2O$.

88. $KI + H_2O_2 + HCl \rightarrow KCl + H_2O + I_2$.

89. $KIO_3 + KI + HCl \rightarrow KCl + H_2O + I_2$.

90. $CuSO_4 + KI \rightarrow CuI + I_2 + K_2SO_4$.

91. $Na_2S_2O_3 + I_2 \rightarrow Na_2S_4O_6 + NaI$.

92. $S_2O_3^{--} + I_2 + OH^- \rightarrow SO_4^{--} + I^- + H_2O$.

93. $I^- + Cl_2 + H_2O \rightarrow IO_3^- + Cl^- + H^+$.

94. $HCNS + I_2 + H_2O \rightarrow ICN + SO_4^{--} + H^+ + I^-$.

95. $Fe_2O_3 + KI + HCl \rightarrow FeCl_2 + KCl + I_2 + H_2O$.

96. $H(SbO)C_4H_4O_6 + I_2 + H_2O \rightarrow H(SbO_2)C_4H_4O_6 + HI$.

97. $ZnSO_4 + K_3Fe(CN)_6 + KI \rightarrow K_2Zn_3[Fe(CN)_6]_2 \ (ppt.) + K_2SO_4 + I_2$.

98. $Pb_3O_4 + H^+ + I^- \rightarrow PbI_2 + I_2 + H_2O$.

99. $NO_2^- + I^- + H^+ \rightarrow NO + I_2 + H_2O$.

100. $H_2S_2O_3 + H_3AsO_3 \rightarrow As_2S_3 + SO_2 + H_2S_4O_6 + H_2O$.

4

THE LAW OF MASS ACTION: CHEMICAL EQUILIBRIUM

In 1879, Guldberg and Waage formulated the generalization known as the **law of mass action**, namely, **the rate of reaction is proportional to the active masses of the reactants**. This law is the basis for many important principles and procedures in the various branches of chemistry; a thorough understanding of the law and of its applications are essential in the theory and practice of analytical chemistry.

In the strict (thermodynamic) sense, the term "active masses," as used above, should now be replaced by *activities* (chemical potentials).

For the reaction represented by

$$A + B \rightarrow C + D \tag{4-1}$$

the rate R of the reaction of A with B is proportional to the activity of A and to the activity of B. Mathematically, a proportionality becomes an equality by the introduction of a proportionality constant. A mathematical formulation of the law of mass action for the reaction of A with B is

$$R = ka_A a_B \tag{4-2}$$

in which the term k is the rate constant for the reaction. If the reaction represented above is reversible, that is,

$$A + B \rightleftharpoons C + D \tag{4-3}$$

the rate of the forward (left-to-right) reaction is represented by

$$R_1 = k_1 a_A a_B \tag{4-4}$$

and the rate of the reverse reaction is represented by

$$R_2 = k_2 a_C a_D \tag{4-5}$$

in which k_1 and k_2 are the rate constants for the forward and the reverse reactions, respectively.

If A and B are brought together under reacting conditions, the forward reaction is initially rapid, because of the relatively high activities of A and B. As the reaction progresses, the activities of A and B decrease as they are converted to C and D, and the rate of the forward reaction therefore decreases. The rate of the reverse reaction, initially zero because no C and D are present, becomes greater as more and more C and D are formed. As a result of the decreasing rate of the forward reaction and the increasing rate of the reverse reaction, a condition will eventually be reached at which the two rates become equal; that is, $R_1 = R_2$, and the system has reached a condition of *equilibrium*. From equations (4-4) and (4-5),

$$k_1 a_A\, a_B = k_2\, a_C\, a_D \tag{4-6}$$

By rearrangement of terms, and noting that the ratio of two constants is also constant, the expression becomes

$$K_{eq} = \frac{k_1}{k_2} = \frac{a_C\, a_D}{a_A\, a_B} \tag{4-7}$$

K_{eq} is known as the **equilibrium constant** for the reaction written in equation (4-3) above, and under given conditions (e.g., at constant temperature) K_{eq} will have the same numerical value, regardless of the initial activities of the components A, B, C, and D that may be brought together, and regardless of whether the equilibrium is approached by mixing only A and B initially, or by mixing only C and D.

The equilibrium state of the system could be approached from the opposite direction, that is, by starting with C and D:

$$C + D \rightleftarrows A + B \tag{4-8}$$

By reasoning analogous to that used above, the equilibrium constant for reaction (4-8) is given by

$$K'_{eq} = \frac{k_2}{k_1} = \frac{a_A\, a_B}{a_C\, a_D} \tag{4-9}$$

K'_{eq} is the equilibrium constant for the reaction *as written* in equation (4-8). The two equilibrium constants are reciprocally related, that is, $K_{eq} = 1/K'_{eq}$.

In the formulation of the equilibrium constant, substances that appear as products (on the right of the reaction arrows) are placed in the numerator, and substances that appear as reactants (on the left of the reaction arrows) are placed in the denominator. Thus, equations (4-3) and (4-8) represent identical equilibrium systems, but the equilibrium constants for these reactions have a reciprocal relation, because of the way in which the equations are written.

When more than one molecule of the same substance enters into the reaction, for example, $2A + B \rightarrow C$, the equation for the rate of reaction is slightly more complicated. Without giving here the detailed proof, it can be shown that in this case

$$R = k a_A\, a_A\, a_B = k a_A^{\,2} a_B \tag{4-10}$$

For the perfectly general case represented by the reaction equation

$$mA + nB \rightleftarrows rC + sD \tag{4-11}$$

where m, n, r, and s are the number of molecules of A, B, C, and D, respectively, the expression for the equilibrium constant is

$$K_{eq} = \frac{a_C^{\,r} a_D^{\,s}}{a_A^{\,m} a_B^{\,n}} \tag{4-12}$$

In considering equilibrium constants, it is convenient to adopt certain arbitrary standard states and assign to them a value of unit activity. A pure solid is considered to be at standard state or unit activity; a pure liquid at a specified temperature is at unit activity; a gas has unit activity when at a partial pressure of one atmosphere. For solutes in solution, activity is defined by the relation

$$a = Cf \tag{4-13}$$

where f, the *activity coefficient*, is a number (usually less than one) by which the concentration C must be multiplied to give the activity a. The standard state is therefore that concentration which, multiplied by its activity coefficient, gives unity as the product. The calculation of activity coefficients in ionic solutions is discussed briefly at the end of this chapter.

Substituting the definition of activity, equation (4-13), into equation (4-12) gives

$$K_{eq} = \frac{(C_C f_C)^r (C_D f_D)^s}{(C_A f_A)^m (C_B f_B)^n} \tag{4-14}$$

With increasing dilution, the activity coefficient f approaches unity (hence a approaches C), whereupon equation (4-14) becomes

$$K_{eq} = \frac{C_C^{\,r} C_D^{\,s}}{C_A^{\,m} C_B^{\,n}} \tag{4-15}$$

Equations (4-12), (4-14), and (4-15) are mathematical statements of the **law of chemical equilibrium**, which is merely an application of the law of mass action to an equilibrium reaction. In words, the equilibrium law may be stated thus: For a reaction at equilibrium, the product of the molar concentrations (activities) of the substances formed divided by the product of the molar concentrations (activities) of the reactants is a constant, provided each concentration (activity) is raised to the power that is the coefficient of that substance in the equation for the reaction. *The system must be at equilibrium if K_{eq} is to be constant.* Most of the reactions of analytical chemistry take place in dilute solution, and equilibrium calculations are based on concentrations expressed in the units moles of solute per liter of solution, usually denoted by enclosing the formula of the solute species in brackets; thus, [A] represents the equilibrium concentration, in moles per liter, of the species A. Equation (4-15) is therefore usually written

$$K_{eq} = \frac{[C]^r[D]^s}{[A]^m[B]^n} \qquad (4\text{-}16)$$

A large value for K_{eq} indicates a reaction that is very extensive in the direction left to right as the equation is written; in other words, at equilibrium there is a large ratio of products to reactants. Conversely, a very small value of K_{eq} indicates a reaction that is quite incomplete at equilibrium.

The numerical value of the equilibrium constant of a reaction gives no information whatever about the time required for equilibrium to be attained—it merely shows the extent to which reaction has occurred when the equilibrium state is reached. Under certain conditions, some reactions are so slow that a very long time is required for attainment of equilibrium; in other cases, especially reactions of ionogens, the reactions are virtually instantaneous. Most of the reactions of analytical chemistry are in the latter category.

Displacement of Equilibria

The rate constants k_1 and k_2 in equations (4-4) and (4-5), and hence the equilibrium constant K_{eq}, include the influence of all the variables (inherent reaction tendency, temperature, etc.) except the concentrations of the substances involved in the reaction.

A study of equilibrium systems led Le Chatelier, in 1884, to the formulation of a principle that appears to have universal application in a wide variety of fields, and is so firmly established as to constitute a fundamental law. **If some change of conditions (commonly referred to as a stress) is imposed on an equilibrium system, the system will readjust itself to undo or counteract the effect of the change.** For example, an increase in temperature favors the endothermic process in an equilibrium system, because this process absorbs heat from the environment and tends to lower the temperature. In a gas phase reaction involving a change in the number of gas molecules, increase of pressure favors the reaction that results in the formation of fewer molecules, because this change tends to decrease the pressure. A catalyst changes the speed of two opposing reactions to the same extent; hence it merely changes the rate at which the system reaches equilibrium.

Of greatest importance in analytical chemistry are the effects of changes of concentration. The law of mass action is, in fact, a specific case of the more general principle of Le Chatelier. Consider, again, the equilibrium system $A + B \rightleftarrows C + D$. If the concentration of A is increased, the system will readjust in the direction that will consume A, that is, by reaction of A with B to produce C and D. A new equilibrium condition is reached, which is more complete in the direction of formation of C and D, but always with new concentrations of all components such that K_{eq} is maintained at a constant value. Displacement of the equilibrium system in the same direction may be accomplished by increasing the concentration of B. It is common practice, in many operations of quantitative analysis, to make a reaction more extensive (more nearly complete) by the use of an excess of a reactant. The same end is attained by removing C or D from the "sphere of action," that is, from reacting conditions. If C or D is removed, for example by precipitation or gas evolution, the system readjusts by further reaction of A and B to produce more C and D, to compensate for the removal of the product or products from the system. A new equilibrium is established, still with the same numerical value of K_{eq}, but representing a more complete conversion of A and B to C and D. Many reactions of quantitative analysis involve this method of displacement of equilibria. From the foregoing it is apparent that the equilibrium can be displaced in the reverse direction by the addition of C or D, or by the removal of A or B.

In Chaps. 5, 6, and 7 the important applications of the mass law to reactions of ionogens are discussed in detail.

Ionic Strength and Activity

The behavior of ions in solution is influenced by a number of factors, chief among which are the mutual attraction of ions of unlike charge and repulsion of ions of like charge (Coulomb's law), and the influence of thermal agitation (Boltzmann distribution law) to counteract the electrical attraction and repulsion. The effects are dependent upon the *total* ionic composition of the solution, expressed by the **ionic strength** of the solution:

$$\mu = \tfrac{1}{2} \sum C_i Z_i^2 \tag{4-17}$$

where μ is the ionic strength, C_i is the molar concentration of an ion, and Z_i is its ionic charge. The product $C_i Z_i^2$ is summed for all the ions in the solution, then divided by two to give the ionic strength.

EXAMPLE 1

Calculate the ionic strength of a solution that is 0.30 M in KNO_3 and 0.10 M in $CaCl_2$.

$$C_{K^+} = 0.30, \qquad C_{NO_3^-} = 0.30, \qquad C_{Ca^{++}} = 0.10, \qquad C_{Cl^-} = 0.20$$
$$\mu = \tfrac{1}{2}[(0.30 \times 1^2) + (0.30 \times 1^2) + (0.10 \times 2^2) + (0.20 \times 1^2)]$$
$$= \tfrac{1}{2}(0.30 + 0.30 + 0.40 + 0.20) = 0.60$$

The definition of ionic strength, equation (4-17), shows that the following relations exist between μ and C for ionogens of the various ion types: for 1-1 type (e.g., KNO_3), $\mu = C$; for 2-1 type ($CaCl_2$) or 1-2 type (Na_2SO_4), $\mu = 3C$; for 2-2 type ($ZnSO_4$), $\mu = 4C$; for 3-1 type ($AlCl_3$) or 1-3 type (Na_3PO_4), $\mu = 6C$.

Debye and Hückel[1] derived the following expression relating the ionic strength to the activity coefficient of an ion:

$$-\log f_i = AZ^2 \sqrt{\mu} \quad \text{or} \quad \log f_i = -AZ^2 \sqrt{\mu} \qquad (4\text{-}18)$$

The constant, A, includes such factors as the dielectric constant of the solvent, the absolute temperature, the Boltzmann distribution constant, the radius of the ionic atmosphere, and the conversion factor from natural to common logarithms. For aqueous solutions at 25°C, $A = 0.50$; equation (4-18) therefore becomes

$$\log f_i = -0.50Z^2 \sqrt{\mu} \qquad (4\text{-}19)$$

EXAMPLE 2

Calculate the activity coefficient of each ion in Example 1.

$$\log f_{K+} = -0.50 \times 1^2 \times \sqrt{0.60} = -0.50 \times 0.77 = -0.38 = \bar{1}.62$$

$$f_{K+} = \text{antilog } \bar{1}.62 = 0.42$$

This is also the activity coefficient of the other univalent ions, NO_3^- and Cl^-.

$$\log f_{Ca++} = -0.50 \times 2^2 \times \sqrt{0.60} = -0.50 \times 4 \times 0.77 = -1.54$$

$$= \bar{2}.46$$

$$f_{Ca++} = \text{antilog } \bar{2}.46 = 0.029$$

It should be noted that the activity coefficient of a given ion is determined by its charge and the total ionic strength of the solution, and not primarily by its own concentration in the solution.

Development of the Debye-Hückel limiting law, as expressed by equation (4-19), assumed the ions to be point charges. An extension of equation (4-19) which takes into account the ion size (many ions are in the range of three to six angstrom units) is

$$\log f_i = -\frac{0.50Z_i^2 \sqrt{\mu}}{1 + \sqrt{\mu}} \qquad (4\text{-}20)$$

This relation is often called the "extended Debye-Hückel equation." It gives closer agreement with experimental values than does equation (4-19), especially at ionic strengths higher than about 0.01.

From known concentrations, activity coefficients and activities can be calculated for use in equilibrium constant expressions. If the equilibrium constant based on activities, equation (4-12), is represented by K_{act}, and the constant based

[1] P. Debye and E. Hückel, *Physik. Z.*, **24**, 185 (1923).

on concentrations, equation (4-15) or (4-16), is represented by K_{conc}, then equation (4-14) can be written

$$K_{act} = K_{conc} \frac{f_C^r f_D^s}{f_A^m f_B^n} \quad \text{or} \quad K_{conc} = K_{act} \frac{f_A^m f_B^n}{f_C^r f_D^s} \quad (4\text{-}21)$$

It is often convenient to express quantities in terms of their logarithms. Solving equation (4-21) by logarithms:

$$\log K_{conc} = \log K_{act} + m \log f_A + n \log f_B - r \log f_C - s \log f_D \quad (4\text{-}22)$$

By use of the definitions $pK_{conc} = -\log K_{conc}$, and $pK_{act} = -\log K_{act}$ (analogous to the definition of $pH = -\log [H^+]$; see p. 53), equation (4-22) becomes

$$pK_{conc} = pK_{act} + r \log f_C + s \log f_D - m \log f_A - n \log f_B \quad (4\text{-}23)$$

Values of the activity coefficients can be calculated from the ionic strength of the solution, using the Debye-Hückel equations (4-19) or (4-20).

EXAMPLE 3

Express the equilibrium constant of the reaction $CuCl_4^{--} \rightleftharpoons Cu^{++} + 4Cl^-$ as a function of the ionic strength of the solution.
By equation (4-19):

$$\log f_{Cu^{++}} = -0.50 \times 2^2 \times \sqrt{\mu} = -2\sqrt{\mu}$$

$$\log f_{Cl^-} = -0.50 \times 1^2 \times \sqrt{\mu} = -0.50\sqrt{\mu}$$

$$\log f_{CuCl_4^{--}} = -0.50 \times 2^2 \times \sqrt{\mu} = -2\sqrt{\mu}$$

By equation (4-23):

$$pK_{conc} = pK_{act} + \log f_{Cu^{++}} + 4 \log f_{Cl^-} - \log f_{CuCl_4^{--}}$$

$$= pK_{act} - 2\sqrt{\mu} - 2\sqrt{\mu} + 2\sqrt{\mu} = pK_{act} - 2\sqrt{\mu}$$

For a solution of any given ionic strength, the relation of K_{conc} to K_{act} can be calculated. For example, if the ionic strength of the above solution is 0.10, $pK_{conc} = pK_{act} - 2\sqrt{0.10} = pK_{act} - 0.64$.

Applications of the influence of ionic strength on the solubility of slightly soluble ionogens and on the extent of ionization of weak electrolytes will be made in the following chapters.

PROBLEMS

See Problems 5-31 and 6-34 for some applications of ionic strength and activity coefficients in ionic equilibria.

4-1 For the solution specified below, calculate (1) the ionic strength of the solution; (2) the activity coefficient of each ionic species, using the Debye-Hückel limiting law;

(3) the activity coefficient of each ionic species, using the extended Debye-Hückel equation.

(a) 0.20 M $BaCl_2$ solution.

(b) 0.060 M $K_4Fe(CN)_6$ solution.

(c) Solution that is 0.50 M in $NaNO_3$ and 0.20 M in $BaCl_2$.

(d) Solution that is 0.08 M in KCl, 0.025 M in $CaCl_2$, and 0.050 M in $FeCl_3$.

(e) Solution that is 0.030 M in $NaCl$, 0.050 M in $Zn(NO_3)_2$, and 0.010 M in $Al_2(SO_4)_3$.

Ans. (a) (1) 0.60. (2) $f_{Ba^{++}} = 0.029$, $f_{Cl^-} = 0.412$. (3) $f_{Ba^{++}} = 0.135$, $f_{Cl^-} = 0.605$.

4-2   For the reaction given below, express pK_{conc} as a function of ionic strength, using the Debye-Hückel limiting law.

(a) $HS^- \rightleftarrows H^+ + S^{--}$.

(b) $Cu(CN)_3^{--} \rightleftarrows Cu^+ + 3CN^-$.

(c) $PtCl_6^{--} \rightleftarrows Pt^{4+} + 6Cl^-$.

(d) $Ag(S_2O_3)_2^{---} \rightleftarrows Ag^+ + 2S_2O_3^{--}$.

(e) $AlF_6^{---} \rightleftarrows Al^{+++} + 6F^-$.   *Ans.* (a) $pK_{conc} = pK_{act} - 2\sqrt{\mu}$.

5

ACID-BASE EQUILIBRIA

An important phase of analytical chemistry and, indeed, of many other branches of science, involves the theory and application of acid-base equilibria, not only in water solution but also in nonaqueous solvents. The classical and the modern definitions of acids and bases have been given in Chap. 3. The classical Arrhenius theory of ionization is adequate for many purposes, whereas the Brønsted-Lowry concept of acids and bases is more general and emphasizes the role of the solvent in the acid-base reaction. The discussion in this chapter will be limited to acid-base systems in water solution. Acid-base equilibria in nonaqueous solvents is treated in more advanced texts.[1,2]

THE WATER EQUILIBRIUM: pH

In the Brønsted-Lowry concept of acids and bases an acid is a proton donor and a base is a proton acceptor. In water solution the solvent itself is an acid and/or a base, undergoing self-ionization or **autoprotolysis**:

$$H_2O + H_2O \rightleftharpoons H_3O^+ + OH^- \qquad (5\text{-}1)$$

Water is therefore an **amphoprotic solvent**. The hydronium ion, H_3O^+, is the simplest representation of a hydrated proton, although the actual species in solution contains more than one molecule of water associated with the proton. For simplicity in writing equations it is customary to write merely H^+, rather than H_3O^+, just as it is customary to represent the copper(II) cation by Cu^{++}

[1] H. A. Laitinen, *Chemical Analysis*, New York, McGraw-Hill, 1960, chap. 4.
[2] H. F. Walton, *Principles and Methods of Chemical Analysis*, 2nd ed., Englewood Cliffs, N. J., Prentice-Hall, 1964, chap. 5.

rather than by $Cu(H_2O)_4^{++}$. The ionization of water is therefore simply represented by

$$H_2O \rightleftharpoons H^+ + OH^- \qquad (5-2)$$

As a result of the slight ionization of water, it has a small, but measurable, conductance; it also exhibits certain properties characteristic of its ions, but only to a limited degree owing to the very low concentrations of the ions. The equilibrium (ionization) constant for water is formulated as follows:[3]

$$K_{ion} = \frac{[H^+][OH^-]}{[H_2O]} = 1.82 \times 10^{-16} \qquad (at\ 25°C) \qquad (5-3)$$

In water and dilute aqueous solutions, $[H_2O]$, the concentration of water in moles per liter, is constant and at 25° has a numerical value of $997/18.0 = 55.3$. Combining this constant with the ionization constant of water gives

$$K_w = [H^+][OH^-] = 55.3(1.82 \times 10^{-16}) = 1.01 \times 10^{-14} \qquad (5-4)$$

generally used merely as 1.0×10^{-14}. K_w is called the **ion product constant of water**, or sometimes simply the "water constant." This relation shows that in pure water, at 25°C, $[H^+] = [OH^-] = \sqrt{K_w} = 1.0 \times 10^{-7}$, and that in aqueous solutions the hydrogen ion concentration is inversely proportional to the hydroxyl ion concentration; if the concentration of one ion is increased, the concentration of the other ion is decreased correspondingly, in order to maintain K_w at 1.0×10^{-14}. An acidic solution is one in which the hydrogen ion concentration is greater than the hydroxyl ion concentration, and an alkaline solution is one in which the hydroxyl ion concentration is greater than the hydrogen ion concentration. For any given concentration of hydrogen (or hydroxyl) ion, the corresponding concentration of hydroxyl (or hydrogen) ion is easily calculated from K_w.

The pH Scale. The very small numbers representing the low concentrations of hydrogen or hydroxyl ion in the water system are somewhat cumbersome to express even in written form, e.g., $[H^+] = 1.0 \times 10^{-5}$. They are even more cumbersome if expressed in words. In 1909 Sørensen introduced the term pH, defined in relation to hydrogen ion concentration, which greatly simplified the expression of hydrogen ion concentration. The term pH is defined as follows:

$$pH = \log(1/[H^+]) = -\log[H^+] \qquad (5-5)$$

Thus, if $[H^+] = 1.0 \times 10^{-5}$, $pH = -\log(1.0 \times 10^{-5}) = -(-5.00) = 5.00$. If $[H^+] = 5.0 \times 10^{-4}$, $pH = -\log(5.0 \times 10^{-4}) = -(0.70 - 4) = -(-3.30) = 3.30$.

The general form of the pH definition has been carried over to use in expressing other very small quantities; for example, $pOH = -\log[OH^-]$; $pK_w = -\log K_w$;

[3] Students not thoroughly familiar with the exponential notation for very small or very large numbers and the arithmetical operations of roots and powers of exponentials should study Appendix VII.

$pK_a = -\log K_a$; $pK_{sp} = -\log K_{sp}$. Because the process of multiplication is accomplished by the addition of logarithms, for the relation $K_w = [H^+][OH^-] = 1.0 \times 10^{-14}$ we may write its counterpart:

$$pK_w = pH + pOH = 14.00 \qquad (5\text{-}6)$$

The following statements summarize the relations just discussed:

1. In water and in neutral aqueous solutions (at 25°C), $[H^+] = [OH^-] = 1.0 \times 10^{-7}$, and $pH = pOH = 7.00$.

2. In an acidic solution the hydrogen ion concentration is greater than the hydroxyl ion concentration, the pH is less than 7.00, and the pOH is greater than 7.00.

3. In an alkaline solution the hydroxyl ion concentration is greater than the hydrogen ion concentration, the pOH is less than 7.00, and the pH is greater than 7.00.

4. A tenfold change in hydrogen or in hydroxyl ion concentration corresponds to a change of one unit in pH or pOH, because $\log 10 = 1.00$.

The numerical interrelations are summarized in Table 5-1.

Table 5-1   Relations Based on the Ionization of Water
$K_w = [H^+][OH^-] = 1.0 \times 10^{-14}$; $pK_w = pH + pOH = 14.00$

$[H^+]$	pH	$[OH^-]$	pOH	Reaction[a]
1.0×10^{-0}	0.00	1.0×10^{-14}	14.00	↑
1.0×10^{-1}	1.00	1.0×10^{-13}	13.00	
1.0×10^{-2}	2.00	1.0×10^{-12}	12.00	
1.0×10^{-3}	3.00	1.0×10^{-11}	11.00	
1.0×10^{-4}	4.00	1.0×10^{-10}	10.00	
1.0×10^{-5}	5.00	1.0×10^{-9}	9.00	
1.0×10^{-6}	6.00	1.0×10^{-8}	8.00	
1.0×10^{-7}	7.00	1.0×10^{-7}	7.00	Neutral
1.0×10^{-8}	8.00	1.0×10^{-6}	6.00	
1.0×10^{-9}	9.00	1.0×10^{-5}	5.00	
1.0×10^{-10}	10.00	1.0×10^{-4}	4.00	
1.0×10^{-11}	11.00	1.0×10^{-3}	3.00	
1.0×10^{-12}	12.00	1.0×10^{-2}	2.00	
1.0×10^{-13}	13.00	1.0×10^{-1}	1.00	
1.0×10^{-14}	14.00	1.0×10^{-0}	0.00	↓

[a] From "Neutral" up, acidity is increasing; from "Neutral" down, alkalinity is increasing.

Interconversion of $[H^+]$, pH, $[OH^-]$, and pOH.   By means of the definition of the terms pH, pOH, and pK_w and their interrelations, the arithmetic con-

(3) the activity coefficient of each ionic species, using the extended Debye-Hückel equation.

   (*a*) 0.20 *M* $BaCl_2$ solution.

   (*b*) 0.060 *M* $K_4Fe(CN)_6$ solution.

   (*c*) Solution that is 0.50 *M* in $NaNO_3$ and 0.20 *M* in $BaCl_2$.

   (*d*) Solution that is 0.08 *M* in KCl, 0.025 *M* in $CaCl_2$, and 0.050 *M* in $FeCl_3$.

   (*e*) Solution that is 0.030 *M* in NaCl, 0.050 *M* in $Zn(NO_3)_2$, and 0.010 *M* in $Al_2(SO_4)_3$.

     Ans. (*a*) (1) 0.60. (2) $f_{Ba^{++}} = 0.029$, $f_{Cl^-} = 0.412$. (3) $f_{Ba^{++}} = 0.135$, $f_{Cl^-} = 0.605$.

  4-2   For the reaction given below, express pK_{conc} as a function of ionic strength, using the Debye-Hückel limiting law.

   (*a*) $HS^- \rightleftarrows H^+ + S^{--}$.

   (*b*) $Cu(CN)_3^{--} \rightleftarrows Cu^+ + 3CN^-$.

   (*c*) $PtCl_6^{--} \rightleftarrows Pt^{4+} + 6Cl^-$.

   (*d*) $Ag(S_2O_3)_2^{---} \rightleftarrows Ag^+ + 2S_2O_3^{--}$.

   (*e*) $AlF_6^{---} \rightleftarrows Al^{+++} + 6F^-$.   *Ans.* (*a*) $pK_{conc} = pK_{act} - 2\sqrt{\mu}$.

5

ACID-BASE EQUILIBRIA

An important phase of analytical chemistry and, indeed, of many other branches of science, involves the theory and application of acid-base equilibria, not only in water solution but also in nonaqueous solvents. The classical and the modern definitions of acids and bases have been given in Chap. 3. The classical Arrhenius theory of ionization is adequate for many purposes, whereas the Brønsted-Lowry concept of acids and bases is more general and emphasizes the role of the solvent in the acid-base reaction. The discussion in this chapter will be limited to acid-base systems in water solution. Acid-base equilibria in nonaqueous solvents is treated in more advanced texts.[1,2]

THE WATER EQUILIBRIUM: pH

In the Brønsted-Lowry concept of acids and bases an acid is a proton donor and a base is a proton acceptor. In water solution the solvent itself is an acid and/or a base, undergoing self-ionization or **autoprotolysis**:

$$H_2O + H_2O \rightleftharpoons H_3O^+ + OH^- \tag{5-1}$$

Water is therefore an **amphiprotic solvent**. The hydronium ion, H_3O^+, is the simplest representation of a hydrated proton, although the actual species in solution contains more than one molecule of water associated with the proton. For simplicity in writing equations it is customary to write merely H^+, rather than H_3O^+, just as it is customary to represent the copper(II) cation by Cu^{++}

---

[1] H. A. Laitinen, *Chemical Analysis*, New York, McGraw-Hill, 1960, chap. 4.
[2] H. F. Walton, *Principles and Methods of Chemical Analysis*, 2nd ed., Englewood Cliffs, N. J., Prentice-Hall, 1964, chap. 5.

52

versions are simple if one remembers the fundamentals of the use of logarithms; see Appendix VII, especially the section on negative logarithms, p. 685.

EXAMPLE 1

In a certain solution $[H^+] = 5.0 \times 10^{-6}$. Calculate (a) pH; (b) pOH; (c) $[OH^-]$.

(a) $pH = -\log[H^+] = -\log(5.0 \times 10^{-6}) = -(0.70 - 6) = -(-5.30) = 5.30$.

(b) $pH + pOH = pK_w = 14.00$. Therefore, $pOH = pK_w - pH = 14.00 - 5.30 = 8.70$.

(c) $pOH = -\log[OH^-]$; therefore, $[OH^-] = 10^{-pOH} = 10^{-8.70} = 10^{\bar{9}.30} = 2.0 \times 10^{-9}$. Alternate method: $[OH^-] = K_w/[H^+] = (1.0 \times 10^{-14})/(5.0 \times 10^{-6}) = 2.0 \times 10^{-9}$.

IONIZATION OF ACIDS AND BASES

Certain soluble electrolytes exhibit the properties of their ions to only a small extent because of low concentrations of the ions. For example, an aqueous solution of hydrogen acetate (acetic acid) exhibits acidic properties to a limited extent only. Measurement of the ion concentrations by several independent methods shows them to be very much less than the total "analytical concentration" of the acetic acid solute. (For convenience in the formulations that follow, the acetate group, $C_2H_3O_2$, will be abbreviated "Ac.") By classical (Arrhenius) theory, only a small fraction of the HAc is ionized:

$$HAc \rightleftharpoons H^+ + Ac^-$$

Applying the mass law to this ionization equilibrium,

$$K_{ion} = \frac{[H^+][Ac^-]}{[HAc]}$$

K_{ion} is the equilibrium constant for the ionization of the acid, and is usually designated by K_a. By the Brønsted-Lowry concept,

$$HAc + H_2O \rightleftharpoons H_3O^+ + Ac^-$$

for which the mass law expression is

$$K_{eq} = \frac{[H_3O^+][Ac^-]}{[H_2O][HAc]}$$

where K_{eq} is the equilibrium constant for the acid-base reaction. But H_2O, being at standard state, need not be written in the K expression, and for simplicity H_3O^+ may be written as H^+. The two expressions then become identical:

$$K_a = \frac{[H^+][Ac^-]}{[HAc]} \tag{5-7}$$

From the degree of ionization and the total "analytical concentration" of the acid, the ionization constant can be calculated. Let M represent the molar concentration of the solute, and α represent the fraction of the solute that is ionized; then $[H^+] = M\alpha$, $[Ac^-] = M\alpha$, and $[HAc] = M(1 - \alpha)$. Consequently,

$$K_a = \frac{(M\alpha)(M\alpha)}{M(1 - \alpha)} = \frac{M\alpha^2}{1 - \alpha} \tag{5-8}$$

Equation (5-8), known as the **Ostwald dilution law**, relates the degree of ionization to the concentration (dilution) of the weak ionogen. The Ostwald dilution law is a special case of the Law of Mass Action as applied to the ionization of a weak electrolyte.

The following examples illustrate several types of calculations based upon the mathematical relations in ionization constants.

EXAMPLE 2

In 0.10 M solution, HAc is 1.34% ionized. Calculate the ionization constant K_a.
Step 1. Write the ionization equation:

$$HAc \rightleftharpoons H^+ + Ac^-$$

Step 2. Formulate the mathematical expression of K_a:

$$K_a = \frac{[H^+][Ac^-]}{[HAc]}$$

Step 3. Compute the molar concentrations of the different solute species, from the information given. If the acetic acid is 1.34% ionized, then α, the fraction ionized, is $1.34/100 = 0.0134$, and $[H^+] = [Ac^-] = M\alpha = 0.10 \times 0.0134 = 1.34 \times 10^{-3}$. $[HAc] = M(1 - \alpha) = 0.10(1 - 0.0134) = 0.0987 = 9.87 \times 10^{-2}$.

Step 4. Substitute the numerical values into the K_a expression from Step 2, and solve:

$$K_a = \frac{(1.34 \times 10^{-3})(1.34 \times 10^{-3})}{9.87 \times 10^{-2}} = 1.82 \times 10^{-5}$$

The above calculation can be simplified, without introducing much error, by noting that when α is small, $1 - \alpha$ is not appreciably different from 1, so that $[HAc]$ is practically equal to M, and

$$K_a = \frac{(1.34 \times 10^{-3})(1.34 \times 10^{-3})}{0.10} = 1.80 \times 10^{-5}$$

Table 5-2 shows the degree of ionization of acetic acid of several different concentrations and the values of K_a calculated as illustrated above. The constancy of the values for K_a shows that acetic acid follows the dilution law, that is, the mass law applies to the ionization of acetic acid. The data of Table 5-2 also show one of the assumptions of the classical theory of ionization, namely, that dilution increases the extent of ionization. The dilution law, in its simplest form, does not apply to the strong (i.e., highly ionized) electrolytes such as

Table 5-2   Ionization Constant of Acetic Acid at 25°C,
Calculated from Conductance Data

M	α	$[H^+] = [Ac^-]$ $= M\alpha$	$[HAc] =$ $M(1 \times \alpha)$	$K_a \times 10^5$
2.0	0.0030	0.0060	1.99	1.81
1.0	0.0043	0.0043	0.996	1.86
0.50	0.0060	0.0030	0.498	1.81
0.20	0.0094	0.00186	0.198	1.75
0.10	0.0134	0.00134	0.0987	1.82
0.050	0.0191	0.00096	0.0490	1.87
0.010	0.0415	0.00042	0.00958	1.85
0.0010	0.125	0.000125	0.00088	1.77
				Average: 1.82

hydrochloric acid, potassium chloride, and sodium hydroxide. These substances, even in quite concentrated solution, are extensively ionized, and the degree of ionization does not change as rapidly with dilution as required by the dilution law; values of K_a, the apparent ionization constant, obtained from measurements and calculations similar to those illustrated for acetic acid, are not constant for the strong electrolytes, but decrease rapidly with dilution.

Any term in the K_a expression can be solved if numerical values for the other terms are known.

EXAMPLE 3

K_a for HAc = 1.8×10^{-5}. Calculate the hydrogen ion concentration, the percent ionization, and the pH of 0.20 M acetic acid. Write the ionization equation and formulate the K_a expression as before. Now let $X = [H^+]$; then $X = [Ac^-]$ also, because the ionization of one molecule of acetic acid gives one hydrogen ion and one acetate ion. $[HAc] = 0.20 - X$; that is, the concentration of acetic acid remaining un-ionized is the total solute concentration minus the amount that is ionized.

$$K_a = \frac{X \cdot X}{0.20 - X} = \frac{X^2}{0.20 - X} = 1.8 \times 10^{-5}$$

This equation, in X^2 and X, is a quadratic equation, which must be solved for X either by the quadratic formula or by the method of successive approximations. Solving by the quadratic formula[4] gives $X = 1.9 \times 10^{-3} = [H^+] = [Ac^-]$; it then follows that

$$\text{percent ionization} = \frac{1.9 \times 10^{-3}}{0.20} \times 100 = 0.95$$

[4] In a quadratic equation, which has the form $aX^2 + bX + c = 0$, the unknown term X is found by use of the formula

$$X = \frac{-b \pm \sqrt{b^2 - 4ac}}{2a}$$

The quadratic equation can be avoided, without introducing appreciable error, by noting that in the weak ionogen $[H^+]$ is small, so that the concentration of acetic acid that is present in un-ionized form is not appreciably different from its total concentration. Thus, in this example, $0.20 - X$ is approximately equal to 0.20, because X is small relative to 0.20. The calculation then simplifies to

$$X^2/0.20 = 1.8 \times 10^{-5}$$

$$X = \sqrt{3.6 \times 10^{-6}} = 1.9 \times 10^{-3} = [H^+]$$

which is the same as the value calculated by the quadratic equation.[5]

$pH = -\log[H^+] = -\log 1.9 \times 10^{-3} = -(0.28 - 3) = 2.72$. Alternatively, pH may be calculated as follows: $[H^+]^2 = 3.6 \times 10^{-6}$; $\log[H^+]^2 = \log(3.6 \times 10^{-6}) = -5.44$; $\log[H^+] = -5.44/2 = -2.72$; $pH = 2.72$.

EXAMPLE 4

At what molar concentration is acetic acid 2.0% ionized? Let $Y = [HAc]$; then $0.020\,Y = [H^+] = [Ac^-]$.

$$K_a = \frac{[H^+][Ac^-]}{[HAc]} = \frac{(0.020\,Y)(0.020\,Y)}{Y} = 1.8 \times 10^{-5}$$

$$4.0 \times 10^{-4}\,Y = 1.8 \times 10^{-5}$$

$$Y = 4.5 \times 10^{-2} = 0.045 = [HAc]$$

That is, acetic acid is 2.0% ionized in $0.045\ M$ solution.

A table of ionization constants of weak acids is given in Appendix II.

Weak Bases.   Exactly the same considerations that were discussed for acetic acid, as a typical weak acid, apply also to weak bases. Ammonium hydroxide is the most common soluble weak base. Ammonium hydroxide, a solution of ammonia in water, has properties characteristic of a low concentration of NH_4^+ and OH^- (as well as simply dissolved NH_3). The equilibrium may be written

$$NH_3 + H_2O \rightleftharpoons NH_4^+ + OH^-$$

but for the sake of simplicity in formulations, one may write

$$NH_4OH \rightleftharpoons NH_4^+ + OH^-$$

from which

$$K_b = \frac{[NH_4^+][OH^-]}{[NH_3]} = \frac{[NH_4^+][OH^-]}{[NH_4OH]} = 1.8 \times 10^{-5} \qquad (5\text{-}9)$$

[5] Whether or not the amount of acid that ionizes can be neglected in problems of this type depends upon both the magnitude of K_a and the concentration of the acid. At very low concentration, even the very weak acids are moderately extensively ionized, and acids that are only slightly weak (e.g., K_a about 10^{-3} or 10^{-4}) are considerably ionized even at moderate concentrations. If a difference of about 5% between the exact and the approximate calculation is allowable, then approximate calculations may be used; otherwise, the exact solution is required.

[Note: it is purely accidental that the ionization constant of ammonium hydroxide has the same numerical value as the ionization constant of acetic acid.] Ammonium hydroxide follows the Ostwald dilution law, that is, the mass law applies to the solution as an equilibrium system. Calculations in the ammonium hydroxide equilibrium system are entirely analogous to those previously illustrated for acetic acid.

Ionization constants of some weak bases are given in Appendix III.

Polyprotic Acids

Acids may be classified on the basis of the number of protons available from one molecule of the acid; thus, HAc is a **monoprotic** acid, H_2S is a **diprotic** acid, and H_3PO_4 is a **triprotic** acid. Experiment has shown that in all polyprotic acids, the ionization takes place in steps or stages, each step having its own characteristic ionization constant. For hydrosulfuric acid, H_2S,

$$H_2S \rightleftharpoons H^+ + HS^- \qquad (5\text{-}10)$$

$$HS^- \rightleftharpoons H^+ + S^{--} \qquad (5\text{-}11)$$

In all cases of polyprotic acids, the extent of ionization decreases with each succeeding step in the ionization. The ionization constant for each step is formulated in the usual way:

$$K_{a_1} = \frac{[H^+][HS^-]}{[H_2S]} = 1.0 \times 10^{-7} \qquad (5\text{-}12)$$

$$K_{a_2} = \frac{[H^+][S^{--}]}{[HS^-]} = 1.2 \times 10^{-13} \qquad (5\text{-}13)$$

Because the second ionization is so extremely slight, as shown by the small numerical value for the second ionization constant in equation (5-13), it does not contribute appreciably to the total hydrogen ion concentration of the solution; for all practical purposes, $[H^+] = [HS^-]$. Hence, from equation (5-13), $[S^{--}] = 1.2 \times 10^{-13}$. The generalization can be made that in all cases of weak diprotic acids, the concentration of the divalent anion is numerically equal to the second-stage ionization constant.

Multiplying equation (5-12) by equation (5-13) gives

$$K_{a_1} \times K_{a_2} = \frac{[H^+][HS^-]}{[H_2S]} \times \frac{[H^+][S^{--}]}{[HS^-]} = (1.0 \times 10^{-7})(1.2 \times 10^{-13})$$

But the product of two constants is a constant, therefore

$$K_{H_2S} = \frac{[H^+]^2[S^{--}]}{[H_2S]} = 1.2 \times 10^{-20} \qquad (5\text{-}14)$$

Equation (5-14) represents the situation as it would be if the diprotic ionization of H_2S occurred in a single equilibrium step:

$$H_2S \rightleftharpoons 2H^+ + S^{--}$$

The analytical uses of hydrogen sulfide are based upon the sulfide ion as a precipitant for cations to form insoluble sulfides, and many separations are based upon control of the sulfide ion concentration by controlling the hydrogen ion concentration of the solution. Furthermore, hydrogen sulfide is generally used by saturating the solution with the gas. In water and in acid solutions at room temperature and pressure, the solubility of hydrogen sulfide is very nearly 0.10 *M*. Because $[H_2S]$ is nearly constant at 0.10, equation (5-14) can be simplified by writing

$$\frac{[H^+]^2[S^{--}]}{0.10} = 1.2 \times 10^{-20} \quad \text{or} \quad K_{ip} = [H^+]^2[S^{--}] = 1.2 \times 10^{-21}$$

$$(5-15)$$

K_{ip} is the ion product constant of hydrogen sulfide; it should be noted carefully that this is *not* an ionization constant; it was derived from the ionization constant by introducing a constant value for $[H_2S]$. K_{ip} is therefore analogous in form to the ion product constant of water, K_w.

Equation (5-15) shows that the sulfide ion concentration of a solution of hydrogen sulfide is inversely proportional to the *square* of the hydrogen ion concentration of the solution; consequently, the sulfide ion concentration of a solution is very extensively influenced by the acidity.

The same general considerations discussed above for hydrosulfuric acid apply to the ionization of phosphoric acid, except that in the latter case ionization takes place in three steps:

$$H_3PO_4 \rightleftharpoons H^+ + H_2PO_4^- \qquad K_{a_1} = \frac{[H^+][H_2PO_4^-]}{[H_3PO_4]} = 7.5 \times 10^{-3}$$

$$H_2PO_4^- \rightleftharpoons H^+ + HPO_4^{--} \qquad K_{a_2} = \frac{[H^+][HPO_4^{--}]}{[H_2PO_4^-]} = 6.2 \times 10^{-8}$$

$$HPO_4^{--} \rightleftharpoons H^+ + PO_4^{---} \qquad K_{a_3} = \frac{[H^+][PO_4^{---}]}{[HPO_4^{--}]} = 4.7 \times 10^{-13}$$

Common Ion Effect

As an equilibrium process, the ionization of a weak acid or of a weak base can be influenced by changes in concentration of an ion produced by the ionogen. Referring again to the case of acetic acid, $HAc \rightleftharpoons H^+ + Ac^-$, this equilibrium can be displaced, from left to right as written, by removing hydrogen ion from the solution by the addition of a base such as sodium hydroxide (i.e., by OH^-); more acetic acid will ionize to readjust the system, according to the Le Chatelier principle. Conversely, this system can be displaced in the reverse direction by the addition of acetate ion (sodium acetate), whereupon the acetate ion combines with some of the hydrogen ion of the solution to form un-ionized acetic acid. This effect is very easily demonstrated experimentally. The common properties associated with acids are the properties of hydrogen ion, and will be exhibited to a pronounced degree if hydrogen ion is present in high concentration, but only to a slight degree if present in low concentration. By the addition of sodium acetate (or any other source of high concentration of acetate ion) to a solution of acetic acid, the acidic properties are decreased, showing that the hydrogen ion concentration has been decreased. The extent of ionization of acetic acid can be suppressed also by the addition of a strong acid, such as hydrochloric acid; in this case the additional hydrogen ions would react with acetate ions and decrease the concentration of the latter. The process in which the ionization of an electrolyte is suppressed by the addition of one of its ions is called the **common ion effect**; it finds many applications in analytical chemistry.

The ionization of ammonium hydroxide,

$$NH_4OH \rightleftharpoons NH_4^+ + OH^- \quad \text{or} \quad NH_3 + H_2O \rightleftharpoons NH_4^+ + OH^-$$

can be displaced by the same general methods as those illustrated with acetic acid; for example, addition of NH_4^+ (e.g., NH_4Cl) lowers the concentration of hydroxyl ion by the common ion effect and the solution containing both NH_3 and NH_4Cl exhibits alkaline properties to a lesser extent than the ammonium hydroxide solution alone.

EXAMPLE 5

K_a of HAc $= 1.8 \times 10^{-5}$. By what amount is the $[H^+]$ of a 0.20 M solution of HAc decreased by making the solution also 0.10 M in NaAc?

$$K_a = \frac{[H^+][Ac^-]}{[HAc]} = 1.8 \times 10^{-5}$$

In acetic acid alone, $[H^+] = [Ac^-]$; given $[HAc] = 0.20$. $[H^+]^2/0.20 = 1.8 \times 10^{-5}$, from which $[H^+] = 1.9 \times 10^{-3}$. In the presence of sodium acetate, $[Ac^-] = 0.10$ and $[HAc] = 0.20$; therefore

$$[H^+] = \frac{K_a[HAc]}{[Ac^-]} = \frac{(1.8 \times 10^{-5})(0.20)}{0.10} = 3.6 \times 10^{-5}$$

By the addition of the sodium acetate, the hydrogen ion concentration has been decreased to less than $\frac{1}{50}$ of its former value.

EXAMPLE 6

What is the molar concentration of acetic acid in a solution that is 0.10 M in acetate ion and 1.0×10^{-5} M in hydrogen ion?

$$[HAc] = \frac{[H^+][Ac^-]}{K_a} = \frac{(1.0 \times 10^{-5})(0.10)}{1.8 \times 10^{-5}} = 5.6 \times 10^{-2}$$

EXAMPLE 7

What is the hydrogen ion concentration of a solution made by mixing equal volumes of 0.10 M HCl and 0.40 M NaAc? Because acetic acid is weakly ionized, mixing a strong acid with a highly ionized acetate results in reaction to form acetic acid: $H^+ + Ac^- \rightarrow HAc$. The reaction consumes one gram-ion of hydrogen and one gram-ion of acetate, and forms one gram-mole of acetic acid. Hence, 0.10 gram-ion of H^+ reacts with 0.10 gram-ion of Ac^-, forming 0.10 gram-mole of HAc, and leaves 0.30 gram-ion of Ac^- in excess. However, by mixing equal volumes of the two solutions, each concentration is decreased to one-half the above values, so that [HAc] = 0.050 and $[Ac^-]$ = 0.15.[6]

$$[H^+] = \frac{K_a[HAc]}{[Ac^-]} = \frac{(1.8 \times 10^{-5})(0.050)}{0.15} = 6.0 \times 10^{-6}$$

(In this example, the *ratio* of [HAc] to $[Ac^-]$ is the determining factor in fixing the hydrogen ion concentration, so it would make no difference whether one used the "original" concentrations without considering the dilution, or the actual molar concentrations. However, there are some equilibrium problems, notably in connection with solubility product constants, in which the actual concentrations must be used.)

EXAMPLE 8

What must be the ratio of the molar concentrations of sodium acetate and acetic acid to give a solution in which the hydrogen ion concentration is 4.5×10^{-5} M?

$$\frac{[Ac^-]}{[HAc]} = \frac{K_a}{[H^+]} = \frac{1.8 \times 10^{-5}}{4.5 \times 10^{-5}} = 0.40$$

Buffer Action. A solution is said to be buffered if it resists change of its hydrogen or hydroxyl ion concentration. Such a solution must contain a component that is an acid (a proton donor) so that it will react with a base, and also a component that is a base (a proton acceptor) so that it will react with an acid. A solution containing a weak acid and its highly ionized salt (i.e., its conjugate base), or a weak base and its highly ionized salt (i.e., its conjugate acid), acts as a buffer. For example, if a strong base (i.e., OH^-) is added to a solution containing acetic acid and sodium acetate, the OH^- reacts with the H^+ of the acid:

$$HAc \rightleftharpoons H^+ + Ac^-$$
$$+$$
$$OH^-$$
$$\Updownarrow$$
$$H_2O$$

[6] Strictly, [HAc] = 0.050 − $[H^+]$ and $[Ac^-]$ = 0.15 + $[H^+]$, because $[Ac^-]$ from the ionization of HAc is equal to $[H^+]$ from the same source. However, $[H^+]$ is so small, compared to 0.050 and 0.15, respectively, that it can be dropped from these terms without appreciable error, thus avoiding solution of a quadratic equation. This principal is generally applicable to calculations based on mass law expressions.

Removal of the hydrogen ion displaces the ionization equilibrium of the acetic acid to replenish the solution in hydrogen ion, so that the concentration of hydrogen ion is essentially unchanged until enough base has been added to be almost stoichiometrically equal to the acetic acid present. Similarly, if a strong acid is added to the buffer mixture, the hydrogen ion is removed by reaction with the acetate ion: $H^+ + Ac^- \rightarrow HAc$, and the hydrogen ion concentration of the solution does not change appreciabiy until nearly the stoichiometric amount of strong acid has been added.

A single compound having appropriate acidic and basic properties may be a buffer. For example, a solution of sodium bicarbonate has some buffer action, because the bicarbonate ion, HCO_3^-, can either furnish protons or accept protons, by reaction with either bases or acids:

$$HCO_3^- + OH^- \rightarrow H_2O + CO_3^{--}$$

$$HCO_3^- + H^+ \rightarrow H_2CO_3$$

Sodium bicarbonate is the "half-neutralized" salt of the weak diprotic acid, H_2CO_3. In general, the partly neutralized salts of weak polyprotic acids exhibit some buffer action, although the buffer capacity (see p. 76) is small.

Example 8 showed that a mixture of an acetate salt and acetic acid, in a mole ratio of 2:5, would give a solution in which $[H^+] = 4.5 \times 10^{-5}$. Although only the mole *ratio* of the base (acetate ion) to the acid in the buffer determines the hydrogen ion *concentration* of the mixture, the buffer *capacity* depends upon the actual amounts of the buffer components, and controls the amount of acid or of base that may be added without consuming all the buffering component.

EXAMPLE 9

For a certain weak acid HA, $K_a = 1.0 \times 10^{-5}$. A buffer solution is prepared which is 0.10 M in HA and 0.10 M in its sodium salt, NaA. Calculate (a) the pH of the original buffer solution; (b) the pH after the addition of 0.010 mole of HCl to a liter of the buffer; (c) the pH after the addition of 0.010 mole of NaOH to a liter of the buffer.

(a) In the original buffer, $[H^+] = K_a[HA]/[A^-] = 1.0 \times 10^{-5} \times 0.10/0.10 = 1.0 \times 10^{-5}$, and $pH = 5.00$.

(b) 0.010 mole of H^+ (added as HCl) reacts with 0.010 mole of A^- (in the buffer), forming 0.010 mole of HA. The new concentrations are $[HA] = 0.11$ and $[A^-] = 0.09$. $[H^+] = 1.0 \times 10^{-5} \times 0.11/0.09 = 1.2 \times 10^{-5}$, and $pH = 4.92$.

(c) 0.010 mole of OH^- (added as NaOH) reacts with 0.010 mole of H^+ (furnished by HA in the buffer), forming 0.010 mole of A^-. The new concentrations are $[HA] = 0.09$ and $[A^-] = 0.11$. $[H^+] = 1.0 \times 10^{-5} \times 0.09/0.11 = 8.2 \times 10^{-6}$, and $pH = 5.08$.

The above example shows that although the acid-base ratio has changed by about $\pm 20\%$, the pH of the solution has changed by only ± 0.08 unit. If only HA, 0.10 M were present in the original solution, the pH would be 3.00; addition of 0.010 mole of strong acid or of strong base would change the pH to about 2.0 and 4.0, respectively. If the same amount (0.010 mole) of strong acid or of strong base is added to a liter of water, the pH is changed from 7.00 to 2.00 and 12.00, respectively.

A solution containing a weak acid, HA, and its highly ionized salt, A^-, is represented by the equilibrium

$$HA \rightleftharpoons H^+ + A^- \tag{5-16}$$

for which the equilibrium constant expression is

$$K_a = \frac{[H^+][A^-]}{[HA]} \quad \text{and} \quad [H^+] = K_a[HA]/[A^-] \tag{5-17}$$

From equation (5-17),

$$pH = pK_a - \log([HA]/[A^-]) = pK_a + \log([A^-]/[HA]) \tag{5-18}$$

The term $[HA]/[A^-]$ is merely the ratio of the molar concentrations of the acid and its conjugate base (salt) in the buffer. Moderate changes in this ratio will not affect the pH of the solution to a great extent. The pH region in which the system exhibits buffer action depends upon the value of K_a. For a solution in which $[HA] = [A^-]$, $pH = pK_a$. By varying the ratio of $[HA]/[A^-]$ from 1/10 to 10/1, the pH will vary over the range $pK_a \pm 1$. For the preparation of buffers in different regions of the pH scale, acids of different pK_a values are chosen.

The same considerations as presented above apply also to a mixture of a weak base (e.g., NH_3) and its conjugate acid (e.g., NH_4^+, an ammonium salt).

Buffer action plays a very important part in many processes of analytical chemistry, industrial chemistry, and biological phenomena. In analytical chemistry it is especially important in effecting certain separations that depend upon careful control of ion concentrations.

Hydrolysis

The ionization of water, although very slight, is the cause of a type of reaction known as **hydrolysis**, which may be defined as the reaction of a substance (atom, molecule, or ion) with the ions of water (H^+, OH^-, or both) to form two products. A further restriction of the definition that is sometimes made is that no electron transfer (redox reaction) is involved.

If one or the other, or both, of the ionic species of water is removed by an irreversible process, the hydrolysis is of necessity complete. This type of reaction is shown by certain binary compounds of nonmetals, for example,

$$PCl_3 + 3HOH \rightarrow 3HCl + H_3PO_3$$

and by certain binary compounds of a metal and a nonmetal which are not salts, for example,

$$Mg_3N_2 + 6HOH \rightarrow 3Mg(OH)_2 + 2NH_3$$

$$CaC_2 + 2HOH \rightarrow Ca(OH)_2 + C_2H_2$$

If the "removal" of one or both of the ions of water by solute species is reversible, an equilibrium system is established, and the extent of reaction depends upon several factors (to be discussed later). Such a condition is represented by the classical hydrolysis reaction of certain salts.[7]

1. Reaction of anions of weak acids (i.e., anion bases); for example,

$$Ac^- + HOH \rightleftharpoons HAc + OH^- \tag{5-19}$$

A solution of sodium actetate is slightly alkaline to indicators, that is, $[OH^-] > [H^+]$, as a result of the removal of some H^+ of water by reaction with Ac^-, and therefore an accumulation of OH^- as demanded by K_w. The equilibrium constant for reaction (5-19) can be formulated in the usual way:

$$K_{hydr} = \frac{[HAc][OH^-]}{[Ac^-][H_2O]} = \frac{[HAc][OH^-]}{[Ac^-]} \tag{5-20}$$

The factor of principal interest in analytical chemistry is the $[OH^-]$ of the solution. Two simple simultaneous equilibria are involved, in which Ac^- and OH^- are competing for H^+:

$$K_a = \frac{[H^+][Ac^-]}{[HAc]} \quad \text{or} \quad [H^+] = \frac{K_a[HAc]}{[Ac^-]}$$

$$K_w = [H^+][OH^-] \quad \text{or} \quad [H^+] = K_w/[OH^-]$$

Hence,

$$\frac{K_a[HAc]}{[Ac^-]} = \frac{K_w}{[OH^-]} \quad \text{and} \quad [HAc][OH^-] = K_w[Ac^-]/K_a$$

In the equilibrium system, $[HAc] = [OH^-]$, and

$$[OH^-] = \sqrt{K_w[Ac^-]/K_a} \tag{5-21}$$

[By simple mathematical manipulation, equation (5-21) can be converted to a formulation expressing directly the *p*H of the solution; see pp. 290–291.]

2. Reaction of cations of weak bases (i.e., cation acids), for example,

$$NH_4^+ + HOH \rightleftharpoons NH_4OH + H^+ \quad (\text{or } NH_3 + H_3O^+) \tag{5-22}$$

---

[7] By the Brønsted-Lowry concept, this type of reaction is simply an acid-base reaction, as may be represented by equation (5-19), in which Ac^-, an anion base, reacts with water (acid) to form the corresponding conjugates, HAc and OH^-. Similar considerations apply to the classical hydrolysis of salt cations (Brønsted acids) such as NH_4^+. Although in modern acid-base treatment the concept of hydrolysis is not *necessary* (and, indeed, is abhorred by some chemists), the term "hydrolysis" for this type of reaction, and "neutralization" for the reverse reaction, are firmly entrenched in chemical terminology; these are useful terms to designate the "direction" of reaction in certain acid-base conjugate systems. A tie-in of historical and modern approach, as given in this chapter, is believed by the author to have some merit.

By reasoning which is entirely analogous to that used in the previous example, it can be shown that

$$[H^+] = \sqrt{K_w[NH_4^+]/K_b} \qquad (5\text{-}23)$$

The student should work through the steps involved and confirm this relation. [Equation (5-23) is easily converted to a formulation for the pH of the solution; see p. 295.]

The hydrolysis of salt anions or cations is of great importance in certain acid-base titrations in which the solution is *not* neutral at the stoichiometric point, and an indicator must be chosen such that its color change interval includes the pH of the solution.

3. Simultaneous reaction of cations and anions. The reaction of ammonium acetate with water,

$$NH_4^+ + Ac^- + HOH \rightleftharpoons NH_4OH + HAc$$

is more extensive than the reaction of either sodium acetate or ammonium chloride, because both the H^+ and OH^- of water are removed by formation of the weak acid and the weak base. Whether the resulting solution is acidic, alkaline, or neutral depends upon the relative strengths of the acid and the base. In the case of ammonium acetate, K_a and K_b happen to have the same numerical value, and the solution is neutral. If K_b is larger than K_a, the solution is alkaline; if K_a is larger than K_b, the solution is acidic. A neutral test with indicators is *not* a valid criterion for the absence of hydrolysis in salt solutions.

4. Many organic compounds, other than the salts derived from inorganic bases and weak organic acids, react reversibly with water. Esters, such as ethyl acetate, react to give the corresponding alcohol and acid:

$$C_2H_5 \cdot C_2H_3O_2 + HOH \rightleftharpoons C_2H_5OH + HC_2H_3O_2$$

The ester may be prepared by the reverse reaction, known as "esterification." Esters are not ionogens, and the hydrolysis and the esterification reactions are characterized by being slow, whereas salt hydrolysis and the reverse reaction, neutralization, are instantaneous reactions.

If hydrolysis is defined without the restriction that no redox reaction shall occur, the following reactions may also be classified as hydrolysis:

$$2Na + 2HOH \rightarrow 2Na^+ + 2OH^- + H_2$$

$$Cl_2 + HOH \rightarrow H^+ + Cl^- + HOCl$$

$$4P + 6HOH \rightarrow PH_3 + 3H_3PO_2$$

The first reaction is very rapid, the second is slow, and the third does not take place with measurable rate except in the presence of alkali to neutralize the H_3PO_2 formed.

Extent of Hydrolysis. The extent to which hydrolysis occurs depends upon a number of factors.

1. *Nature of reactants and products.* In salt hydrolysis the extent of reaction, at a given temperature and concentration of solute, depends upon the strength of the acid and/or base formed. If K_a and/or K_b is rather large (e.g., 10^{-5} M) compared with K_w (10^{-14}) the system comes to equilibrium when only a small fraction of the solute has reacted. As the value of K_a and/or K_b for the different solutes become smaller, hydrolysis is more extensive, and it can be essentially complete if these K-values are approximately the same as K_w.

2. *Concentration of solute.* The equilibrium (hydrolysis) constant formulated as equation (5-20) is the mass law expression for the reaction of equation (5-19). At constant temperature, decreasing the concentration of Ac^- is tantamount to increasing the concentration of water (which is the cause of hydrolysis) relative to the Ac^-, and the smaller its concentration the larger the fraction of the solute that is hydrolyzed.

3. *Temperature.* The degree of ionization of water increases more rapidly with increasing temperature than does the ionization of weak acids or weak bases. At 25°C, $K_w = 1.0 \times 10^{-14}$, and $[H^+] = [OH^-] = 1.0 \times 10^{-7}$; at 100°C, $K_w = 5.0 \times 10^{-13}$, and $[H^+] = [OH^-] = 7.0 \times 10^{-7}$. Since these ions are the cause of hydrolysis, it becomes more extensive at the higher temperature.

GENERALIZED TREATMENT OF ACID-BASE EQUILIBRIA IN WATER

Let A represent an acid and B its conjugate base;[8,9] then, in aqueous solution,

$$A + H_2O \rightleftarrows H_3O^+ + B \tag{5-24}$$

But this system contains two acid-base pairs or conjugates, the separate equilibria for which are

$$A \rightleftarrows H^+ + B \tag{5-25}$$

$$H_2O \rightleftarrows H^+ + OH^- \tag{5-26}$$

In the following formulations, C represents the analytical concentration of a solute, without regard to the relative amounts of ionized or un-ionized forms, and a bracketed symbol represents the *equilibrium* concentration of the indicated species. In the water solution of A, the equilibrium concentration of A is the analytical concentration of the acid minus the amount that is ionized into H^+ (and B); water also contributes H^+ to the system. The H^+ from the acid A is therefore the equilibrium hydrogen ion concentration, $[H^+]$, minus the H^+ furnished by the water, and this is equal to $[OH^-]$. Therefore

$$[A] = C_A - ([H^+] - [OH^-]) \tag{5-27}$$

[8] J. E. Ricci, *Hydrogen Ion Concentration*, Princeton, N. J., Princeton Univ. Press, 1952.
[9] H. A. Laitinen, *op. cit.*

Similarly, if B is added to water,

$$[B] = C_B + ([H^+] - [OH^-]) \tag{5-28}$$

The equilibrium constant for reaction (5-25) is

$$K_{eq} = \frac{[H^+][B]}{[A]} = K_a \tag{5-29}$$

K_a is the ionization constant of the acid A. Rearranging, and substituting equations (5-27) and (5-28) into (5-29) gives

$$[H^+] = K_a \frac{[A]}{[B]} = K_a \frac{C_A - [H^+] + [OH^-]}{C_B + [H^+] - [OH^-]} \tag{5-30}$$

This is a *general* equation for the hydrogen ion concentration of a solution made by adding an acid, or its conjugate base, or both, to water. For certain conditions and types of solutes the above equations devolve to simpler expressions, as indicated below.

Strong Acid

A strong acid is considered to be completely ionized, that is, equation (5-25) is complete as written, and $[A] = 0$. By equation (5-27),

$$0 = C_A - [H^+] + [OH^-] \quad \text{or} \quad [H^+] = C_A + [OH^-] \tag{5-31}$$

For the usual concentrations of acid, $C_A \gg [OH^-]$, and $[H^+] = C_A$. However, if C_A is of about the same order as the concentration of H^+ of water (10^{-7} M), the H^+ furnished by water cannot be neglected. Since $[OH^-] = K_w/[H^+]$,

$$[H^+] = C_A + K_w/[H^+] \quad \text{or} \quad [H^+]^2 - C_A[H^+] - K_w = 0 \tag{5-32}$$

and the quadratic equation must be solved, or equation (5-31) used for calculation by successive approximations.

EXAMPLE 10

Calculate $[H^+]$ and pH of 5.0×10^{-7} M HCl. By successive approximations (successive steps are indicated by subscripts): Using equation (5-31), and $[OH^-] = K_w/[H^+]$,

$$[H^+]_1 = 5.0 \times 10^{-7} \qquad [OH^-]_1 = \frac{1.0 \times 10^{-14}}{5.0 \times 10^{-7}} = 0.2 \times 10^{-7}$$

$$[H^+]_2 = 5.2 \times 10^{-7} \qquad [OH^-]_2 = \frac{1.0 \times 10^{-14}}{5.2 \times 10^{-7}} = 0.19 \times 10^{-7}$$

$$[H^+]_3 = 5.19 \times 10^{-7}$$

The second approximation was sufficient, and $pH = 6.28$.

By the quadratic equation (5-32),

$$[H^+]^2 - 5.0 \times 10^{-7}[H^+] - 1.0 \times 10^{-14} = 0$$

Solving, $[H^+] = 5.2 \times 10^{-7}$, and $pH = 6.28$. The second approximation, above, is identical with the rigorous solution to the problem.

Strong Base

If a strong (completely ionized) base is added to water, $[B] = 0$, and from equation (5-28)

$$0 = C_B + [H^+] - [OH^-] \quad \text{or} \quad [OH^-] = C_B + [H^+]$$

and

$$[OH^-] = C_B + K_w/[OH^-] \quad \text{or} \quad [OH^-]^2 - C_B[OH^-] - K_w = 0 \quad (5\text{-}33)$$

For the usual concentrations of base, $C_B \gg [H^+]$, and $[OH^-] = C_B$.

Weak Acid

If a weak acid A (but not its conjugate base B) is added to water, $C_B = 0$, $[H^+] \gg [OH^-]$, and equation (5-30) becomes

$$[H^+] = K_a \frac{C_A - [H^+]}{[H^+]} \tag{5-34}$$

from which

$$[H^+] = \sqrt{K_a(C_A - [H^+])} \quad \text{or} \quad [H^+]^2 + K_a[H^+] - K_aC_A = 0 \tag{5-35}$$

If the degree of ionization of the acid is small with respect to C_A, that is, if $[H^+] \ll C_A$,

$$[H^+] = \sqrt{K_aC_A} \tag{5-36}$$

Otherwise, $[H^+]$ must be calculated by successive approximations using equation (5-36), or by solving the quadratic equation (5-35). Note that equations (5-35) and (5-36) are identical with the formulations used in Example 3, pp. 57–58.

EXAMPLE 11

Calculate $[H^+]$ of 5.0×10^{-3} M solution of a monoprotic acid for which $K_a = 2.0 \times 10^{-4}$.

By successive approximations, using equation (5-36),

$$[H^+]_1 = \sqrt{(2.0 \times 10^{-4})(5.0 \times 10^{-3})} = \sqrt{1.0 \times 10^{-6}}$$

$$= 1.0 \times 10^{-3}$$

But 1.0×10^{-3} is not negligible in comparison to 5.0×10^{-3}.

$$[H^+]_2 = \sqrt{(2.0 \times 10^{-4})(5.0 \times 10^{-3} - 1.0 \times 10^{-3})}$$

$$= \sqrt{8.0 \times 10^{-7}} = 9.0 \times 10^{-4}$$

$$[H^+]_3 = \sqrt{(2.0 \times 10^{-4})(5.0 \times 10^{-3} - 0.9 \times 10^{-3})}$$

$$= \sqrt{8.2 \times 10^{-7}} = 9.0 \times 10^{-4}$$

and the second approximation was sufficient.

By quadratic equation (5-35),

$$[H^+]^2 - 2.0 \times 10^{-4}[H^+] - (2.0 \times 10^{-4})(5.0 \times 10^{-3}) = 0$$

from which

$$[H^+] = 9.0 \times 10^{-4}$$

the same as obtained in the second approximation above.

Whenever $C_A = K_a$, no answer is possible using the successive approximation method, and the quadratic equation must be solved.

Weak Base

If a weak base (but not its conjugate acid) is added to water, $C_A = 0$, $[OH^-] \gg [H^+]$, and equation (5-30) becomes

$$[H^+] = K_a \frac{[OH^-]}{C_B - [OH^-]} = K_w/[OH^-] \qquad (5\text{-}37)$$

from which

$$[OH^-] = \sqrt{(K_w/K_a)(C_B - [OH^-])} \qquad (5\text{-}38)$$

If $C_B \gg [OH^-]$,

$$[OH^-] = \sqrt{(K_w/K_a)C_B} \qquad (5\text{-}39)$$

The last two equations are of the same general form as equations (5-35) and (5-36) for $[H^+]$ of a weak acid if K_w/K_a is replaced by K_b, the classical ionization constant of a weak base. In equation (5-39), K_a is the acid ionization constant of the conjugate of the weak base. If the base is the anion of a weak acid undergoing the classical hydrolysis reaction

$$B^- + H_2O \rightleftharpoons OH^- + HB$$

the equilibrium (hydrolysis) constant of the reaction is

$$K_h = \frac{[OH^-][HB]}{[B^-]} \qquad (5\text{-}40)$$

Multiplying by $[H^+]/[H^+]$ and making the appropriate substitutions,

$$K_h = \frac{[HB][OH^-][H^+]}{[B^-][H^+]} = K_w/K_a \tag{5-41}$$

If B is a classical molecular weak base (e.g., NH_3),

$$B + H_2O \rightleftharpoons BH^+ + OH^- \tag{5-42}$$

$$K_{eq} = K_b = ([BH^+][OH^-])/[B] \tag{5-43}$$

which is identical with equation (5-39) when K_w/K_a of that equation is replaced by K_b.

From the foregoing it is apparent that the concept of "hydrolysis" of anions of weak acids and cations of weak bases can be treated as conjugate acid-base reactions in the water system, noting that $K_b = K_w/K_a$, and $K_a = K_w/K_b$. For example, the "basic" ionization constant of fluoride ion $= K_w/(K_a$ for HF), that is, $K_b = (1.0 \times 10^{-14})/(2.4 \times 10^{-4}) = 4.2 \times 10^{-11}$. The "acid" ionization constant of ammonium ion $= K_w/(K_b$ for ammonia), that is, $K_a = (1.0 \times 10^{-14})/(1.8 \times 10^{-5}) = 5.6 \times 10^{-10}$. Some writers prefer to give a single table of acid ionization constants, including the cations of weak bases, rather than separate tables of constants for weak acids and weak bases. From such tables, the ionization constant of the weak base is obtained by dividing K_w by the K_a value for the conjugate acid. For example, given K_a for $NH_4^+ = 5.6 \times 10^{-10}$, K_b for $NH_3 = 1.8 \times 10^{-5}$.

Weak Acid and Its Conjugate Base

If both A and B are added to water, the solution may be either acidic or alkaline. If the solution is acidic, $[H^+] \gg [OH^-]$, and equation (5-30) becomes

$$[H^+] = K_a \frac{C_A - [H^+]}{C_B + [H^+]} \tag{5-44}$$

If $[H^+] \ll C_A$ and C_B (acidic solution),

$$[H^+] = K_a \frac{C_A}{C_B} \tag{5-45}$$

This relation, known as the Henderson equation, is identical with the equations used in Examples 5 through 8 for calculating the $[H^+]$ resulting from the common ion effect, and the $[H^+]$ of buffer solutions. It is also used in calculating the pH of the solution during titration of weak acids by strong bases, as illustrated on pp. 287–289.

If $[OH^-] \gg [H^+]$ (alkaline solution), equation (5-30) becomes

$$[H^+] = K_a \frac{C_A + [OH^-]}{C_B - [OH^-]} \tag{5-46}$$

and if $[OH^-] \ll C_A$ and C_B, the equation again reduces to equation (5-45).

Polyprotic Acids

In aqueous solution of a polyprotic acid, H_nA, several equilibria are involved. For a diprotic acid,

$$H_2A \rightleftarrows H^+ + HA^- \qquad K_1 = \frac{[H^+][HA^-]}{[H_2A]} \qquad (5\text{-}47)$$

$$HA^- \rightleftarrows H^+ + A^{--} \qquad K_2 = \frac{[H^+][A^{--}]}{[HA^-]} \qquad (5\text{-}48)$$

$$C_A = [H_2A] + [HA^-] + [A^{--}] \qquad (5\text{-}49)$$

$$[H^+] = [HA^-] + 2[A^{--}] \qquad \text{(electroneutrality rule)} \qquad (5\text{-}50)$$

Rigorous solution of these four equations for the four unknowns, which is mathematically cumbersome, can be avoided by making some simplifying assumptions. Usually, only the first ionization step needs to be considered for hydrogen ion concentration, in which case

$$[H^+] = [HA^-] \qquad (5\text{-}51)$$

$$[H^+] = \sqrt{K_1(C_A - [H^+])} \qquad (5\text{-}52)$$

$$[H^+] = \sqrt{K_1 C_A} \qquad (5\text{-}53)$$

Equations (5-52) and (5-53) are identical with equations (5-35) and (5-36) for a weak monoprotic acid. For very dilute solutions (e.g., 10^{-3} M) of diprotic acids of K_1 less than about 10^{-5}, equations (5-51) and (5-53) are valid, even when K_2 is only an order of magnitude smaller than K_1. Even for very dilute solution of H_2A, for which $K_1 = 10^{-3}$ and $K_2 = 10^{-4}$, a second approximation calculation is usually sufficient. From equation (5-48) and (5-51) it follows that

$$[A^{--}] \approx K_2 \qquad (5\text{-}54)$$

as has already been illustrated for hydrogen sulfide (p. 59).

It is often necessary to calculate the relative amounts of the various species in solution at a given pH, as for example in calculating the amounts of buffer components to prepare a solution of a certain pH, or in calculating the solubility of a salt of a weak acid in a solution of a given pH.

Consider the conjugate system of a monoprotic acid:

$$HA \rightleftarrows H^+ + A^- \qquad K_a = \frac{[H^+][A^-]}{[HA]} \qquad (5\text{-}55)$$

Let α_0 be the fraction of the total concentration in the form of HA, and α_1 the fraction in the form of A^-. Then

$$\alpha_0 = \frac{[HA]}{[HA] + [A^-]}$$

From equation (5-55),

$$[HA] = \frac{[H^+][A^-]}{K_a}$$

Hence,

$$\alpha_0 = \frac{[H^+][A^-]/K_a}{\frac{[H^+][A^-]}{K_a} + [A^-]} = \frac{[H^+][A^-]}{K_a} \cdot \frac{K_a}{[A^-]([H^+] + K_a)}$$

$$= \frac{[H^+]}{[H^+] + K_a} \tag{5-56}$$

Similarly,

$$\alpha_1 = \frac{K_a}{[H^+] + K_a} \tag{5-57}$$

For a diprotic acid, H_2A,

$$H_2A \rightleftharpoons H^+ + HA^- \qquad K_1 = \frac{[H^+][HA^-]}{[H_2A]} \quad \text{and} \quad [HA^-] = \frac{K_1[H_2A]}{[H^+]} \tag{5-58}$$

$$HA^- \rightleftharpoons H^+ + A^{--} \qquad K_2 = \frac{[H^+][A^{--}]}{[HA^-]} \quad \text{and} \quad [A^{--}] = \frac{K_1K_2[H_2A]}{[H^+]^2} \tag{5-59}$$

$$C_A = [H_2A] + [HA^-] + [A^{--}] \tag{5-60}$$

Substituting from equations (5-58) and (5-59) into (5-60) gives

$$C_A = [H_2A] + \frac{K_1[H_2A]}{[H^+]} + \frac{K_1K_2[H_2A]}{[H^+]^2}$$

$$= \frac{[H_2A][H^+]^2 + K_1[H_2A][H^+] + K_1K_2[H_2A]}{[H^+]^2}$$

$$= \frac{[H_2A]([H^+]^2 + K_1[H^+] + K_1K_2)}{[H^+]^2} = \frac{[H_2A]D}{[H^+]^2} \tag{5-61}$$

where D represents the terms within the parentheses. Again, letting α represent the fraction of a given species,

$$\alpha_0 = \frac{[H_2A]}{C_A} = \frac{[H_2A][H^+]^2}{[H_2A]D} = \frac{[H^+]^2}{D} = \frac{[H^+]^2}{[H^+]^2 + K_1[H^+] + K_1K_2} \tag{5-62}$$

$$\alpha_1 = \frac{[HA^-]}{C_A} = \frac{\frac{K_1[H_2A]}{[H^+]}[H^+]^2}{[H_2A]D} = \frac{K_1[H^+]}{D} = \frac{K_1[H^+]}{[H^+]^2 + K_1[H^+] + K_1K_2} \tag{5-63}$$

$$\alpha_2 = \frac{[A^{--}]}{C_A} = \frac{\dfrac{K_1 K_2 [H_2 A]}{[H^+]^2} [H^+]^2}{[H_2 A] D} = \frac{K_1 K_2}{D} = \frac{K_1 K_2}{[H^+]^2 + K_1 [H^+] + K_1 K_2}$$

$$(5\text{-}64)$$

For the general case of a polyprotic acid, $H_n A$, the denominator in the α expression is a polynomial of $n + 1$ terms:

$$[H^+]^n + K_1 [H^+]^{n-1} + K_1 K_2 [H^+]^{n-2} + \cdots + K_1 K_2 \cdots K_n \qquad (5\text{-}65)$$

and the fractions of the different species $H_n A$, $H_{n-1} A^-$, $H_{n-2} A^{--}$, ..., A^{-n} are given by using each term in turn as the numerator.

EXAMPLE 12

For $H_2 A$, $K_1 = 5.0 \times 10^{-2}$ and $K_2 = 4.0 \times 10^{-5}$. Calculate the fraction of each species at (a) pH 3.0; (b) pH 5.0.

(a) For $pH = 3.0$ the denominator of the fraction is

$$D = (1.0 \times 10^{-3})^2 + (5.0 \times 10^{-2})(1.0 \times 10^{-3}) + (5.0 \times 10^{-2})(4.0 \times 10^{-5})$$
$$= 1.0 \times 10^{-6} + 5.0 \times 10^{-5} + 2.0 \times 10^{-6} = 5.3 \times 10^{-5}$$

$$\alpha_0 = (1.0 \times 10^{-6})/(5.3 \times 10^{-5}) = 1.9 \times 10^{-2} = \underline{0.019}$$

$$\alpha_1 = (5.0 \times 10^{-5})/(5.3 \times 10^{-5}) = 9.4 \times 10^{-1} = \underline{0.94}$$

$$\alpha_2 = (2.0 \times 10^{-6})/(5.3 \times 10^{-5}) = 3.8 \times 10^{-2} = \underline{0.038}$$

$$\text{Sum:} \quad 1.00$$

(b) For $pH = 5.0$, $D = 2.5 \times 10^{-6}$, from which α_0 is negligible, $\alpha_1 = 0.20$, and $\alpha_2 = 0.80$. (The student should confirm the calculations.)

Whenever the successive K values are quite well separated (e.g., $K_1/K_2 \geq 10^4$), at any given pH value no more than two adjacent species can be present in significant amounts. On the other hand, when the successive K values are quite close together, as in citric acid (triprotic), at intermediate values of pH the several species may be present in significant amounts.

A convenient way to represent the influence of pH on the species present is to plot the fraction of each species against pH, as shown in Fig. 5-1 for carbonate solutions. When two adjacent species are present in equal amounts, $pH = pK$ for the conjugate pair represented, and the region around this point, where the composition vs. pH curves are steep, is a good buffer region; moderate changes in the acid/base ratio cause little change in the pH of the solution. A diprotic acid-base system has two buffer regions centering around pH values corresponding to pK_1 and pK_2 (see Fig. 5-1). An aqueous solution containing only the acid salt HA^- (e.g., $NaHCO_3$ or HCO_3^-) has some buffer action, but its buffer capacity is at a minimum, as shown by the fact that the composition vs. pH curve has zero slope. Such a solution corresponds to the first end point in

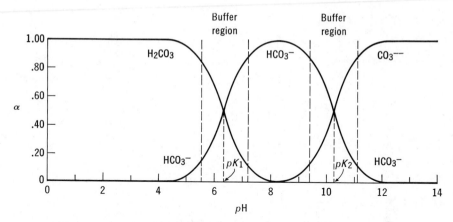

Fig. 5-1   Fraction of various carbonate species at different pH values.

the titration of a weak diprotic acid, where the plot of pH vs. composition has maximum slope (see Fig. 23-4).

Ampholytes

The anion HA^- formed in the first ionization step of a diprotic acid H_2A, is amphoprotic; that is, it can furnish protons or react with protons:

$$HA^- \rightleftarrows H^+ + A^{--} \qquad K_2 = \frac{[H^+][A^{--}]}{[HA^-]} \qquad \text{and} \qquad [A^{--}] = \frac{K_2[HA^-]}{[H^+]}$$

$$(5\text{-}66)$$

$$HA^- + H^+ \rightleftarrows H_2A \qquad \frac{1}{K_1} = \frac{[H_2A]}{[H^+][HA^-]} \qquad \text{and} \qquad [H_2A] = \frac{[H^+][HA^-]}{K_1}$$

$$(5\text{-}67)$$

The ionization of water may also be involved:

$$H_2O \rightleftarrows H^+ + OH^- \qquad K_w = [H^+][OH^-] \qquad \text{and} \qquad [OH^-] = K_w/[H^+]$$

$$(5\text{-}68)$$

The equilibrium concentration of hydrogen ion is composed of the H^+ from the ionization of HA^- ($=[A^{--}]$) plus the H^+ from water ($=[OH^-]$) minus the H^+ consumed by reaction with HA^- ($=[H_2A]$); that is,

$$[H^+] = [A^{--}] + [OH^-] - [H_2A] \qquad (5\text{-}69)$$

Substituting from equations (5-66), (5-67), and (5-68):

$$[H^+] = \frac{K_2[HA^-]}{[H^+]} + \frac{K_w}{[H^+]} - \frac{[H^+][HA^-]}{K_1} \qquad (5\text{-}70)$$

Clearing fractions,

$$[H^+]^2 K_1 = K_1 K_2 [HA^-] + K_1 K_w - [H^+]^2 [HA^-] \tag{5-71}$$

and rearranging gives

$$[H^+]^2 (K_1 + [HA^-]) = K_1 K_2 [HA^-] + K_1 K_w \tag{5-72}$$

$$[H^+] = \sqrt{\frac{K_1 K_2 [HA^-] + K_1 K_w}{K_1 + [HA^-]}} = \sqrt{\frac{K_1 (K_2 [HA^-] + K_w)}{K_1 + [HA^-]}} \tag{5-73}$$

Usually, $K_w \ll K_2[HA^-]$, hence

$$[H^+] = \sqrt{\frac{K_1 K_2 [HA^-]}{K_1 + [HA^-]}} \tag{5-74}$$

If $K_1 \ll [HA^-]$,

$$[H^+] \approx \sqrt{K_1 K_2} \tag{5-75}$$

and $[H^+]$ is independent of the concentration of HA^-.

If $K_1 K_2 > K_w$, the solution is acidic; if $K_1 K_2 < K_w$, the solution is alkaline. In either case, for most values of K_1 and K_2 and reasonable values of $[HA^-]$, K_1 is small compared to $[HA^-]$, $K_1 K_w/[HA^-]$ is small compared to $K_1 K_2$, and equation (5-73) reduces to equation (5-75).

By analogous derivations for a triprotic acid H_3A, it can be shown that in a solution of HA^{--}

$$[H^+] \approx \sqrt{K_2 K_3} \tag{5-76}$$

Equations (5-75) and (5-76) give the hydrogen ion concentration at intermediate stoichiometric points in the titration of polyprotic acids by alkali (see pp. 296–297), or of their alkali salts by acid (see pp. 302–303).

Buffer Capacity

Buffer capacity is defined quantitatively as the number of moles of strong acid or strong base required to change the pH of a liter of solution by one pH unit. In the titration of an acid by a base (or conversely), the slope of the titration curve (see Figs. 23-1 to 23-5) is inversely related to the buffer capacity of the solution. The curve of pH vs. composition (ml of titrant or percent titration) is quite flat (small slope) during most of the titration, because the solution has high buffer capacity; the pH is changed very little by addition of small increments of titrant. Near the stoichiometric point the titration curve is very steep; addition of a small amount of titrant gives a marked change in pH, because the solution has small buffer capacity.

Because buffer capacity, often represented by β, varies with solution composition, and hence with pH, it is best represented by a differential (rate of change):

$$\beta = -\frac{dA}{dpH} = \frac{dB}{dpH} \tag{5-77}$$

where dA or dB represents the number of moles of strong acid or strong base required to produce a change of $dp\text{H}$. (The negative sign indicates that addition of acid decreases the $p\text{H}$.) At any point on the titration curve, β is therefore the reciprocal of the slope of the curve. It can be shown[10] that in a buffer solution consisting of a conjugate acid-base pair,

$$\beta = 2.3 \frac{C_A C_B}{C_A + C_B} \tag{5-78}$$

The solution has its maximum buffer capacity when $C_A = C_B$, and for any given ratio C_A/C_B (which determines the $p\text{H}$), β is proportional to the total concentration of buffer components. The buffer capacity of a solution containing only strong acid or strong base is given by

$$\beta = 2.3 C_A \qquad \text{or} \qquad \beta = 2.3 C_B \tag{5-79}$$

For a solution of an acid salt, e.g., NaHA (HA^-),

$$\beta = 2.3 \times 2C \times \sqrt{K_2/K_1} \tag{5-80}$$

The buffer capacity is proportional to the salt concentration, whereas the $p\text{H}$ is independent of concentration; see equation (5-75).

EXAMPLE 13

Calculate the buffer capacity of 0.20 M HCl. $\beta = 2.3 \times 0.20 = 0.46$. Although 0.46 mole of base is far in excess of the amount of acid present, it should be noted that the buffer capacity is inversely proportional to the slope of the titration curve *at the solution composition given*. Addition of base or acid changes the composition of the solution.

EXAMPLE 14

Calculate the buffer capacity of a solution that is 0.060 M in HA and 0.040 M in NaA. K_a of HA $= 1.0 \times 10^{-5}$.

$$\beta = 2.3 \frac{0.060 \times 0.040}{0.060 + 0.040} = 0.055.$$

EXAMPLE 15

Calculate the buffer capacity of a 0.10 M solution of NaHA; for the diprotic acid H_2A, $K_1 = 1.0 \times 10^{-3}$ and $K_2 = 9.0 \times 10^{-7}$.

$$\beta = 2.3 \times 2 \times 0.10 \times \sqrt{(9.0 \times 10^{-7})/(1.0 \times 10^{-3})} = 0.014.$$

PROBLEMS

Ionization constants of weak acids and weak bases will be found in Appendixes II and III. Formula weights of most of the compounds used in problems in this text will be found in the end papers at the back of the book.

[10] J. E. Ricci, *op. cit.*

78   Quantitative Chemical Analysis

5-1 Calculate pH, pOH, and $[OH^-]$ corresponding to the molar concentration of hydrogen ion given.

(a) 5.0×10^{-3} (e) 2.5×10^{-3} (i) 4.0×10^{-13}
(b) 8.0×10^{-10} (f) 8.5×10^{-6} (j) 2.4×10^{-8}
(c) 4.5×10^{-5} (g) 1.2×10^{-10} (k) 0.80
(d) 2.0×10^{-12} (h) 5.0×10^{-7} (l) 2.0

Ans. (a) 2.30; 11.70; 2.0×10^{-12}. (b) 9.10; 4.90; 1.25×10^{-5}.

5-2 Calculate $[H^+]$, $[OH^-]$, and pOH corresponding to the pH given.

(a) 3.25   (d) -0.48 (g) 7.04   (i) 11.12
(b) 10.90   (e) 4.07   (h) 9.30   (k) 12.50
(c) 0.70   (f) 5.42   (i) 10.92   (l) 13.26

Ans. (a) 5.6×10^{-4}; 1.8×10^{-11}; 10.75. (b) 1.3×10^{-11}; 7.9×10^{-4}; 3.10.

5-3 Calculate pH, $[H^+]$, and $[OH^-]$ corresponding to the pOH given.

(a) 4.07   (d) 11.57   (g) 5.26   (j) 11.90
(b) 10.92   (e) 0.00   (h) 7.70   (k) 12.24
(c) 7.12   (f) 3.80   (i) 10.49   (l) 14.70

Ans. (a) 9.93; 1.2×10^{-10}; 8.5×10^{-5}. (b) 3.08; 8.3×10^{-4}; 1.2×10^{-11}.

5-4 Calculate pH, pOH, and $[H^+]$ corresponding to the molar concentration of hydroxyl ion given.

(a) 1.2×10^{-10} (e) 9.0×10^{-4} (i) 3.8×10^{-8}
(b) 3.4×10^{-2} (f) 5.5×10^{-11} (j) 8.3×10^{-10}
(c) 4.8×10^{-5} (g) 6.4×10^{-6} (k) 0.63
(d) 1.1×10^{-8} (h) 3.1×10^{-13} (l) 4.0

Ans. (a) 4.08; 9.92; 8.3×10^{-5}. (b) 12.53; 1.47; 3.0×10^{-13}.

5-5 Calculate the hydrogen ion concentration (for acids) or the hydroxyl ion concentration (for bases), and also the pH of the solution given.

(a) 0.10 M acetic acid   (f) 0.20 M formic acid
(b) 0.25 M ammonium hydroxide   (g) 0.040 M hypochlorous acid
(c) 0.70 M hydrofluoric acid   (h) 0.020 M ammonia
(d) 0.030 M boric acid   (i) 0.50 M ethylamine
(e) 0.15 M benzoic acid   (j) 0.40 M pyridine

Ans. (a) 1.3×10^{-3}; 2.89. (b) 2.1×10^{-3}; 11.32.

5-6 Calculate the percentage of ionization of the solute in the solution given.

(a) 0.050 M benzoic acid   (f) 0.40 M hydrocyanic acid
(b) 0.025 M formic acid   (g) 0.50 M nitrous acid
(c) 0.40 M hypochlorous acid (h) 0.080 M ammonia
(d) 0.050 M acetic acid   (i) 0.030 M ammonia
(e) 0.20 M boric acid   (j) 0.30 M ammonia

Ans. (a) 3.64. (b) 7.9.

5-7 At what molar concentration does the solute have the percentage of ionization given?

(a) Acetic acid, 1.3%   (f) Hydrazoic acid, 1.3%
(b) Nitrous acid, 4.5%   (g) Hydrazonium hydroxide, 3.0%
(c) Benzoic acid, 2.5%   (h) Ammonia, 2.5%
(d) Hydrofluoric acid, 5.0% (i) Ammonia, 8.0%
(e) Acetic acid, 4.0%   (j) Ammonia, 10.0%

Ans. (a) 0.105. (b) 0.243.

5-8   Calculate the pH of a solution of the composition given.

(*a*) 0.10 M in benzoic acid and 0.50 M in sodium benzoate.

(*b*) 0.50 M in ammonia and 0.10 M in ammonium chloride.

(*c*) 0.30 M in nitrous acid and 0.50 M in sodium nitrite.

(*d*) 1.0 M in ammonia and 0.25 M in ammonium sulfate.

(*e*) 0.20 M in acetic acid and 0.10 M in sodium acetate.

(*f*) 0.10 M in acetic acid and 0.20 M in sodium acetate.

(*g*) 0.050 M in acetic acid and 0.10 M in sodium acetate.

(*h*) 0.25 M in ammonia and 0.20 M in ammonium sulfate.

(*i*) Solution made by mixing equal volumes of 0.20 M acetic acid and 0.12 M sodium hydroxide.

(*j*) Solution made by mixing equal volumes of 0.50 M ammonia and 0.40 M hydrochloric acid.   *Ans.* (*a*) 4.89.   (*b*) 8.95.

5-9   Calculate the weight in grams of the corresponding sodium salt that must be present in 100 ml of the acid solution to give the specified pH.

(*a*) 0.040 M benzoic acid, pH 4.30.   *Ans.* 0.76.

(*b*) 0.25 M formic acid, pH 2.68.   *Ans.* 0.136.

(*c*) 0.50 M nitrous acid, pH 3.10.

(*d*) 0.040 M acetic acid, pH 5.20.

(*e*) 0.080 M hypochlorous acid, pH 6.40.

(*f*) 0.10 M benzoic acid, pH 4.30.

(*g*) 0.050 M benzoic acid, pH 3.66.

(*h*) 1.0 M nitrous acid, pH 3.40.

(*i*) 0.50 M nitrous acid, pH 2.60.

(*j*) 0.050 M hydrazoic acid, pH 4.72.

5-10   How many grams of NH_4Cl must be added to 200 ml of 0.50 M ammonia to give a solution of pH (*a*) 10.00, (*b*) 9.36, (*c*) 8.70?   *Ans.* (*a*) 0.97, (*b*) 4.2.

5-11   How many grams of ammonium chloride must be added to 500 ml of 0.30 M ammonia to give a solution of pH (*a*) 8.95, (*b*) 9.26, (*c*) 10.20?

5-12   In what mole ratio must sodium acetate and acetic acid be mixed to give a solution of pH (*a*) 3.70, (*b*) 4.74, (*c*) 4.92, (*d*) 5.22?   *Ans.* (*a*) 0.090/1.0.

5-13   Exactly one gram of mixture composed only of Na_2CO_3 and $NaHCO_3$ is dissolved in water, giving a solution of pH 10.00. Calculate the percentage of Na_2CO_3 in the mixture.   *Ans.* 41.3.

5-14   Calculate the pH and the percentage of hydrolysis of the solute in the solution given.

(*a*) 0.20 M KCN   (*c*) 0.30 M NH_4Cl

(*b*) 0.40 M Na_2CO_3 (*d*) 0.030 M NH_4Cl

         Ans. (*a*) pH 11.30, 1.0%; (*b*) pH 11.92, 2.08%; (*c*) pH 4.89, 0.0043%.

5-15   Calculate the mole ratio of KH_2PO_4 to K_2HPO_4 in a phosphate buffer of pH (*a*) 6.50, (*b*) 7.21, (*c*) 7.81.   *Ans.* (*a*) 5.2/1.0.

5-16   Calculate the buffer capacity of each solution in Problems 5-8, 5-9, 5-10, and 5-11.

5-17   A solution has a total concentration of $[NH_3] + [NH_4Cl] = 0.10$ M; calculate the molar concentration of NH_3 and of NH_4Cl if the pH of the solution is (*a*) 8.95, (*b*) 9.56.

5-18   Each of the following is saturated with hydrogen sulfide gas at room temperature, at which the molar solubility of H_2S is 0.10. Calculate the molar concentration of sulfide ion in the solution. (Use the combined constant, K_1K_2, for hydrogen sulfide.)

(*a*) Water

(*b*) 0.20 M hydrochloric acid

(*c*) 0.20 M sulfuric acid

(*d*) 0.20 M acetic acid

(*e*) A solution of pH 3.40

(*f*) A solution which is 0.20 M in acetic acid and 0.10 M in sodium acetate

5-19 Calculate the pH and the percent hydrolysis of a 0.10 M solution of the salt given. (Note: If K_a or K_b is of about the same magnitude as K_w, quadratic solution of the problem is required.)

(*a*) $NaC_2H_3O_2$

(*b*) $NaBO_2$

(*c*) NH_4Cl

(*d*) $NaClO$

(*e*) $C_6H_5NH_3Cl$

(*f*) KNO_2

(*g*) C_5H_5NHCl

(*h*) Na_2S

(*i*) K_3PO_4

5-20 Calculate the pH of a 0.10 M solution of the solute given.

(*a*) H_2S

(*b*) $NaHS$

(*c*) $H_2C_2O_4$

(*d*) KHC_2O_4

(*e*) $NaHCO_3$

(*f*) $H_2C_8H_4O_4$ (phthalic)

(*g*) $KHC_8H_4O_4$

(*h*) $KHC_4H_4O_6$ (tartrate)

(*i*) $NaHSO_3$

(*j*) H_3PO_4

(*k*) KH_2PO_4

(*l*) K_2HPO_4

5-21 Calculate the mole ratio of K_2HPO_4 to K_3PO_4 in a phosphate buffer solution of pH (*a*) 12.03, (*b*) 12.21, (*c*) 12.33.

5-22 Calculate the mole ratio of KH_2PO_4 to K_2HPO_4 in a phosphate buffer solution of pH (*a*) 7.81, (*b*) 7.21, (*c*) 6.50.

5-23 Calculate the mole ratio of KH_2PO_4 to H_3PO_4 in a phosphate buffer solution of pH (*a*) 1.60, (*b*) 2.12, (*c*) 2.82.

5-24 Assume that the total phosphate-species concentration is 1.0 M in each of the solutions of Problems 5-21 through 5-23. Calculate the buffer capacity of each solution.

5-25 Assume that the total phosphate-species concentration is 1.0 M in each of the solutions of Problems 5-21 through 5-23. How many grams of each buffer component are present in 250 ml of solution?

5-26 Calculate the mole ratio of Na_2CO_3 to $NaHCO_3$ in a carbonate buffer solution of pH (*a*) 10.55, (*b*) 10.25, (*c*) 9.85.

5-27 Calculate the buffer capacity of each solution of Problem 5-26, if the total carbonate-species concentration is 1.0 M.

5-28 If the total carbonate-species concentration in each solution of Problem 5-26 is 1.0 M, how many grams of each buffer component are present in 500 ml of solution?

5-29 Calculate the fraction of each solute species, at pH increments of one unit (or, if necessary to get appropriate plotting points, at 0.5 pH unit), over the pH range specified. Plot on separate graphs the fraction of each species against pH and mark the good buffer regions.

(*a*) Oxalate, over the pH range 0 to 7.

(*b*) Sulfide, over the pH range 4 to 14.

(*c*) Phthalate, over the pH range 0 to 8.

(*d*) Phosphate, over the pH range 1 to 13.

(*e*) Tartrate, over the pH range 1 to 7.

(*f*) Citrate, over the pH range 1 to 8.

(*g*) EDTA (H_4Y), over the pH range 0 to 12.

5-30 Ten ml of 0.0020 M HCl is diluted with pure water to one liter; 10 ml of the resulting solution is diluted with pure water to one liter. Calculate the pH of the final solution.

5-31 Using the Debye-Hückel limiting law, (1) write the mathematical expression for the equilibrium (activity) constant (expressed as pK_{act}) and (2) calculate pK_{act} at an ionic strength of 0.040. [Parts (c) to (e) refer to ionization steps of EDTA.]

(a) $H_2PO_4^- \rightleftharpoons H^+ + HPO_4^{--}$.

(b) $HPO_4^{--} \rightleftharpoons H^+ + PO_4^{---}$.

(c) $H_3Y^- \rightleftharpoons H^+ + H_2Y^{--}$.

(d) $H_2Y^{--} \rightleftharpoons H^+ + HY^{---}$.

(e) $HY^{---} \rightleftharpoons H^+ + Y^{4-}$.

6

SLIGHTLY SOLUBLE
IONOGENS: SOLUBILITY
PRODUCT CONSTANTS

One of the very important applications of the equilibrium law involves the equilibrium between a slightly soluble electrolyte and its ions in solution. For example, in a saturated aqueous solution of silver chloride, the following equilibrium exists:

$$\text{AgCl (solid)} \rightleftharpoons \text{Ag}^+ + \text{Cl}^- \tag{6-1}$$

Following the usual conventions for formulation of equilibrium constants,

$$K_{eq} = \frac{[\text{Ag}^+][\text{Cl}^-]}{[\text{AgCl}_{solid}]} \tag{6-2}$$

But solid AgCl is at standard state (unit activity), and the equilibrium is independent of the *amount* of solid solute in contact with the solution. The equilibrium is therefore represented by the *solubility product constant*, K_{sp}:

$$K_{sp} = [\text{Ag}^+][\text{Cl}^-] \tag{6-3}$$

Because the concentration of each ion is expressed in moles per liter, the K_{sp} in this case has the dimensions (moles/liter)^2.

When one molecule of a slightly soluble ionogen furnishes more than one ion of the same kind, the concentration of that ion must be raised to the corresponding power. For example,

$$\text{Ag}_2\text{S} \rightleftharpoons 2\text{Ag}^+ + \text{S}^{--} \tag{6-4}$$

and

$$K_{sp} = [\text{Ag}^+]^2[\text{S}^{--}] \tag{6-5}$$

In this case, the K_{sp} has the dimensions of (moles/liter).[3] The formulation can be made general by writing

$$M_xA_y\,(\text{solid}) \rightleftharpoons xM^{y+} + yA^{x-} \tag{6-6}$$

for which

$$K_{sp} = [M^{y+}]^x[A^{x-}]^y \tag{6-7}$$

The K_{sp} has the dimensions (moles/liter)$^{x+y}$. For the sake of simplicity in subsequent treatment and illustrative calculations, the dimensions of the K_{sp} will be omitted and only the numerical value used.

Equation (6-7) is a mathematical statement of the **solubility product principle (law)**; namely, in a saturated solution of a slightly soluble ionogen, the product of the molar concentrations of the ions, each raised to the power that is the number of that kind of ion obtained per molecule of compound, is a constant.

In terms of the molar solubility of the ionogen, the form of the K_{sp} expression can be generalized for solutes of different ion types. For silver chloride, equation (6-1), if s represents the molar solubility of silver chloride, then $[Ag^+] = s$, and $[Cl^-] = s$; hence

$$K_{sp} = [Ag^+][Cl^-] = s \times s = s^2$$

For barium sulfate,

$$BaSO_4 \rightleftharpoons Ba^{++} + SO_4^{--}$$

if s represents the molar solubility, then $[Ba^{++}] = s$, $[SO_4^{--}] = s$, and

$$K_{sp} = [Ba^{++}][SO_4^{--}] = s \times s = s^2$$

For calcium fluoride,

$$CaF_2 \rightleftharpoons Ca^{++} + 2F^-$$

if s represents the molar solubility, then $[Ca^{++}] = s$ and $[F^-] = 2s$, because each molecule of CaF_2 produces two fluoride ions. Hence,

$$K_{sp} = [Ca^{++}][F^-]^2 = s \times (2s)^2 = 4s^3$$

Similar K_{sp} expressions in terms of the molar solubility s can be derived for compounds of any other ion type.

A comparison of the K_{sp} values of two substances gives little information about their relative solubilities (and conversely), unless the compounds furnish the same number of ions per molecule. Suppose that two substances, MA and MA$_2$, have the same numerical value for the K_{sp}, for example, 4.0×10^{-18}. For the compound MA, the molar solubility s is

$$\sqrt{4.0 \times 10^{-18}} = 2.0 \times 10^{-9}$$

For the compound MA$_2$, the molar solubility, s, is

$$\sqrt[3]{(4.0 \times 10^{-18})/4} = 1.0 \times 10^{-6}$$

The molar solubility of MA_2 is 500 times greater than that of MA. Conversely, suppose two compounds, MA and M_2A, have the same molar solubility, for example, 2.0×10^{-5}. The K_{sp} of MA is

$$s^2 = (2.0 \times 10^{-5})^2 = 4.0 \times 10^{-10}$$

The K_{sp} of M_2A is

$$4s^3 = 4(2.0 \times 10^{-5})^3 = 3.2 \times 10^{-14}$$

These examples clearly illustrate the effects of roots and powers of small numbers.

The following examples are illustrative of the types of calculations commonly encountered, based on the solubility product principle thus far discussed.

Calculation of the K_{sp} From the Solubility

EXAMPLE 1

The solubility of silver chloride at 25°C is 0.00019 g per 100 ml. Calculate its K_{sp}.

Step 1. Write the ionic equation for the solubility equilibrium:

$$AgCl \rightleftharpoons Ag^+ + Cl^-$$

Step 2. Formulate the K_{sp} expression:

$$K_{sp} = [Ag^+][Cl^-]$$

Step 3. Calculate the molar concentrations of the ions. The solubility was given as 0.00019 g per 100 ml, which is the same as 0.0019 g per liter (1000 ml). The molecular weight of AgCl is 143. The molar solubility is therefore $0.0019/143 = 1.33 \times 10^{-5}$. Each molecule of silver chloride that dissolves gives one Ag^+ and one Cl^-; therefore, $[Ag^+] = 1.33 \times 10^{-5}$ and $[Cl^-] = 1.33 \times 10^{-5}$.

Step 4. Substitute the known concentrations into the K_{sp} expression of Step 2, and solve:

$$K_{sp} = [Ag^+][Cl^-] = (1.33 \times 10^{-5})(1.33 \times 10^{-5}) = 1.8 \times 10^{-10}$$

(K_{sp} values listed in most tables are given only to two significant figures.)

EXAMPLE 2

The solubility of silver phosphate, Ag_3PO_4, is 0.20 mg per 100 ml. Calculate its K_{sp}.

Step 1.

$$Ag_3PO_4 \rightleftharpoons 3Ag^+ + PO_4^{---}$$

Step 2.

$$K_{sp} = [Ag^+]^3[PO_4^{---}]$$

Step 3. 0.20 mg per 100 ml is the same concentration as 0.0020 g per liter. The molecular weight of Ag_3PO_4 is 419. The molar solubility of Ag_3PO_4 is $0.0020/419 = 4.8 \times 10^{-6}$. Each molecule of Ag_3PO_4 gives three Ag^+ and one PO_4^{---}. Therefore, $[Ag^+] = 3(4.8 \times 10^{-6}) = 1.44 \times 10^{-5}$ and $[PO_4^{---}] = 4.8 \times 10^{-6}$.

Step 4.

$$K_{sp} = [Ag^+]^3[PO_4^{---}] = (1.44 \times 10^{-5})^3(4.8 \times 10^{-6})$$
$$= 1.4 \times 10^{-20}$$

It should be noted that the silver ion concentration was *not* multiplied by three and then cubed (a common student misconception); another number, namely, the molar solubility, was multiplied by three in order to obtain the numerical value for the silver ion concentration; this concentration was then cubed, conforming to the requirements of the solubility product law.

A comparison of the above examples shows that the K_{sp} of Ag_3PO_4 is very much smaller than that of AgCl, whereas the molar solubility of AgCl is only about three times that of Ag_3PO_4.

Calculation of Solubility From K_{sp}

EXAMPLE 3

The K_{sp} of $Ag_2CrO_4 = 1.3 \times 10^{-12}$. Calculate the molar solubility, the molar concentration of its ions, and its solubility in grams per 100 ml.
Step 1.

$$Ag_2CrO_4 \rightleftharpoons 2Ag^+ + CrO_4^{--}$$

Step 2.

$$K_{sp} = [Ag^+]^2[CrO_4^{--}] = 1.3 \times 10^{-12}$$

Step 3. Deduce the concentration of each kind of ion in terms of the molar solubility. If s is the molar solubility, then $[Ag^+] = 2s$ and $[CrO_4^{--}] = s$.
Step 4. Substitute into the K_{sp} expression of Step 2, and solve.

$$K_{sp} = [Ag^+]^2[CrO_4^{--}] = (2s)^2(s) = 4s^3 = 1.3 \times 10^{-12}$$

$$s = \sqrt[3]{(1.3 \times 10^{-12})/4} = \sqrt[3]{325 \times 10^{-15}} = 6.9 \times 10^{-5}$$

$$[Ag^+] = 2s = 1.4 \times 10^{-4}; \quad [CrO_4^{--}] = s = 6.9 \times 10^{-5}$$

The molecular weight of Ag_2CrO_4 is 332; the solubility in grams per liter is $6.9 \times 10^{-5} \times 332 = 2.3 \times 10^{-2}$, which is the same concentration as 2.3×10^{-3} g per 100 ml.

The solubility product constant for a slightly soluble ionogen establishes the criterion for the formation of a precipitate. If the product of the molar concentrations of the ions, with their appropriate powers as required by the law (this product is sometimes called the "ion concentration product," abbreviated ICP) is less than the K_{sp} of the compound formed by their union, the solution is unsaturated and no precipitate can form. If the ion concentration product is exactly equal to the K_{sp}, no precipitate forms, but the solution is saturated with the solute, that is, the solution contains the equilibrium amount of solute. If the ion concentration product is greater than the K_{sp}, a precipitate can form, and will do so unless the phenomenon of supersaturation occurs. A super-saturated solution contains more than the equilibrium amount of solute; this represents an unstable or metastable condition, and the system can convert to the equilibrium (stable) condition by the separation of the solid phase in the amount that is in excess of the solubility. The precipitation of a solute when its solubility product constant is exceeded is another example of the operation of Le Chatelier's principle; the stress imposed by an ion concentration product greater than the K_{sp} is relieved by separation of the solid phase, the formation of which removes ions from solution so that their concentrations are lowered to the equilibrium values.

EXAMPLE 4

The K_{sp} for $BaSO_4 = 1.0 \times 10^{-10}$. If 0.0010 mole of Ba^{++} and 0.00010 mole of SO_4^{--} are brought together in a liter of solution, will $BaSO_4$ be precipitated?

Step 1.
$$BaSO_4 \rightleftharpoons Ba^{++} + SO_4^{--}$$

Step 2.
$$K_{sp} = [Ba^{++}][SO_4^{--}] = 1.0 \times 10^{-10}$$

Step 3. Given: $[Ba^{++}] = 1.0 \times 10^{-3}$, $[SO_4^{--}] = 1.0 \times 10^{-4}$

Step 4. $ICP = (1.0 \times 10^{-3})(1.0 \times 10^{-4}) = 1.0 \times 10^{-7}$ which is much greater than the K_{sp}, 1.0×10^{-10}, therefore $BaSO_4$ will be precipitated.

There are two other methods of solving this problem. From the given concentration of Ba^{++}, calculate the equilibrium concentration of SO_4^{--} and compare it with the concentration of SO_4^{--} given. Or, from the given concentration of SO_4^{--}, calculate the concentration of Ba^{++} at equilibrium, and compare it with the concentration of Ba^{++} given.

EXAMPLE 5

Calculate the concentration of sulfide ion required to start precipitation of FeS from a solution that is 1.0×10^{-4} M in Fe^{++}; the K_{sp} of $FeS = 5.0 \times 10^{-18}$.

Step 1.
$$FeS \rightleftharpoons Fe^{++} + S^{--}$$

Step 2.
$$K_{sp} = [Fe^{++}][S^{--}] = 5.0 \times 10^{-18}$$

Step 3.
$$Given [Fe^{++}] = 1.0 \times 10^{-4}$$

Step 4.
$$[S^{--}] = K_{sp}/[Fe^{++}] = (5.0 \times 10^{-18})/(1.0 \times 10^{-4})$$
$$= 5.0 \times 10^{-14}$$

This concentration of sulfide ion will just saturate the solution with FeS; any greater concentration of sulfide ion will start precipitation of FeS.

DISSOLUTION OF SLIGHTLY SOLUBLE COMPOUNDS

The solubility product constant is also the criterion for the dissolution of a precipitate. A precipitate, once formed under suitable conditions, can be dissolved by any process that makes the ion concentration product smaller than the solubility product constant. There are several ways of lowering the concentration of the ions and thus causing the dissolution of the slightly soluble ionogen.

1. Addition of More Solvent. Decreasing the concentration of the ions in solution by adding more solvent causes the system to readjust by favoring the process which forms more ions, namely, the dissolution of the solid phase. Note that K_{sp} is not changed by adding more solvent.

2. Change of Temperature. The K_{sp} of a slightly soluble ionogen has a characteristic value only at a given temperature. At different temperatures, the saturated solution contains different equilibrium amounts of solute, and therefore it is represented by different numerical values for the K_{sp}. The dissolution of most solids in water is an endothermic process (heat is absorbed from the environment), in which case increasing the temperature increases the solubility of the solid. If such a system at solubility equilibrium at one temperature is subjected to an increase in temperature, the ion concentration product that was equal to the K_{sp} at the lower temperature is less than the K_{sp} at the higher temperature. A change therefore occurs that increases the ion concentration product to a value equal to the K_{sp} characteristic of the higher temperature, that is, more solute dissolves.

3. Removal of Ions by Chemical Reaction. A common application of this principle is the dissolution of slightly soluble salts of weak acids in strong acids. Consider, for example, the action of strong acid (high concentration of hydrogen ion) on a suspension of silver cyanide. The action can be interpreted conveniently by reference to a "box diagram equation" as follows:

$$AgCN \text{ (solid)} \rightleftharpoons Ag^+ + CN^-$$
$$+$$
$$H^+$$
$$\downarrow\uparrow$$
$$HCN \text{ (weak acid)}$$

There are two ionic species competing for CN^-, namely, Ag^+ to form the insoluble AgCN, and H^+ to form the weakly ionized HCN. If a strong acid is added to an aqueous suspension of AgCN, the concentration of CN^- is decreased by its reaction with H^+ to form HCN. Applying the Le Chatelier principle, the solubility equilibrium adjusts for this change by dissolution of some of the solid AgCN to replenish the solution in CN^-. At this new equilibrium condition, the product $[Ag^+][CN^-]$ is still equal to K_{sp} so long as any solid AgCN remains to keep the solution saturated, but now $[Ag^+]$ is greater than $[CN^-]$ because some of the latter has been removed from the system by the formation of HCN. Because $[Ag^+]$ is equal to the molar solubility of AgCN under these conditions, the solubility of AgCN has been increased by the addition of H^+. For a given concentration of H^+, the CN^- concentration of the solution has a value that will satisfy simultaneously the solubility product constant of AgCN and the ionization constant of HCN. This condition is a requirement of the two competing equilibria, and it is also a common sense conclusion, because a solution can have but *one* concentration of a given ionic species or solute. The mathematical considerations are as follows:

$$K_{sp} = [Ag^+][CN^-] \quad \text{and} \quad [Ag^+] = K_{sp}/[CN^-] \tag{6-8}$$

$$K_a = \frac{[H^+][CN^-]}{[HCN]} \quad \text{and} \quad [CN^-] = K_a[HCN]/[H^+] \tag{6-9}$$

Substituting,

$$[Ag^+] = \frac{K_{sp}}{K_a[HCN]/[H^+]} = \frac{K_{sp}[H^+]}{K_a[HCN]} \tag{6-10}$$

For every CN^- removed (by reaction with H^+), one molecule of HCN is formed and one ion of Ag^+ is formed; that is, $[HCN] = [Ag^+]$. (Strictly, $[HCN]$ is not quite equal to $[Ag^+]$ because of the slight ionization of HCN; however, in the presence of excess H^+ the amount of HCN that is ionized is so small that it can be ignored without introducing appreciable error in the computation.) Therefore,

$$[Ag^+]^2 = \frac{K_{sp}[H^+]}{K_a} \quad \text{and} \quad [Ag^+] = \sqrt{\frac{K_{sp}[H^+]}{K_a}} \tag{6-11}$$

$[Ag^+]$, which is also the molar solubility of AgCN, can be calculated from the constants and the known hydrogen ion concentration of the solution. On the basis of these considerations, it follows that a given sample of AgCN can be *completely* dissolved by the addition of *sufficient* acid.

EXAMPLE 6

How many moles of AgCN will dissolve in a liter of 2 M nitric acid? K_{sp} of AgCN $= 1.6 \times 10^{-14}$. K_a of HCN $= 4.9 \times 10^{-10}$. Using equation (6-11), and assuming that the amount of H^+ consumed in the reaction is small compared to 2 M,

$$[Ag^+] = \sqrt{\frac{(1.6 \times 10^{-14})(2)}{4.9 \times 10^{-10}}} = \sqrt{65 \times 10^{-6}} = 8.0 \times 10^{-3}$$

This problem can be approached in another way. The dissolution reaction is

$AgCN + H^+ \rightarrow Ag^+ + HCN$, for which the equilibrium constant expression is $K_{eq} = [Ag^+][HCN]/[H^+]$. Multiplying by $[CN^-]/[CN^-]$ and substituting the appropriate constants gives

$$K_{eq} = \frac{[Ag^+][CN^-][HCN]}{[H^+][CN^-]} = \frac{K_{sp}}{K_a}$$

At equilibrium, $[Ag^+] = [HCN] = \sqrt{K_{eq}[H^+]} = \sqrt{K_{sp}[H^+]/K_a}$ which is identical with equation (6-11).

Silver cyanide is also soluble in ammonia solution:

$$AgCN \text{ (solid)} \rightleftharpoons Ag^+ + CN^-$$
$$+$$
$$2NH_3$$
$$\updownarrow$$
$$[Ag(NH_3)_2]^+ \text{ (weakly dissociated complex ion)}$$

Reasoning entirely analogous to that used for the dissolution of AgCN in acid is applicable to its dissolution in ammonia; the sole difference is that in the latter case Ag^+ is removed from solution by the formation of the weakly dissociated complex ion, $[Ag(NH_3)_2]^+$. Illustrative calculations involving complex ion formation are given in Chapter 7.

The Common Ion Effect in Precipitation

In a saturated solution of a slightly soluble ionogen made by dissolving the equilibrium amount of solute in water, or by bringing together in solution the stoichiometric amounts of the reacting ions, the concentrations of cation and anion are represented by the ionization equation of the solute. In the case of silver chloride, $AgCl \text{ (solid)} \rightleftharpoons Ag^+ + Cl^-$, for which $K_{sp} = 1.8 \times 10^{-10}$. Under the circumstances described above, $[Ag^+] = [Cl^-] = \sqrt{1.8 \times 10^{-10}} = 1.3 \times 10^{-5}$, which is the molar solubility of silver chloride in water. If more chloride ion (e.g., NaCl or HCl) is added to the solution, the equilibrium system will be displaced in accordance with Le Chatelier's principle, in the direction that tends to nullify the increased concentration of Cl^-; that is, Cl^- will react with Ag^+ to form more AgCl. But the solution was already saturated with AgCl; formation of an additional amount results in its precipitation. The K_{sp} formulation shows that as $[Cl^-]$ increases, $[Ag^+]$ must undergo a proportional decrease in order to maintain a constant value for the ion product. The displacement of the equilibrium system just illustrated is an example of the **common ion effect**; advantage is taken of this effect in many processes in quantitative analysis. The operation of this effect is the reason for adding a slight excess of precipitant in all precipitation reactions, for it results in a decreased solubility of the substance precipitated.

The K_{sp} formulation for silver chloride permits the calculation of the solubility of silver chloride in solutions containing known amounts of Cl^- (or of

Ag^+) in excess of the stoichiometric concentration (1.3×10^{-5} M). For example, if additional Cl^- is added until its molar concentration is 1.0×10^{-3}, the concentration of Ag^+, and therefore also the solubility of AgCl, may be computed:

$$[Ag^+] = K_{sp}/[Cl^-] = (1.8 \times 10^{-10})/(1.0 \times 10^{-3}) = 1.8 \times 10^{-7}$$

The solubility of silver chloride in 1.0×10^{-3} M Cl^- solution is smaller than its solubility in water by a factor of about 100.

On the basis of the above discussion it might be supposed that the solubility of silver chloride could be decreased almost indefinitely by continuing to increase the concentration of chloride (or silver) ion. Actually, this is not the case, and the practical limit in decreasing the solubility of most slightly soluble solutes is approximately 0.1 molar concentration of the common ion. One reason for the limitation, in some cases, is the fact that at high concentrations of the common ion another reaction comes into prominence, involving the formation of soluble but weakly dissociated products, such as complex ions. For silver chloride, high concentrations of chloride cause the formation of complex ions, such as $AgCl_2^-$ and $AgCl_3^{--}$, the salts of which are soluble; thus, AgCl (solid) + Cl^- (high concentration) $\rightarrow AgCl_2^-$. Another reason for avoiding large excesses of precipitant is discussed briefly in the next section.

Table 6-1 shows the way in which the solubility of silver chloride changes

Table 6-1 Solubility of Silver Chloride
in Solutions of Sodium Chloride[a]

Molarity of NaCl	Molar Solubility of AgCl $\times 10^5$
0.000 (water)	1.1
0.00386	0.072
0.00924	0.091
0.0176	0.131
0.0365	0.189
0.0884	0.361
0.356	1.74
0.511	2.80
0.975	8.06

[a] Taken from G. S. Forbes and H. I. Cole, *J. Am. Chem. Soc.*, **43**, 2492 (1921); data rounded to not more than three significant figures.

on the addition of excess chloride ion; on addition of small amounts of sodium chloride to the saturated solution the solubility of silver chloride decreases, but it then increases at high concentrations of chloride ion.

The Diverse Ion Effect

Solubility measurements on a large number of slightly soluble ionogens have shown that they are more soluble in solutions of salts than they are in water, even though no chemical reaction occurs with the ions of the soluble salts. For example, silver chloride and barium sulfate are more soluble in potassium nitrate solution than they are in water, as shown in Table 6-2. This is known as the **diverse ion**

Table 6-2   Solubility of Silver Chloride[a] and of Barium Sulfate[b] in Potassium Nitrate Solution

Molar concentration of KNO_3	Molar Solubility $\times 10^5$	
	AgCl	BaSO₄
0.000	1.28	0.96
0.001	1.32	1.16
0.005	1.38	1.42
0.010	1.43	1.70
0.036	——	2.45

[a] S. Popoff and E. W. Neuman, *J. Phys. Chem.*, **34**, 1853 (1930).
[b] E. W. Neuman, *J. Am. Chem. Soc.*, **55**, 879 (1933).

effect, or sometimes as the neutral salt effect, and is due to the influence of the ionic strength of the solution on the activity coefficient of the ions of the slightly soluble ionogen. The relation of activity coefficient to ionic strength and to equilibrium constants has been discussed and illustrated in Chap. 4.

For the slightly soluble ionogen MA:

$$MA \rightleftharpoons M^+ + A^-$$

$$K_{ap} = a_{M^+} \cdot a_{A^-} = ([M^+] \cdot f_{M^+})([A^-] \cdot f_{A^-}) = K_{sp} \cdot f_{M^+} \cdot f_{A^-}$$

where K_{ap} is the *activity product constant*, K_{sp} is the solubility product constant (based on concentrations), a is the activity, and f is the activity coefficient of the ion designated by the subscript. Similarly, for a slightly soluble ionogen of the type MA_2:

$$K_{ap} = a_{M^{++}} \cdot a_{A^-}^2 = ([M^{++}] \cdot f_{M^{++}})([A^-]^2 \cdot f_{A^-}^2) = K_{sp} \cdot f_{M^{++}} \cdot f_{A^-}^2$$

and so on for other ion types. From the known (experimentally determined) solubility of an ionogen, its K_{sp} and the ion activity coefficients can be determined, and hence also its K_{ap}. Once the K_{ap}, which is a true constant, is determined, the solubility of the compound in solutions of known ionic strength can be calculated.

EXAMPLE 7

The solubility of AgCl in water (at a certain temperature) is 1.34×10^{-5} mole per liter. Calculate its molar solubility in 0.010 M KNO$_3$ solution.

$$K_{sp} = [Ag^+][Cl^-] = (1.34 \times 10^{-5})^2 = 1.80 \times 10^{-10}$$

$$\mu = 1.34 \times 10^{-5}$$

$$\log f_{Ag^+} = \log f_{Cl^-} = -0.50 \times 1^2 \times \sqrt{1.34 \times 10^{-5}}$$

$$= -0.50 \times 3.7 \times 10^{-3} = -0.0018 = \bar{1}.998$$

$$f_{Ag^+} = f_{Cl^-} = 0.995$$

$$K_{ap} = K_{sp} \cdot f^2 = 1.80 \times 10^{-10} \times 0.995^2 = 1.78 \times 10^{-10}$$

In 0.010 M KNO$_3$ solution, $\mu = 0.010$. (The Ag$^+$ and Cl$^-$, each at 1.34×10^{-5} M, make negligible contribution to μ in comparison with 0.010 M KNO$_3$.)

$$\log f_{Ag^+} = \log f_{Cl^-} = -0.50 \times 1^2 \times \sqrt{0.010} = -0.050 = \bar{1}.95$$

$$f_{Ag^+} = f_{Cl^-} = 0.89$$

$$K_{sp} = K_{ap}/f^2 = 1.78 \times 10^{-10}/0.89^2 = 2.24 \times 10^{-10}$$

$$\text{Molar solubility} = [Ag^+] = [Cl^-] = \sqrt{K_{sp}} = \sqrt{2.24 \times 10^{-10}}$$

$$= 1.50 \times 10^{-5}$$

In 0.010 M KNO$_3$, the solubility of silver chloride is about 12% greater than its solubility in water.

When the soluble ionogen has an ion in common with the precipitate, both the common ion effect and the ionic strength effect are involved in influencing the solubility of the precipitate.

EXAMPLE 8

K_{sp} of CaF$_2$ = 4.0×10^{-11}. Calculate the solubility of CaF$_2$ (a) in water; (b) in 0.010 M NaF, ignoring activities; (c) in 0.010 M NaF, considering activities.

(a) If s = molar solubility of CaF$_2$, then [Ca^{++}] = s, [F$^-$] = $2s$, and K_{sp} = $4s^3$ = 4.0×10^{-11}, from which $s = 2.15 \times 10^{-4}$.

(b) $s = [Ca^{++}] = K_{sp}/[F^-]^2 = 4.0 \times 10^{-11}/0.010^2 = 4.0 \times 10^{-7}$.

(c) In saturated solution of CaF$_2$, $\mu = 3s = 3(2.15 \times 10^{-4}) = 6.45 \times 10^{-4}$, and $\sqrt{\mu} = 0.0254$.

$$\log f_{Ca^{++}} = -0.50 \times 2^2 \times 0.0254 = -0.0508 = \bar{1}.949$$

$$f_{Ca^{++}} = 0.89$$

$$\log f_{F^-} = -0.50 \times 1^2 \times 0.0254 = -0.0127 = \bar{1}.987$$

$$f_{F^-} = 0.97$$

$K_{ap} = K_{sp} \cdot f_{Ca^{++}} \cdot f_{F^-}^2 = 4.0 \times 10^{-11} \times 0.89 \times 0.97^2 = 3.35 \times 10^{-11}$. In 0.010 M NaF, $\mu = 0.010$ (the CaF_2 makes negligible contribution), and $\sqrt{\mu} = 0.10$.

$$\log f_{Ca^{++}} = -0.50 \times 2^2 \times 0.10 = -0.20 = \bar{1}.80$$

$$f_{Ca^{++}} = 0.63$$

$$\log f_{F^-} = -0.50 \times 1^2 \times 0.10 = -0.050 = \bar{1}.95$$

$$f_{F^-} = 0.89$$

$$K_{sp} = \frac{K_{ap}}{f_{Ca^{++}} \cdot f_{F^-}^2} = \frac{3.35 \times 10^{-11}}{0.63 \times 0.89^2} = \frac{3.35 \times 10^{-11}}{0.50}$$

$$= 6.7 \times 10^{-11}$$

$$s = [Ca^{++}] = K_{sp}/[F^-]^2 = 6.7 \times 10^{-11}/0.010^2 = 6.7 \times 10^{-7}$$

The above example illustrates the decrease in solubility caused by the common ion effect [compare (*a*) and (*b*)], and also the effect of the ionic strength in increasing the solubility [compare (*b*) and (*c*)]. In gravimetric precipitation methods, maximum precipitation of the desired constituent is effected by use of a *slight* excess of the precipitant to take advantage of the common ion effect, but a *large* excess of precipitant should be avoided. In addition to the increased solubility caused by high ionic strength due to a high concentration of precipitant, a large excess of reagent sometimes results in increased solubility due to formation of soluble complexes, as indicated in the previous section.

Fractional Precipitation

Many of the separations in both qualitative and quantitative analysis are based upon differences in the solubilities of substances. In precipitation reactions, these differences in solubility permit fractional precipitation, that is, precipitation of one substance (or a group of substances) under conditions that will not allow precipitation of others. (By the same principle, solubility differences permit the dissolution of one substance, or a group of substances, but not others.)

$$K_{sp} \text{ of } AgCl = 1.8 \times 10^{-10} \qquad K_{sp} \text{ of } AgI = 8.3 \times 10^{-17}.$$

Assume a solution that is $1.0 \times 10^{-3} M$ in chloride ion and $1.0 \times 10^{-3} M$ in iodide ion, and that silver ion is added slowly and continuously to this mixture. The K_{sp} of AgI will be exceeded and AgI precipitated before the K_{sp} of AgCl is reached. This conclusion is reached by calculating the silver ion concentration required for solubility equilibrium for each salt. For AgI,

$$[Ag^+] = K_{sp}/[I^-] = (8.3 \times 10^{-17})/(1.0 \times 10^{-3})$$

$$= 8.3 \times 10^{-14}$$

For AgCl,

$$[Ag^+] = K_{sp}/[Cl^-] = (1.8 \times 10^{-10})/(1.0 \times 10^{-3})$$

$$= 1.8 \times 10^{-7}$$

Because a smaller concentration of silver ion is required to reach the solubility equilibrium for AgI than for AgCl, the former precipitates first. On further addition of silver ion beyond 8.3×10^{-14} M, only AgI precipitates until the silver ion concentration reaches 1.8×10^{-7}, the saturation concentration for silver chloride under the conditions given for the chloride ion concentration. When silver chloride just begins to precipitate, that is, when $[Ag^+]$ is just greater than 1.8×10^{-7}, the concentration of the iodide ion has been decreased, by precipitation as AgI, to a value calculated by

$$[I^-] = K_{sp}/[Ag^+] = (8.3 \times 10^{-17})/(1.8 \times 10^{-7}) = 4.6 \times 10^{-10}$$

Up to this point, the iodide ion has been separated from the chloride ion by **fractional precipitation** of AgI. Continued addition of silver ion causes precipitation of AgCl along with AgI. The ratio of $[I^-]$ to $[Cl^-]$ in the solution (which is saturated with both AgI and AgCl) can be calculated from the K_{sp} values by noting that the concentration of silver ion is the same in each separate solubility equilibrium:

$$\frac{K_{sp}}{K_{sp}} = \frac{[\cancel{Ag^+}][I^-]}{[\cancel{Ag^+}][Cl^-]} = \frac{8.3 \times 10^{-17}}{1.8 \times 10^{-10}}$$

hence,

$$[I^-]/[Cl^-] = 4.6 \times 10^{-7}$$

From the point at which both salts are precipitating, it follows that $1/4.6 \times 10^{-7} = 2.2 \times 10^6$ molecules of AgCl must precipitate for every molecule of AgI that precipitates, in order to maintain the ratio of ions calculated above.

Now assume a solution that is 0.10 M in Cl^- and 1.0×10^{-8} M in I^-. Upon addition of Ag^+ to this mixture AgCl is precipitated first.

$$[Ag^+] = K_{sp}/[Cl^-] = (1.8 \times 10^{-10})/(1.0 \times 10^{-1}) = 1.8 \times 10^{-9}$$

which is smaller than

$$[Ag^+] = K_{sp}/[I^-] = (8.3 \times 10^{-17})/(1.0 \times 10^{-8}) = 8.3 \times 10^{-9}$$

From the foregoing, two important requisites for fractional precipitation can be deduced: (1) The solubilities of the substances to be separated by a common precipitant must be widely different. (2) The concentrations of the ions to be separated by reaction with the precipitating ion must not be widely disproportionate to the difference in solubilities of the compounds formed.

Transposition of Insoluble Compounds

If, to an aqueous suspension of a slightly soluble ionogen, an ion is added that forms a less soluble compound with one of the ions of the first substance, the first compound will transpose to the second. For example, addition of chloride ion to a suspension of silver chromate causes the latter to transpose to silver chloride:

$$Ag_2CrO_4 + 2Cl^- \rightarrow CrO_4^{--} + 2AgCl$$

The transposition is readily observed; silver chromate is red-orange in color; upon addition of chloride ion, the red-orange solid disappears by transposition to a white precipitate of silver chloride suspended in a yellow solution (CrO_4^{--}). Transposition occurs because the silver ion concentration, in solubility equilibrium with the amount of chloride ion present, is less than the silver ion concentration in the saturated solution of silver chromate. Up to a certain point, both silver chromate and silver chloride solids will be present, but if the chloride ion concentration is made sufficiently high, all the silver chromate will be transposed to silver chloride. The K_{sp} values of the two compounds permit calculation of the equilibrium concentrations. K_{sp} of silver chromate is 1.3×10^{-12}; K_{sp} of silver chloride is 1.8×10^{-10}. In a solution saturated with both salts,

$$[Ag^+][Cl^-] = 1.8 \times 10^{-10}$$

and

$$[Ag^+] = (1.8 \times 10^{-10})/[Cl^-]$$

$$[Ag^+]^2[CrO_4^{--}] = 1.3 \times 10^{-12}$$

and

$$[Ag^+] = \sqrt{(1.3 \times 10^{-12})/[CrO_4^{--}]}$$

At equilibrium these concentrations of Ag^+ must be equal,

$$\frac{1.8 \times 10^{-10}}{[Cl^-]} = \sqrt{\frac{1.3 \times 10^{-12}}{[CrO_4^{--}]}}$$

and

$$\frac{[Cl^-]}{\sqrt{[CrO_4^{--}]}} = \frac{1.8 \times 10^{-10}}{\sqrt{1.3 \times 10^{-12}}} = 1.6 \times 10^{-4}$$

These considerations are used in the indicator action in the titrimetric determination of chloride by the Mohr method, in which chloride ion is titrated by silver ion in the presence of chromate ion as the indicator. Silver chromate cannot form permanently in the mixture until virtually all the chloride ion is precipitated as silver chloride.

Even though a first compound may be somewhat less soluble than a second, extensive transposition of the first to the second may be accomplished by the use of a very high concentration of transposing reagent. K_{sp} of $BaSO_4 = 1.0 \times 10^{-10}$;

K_{sp} of $BaCO_3 = 5.1 \times 10^{-9}$. Although barium sulfate is less soluble than barium carbonate, transposition of barium sulfate according to the reaction

$$BaSO_4 + CO_3^{--} \rightarrow SO_4^{--} + BaCO_3$$

can be made by boiling solid barium sulfate with a concentrated solution of sodium carbonate. From the K_{sp} values it is possible to calculate the carbonate ion concentration required to transpose a given amount of barium sulfate, or to calculate the amount of barium sulfate that can be transposed by a given carbonate ion concentration.

$$\frac{[Ba^{++}][CO_3^{--}]}{[Ba^{++}][SO_4^{--}]} = \frac{5.1 \times 10^{-9}}{1.0 \times 10^{-10}} = 5.1 \times 10^1 = 51$$

$$[CO_3^{--}] = 51[SO_4^{--}]$$

or

$$[SO_4^{--}] = [CO_3^{--}]/51 = 2.0 \times 10^{-2}[CO_3^{--}]$$

In analytical chemistry advantage is taken of this transposition in order to effect a "decomposition" of barium sulfate, which is not appreciably soluble in any common reagent; after transposing the barium sulfate with sodium carbonate, the insoluble barium carbonate is filtered off, leaving the sulfate ion in the filtrate. The barium carbonate is then dissolved in acid, putting the barium ion into solution.

Transpositions with sodium carbonate are frequently done by **fusion** of the insoluble compound with sodium carbonate. After the melt has cooled it is extracted with water, which then contains the anion of the original insoluble compound (along with the excess of sodium carbonate). The insoluble carbonate formed by transposition is filtered off and dissolved in acid, which puts the cation of the original compound into solution.

PROBLEMS

Solubility product constants will be found in Appendix I. Formula weights of the compounds are given on the end papers at the back of the book. In solving these problems, ignore activities except where the problem statement indicates the contrary.

6-1 From the solubility given, calculate the K_{sp} of the compound.

Compound	Solubility, mg/100 ml	Compound	Solubility, mg/100 ml
(a) AgBr	0.013	(h) Hg_2I_2	1.46×10^{-5}
(b) CaF_2	1.7	(i) SrC_2O_4	0.415
(c) Hg_2Br_2	0.0014	(j) $Pb_3(PO_4)_2$	1.2×10^{-4}
(d) $Sr_3(PO_4)_2$	0.012	(k) Ag_2S	1.1×10^{-13}
(e) CuI	0.020	(l) $MgNH_4PO_4$	0.86
(f) $Fe(OH)_3$	3.8×10^{-6}	(m) TlBr	54
(g) Ag_2CrO_4	2.24	(n) $AgIO_3$	5.0

Ans. (a) 4.8×10^{-13}. (b) 4.3×10^{-11}. (c) 6.2×10^{-23}.

6-2 From the K_{sp} of the compound given, calculate (1) the molar solubility, and (2) the solubility in mg/100 ml.

(a) $Fe(OH)_2$ (f) $Ca(IO_3)_2$ (k) $Mn(OH)_2$

(b) $Fe(OH)_3$ (g) Hg_2Cl_2 (l) Bi_2S_3

(c) Hg_2I_2 (h) $Mg(OH)_2$ (m) Tl_2S

(d) $Pb_3(PO_4)_2$ (i) $Pb(IO_3)_2$ (n) $Pb_3(AsO_4)_2$

(e) AgI (j) $Cr(OH)_3$ (o) $Ce(IO_3)_3$

Ans. (a) 7.0×10^{-6}; 6.3×10^{-2}.

(b) 3.6×10^{-10}; 3.9×10^{-6}.

(c) 2.24×10^{-10}; 1.46×10^{-5}.

6-3 Calculate the molar concentration of bromide ion required to start precipitation from 0.0010 M solution of (a) Ag^+, (b) Pb^{++}.

Ans. (a) $>5.0 \times 10^{-10}$.   (b) >0.197.

6-4 Calculate the molar concentration of sulfide ion required to start precipitation of the metal sulfide from the solution given.

(a) Saturated aqueous solution of $AgCl$.

(b) Solution containing 50 mg of Cd^{++}/100 ml.

Ans. (a) $>1.8 \times 10^{-42}$.   (b) $>1.59 \times 10^{-24}$.

6-5 Calculate the concentration (1) in moles per liter, and (2) in mg/100 ml, of the cation remaining unprecipitated from solution in which the sulfide ion concentration is 2.0×10^{-10} M.

(a) Bi^{+++}.   *Ans.* 3.5×10^{-34}; 7.3×10^{-30}.

(b) Mn^{++}.   *Ans.* 5.5×10^{-6}; 3.0×10^{-2}.

6-6 Calculate the solubility (1) in moles per liter, and (2) in mg/100 ml, of the following under the conditions stated.

(a) Ag_2CrO_4 in a solution that is 0.0010 M in CrO_4^{--}.

(b) Ag_2CrO_4 in a solution that is 0.0010 M in Ag^+.

(c) $Ba_3(PO_4)_2$ in a solution that is 0.0010 M in PO_4^{---}.

Ans. (a) 1.8×10^{-5}; 0.60.

(b) 1.3×10^{-6}; 4.3×10^{-2}.

(c) 6×10^{-12}; 3.6×10^{-7}.

6-7 A certain solution is 0.010 M in Sr^{++} and 0.10 M in Ca^{++}.

(a) Upon the slow addition of ammonium oxalate to the mixture, which salt, SrC_2O_4 or CaC_2O_4, will precipitate first? Make calculations to prove your answer, and explain briefly.

(b) Calculate the molar concentration ratio $[Sr^{++}]/[Ca^{++}]$ when the solution is saturated with both oxalates.

(c) Calculate the concentration of the cation first precipitated when the second cation begins to precipitate as its oxalate.

Ans. (a) CaC_2O_4.   (b) $0.43/1.0$.   (c) $[Ca^{++}] = 0.023$.

6-8 Equal volumes of saturated aqueous solution of $BaSO_4$ and Ag_2CrO_4 are mixed. [*Note:* By mixing equal volumes of the two solutions, the available concentration of each ion is decreased to one-half its original concentration.]

(a) Will a precipitate of $BaCrO_4$ form? Prove by calculation.

Ans. Yes. ICP = 1.7×10^{-10}, which is larger than K_{sp}.

(b) Will a precipitate of Ag_2SO_4 form? Prove by calculation.

Ans. No. ICP = 2.3×10^{-14}, which is smaller than K_{sp}.

6-9 How many grams of CaF_2 can be transposed to $CaCO_3$ by treating excess CaF_2

with 200 ml of solution in which the final concentration of carbonate ion is 0.10 M?

Ans. 0.225.

6-10 A certain solution is 0.010 M in Zn^{++} and 0.010 M in Mn^{++}. Calculate the permissible pH range (minimum and maximum pH) so that when the solution is saturated with H_2S (0.1 M) a quantitative separation of Zn^{++} from Mn^{++} can be made. [*Note:* Assume an ion to be quantitatively precipitated when its molar concentration is decreased to 10^{-6} M or less.] *Ans. pH range 1.41 to 3.98.*

6-11 Calculate the pH range that will permit the quantitative separation of Fe^{+++} from Fe^{++} by hydroxide precipitation from a solution in which each ion is 0.010 M. [See *Note* in Problem 6-10.]

6-12 Calculate the molar concentration of iodide ion required to start precipitation from the solution given.

(*a*) 1.0×10^{-4} M Ag^+.
(*b*) 0.0010 M Pb^{++}.
(*c*) 0.10 M Tl^+.
(*d*) 0.0010 M Hg_2^{++}.
(*e*) 1.0×10^{-7} M Hg_2^{++}.
(*f*) 0.010 M Hg^{++}.

6-13 Calculate the molar concentration of sulfide ion required to start precipitation from 1.0×10^{-4} M solution of the cation given.

(*a*) Ag^+ (*c*) Hg^{++} (*e*) Cd^{++} (*g*) Fe^{++}
(*b*) Pb^{++} (*d*) Bi^{+++} (*f*) Mn^{++} (*h*) Zn^{++}

6-14 Calculate the molar concentration of hydroxyl ion required to start precipitation from the solution given.

(*a*) Solution containing 50 mg of Ag^+ per 100 ml.
(*b*) Solution containing 50 mg of $AgNO_3$ per 100 ml.
(*c*) Solution containing 0.50 mg of Fe^{+++} per liter.
(*d*) Solution containing 100 mg of $MgCl_2$ per 100 ml.
(*e*) Saturated solution of $MnCO_3$.
(*f*) Saturated solution of $Ca(IO_3)_2$.
(*g*) Saturated solution of CuC_2O_4.
(*h*) Saturated solution of FeS.

6-15 How many grams of NH_4Cl must be added to 200 ml of a solution that is 0.010 M in Mg^{++} and 0.10 M in NH_3 in order to prevent the precipitation of $Mg(OH)_2$?

6-16 Calculate the concentration (1) in moles per liter, and (2) in mg/100 ml, of the cation remaining unprecipitated from a solution that has a hydroxyl concentration of 0.0050 M.

(*a*) Ag^+ (*c*) Cd^{++} (*e*) Cr^{+++} (*g*) Mg^{++}
(*b*) Al^{+++} (*d*) Ce^{+++} (*f*) Ni^{++} (*h*) Cu^{++}

6-17 Calculate the concentration (1) in moles per liter, and (2) in mg/100 ml, of the cation remaining unprecipitated from a solution in which the sulfide ion concentration is 2.0×10^{-9} M.

(*a*) Ag^+ (*c*) Bi^{+++} (*e*) Cu^+ (*g*) Co^{++}
(*b*) Pb^{++} (*d*) Cu^{++} (*f*) Hg_2^{++} (*h*) Ni^{++}

6-18 Calculate the volume of water required to just dissolve the substance given.

(*a*) 10.0 mg of PbF_2.
(*b*) 0.50 mg of $BaSO_4$.
(*c*) 20 mg of $Ca(IO_3)_2$.
(*d*) 1.0 mg of MnS.
(*e*) 1.0 μg (1.0 *microgram* = 10^{-6} g) of $Fe(OH)_3$.
(*f*) A *single molecule* of HgS (one mole = 6.0×10^{23} molecules).

6-19 In each case show whether or not a precipitate will form; assume absence of supersaturation.

(a) Equal volumes of 0.010 M $CaCl_2$ and 0.010 M NaOH are mixed.

(b) 100 ml of 0.0015 M Ag^+ is mixed with 200 ml of 0.0010 M PO_4^{---}.

(c) 1.0 ml of 0.10 M Sr^{++} is added to one liter of 0.050 M CrO_4^{--}.

(d) 1.0 μg of Ag^+ and 1.0 μg of I^- are added to 500 ml of water.

(e) 1.0 mg of $Ca(NO_3)_2$ and 1.0 mg of $(NH_4)_2C_2O_4$ are added to one liter of water.

6-20   Calculate the solubility (1) in moles per liter and (2) in mg/100 ml of the given compound under the conditions stated.

(a) CaC_2O_4 in a solution that is 0.0010 M in $C_2O_4^{--}$.

(b) $BaSO_4$ in a solution that is 0.0010 M in SO_4^{--}.

(c) $Ca_3(PO_4)_2$ in a solution that is 1.0×10^{-5} M in PO_4^{---}.

(d) $Ca_3(PO_4)_2$ in a solution that is 1.0×10^{-5} M in Ca^{++}.

(e) Hg_2I_2 in a solution that is 1.0×10^{-4} M in I^-.

(f) Hg_2I_2 in a solution that is 1.0×10^{-4} M in Hg_2^{++}.

(g) $Pb(IO_3)_2$ precipitated by mixing 100 ml of 0.10 M $Pb(NO_3)_2$ with 300 ml of 0.10 M KIO_3.

6-21   Calculate the solubility loss, in milligrams, (1) in the precipitation mixture and (2) in the wash water, when $BaSO_4$ is precipitated under the conditions stated. [Assume that the supernatant solution is drained completely from the precipitate before washing.]

(a) Exactly equivalent amounts of Ba^{++} and SO_4^{--} are mixed in a volume of 200 ml; volume of wash water, 200 ml.

(b) Volume of reaction mixture, 300 ml, and solution is 0.0020 M in SO_4^{--}; volume of wash water, 150 ml.

(c) What is the percent error due to solubility loss, in each of the above cases, if the precipitate weighs 0.50 g? 0.050 g?

6-22   Calculate the solubility loss, in milligrams, (1) in the precipitation mixture and (2) in the wash water, when PbI_2 is precipitated under the conditions stated. [Same assumption as in Problem 6-21.]

(a) Exactly equivalent amounts of Pb^{++} and I^- are used, in a volume of 250 ml; volume of wash water, 100 ml.

(b) Volume of solution, 250 ml; supernatant solution is 0.0050 M in I^-; volume of wash water, 100 ml.

(c) Same as (b), except supernatant solution is 0.0050 M in Pb^{++}.

6-23   A certain solution is 0.10 M in Br^- and 0.0010 M in I^-.

(a) Upon the slow addition of silver nitrate to the above mixture, which silver salt, AgBr or AgI, will precipitate first? Make calculations to prove your answer, and explain briefly.

(b) Calculate the molar concentration ratio $[Br^-]/[I^-]$ when the solution is saturated with both silver salts.

(c) Calculate the concentration of the anion first precipitated when the second anion begins to precipitate as its silver salt.

6-24   Repeat the calculations as in Problem 6-23 for a solution that is 0.10 M in CNS^- and 0.0010 M in Br^-. In part (b) calculate the molar concentration ratio $[CNS^-]/[Br^-]$ when the solution is saturated with both silver salts.

6-25   A certain solution is 0.10 M in Ca^{++} and 0.010 M in Ba^{++}.

(a) Upon the slow addition of ammonium oxalate to the mixture, which salt, CaC_2O_4 or BaC_2O_4, will precipitate first? Make calculations to prove your answer, and explain briefly.

(b) Calculate the molar concentration ratio $[Ca^{++}]/[Ba^{++}]$ when the solution is saturated with both oxalates.

(c) Calculate the concentration of the cation first precipitated when the second cation begins to precipitate as its oxalate.

(d) Repeat the calculations of (a), (b), and (c) for a solution that is 0.010 M in Ca^{++} and 0.10 M in Ba^{++}. Is fractional precipitation as oxalate a feasible method of effecting an analytical separation of Ca^{++} from Ba^{++}? Explain.

6-26 A certain solution contains equal molar concentrations of Pb^{++} and Ba^{++}. Make calculations and give appropriate explanations to show whether or not separation of these ions from one another is feasible by fractional precipitation as (a) carbonate; (b) sulfate; (c) oxalate; (d) fluoride; (e) chromate.

6-27 Equal volumes of saturated solution of the substances given are mixed. Make calculations and explanations as indicated. [See *Note* in Problem 6-8.]

(a) CdC_2O_4 and $CuCO_3$. Will $CdCO_3$ precipitate? Will CuC_2O_4 precipitate?

(b) $CaSO_4$ and BaC_2O_4. Will CaC_2O_4 precipitate? Will $BaSO_4$ precipitate?

6-28 Saturated aqueous solutions of the substances given are mixed in the ratio of 200 ml of the first with 100 ml of the second. Make calculations and appropriate explanations.

(a) $SrCrO_4$ and $PbCO_3$. Will $SrCO_3$ precipitate? Will $PbCrO_4$ precipitate?

(b) Ag_2CrO_4 and $BaSO_4$. Will Ag_2SO_4 precipitate? Will $BaCrO_4$ precipitate?

6-29 How many grams of CaF_2 can be transposed to $CaCO_3$ by treating excess CaF_2 with 100 ml of solution in which the final carbonate ion concentration is 0.10 M?

6-30 How many grams of $BaSO_4$ can be transposed to $BaCO_3$ by treating excess $BaSO_4$ with 250 ml of solution in which the final carbonate ion concentration is 0.050 M?

6-31 How many grams of $Sr_3(PO_4)_2$ can be transposed to $SrCO_3$ by treating excess $Sr_3(PO_4)_2$ with 200 ml of solution in which the final carbonate ion concentration is 0.50 M?

6-32 How many grams of AgCNS can be transposed to AgCl by treating excess AgCNS with 250 ml of solution in which the final chloride ion concentration is 0.10 M? How many grams of NaCl must be added to attain the equilibrium conditions?

6-33 How many grams of the water-insoluble compound given can be dissolved in 200 ml of strong acid (e.g., HNO_3) at equilibrium with the hydrogen ion concentration stated?

(a) CaF_2; $[H^+] = 0.20$.

(b) BaF_2; $[H^+] = 0.050$.

(c) SnS; $[H^+] = 0.10$. $(SnS + 2H^+ \rightleftharpoons Sn^{++} + H_2S)$

(d) FeS; $[H^+] = 0.10$.

(e) $CaSO_4$; $[H^+] = 0.20$. $(CaSO_4 + H^+ \rightleftharpoons Ca^{++} + HSO_4^-)$

(f) Ag_2CrO_4; $[H^+] = 0.020$. $(Ag_2CrO_4 + H^+ \rightleftharpoons 2Ag^+ + HCrO_4^-)$

6-34 Calculate the molar solubility of the given compound in the electrolyte solutions stated; use activity coefficients calculated from the Debye-Hückel limiting law.

(a) HgI_2 in (1) 0.020 M KNO_3; (2) 0.020 M K_2SO_4.

(b) $PbCl_2$ in (1) 0.010 M $NaNO_3$; (2) 0.010 M $Ca(NO_3)_2$.

(c) MgF_2 in (1) 0.020 M $MgCl_2$; (2) 0.010 M NaF.

(d) Ag_2CrO_4 in (1) 0.10 M KNO_3; (2) 0.010 M $Mg(NO_3)_2$; (3) 0.010 M $MgCrO_4$.

7

COMPLEX IONS

Before discussing the formation of complex ions and their application in analytical chemistry, it is appropriate to review the mode of formation of the different kinds of chemical bonds.

Metal atoms that have only a few electrons in the outermost electron shell tend to lose these electrons by transfer to other atoms, and thus acquire the stable electron configuration of the next lower inert gas. Similarly, nonmetal atoms having only a few less than eight electrons in the outer shell tend to gain electrons by transfer from other atoms, and thus acquire the stable electron configuration of the next higher inert gas. For example in the reaction of sodium with chlorine, an electron is *transferred* from the sodium atom to the chlorine atom, forming a sodium ion and a chloride ion:

$$Na + :\overset{\frown}{\underset{..}{Cl}}: \rightarrow Na^+ + :\underset{..}{\overset{..}{Cl}}:^-$$

The oppositely charged ions are held in the crystal lattice of sodium chloride by forces that are principally electrostatic. This type of chemical bond, formed by electron transfer from one atom to another, is called an **electrovalent** or a **polar** bond.

Some atoms can complete an octet of electrons by mutual sharing of electrons between atoms. Several of the nonmetallic elements complete an octet of electrons by sharing electrons with other atoms of the same element, forming diatomic molecules; thus,

$$:\underset{..}{Cl}. + \cdot\underset{..}{\overset{..}{Cl}}: \rightarrow :\underset{..}{\overset{..}{Cl}}:\underset{..}{\overset{..}{Cl}}:$$

Molecular chlorine, Cl_2, may be represented by writing Cl—Cl, the dash

101

between the atoms indicating a pair of electrons shared between the two atoms. Similarly, in carbon tetrachloride the electron arrangement can be represented as follows (the crosses designate electrons furnished by the carbon atom):

$$
\begin{array}{cccc}
& :\overset{\cdot\cdot}{\text{Cl}}: & & \text{Cl} \\
& \overset{\cdot\cdot\ \cdot\times\ \cdot\cdot}{:\text{Cl}^\times\text{C}_\times\text{Cl}:} & \text{or} & \text{Cl}\!-\!\overset{|}{\underset{|}{\text{C}}}\!-\!\text{Cl} \\
& \overset{\cdot\cdot\ \times\cdot\ \cdot\cdot}{:\underset{\cdot\cdot}{\text{Cl}}:} & & \text{Cl}
\end{array}
$$

A chemical bond formed by the *sharing* of electrons between atoms each of which contributes an electron to the shared pair is known as a **covalent** or a **nonpolar** bond.

Atoms containing unshared pairs of electrons may contribute both of the electrons for a shared pair to atoms having an electron deficiency that can accommodate the pair of electrons. Nitrogen atom in ammonia has a completed octet of electrons, but it has an unshared pair of electrons; the hydrogen ion (a hydrogen atom that has lost its valence electron) can acquire a stable configuration by accepting two electrons donated by the nitrogen atom of ammonia:

$$
\begin{array}{ccc}
\text{H} & & \left[\ \begin{array}{c}\text{H}\\ |\end{array}\ \right]^+ \\
\text{H}:\!\overset{\cdot\cdot}{\underset{\cdot\cdot}{\text{N}}}:\rightarrow\text{H}^+ & \text{or} & \text{H}\!-\!\text{H}\!\rightarrow\!\text{H} \\
\text{H} & & \text{H}
\end{array}
$$

A chemical bond formed by the sharing of a pair of electrons both of which are furnished by one atom is called a **coordinate covalent** or **semipolar** bond. In graphic formulas this type of bond is represented by an arrow drawn from the donor to the acceptor. Once the semipolar bond is formed, it is indistinguishable from the nonpolar bond; these two types of bond differ not in kind, but *in the mode of formation*.

The Lewis system of acids and bases is founded on the semipolar bond; a base is an electron-pair donor, and an acid is an electron-pair acceptor. The Lewis base that serves as the donor is called the **ligand** and is often represented by L in writing general formulas and equations. In complex formation the ligand is usually a neutral molecule (H_2O, NH_3, many organic compounds, especially those containing nitrogen) or an anion (Cl^-, CN^-, SO_4^{--}, etc.).

Coordination Complexes

Almost all of the metal ions can act as Lewis acids in accepting electron pairs from Lewis bases to form **complex ions**. The number of bonds that can attach to a central ion is called the **coordination number** of that ion, and is one of its characteristic properties. The *maximum* coordination number is related to the position of the element in the periodic system, as follows:

Two: the element hydrogen only.

Four: elements of the first (short) period, i.e., lithium through fluorine.

Six: elements of the second (short) period and elements of the first long period, i.e., sodium through bromine.

Eight: the remaining elements, beginning with rubidium.

Coordination numbers less than the maximum are often shown; thus, copper ion, which has a maximum coordination number of six, usually shows a coordination number of only four, as in $Cu(NH_3)_4^{++}$. In a number of instances of the familiar ions, the coordination number usually exhibited is twice the electrovalence or oxidation number of the simple ion, as in $Ag(NH_3)_2^+$, $Zn(NH_3)_4^{++}$, $Co(NO_2)_6^{---}$. $Fe(CN)_6^{---}$.

Formation of Complex Ions. A complex ion may be defined as an ion formed reversibly by the union of ions with molecules or with other ions, with the restriction that no redox change occurs. The following examples are illustrative:

$$Cu^{++} \text{ (ion)} + 4NH_3 \text{ (molecule)} \rightarrow Cu(NH_3)_4^{++}$$

$$Co^{++} \text{ (ion)} + 6H_2O \text{ (molecule)} \rightarrow Co(H_2O)_6^{++}$$

$$Fe^{+++} \text{ (ion)} + 6CN^- \text{ (ion)} \rightarrow Fe(CN)_6^{---}$$

$$SbCl_4^- \text{ (complex ion)} + 2Cl^- \text{ (ion)} \rightarrow SbCl_6^{---}$$

The chemical bond between the central metallic ion and the ligand is a co-ordinate covalent bond, as illustrated by the following:

$$
\begin{bmatrix}
H_3N: & & :NH_3 \\
 & Cu & \\
H_3N: & & :NH_3
\end{bmatrix}^{++}
\quad
\begin{bmatrix}
:Cl:^- & & :Cl:^- \\
 & Pd & \\
:Cl:^- & & :Cl:^-
\end{bmatrix}^{--}
$$

Valence Number of Complexes. The valence number or charge of the complex ion formed is the algebraic sum of the charges of the components. Many complexes are known in which both neutral molecules and ions, or different kinds of molecules, or different kinds of ions, are coordinated to the same central metal ion. From the complex ion $[Pt(NH_3)_6]^{4+}$, ammonia molecules can be replaced by chloride ions to form a series of complexes $[Pt(NH_3)_5Cl]^{+++}$, $[Pt(NH_3)_4Cl_2]^{++}$, $[Pt(NH_3)_3Cl_3]^+$, $Pt(NH_3)_2Cl_4$ (a nonelectrolyte), $[Pt(NH_3)Cl_5]^-$, and $[PtCl_6]^{--}$.

COMPLEX IONS AND THE MASS LAW

Almost all of the metal ions in water solution are "hydrated," that is, they exist as aquo-complexes in which water is the ligand, the coordination occurring by donation of a pair of electrons from the oxygen. For example, the copper (II) cation in water is represented as $Cu(H_2O)_4^{++}$. The formation of other complexes occurs by displacement of coordinated water by another ligand, and the reaction takes place in stages. For example, if M represents a cation of coordination number n, and L represents a ligand other than water,

$$M(H_2O)_n + L \rightleftharpoons H_2O + M(H_2O)_{n-1}L$$

$$M(H_2O)_{n-1}L + L \rightleftharpoons H_2O + M(H_2O)_{n-2}L_2$$

and so on to the formation of the highest complex, ML_n. For simplicity in writing equations, the water of aquo-complexes is usually omitted. Because M can be univalent, divalent, etc., and L can be either neutral or ionic, the ionic charges are omitted in the general treatment given here.

Each stage of coordination has a characteristic formation or stability constant; its reciprocal is the dissociation or instability constant of the complex. Thus,

$$M + L \rightleftharpoons ML \qquad k_1 = \frac{[ML]}{[M][L]} \tag{7-1}$$

$$ML + L \rightleftharpoons ML_2 \qquad k_2 = \frac{[ML_2]}{[ML][L]} \tag{7-2}$$

$$ML_2 + L \rightleftharpoons ML_3 \qquad k_3 = \frac{[ML_3]}{[ML_2][L]} \tag{7-3}$$

$$ML_{n-1} + L \rightleftharpoons ML_n \qquad k_n = \frac{[ML_n]}{[ML_{n-1}][L]} \tag{7-4}$$

The over-all formation constant of a given stage of complexation is represented by the product of the successive k values:

$$M + 2L \rightleftharpoons ML_2 \qquad K_2 = k_1 k_2 = \frac{[ML_2]}{[M][L]^2} \tag{7-5}$$

$$M + 4L \rightleftharpoons ML_4 \qquad K_4 = k_1 k_2 k_3 k_4 = \frac{[ML_4]}{[M][L]^4} \tag{7-6}$$

In a solution containing a cation and a complexing ligand the total (analytical) concentration of the metal is the sum of the equilibrium concentration of each species present; for example,

$$C_M = [M] + [ML] + [ML_2] + [ML_3] + \cdots + [ML_n] \tag{7-7}$$

Substituting the various concentrations from equations (7-1) through (7-4) gives

$$C_M = [M] + k_1[M][L] + k_1k_2[M][L]^2 + k_1k_2k_3[M][L]^3$$
$$+ \cdots k_1k_2k_3 \cdots k_n[M][L]^n \tag{7-8}$$

$$C_M = [M](1 + K_1[L] + K_2[L]^2 + K_3[L]^3 + K_n[L]^n) \tag{7-9}$$

$$C_M = [M]P \tag{7-10}$$

where P represents the polynomial in the parentheses in equation (7-9).
The fraction of each species can be calculated as follows:

$$\alpha_0 = \frac{[M]}{C_M} = \frac{[M]}{[M]P} = \frac{1}{P} \tag{7-11}$$

$$\alpha_1 = \frac{[ML]}{C_M} = \frac{[ML]}{[M]P} = \frac{K_1[M][L]}{[M]P} = \frac{K_1[L]}{P} \tag{7-12}$$

$$\alpha_2 = \frac{[ML_2]}{C_M} = \frac{K_2[L]^2}{P} \tag{7-13}$$

$$\alpha_n = \frac{[ML_n]}{C_M} = \frac{K_n[L]^n}{P} \tag{7-14}$$

in which [L] is the concentration of free ligand at equilibrium. The method is analogous to the calculation of the various species in polyprotic acids at a given hydrogen ion concentration illustrated in Chap. 5.

EXAMPLE 1

Calculate the concentration of each copper species in a liter of solution containing copper(II) and 0.010 mole of free NH_3. The successive formation constants of the complexes are: $k_1 = 9.8 \times 10^3$, $k_2 = 2.2 \times 10^3$, $k_3 = 5.4 \times 10^2$, $k_4 = 93$.
The value of the polynomial, equations (7-9) and (7-10), is

$$P = 1 + 98 + (2.16 \times 10^3) + (1.17 \times 10^4) + (1.09 \times 10^4)$$
$$= 2.49 \times 10^4, \text{ from which}$$

$$\alpha_0 = 1/(2.49 \times 10)^4 = 4.0 \times 10^{-5} \text{ (negligible)}$$

$$\alpha_1 = 98/(2.49 \times 10^4) = 3.93 \times 10^{-3} \qquad = 0.004$$

$$\alpha_2 = (2.16 \times 10^3)/(2.49 \times 10^4) = 8.67 \times 10^{-2} = 0.087$$

$$\alpha_3 = (1.17 \times 10^4)/(2.49 \times 10^4) = 4.70 \times 10^{-1} = 0.470$$

$$\alpha_4 = (1.09 \times 10^4)/(2.49 \times 10^4) = 4.38 \times 10^{-1} = 0.438$$

$$\text{Sum:} \quad 0.999$$

The concentration of each species is obtained by multiplying the total copper concentration by the corresponding value of α. For example, if $C_M = 0.10$, then $[Cu^{++}] = 4.0 \times 10^{-6}$ (negligible), $[Cu(NH_3)^{++}] = 3.9 \times 10^{-4}$, $[Cu(NH_3)_2^{++}] = 8.7 \times 10^{-3}$, and so on.

Often the successive formation constants are not very different, hence there is a considerable range of ligand concentration in which two or more adjacent species are present in roughly comparable amounts, as shown for α_3 and α_4 in the above example. In the presence of a high concentration of ligand, formation of the highest complex is favored, as would be expected from the mass law. For instance, in Example 1 above, if $[NH_3] = 0.10$, about 90% of the copper would be in the form of $Cu(NH_3)_4^{++}$, about 10% in the form of $Cu(NH_3)_3^{++}$, and the Cu^{++} would be only about 10^{-6}%. For most analytical applications interest centers primarily in the concentration of the simple (uncomplexed) cation under conditions of at least a moderate excess of ligand. Under these circumstances the concentration of the simple cation can be estimated satisfactorily from the cumulative formation constant of the highest-order complex. Indeed, in many cases the stepwise formation constants are not available, and the only recourse is then the use of the cumulative constant.

EXAMPLE 2

0.10 mole of copper sulfate and 0.60 mole of ammonia are mixed and diluted to one liter. K_4, the cumulative constant of the four coordination steps, is 1.07×10^{12}. Calculate $[Cu^{++}]$ in the solution.

$$Cu^{++} + 4NH_3 \rightleftarrows Cu(NH_3)_4^{++}$$

$$K_4 = \frac{[Cu(NH_3)_4^{++}]}{[Cu^{++}][NH_3]^4} = 1.07 \times 10^{12}$$

The large value of K_4 shows that the reaction is very extensive, and in the presence of excess ammonia it is virtually complete. In the over-all reaction, 0.10 mole of Cu^{++} reacts with 0.40 mole of NH_3, forming approximately 0.10 mole of $Cu(NH_3)_4^{++}$ and leaving 0.20 mole of NH_3 in excess.

$$[Cu^{++}] = \frac{[Cu(NH_3)_4^{++}]}{K_4[NH_3]^4} = \frac{0.10}{(1.07 \times 10^{12})(0.20)^4} = 5.9 \times 10^{-11}$$

One of the frequent applications of complex formation is the addition of a ligand to form a complex with the cation of a slightly soluble compound in order to dissolve the latter, or in order to prevent its precipitation.

EXAMPLE 3

Calculate the molar solubility of AgBr in an ammonia solution in which the final NH_3 concentration is 0.10 M. The reactions and constants are:

$$AgBr \rightleftarrows Ag^+ + Br^- \qquad K_{sp} = [Ag^+][Br^-] = 5.0 \times 10^{-13}$$

$$Ag^+ + NH_3 \rightleftarrows Ag(NH_3)^+ \qquad k_1 = \frac{[Ag(NH_3)^+]}{[Ag^+][NH_3]} = 1.6 \times 10^3$$

$$Ag(NH_3)^+ + NH_3 \rightleftarrows Ag(NH_3)_2^+ \qquad k_2 = \frac{[Ag(NH_3)_2^+]}{[Ag(NH_3)^+][NH_3]}$$

$$= 6.8 \times 10^3$$

$[Ag^+] = \alpha_0 C_{Ag^+}$, hence $K_{sp} = \alpha_0 C_{Ag^+}[Br^-]$. If s represents the molar solubility under these conditions,

$$s = C_{Ag^+} = [Br^-] = \sqrt{K_{sp}/\alpha_0}$$

By the use of equations (7-7) to (7-11), $\alpha_0 = 9.9 \times 10^{-6}$; hence,

$$s = \sqrt{(5.0 \times 10^{-13})/(9.9 \times 10^{-6})} = 2.24 \times 10^{-4}$$

Because ammonia is present in excess, the over-all formation constant, K_2, of $Ag(NH_3)_2^+$ can be used. The over-all reaction is

$$AgBr \text{ (solid)} + 2NH_3 \rightarrow Ag(NH_3)_2^+ + Br^-$$

The competing or simultaneous equilibria are represented by the constants

$$K_{sp} = [Ag^+][Br^-] = 5.0 \times 10^{-13}$$

$$K_2 = \frac{[Ag(NH_3)_2^+]}{[Ag^+][NH_3]^2} = 1.09 \times 10^7$$

Multiplying these two equations, which eliminates the $[Ag^+]$ between them, gives

$$\frac{[Ag(NH_3)_2^+][Br^-]}{[NH_3]^2} = K_{sp} K_2 = 5.4 \times 10^{-6}$$

This expression is, indeed, the equilibrium constant for the over-all reaction as written above; AgBr, being in the solid state, is at unit activity and does not appear in the equilibrium constant expression. Let $X =$ molar solubility of AgBr under the conditions of the problem; then let $[Ag(NH_3)_2^+] = [Br^-] = X$, and

$$X = \sqrt{(5.4 \times 10^{-6})(0.10)^2} = 2.3 \times 10^{-4}$$

which is practically identical with the value obtained by use of the successive formation constants.

EXAMPLE 4

Calculate the number of moles of KCN that must be added to dissolve 0.10 mole of $Zn(OH)_2$ suspended in a liter of water. K_{sp} of $Zn(OH)_2 = 3.3 \times 10^{-17}$; K_4 of $Zn(CN)_4^{--} = 5.8 \times 10^{16}$. The reaction (assuming no hydrolysis of CN^-, etc.) is

$$Zn(OH)_2 \text{ (solid)} + 4CN^- \rightarrow Zn(CN)_4^{--} + 2OH^-$$

$$\frac{[Zn(CN)_4^{--}][OH^-]^2}{[CN^-]^4} = (3.3 \times 10^{-17})(5.8 \times 10^{16}) = 1.9$$

Dissolution of 0.10 mole of $Zn(OH)_2$ gives 0.10 mole of $Zn(CN)_4^{--}$ and 0.20 mole of OH^-. Then

$$[CN^-] = \sqrt[4]{\frac{(0.10)(0.20)^2}{1.9}} = 0.21$$

This is the *equilibrium* amount of CN^- that must be present in the solution; but the stoichiometry of the reaction requires $4(0.10) = 0.40$ mole of CN^-; total KCN required is therefore $0.40 + 0.21 = 0.61$ mole.

Amphoteric Hydroxides.   Several cations, notably those of zinc, aluminum, chromium(III), lead(II), tin(II), and a few others, are precipitated as hydroxides, which then dissolve in excess alkali by formation of hydroxo-complexes. Each of the successive reactions, as well as the over-all reaction of formation of the hydroxo-complex from its ions, is characterized by an equilibrium constant, as follows:

$$Zn^{++} + 2OH^- \rightarrow Zn(OH)_{2_{(s)}}$$

$$K_{eq} = 1/K_{sp} = 1/([Zn^{++}][OH^-]^2 \tag{7-15}$$

$$Zn(OH)_{2_{(s)}} + 2OH^- \rightarrow Zn(OH)_4^{--}$$

$$K_{eq} = K_{f_{(s)}} = \frac{[Zn(OH)_4^{--}]}{[OH^-]^2} \tag{7-16}$$

For the formation of the complex from its ions,

$$Zn^{++} + 4OH^- \rightarrow Zn(OH)_4^{--}$$

$$K_{eq} = K_f = \frac{[Zn(OH)_4^{--}]}{[Zn^{++}][OH^-]^4} = \frac{K_{f_{(s)}}}{K_{sp}} \tag{7-17}$$

In these expressions, K_{sp} is the solubility product constant of the insoluble hydroxide, K_f is the formation constant of the complex from its ions, and $K_{f_{(s)}}$ is the formation constant of the complex from the insoluble hydroxide. Numerical values for K_{sp} and K_f are available from tables; less often does one find tables giving $K_{f_{(s)}}$ values, but these can be calculated from the other two constants:

$$K_{f_{(s)}} = K_{sp}K_f \tag{7-18}$$

For example, in the case of the zinc compounds,

$$K_{f_{(s)}} = (3.3 \times 10^{-17})(3.1 \times 10^{15}) = 0.10$$

K_{sp} and K_f can be used to calculate the concentrations of the different ionic species at a given pH; $K_{f_{(s)}}$ can also be used to calculate the amount of alkali required to dissolve a given amount of the insoluble hydroxide.

EXAMPLE 5

Calculate the concentration of Zn^{++} and of $Zn(OH)_4^{--}$ in equilibrium with solid $Zn(OH)_2$ at pH 11.0. (See above for values of the constants.) At pH 11.0, $[OH^-] = 10^{-3}$. $[Zn^{++}] = K_{sp}/[OH^-]^2 = (3.3 \times 10^{-17})/(10^{-3})^2 = 3.3 \times 10^{-11}$. $[Zn(OH)_4^{--}] = K_f[Zn^{++}][OH^-]^4 = (3.1 \times 10^{15})(3.3 \times 10^{-11})(10^{-3})^4 = 1.0 \times 10^{-7}$.   Alternatively, $[Zn(OH)_4^{--}] = K_{f_{(s)}}[OH^-]^2 = 0.10(10^{-3})^2 = 1.0 \times 10^{-7}$.

EXAMPLE 6

0.010 mole of solid $Zn(OH)_2$ is suspended in a liter of water. How many moles of NaOH must be added to just dissolve the $Zn(OH)_2$? $K_{f_{(s)}} = 0.10$. From the reaction

$$Zn(OH)_{2_{(s)}} + 2OH^- \rightarrow Zn(OH)_4^{--}$$

it follows that dissolution of 0.010 mole of $Zn(OH)_2$ gives 0.010 mole of $Zn(OH)_4^{--}$. Hence,

$$[OH^-] = \sqrt{\frac{[Zn(OH)_4^{--}]}{K_{f_{(s)}}}} = \sqrt{\frac{0.010}{0.10}} = \sqrt{0.10} = 0.32$$

which is the equilibrium concentration of OH^- when the precipitate has just dissolved. But 0.020 mole of NaOH is consumed in the reaction, hence $0.32 + 0.02 = 0.34$ mole of NaOH must be added. By use of the K_{sp} of $Zn(OH)_2$, the Zn^{++} concentration of the solution can also be calculated:

$$[Zn^{++}] = K_{sp}/[OH^-]^2 = 3.3 \times 10^{-17}/0.32^2 = 3.3 \times 10^{-16}.$$

COMPLEXONES

An important class of reagents that form metal chelate complexes (see Chapter 10) was introduced in the mid-1940s by Schwartzenbach.[1] As a class, these reagents are sometimes referred to as "complexones" or "chelons." Many of these compounds are aminopolycarboxylic acids, the most important being ethylenedinitrilotetraacetic acid, $(HOOCCH_2)_2N-CH_2-CH_2-N(CH_2COOH)_2$, commonly called ethylenediaminetetraacetic acid, or EDTA. This compound is a tetraprotic acid, represented for convenience as H_4Y. The acid is insoluble in water, but its disodium salt, Na_2H_2Y, is water soluble, and it is this compound which is commonly used as the reagent, although still commonly referred to as EDTA. This reagent forms soluble complexes, of widely different stabilities, with all cations. In all cases, the EDTA reacts with the cation in a 1:1 mole ratio as illustrated by the generalized equation

$$M^{n+} + H_2Y^{--} \rightarrow MY^{n-4} + 2H^+ \qquad (7\text{-}19)$$

Because of the 1:1 reaction ratio, equilibrium calculations are simpler than for most other complexes, in which various complexes are formed in stepwise equilibria. Reference to equation (7-19) indicates that the smaller the formation constant of the metal-EDTA complex, the higher must be the *p*H of the solution in order to form the complex. In general (although there are exceptions), complexes with divalent cations are stable in alkaline or slightly acidic solution, those with trivalent cations are stable in solution of *p*H 2 or 1, and those with tetravalent cations are stable in strongly acidic solution. In analytical applications,

[1] G. Schwartzenbach, E. Kampitsch, and R. Steiner, *Helv. Chim. Acta,* **28**, 828 (1945). For a general reference work, see F. J. Welcher, *The Analytical Uses of Ethylenediaminetetraacetic Acid*, Princeton, N. J., Van Nostrand, 1958.

rate of formation of the complex may be important; although most of the EDTA complexes form rapidly, the complexes with iron(III), chromium(III), and aluminum form slowly at room temperature.

EDTA is used extensively as a masking agent to prevent the characteristic reactions of the simple cations; examples will be cited later in this chapter. Its effect is dependent upon several factors, such as the pH (since the last stage of ionization of EDTA is very weak), the stability of the particular metal-EDTA complex, and the extent of the reaction against which the cation is to be masked. The color of simple (aquo) colored cations, such as those of copper, cobalt, nickel, chromium, etc., is enhanced by formation of the metal-EDTA complex, often making the solutions suitable for spectrophotometric measurement. Complexometric titrations using EDTA have wide application; this subject is treated briefly in Chap. 25.

The stability constants of some of the metal-EDTA complexes are given in Appendix IV. Ionization constants of H_4Y are given in Appendix II.

STABILIZATION OF OXIDATION STATES
BY COMPLEX FORMATION

The ease with which ions of some of the elements may be oxidized or reduced, that is, the reduction potential of the system, is often drastically changed by the formation of complexes. Following are some examples.

Salts of cobalt(II) are not oxidized in air in acidic solution, and cobalt(III) salts are spontaneously reduced to cobalt(II). However, $Co(NH_3)_6^{++}$ is readily oxidized to $Co(NH_3)_6^{+++}$ by atmospheric oxygen.

Iron(II) compounds are readily oxidized by atmospheric oxygen to iron(III); $Fe(CN)_6^{4-}$, however, is completely stable toward air oxidation. The iron(II) complexes with dipyridine, represented by $Fe(dipy)_3^{++}$, and with 1,10-phenanthroline, represented by $Fe(phen)_3^{++}$, are more stable than the corresponding iron(III) complexes. These highly colored iron(II) complexes are used as indicators in redox titrimetry and also for the colorimetric determination of iron.

Copper(I) salts are readily oxidized to copper(II), and the latter are reduced to the former only with difficulty. On the other hand, the cyano complex of copper(II), $Cu(CN)_4^{--}$, spontaneously undergoes an internal redox reaction with the formation of $Cu(CN)_3^{--}$, which is stable toward atmospheric oxidation.

The formation of compounds of silver(II) from silver(I) requires use of very potent oxidizing agents, and silver(II) compounds are quite unstable; however, the dipyridine and the 1,10-phenanthroline complexes of silver(II), $Ag(dipy)_2^{++}$ and $Ag(phen)_2^{++}$, are very stable.

In all of the above cases the complexes are so little dissociated, that is, the equilibrium concentrations of the simple cations Co^{+++}, Fe^{++}, Cu^+, Ag^{++} are so small that the properties usually associated with the simple ions are exhibited only to a very small extent, if at all.

ANALYTICAL APPLICATIONS OF COMPLEX FORMATION

There are numerous instances in analytical chemistry where the formation of a complex is necessary for the success of the analysis.

In the titrimetric determination of copper, copper(II) ion oxidizes iodide ion to free iodine, which is titrated; any iron(III) in the solution would also oxidize iodide ion to iodine, and the calculated results for copper would be too high. Interference from iron(III) is eliminated by decreasing its concentration to a negligible amount by the formation of the very stable hexafluoroferrate(III) complex, FeF_6^{---}.

Organic polyhydroxy acids, such as citric and tartaric acids, and their salts form stable complexes with several cations, notably Al^{+++}, Cr^{+++}, Fe^{+++}, and Cu^{++}. These complexes are so stable that many of the usual reactions of the simple cations are not shown by the solutions. For example, addition of tartaric acid to a solution of iron(III) salt will prevent the precipitation of iron(III) hydroxide by ammonium hydroxide. In the precipitation of nickel by dimethylglyoxime, in ammoniacal solution, precipitation of iron(III) hydroxide is prevented by the addition of tartrate. The Fehling test for reducing sugars uses as a reagent a strongly alkaline solution of copper(II) salt, from which the precipitation of copper(II) hydroxide is prevented by complexing the copper(II) with tartrate. In the separation of aluminum from beryllium, the latter is precipitated as its hydroxide (hydrous oxide) at pH 7.5; precipitation of aluminum is prevented by the addition of tartrate to form a stable complex.

The titrimetric determination of iron is based on the oxidation of Fe^{++} to Fe^{+++} by permanganate or other strong oxidants. The determination is carried out in the presence of phosphoric acid, which forms with Fe^{+++} a stable complex $Fe(PO_4)_2^{---}$. Decreasing the concentration of Fe^{+++} by complexation makes the oxidation of Fe^{++} more complete.

The separation of calcium ion from magnesium ion by precipitation of calcium oxalate requires a high concentration of oxalate ion to insure the formation of the oxalato complex of magnesium, $Mg(C_2O_4)_2^{--}$, leaving in solution such a low concentration of Mg^{++} that it is not precipitated.

The separation of Cd^{++} from Cu^{++} can be made on the basis of the different stabilities of their cyano complexes. The ammoniacal solution containing $Cd(NH_3)_4^{++}$ and $Cu(NH_3)_4^{++}$ is treated with potassium cyanide, forming $Cd(CN)_4^{--}$ and $Cu(CN)_3^{--}$ (note the reduction to copper(I) in the cyano complex). When hydrogen sulfide is passed into the solution, only CdS is precipitated. The $Cu(CN)_3^{--}$ is so stable that the equilibrium concentration of Cu^+ is too small to be precipitated by hydrogen sulfide.

As a masking agent, EDTA will prevent the precipitation of the hydroxides (hydrous oxides) of divalent and trivalent cations by ammonia; of sulfides of zinc, nickel, cobalt, and manganese; of calcium by oxalate; of nickel by dimethylglyoxime; etc. In the presence of EDTA, iron(III) will not give a color with thiocyanate, and only mercury and silver give a positive reaction with dithizone. In ammoniacal solution, EDTA dissolves all metal hydroxides and phosphates, also barium sulfate and many other insoluble compounds. Among the many practical uses of EDTA are its application in cleaners for copperware, use of the iron(II) complex for treatment of iron chlorosis of orange trees, and the calcium complex, which is the only injectable antidote for lead poisoning.[2] The calcium EDTA complex is also used as an additive in some foodstuffs.

PROBLEMS

See Appendix IV for formation constants of complex ions, and Appendix I for solubility product constants. Unless the problem states to the contrary, use the over-all formation constant for the highest order complex involved in the reaction. Ignore activities and side reactions such as hydrolysis.

7-1 Calculate the molar concentration of the simple heavy metal cation in the solution made by mixing the reagents given, in a liter of solution. [*Note*: Account must be taken of the amount of ligand that *reacts* with the metal ion.]

(a) 0.050 mole of $AgNO_3$ and 0.25 mole of NH_3.   *Ans.* 2.1×10^{-7}.

(b) 0.050 mole of $AgNO_3$ and 0.25 mole of KCN.   *Ans.* 3.2×10^{-20}.

(c) 0.010 mole of $FeCl_3$ and 0.20 mole of NaF.

(d) 0.020 mole of $AgNO_3$ and 0.080 mole of $Na_2S_2O_3$.

(e) 0.050 mole of $Cd(NO_3)_2$ and 0.25 mole of NH_3.

(f) 0.030 mole of $Cd(NO_3)_2$ and 0.20 mole of KCN.

(g) 0.060 mole of $Hg(NO_3)_2$ and 0.40 mole of KI.

(h) 0.030 mole of $Fe(NO_3)_3$ and 0.30 mole of KCN.

(i) 0.10 mole of $Al(NO_3)_3$ and 1.0 mole of NaF.

(j) 0.10 mole of $ZnCl_2$ and 0.40 mole of Na_4Y (EDTA salt).

7-2 How many moles of complexing agent (NH_3, KCN, etc.) must be *added*, per liter of solution, in order to dissolve the substance given? [*Note*: Account must be taken of the amount of ligand required for the reaction.]

(a) $Na_2S_2O_3$, to dissolve 0.020 mole of AgI.   *Ans.* 0.44.

(b) KCN, to dissolve 0.010 mole of Cu_2S.   *Ans.* 0.0604.

(c) NH_3, to dissolve 0.010 mole of $Zn(OH)_2$.

(d) NH_3, to dissolve 0.010 mole of AgCl.

(e) KCN, to dissolve 0.030 mole of AgI.

(f) KCN, to dissolve 0.0010 mole of Ag_2S.

(g) NH_3, to dissolve 0.020 mole of $Cu(OH)_2$.

(h) NaOH, to dissolve 0.020 mole of $Zn(OH)_2$.

(i) NaF, to dissolve 0.0030 mole of $Al(OH)_3$.

(j) NaOH, to dissolve 0.030 mole of $Al(OH)_3$.

(k) Na_2S, to dissolve 0.010 mole of HgS. For formation of HgS_2^{--} *from its ions*, $K_f = 5.0 \times 10^{54}$; see equation (7-18).

(l) Na_4Y (EDTA salt), to dissolve 0.050 mole of $BaSO_4$.

[2] R. Pribil, *Chelometry*, Prague, Chemapol, 1961.

7-3 One liter of solution made by mixing the solutes given is then made 0.0010 M in sulfide ion. (1) Make calculations to show whether or not any of the metal sulfide will be precipitated. (2) If metal sulfide is precipitated, calculate the concentration of the heavy metal cation remaining in solution at equilibrium. (3) If metal sulfide is not precipitated, calculate the concentration of sulfide ion that would be required to start precipitation.

(a) 0.020 mole of Cd^{++} and 0.12 mole of KCN.

(b) 0.050 mole of Cu^{+} and 0.25 mole of KCN.

(c) 0.025 mole of $AgNO_3$ and 0.50 mole of KCN.

(d) 0.030 mole of $Cd(NO_3)_2$ and 0.20 mole of KCN.

(e) 0.050 mole of Cu^{+} and 0.30 mole of KCN.

(f) 0.040 mole of $AgNO_3$ and 0.10 mole of NH_3.

(g) 0.040 mole of $AgNO_3$ and 0.10 mole of KCN.

(h) 0.040 mole of $AgNO_3$ and 0.10 mole of $Na_2S_2O_3$.

(i) 0.10 mole of $ZnSO_4$ and 0.60 mole of NH_3.

(j) 0.10 mole of $FeSO_4$ and 0.15 mole of Na_4Y (EDTA salt).

(k) 0.060 mole of $ZnSO_4$ and 0.10 mole of Na_4Y (EDTA salt).

(l) 0.050 mole of $Pb(NO_3)_2$ and 0.070 mole of Na_4Y (EDTA salt).

Ans. (a) (1) ICP $= 5.9 \times 10^{-17}$; CdS precipitated. (2) $[Cd^{++}] = 7.1 \times 10^{-24}$.

(b) (1) ICP $= 1.6 \times 10^{-56}$; Cu_2S not precipitated.

(3) $> 6.2 \times 10^3$ M—impossibly high.

7-4 Calculate the molar solubility of the slightly soluble compound given, in a solution of the ligand of the final (equilibrium) concentration stated.

(a) AgBr, 1.0 M NH_3.   (f) HgS, 1.0 M KI.

(b) AgI, 1.0 M NH_3.   (g) PbS, 0.10 M Na_4Y (EDTA salt).

(c) AgI, 0.50 M $Na_2S_2O_3$.   (h) $Al(OH)_3$, 0.10 M KF.

(d) Ag_2S, 0.50 M KCN.   (i) $Cu_3(AsO_4)_2$, 0.10 M NH_3.

(e) CdS, 0.020 M KCN.   (j) ZnS, 0.20 M Na_4Y (EDTA salt).

7-5 Calculate the molar concentration of Zn^{++} and of $Zn(OH)_4^{--}$ in equilibrium with solid $Zn(OH)_2$ at pH (a) 6.00; (b) 8.00; (c) 10.00.

7-6 Calculate the molar concentration of Al^{+++} and of $Al(OH)_4^{-}$ in equilibrium with solid $Al(OH)_3$ at pH (a) 5.00; (b) 7.00; (c) 9.00; (d) 11.00.

7-7 The following mixture is made 1.0 M in NH_3 (NH_4OH). Make calculations to show whether or not either of the metal hydroxides is precipitated.

(a) 0.010 M in Cd^{++} and 0.010 M in Zn^{++}.

(b) 0.010 M in Cu^{++} and 0.010 M in Ni^{++}.

7-8 To a liter of 0.010 M solution of the given cation, 0.030 mole of Na_4Y (EDTA salt) and 10^{-7} mole of S^{--} is added. Make calculations to show whether or not the metal sulfide is precipitated.

(a) Cd^{++}.   (b) Zn^{++}.   (c) Fe^{++}.   (d) Mn^{++}.   (e) Ni^{++}.

7-9 To a liter of 0.010 M solution of the given cation, 0.020 mole of Na_4Y (EDTA salt) and 0.0010 mole of NaOH is added. Make calculations to show whether or not the metal hydroxide is precipitated.

(a) Fe^{+++}.   (b) Fe^{++}.   (c) Pb^{++}.   (d) Cu^{++}.   (e) Ni^{++}.

7-10 For the total metal-ion concentration given, calculate the molar concentration of each metal-containing species in equilibrium with the concentration of ligand stated.

(a) Silver, 0.10 M, $[NH_3] = 0.010$.

(*b*) Cadmium, 0.10 M, $[CN^-] = 0.0010$.

(*c*) Zinc, 0.050 M, $[NH_3] = 0.020$.

(*d*) Mercury, 0.050 M, $[CN^-] = 0.020$.

(*e*) Silver, 0.040 M, $[S_2O_3^{--}] = 0.0050$.

(*f*) Silver, 0.040 M, $[S_2O_3^{--}] = 0.050$.

(*g*) Palladium(II), 0.10 M, $[Cl^-] = 0.0010$.

(*h*) Mercury(II), 0.060 M, $[Br^-] = 0.040$.

(*i*) Nickel, 0.10 M, $[NH_3] = 0.020$.

(*j*) Cadmium, 0.050 M, $[I^-] = 0.020$.

8

RELIABILITY OF MEASUREMENTS

The data of quantitative analysis consist of measurements of some property such as weight, volume, density, electrical conductivity, or absorption of radiant energy. Much of the subject matter of other branches of chemistry, and indeed of many other sciences, is quantitative in that measurements are involved. After measurements have been made, consideration must be given to the reliability of the measurements as representing the amount or quantity of the substance or of the property measured. The material in this chapter is designed to give the student an introduction to some of the factors involved in the evaluation of data.

Precision expresses the **reproducibility** of a measurement, that is, the agreement among themselves of several measurements of the same substance or property. Suppose, for example, that each of five students measures the volume of water contained in a "500-ml" flask by using a 25-ml graduated cylinder and expresses the result to the nearest milliliter. The measured values might be as follows: 501, 496, 503, 490, 500 ml. Similarly, values differing from one another would likely be obtained if measured by the same individual five different times. There may be several reasons why the measured values are not in perfect agreement, that is, several sources of deviation in the measurements. Some possible sources are: spillage in transfer of the liquid from flask to graduate: differences in adjustment of the liquid level at the top mark of the graduate; different drainage in emptying the graduate.

The reproducibility of a measurement is expressed by the **deviation** of that measurement. The deviation D is the difference between an observed (measured) value O and the arithmetic mean (average) M of all the measurements; that is,

$$D = |O - M|$$

where the vertical bars indicate that the difference is taken without regard to sign. The arithmetic mean of the deviations can be used to express the precision or reproducibility of the series of measurements. From the example cited above,

Observed (O)	Deviation $|O - M|$
501	3
496	2
503	5
490	8
500	2
5⟌2490	5⟌20

Mean (M):   498   4 Average deviation

The definition and illustration just given are for **absolute deviation**. Of more practical significance is the **relative deviation**, which is the value of D with respect to M, and may be expressed as a fraction, D/M, or as a percentage, $(D/M) \times 100$, or in parts per thousand, $(D/M) \times 1000$. In the above illustration the average relative deviation is 4/498, or $(4/498) \times 100 = 0.8\%$, or $(4/498) \times 1000 = 8\%_0$. In most measurements of quantitative analysis, deviations should be small, and are most conveniently expressed in parts per thousand, $\%_0$.

Range is simply the difference between the highest and the lowest observed or measured value:

$$R = O_{highest} - O_{lowest}$$

It, too, can be expressed in relative terms. In the above example, $R = 503 - 490 = 13$, and the relative range is $(13/498) \times 1000 = 26\%_0$. As a measure of dispersion of results, range has little value for a large number of measurements; as the number of measurements decreases, range becomes more meaningful; indeed, for only two measurements, the range and the mean give *all* the information about the measurements.

Usually the true value of the quantity measured is unknown to the analyst. In this case, deviations are used to express the reliability of measurements.

Rejection of a Result.   In a series of measurements, it sometimes happens that one value has a deviation considerably greater than the deviations of the other values. The question then arises whether such a value is a valid member of the series. If the cause of the large deviation is known, obviously the result should not be included in the series. For example, in the analysis of multiplicate samples, if it is known that some solution being titrated was spilled, or that some precipitate was lost in transfer, the results of the analysis of that sample cannot possibly be reliable, and the analysis of that sample should be discontinued as soon as such a mistake is made. Often it happens that the cause of a large deviation is unknown. Certain rules can then be applied to decide whether or not the suspected value can be rejected. If, in a series of four or more values, one value appears to differ widely from the other values, the suspected value is temporarily rejected, and the mean of the other measurements and the average deviation are computed. If the deviation of the suspected value from the mean of the other values is more than four times the average deviation, the suspected value may be discarded; otherwise it must be retained, and a new average and average deviation computed.[1] A clue to which value (if any) may be suspected is best obtained by arranging the measurements in order, say from lowest to highest, and then noting the difference between adjacent values. Usually, a suspected value will be the lowest or the highest measurement in the series. Returning to the example of the five measurements of the volume of the flask, it might be suspected that the measurement 490 ml should be discarded. The question is decided by applying the above rule.

	Observed		Deviation
Temporarily rejected:	[490]		[10]
	496		4
	500		0
	501		1
	503		3
Average of four:	500	Average deviation:	2

The deviation 10 of the suspected value is more than four times 2, the average deviation of the other values. The value 490 is therefore rejected, and the average relative deviation of the remaining results is 2/500, or 4‰.

Accuracy deals with the **correctness** of a measurement, or the agreement of the measurements with the "true" value of the quantity measured. There are relatively few instances in which the true value of a quantity is known. The value 12.000 ... for the atomic weight of carbon-12 isotope, is a true value only because it was arbitrarily chosen as a number in terms of which the relative weights of other atoms are now expressed, as determined by experimental measurements. The numbers obtained by *counting* of persons or objects are true values; for example, there is no uncertainty in the number of windows in a certain room, or the number of pages in a certain book. Most of the data of quantitative analysis, however, are obtained not by counting, but by measurement, that is, determining how many small units of measure (grams, milliliters, ohms, divisions on a meter, etc.) are contained in the larger quantity to be measured. Such measurements are subject to discrepancies arising from various sources; the quantity generally used as the "true" value is really the *most probable value*, derived by the application of statistical methods for the evaluation of data obtained by repeated, careful measurement.

[1] Other methods of testing for rejection are treated in books on statistics; see references given later in this chapter.

The situation has been very aptly stated by Gore as follows:

"All experimental measures are variable provided the measuring device is sufficiently sensitive to detect the existent level of variability. This variability is the fundamental determinant of the magnitude of the effects which *can* be detected. Unless measures show variability, the experimenter is at a loss to estimate the magnitude of the smallest effect he can observe, nor can he estimate quantitatively the reliability of a measured difference. Therefore it is desirable that in any experiment the repetitive measurements be variable and, obviously, that the magnitude of the variation be small. One should not often boast when he has made a series of identical measurements."[2]

Error, E, is the difference between an observed or measured value, O, and the true (most probable) value, T. That is,

$$E = O - T$$

In the example given previously for the measurement of the capacity of a flask, if the true volume T is 501 ml, we have

	Observed (O)	Error ($O - T$)
	501	0
	496	−5
	503	+2
Rejected:	[490]	
	500	−1
Mean:	500	Average error: −1

In computing error, account is taken of the sign of the error; the same error, in sign and magnitude, is obtained directly by using the mean of the retained observed values ($500 - 501 = -1$) as by taking the algebraic average of the individual errors ($-4/4 = -1$).

For errors, as for deviations, the absolute error is of little significance; but the error relative to the true value, E/T expressed in suitable units, is of practical importance. The following example will illustrate this point.

Measured value, O	11	101	1001
True value, T	10	100	1000
Absolute error, E	1	1	1
% Relative error, $(E/T) \times 100$	10	1	0.1

Although the absolute error is the same, namely, one unit in each case, the relative errors are widely different. In the example of the volume of the flask, the absolute error is −1 ml; the relative error is −1/501, or −0.2%, or −2‰.

---

[2] W. L. Gore, *Statistical Methods for Chemical Experimentation*, New York, Interscience, 1952, p. 3.

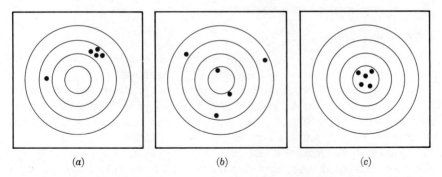

(a)   *(b)*   *(c)*

Fig. 8-1 (*a*) Precise but not accurate. (*b*) Neither precise nor accurate. (*c*) Both precise and accurate.

Measurements may be precise without necessarily being accurate, due to some nearly constant source of error in the measurements. The idea that good precision (small relative deviation) implies good accuracy (small relative error) is a common fallacy in the thinking of many beginning students in quantitative analysis. An illustration will be helpful in distinguishing between precision and accuracy. Figure 8-1 represents three rifle targets at each of which five rounds have been fired. In (*a*) the results are precise but not accurate; the one shot at the "nine o'clock" position might be rejected in evaluation of the precision, just as an analytical result may be rejected if it has a huge deviation. Furthermore, the location of the hits indicates clearly the presence of a constant determinate error, such as an improperly aligned gun sight, or failure to account for wind drift; the cause of the one shot to the left might or might not be known. In (*b*) the hits are neither precise nor accurate; the deviations are both large and random, and probably indicate merely the lack of skill of the rifleman. The possible argument that the average location of the shots is in or near the bull's-eye would not be convincing to the scorekeeper. In (*c*) the hits are both precise and accurate.

It is obviously impossible to achieve high accuracy without high precision. The precision and the accuracy of measurements are often collectively referred to as **reliability**.

Because most true values are determined by measurements that are subject to slight variations, it might appear that the accuracy and the error of the measurements cannot be stated. In the strictest sense this is the case. On the other hand, a value determined by careful measurements is the midvalue of a very narrow range of values within which there is a very high probability that the true value lies. Use of the terms true value, error, and accuracy in their strict sense is then justified in evaluating the reliability of measurements and in discussing the kinds and sources of errors.

CLASSIFICATION OF ERRORS

Determinate Errors

Determinate errors are those that may either be avoided, or for which corrections can be applied after determining their magnitude.

If an error of the same sign and magnitude occurs in the analysis of multiplicate samples, the error is not revealed by lack of precision. Such **constant errors** are therefore insidious because they are unsuspected. They might be revealed, however, by carrying out the analysis by distinctly different methods. It is for this reason that in evaluating a new method of analysis, the results are compared with another method based upon a completely different reaction or principle. It is extremely improbable that errors of the same sign and magnitude would be present in widely different methods, as, for example, the gravimetric, titrimetric, and photometric determination of iron. Any discrepancy in the results of different methods can usually lead to the source of the error.

Variable determinate errors may vary not only in amount but even in sign with varying conditions. In some cases the manner of the variation may be known, hence corrections can be applied; such errors are sometimes called **systematic errors**. For example, the influence of temperature on the volume of glass measuring vessels or on the potential of electrodes is known, and corrections for temperature variation can be applied.

Many kinds or sources of determinate errors can occur in quantitative analysis. Some of the more common ones are mentioned below; others will occur to the student as his knowledge of and experience in the subject are broadened.

1. *Errors due to equipment used* include the use of uncalibrated measuring devices (weights, burets, volumetric flasks), faulty balance construction, and contamination of solutions by chemical attack of the vessels used.

2. *Errors due to reagents* arise because the reagents may contain impurities that interfere with the method of analysis.

3. *Personal errors* arise through the limited ability of the analyst to discern or to judge observations with certainty. Poor color discrimination or even color blindness is often a serious source of error in titrimetric analysis; for, although the origin of the error is known, it may be very difficult either to avoid the error or to evaluate its magnitude. Some kinds of personal errors may be more or less constant, hence not be suspected by any lack of precision; in such instances the analyst must not let judgment be overcome by prejudice to make slightly uncertain measurements agree with one another. As mentioned earlier, some variation is desirable; perfect agreement of multiplicate measurements may be indicative of imperfect sensitivity of the measuring process, but if it results from conscious prejudice it is inexcusable, and the line between prejudice and dishonesty is sometimes difficult to define.

4. *Operational errors* originate in the inexperience or carelessness of the

analyst. Some examples are spillage of materials, loss by bumping during evaporations, adsorption of moisture by hygroscopic substances during weighing, contamination of samples during analysis, improper ignition temperature, failure to apply known corrections, and even errors in arithmetic (which are all too prevalent among students). Careless errors are inexcusable. Operational errors in general diminish with the additional skill, experience, and understanding of the analyst. Most of the illustrations cited might even be considered as indeterminate errors by the beginner, but they are variable determinate errors to an experienced analyst.

5. *Methodic errors* are inherent in the physical and/or chemical properties of the system undergoing analysis. These errors are particularly serious because their magnitude and sign are constant when the conditions of the method are the same in multiplicate analyses. They may be revealed, however, by varying the conditions, or by making the analysis for the desired constituent by another method differing considerably from the first in principle. Some examples of error of method are the solubility of a precipitate in its mother liquor and in wash liquids, decomposition of a precipitate during ignition, and incomplete reaction due to a reversible system at equilibrium. At a fixed set of conditions these errors cannot be eliminated or even diminished, no matter how skillfully the analysis is performed. However, an experienced analyst can exercise judgment in changing the conditions or even the principle of the analysis so as to reveal methodic errors.

A thorough study of some analyses has shown that certain errors of method are independent, in both magnitude and sign, of the amount of the constituent being determined. The introduction of components of glassware (silica, boron, alkalies) is essentially **constant** in multiplicate samples if the concentration of chemicals, the time of contact, and the temperature are identical. On the other hand, some errors are **proportional** to the amount of sample used in the analysis. The amount of moisture tenaciously retained by ignited precipitates, or of other substances adsorbed from solution, is generally proportional to the amount of the desired constituent being worked in the sample.

Certain errors will always have the same sign. Contamination by another constituent, or by components of glassware (e.g., silica), or incomplete expulsion of volatile matter during ignition will always result in a positive error. Solubility losses, incomplete reactions, and losses of material in transfer will always be negative errors. In a series of operations, positive errors in one operation may be more or less cancelled by negative errors in another operation. Recognition of the effects of these kinds of errors is important in attaching the proper significance to the results obtained.

Indeterminate Errors

Even after account has been taken of all known determinate errors there will remain slight variations the source, magnitude, and sign of which cannot be predicted nor estimated. These **indeterminate errors** follow the law of chance or probability, and are therefore often called random errors. The very nature of indeterminate errors makes them impossible of illustration. Any error that can be named or specified is of necessity a determinate error, with magnitude and sign that is related to its cause; it can be evaluated or controlled when the cause can be learned.

The objective of all measurement is to establish the true value of the quantity measured. As mentioned earlier, this is in reality the most probable value obtained by application of the laws of probability to indicate the reliability of the measurements. The laws of probability or rules of chance are almost self-evident:

1. Very large errors occur only seldom.
2. Small errors occur frequently.
3. Positive and negative errors occur with equal frequency; the most probable value is given by the arithmetic mean of the measured values.

These rules apply only to situations involving a very large number of observations or measurements. The probability laws can be represented graphically as in Fig. 8-2, which is called the **normal error curve**, or **normal frequency curve**, or the **Gaussian distribution curve**.

Following are some of the definitions and concepts commonly used in the statistical evaluation of data. The symbols have the following significance:

N = number of measurements
v = observed or measured value
Σ = summation of several numbers

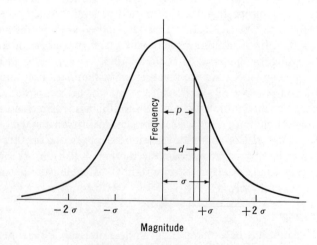

Fig. 8-2 Normal error curve.

1. *Mean.* The mean is the arithmetic average of all measured values; it may be represented by $\bar{v}$.

$$\bar{v} = \frac{v_1 + v_2 + v_3 + \cdots v_n}{N} = \frac{\Sigma v}{N}$$

2. *Median* is the middle value in a series of v's. It is most easily determined by arranging all the v's in ascending or in descending sequence and picking the middle value. When N is an even number, the median is the average of the two middle values in the series.

3. *Mode* is the value of v that occurs most frequently in the series. In a true statistical distribution, where N is very large, the median and the mode are identical.

4. *Deviation* is the difference between a value and the mean, expressed without regard to sign: $|v - \bar{v}|$.

5. *Average deviation of a single measurement* is the average of the deviations; that is,

$$\bar{d} = \frac{\Sigma |v - \bar{v}|}{N}$$

6. *Standard deviation of a single measurement*, for an infinite number of measurements, is designated by the symbol σ, and is given by

$$\sigma = \sqrt{\frac{\Sigma |v - \bar{v}|^2}{N}}$$

When N is small, the standard deviation s is

$$s = \sqrt{\frac{\Sigma |v - \bar{v}|^2}{N - 1}}$$

The term $(N - 1)$ is called the **degrees of freedom**; it is one less than the number of measurements in the set, because the data have been used to establish the average value $\bar{v}$ from which the deviations are obtained. Squaring the deviation gives appropriate importance to large deviations, which influence the standard deviation more than they do the average deviation. This method of taking into account the dispersion of the values gives a better measure of precision than does the average deviation $\bar{d}$. The standard deviation s is always larger than the average deviation $\bar{d}$. Standard deviations calculated from small numbers of measurements are underestimated; on the average, standard deviations calculated from 10, 5 and 2 measurements are 2.5%, 6%, and 20%, respectively, below the true deviation.[3]

7. *Variance* is the square of the standard deviation. A ratio of two variances is called the **F function**; that is, $F = s_1^2/s_2^2$. The F function is used to compare

[3] W. L. Gore, *op. cit.*, p. 26.

the precision of two sets of measurements; tables of F values for different probability levels and different degrees of freedom are published in books on statistics.[4]

8. *Probable deviation of a single measurement* is the deviation having a magnitude such that there are equal numbers of deviations greater and smaller than itself; it is a median deviation. It can be shown from statistics that the probable deviation p is 0.67 of the standard deviation. The positions of the values of $\bar{d}$, σ and p are shown on the normal error curve in Fig. 8-2. The value of σ is the abscissa of the inflection point of the curve; the value of p is the abscissa which divides the area under the curve, on either side, into two equal portions. In a normal distribution, $\sigma > \bar{d} > p$, and these terms are related so that $p = 0.85\bar{d} = 0.67\sigma$.

9. *Precision of the mean.* Statistically, the mean of N measurements is $\sqrt{N}$ times as reliable as a single measurement, from which it follows that

Average deviation of the mean $= \bar{d}/\sqrt{N}$
Standard deviation of the mean $= s/\sqrt{N}$
Probable deviation of the mean $= p/\sqrt{N}$

Some Additional Statistical Concepts

A very large number of measurements must be made in order to obtain a normal or Gaussian error distribution; obviously this is not practical in most analytical work. If only duplicates are analyzed, disagreement exceeding an acceptable amount (which should be predicted in advance of measurement) should lead to a decision to make a third analysis. In a set of three measurements having two values in very close agreement and one value quite divergent, the difference between the lowest and the highest value may be about 30 times as great as the difference between the values in best agreement only about once in twenty times, that is, this situation has a probability of only about 0.05 or 5%.[4] Increasing the number of measurements decreases the error, but the improvement falls off rapidly with increasing number (above about 5 to 10 samples), so that the slight improvement in results may not justify the additional analytical effort.

Confidence Limits. In industrial control laboratories where a raw material or a manufactured product is analyzed over a long time period, it is a matter of great concern to know whether or not the material is "in control." A common practice is to use quality control charts on which the average analysis and/or the range of results is plotted against time. Also, in the analysis of the same homogeneous material by several analysts, or by the same analyst on several

---

[4] W. J. Youden, *Statistical Methods for Chemists*, New York, Wiley, 1951.

occasions, it is important to test the reliability of the analysis. For a series containing a very large number of measurements, values have been computed to show the probability that any given measurement will fall within certain limits around the mean. A few probability values are given in Table 8-1; more extensive tables can be found in books on statistics.[5,6] Thus, if 1000 measurements are made, the probability is that 997 values lie within $\pm 3\sigma$, 955 values lie within $\pm 2\sigma$, 683 lie within $\pm\sigma$, and so on. The "95% confidence limits" are therefore the results that range from -2σ to $+2\sigma$ from the mean; only once in twenty times would a "true" value lie outside these limits.

Table 8-1   Probability of a Given Deviation

Limit of Error in Terms of $\pm\sigma$	Probability That a Result Will Fall Within the Limits
0.5	0.383
1.0	0.683
1.5	0.866
2.0	0.955
2.5	0.988
3.0	0.997
4.0	0.9999

Checking and Improving the Reliability of Analysis

Various practical methods exist for improving and for checking the reliability of analysis. The average of several multiplicates is more reliable than one or only a few analyses; an analyst would not depend upon the results of a single determination if much importance was to be attached to the result. As N approaches infinity, the error of the average approaches zero; but in most analytical work it is completely impractical to run a very large number of analyses. The magnitude of the error of the mean falls off very rapidly with the first few analyses, so that little improvement is attained as more and more measurements are included in the mean.

In a complete analysis of a sample for all known constituents, a summation of all the percentages may be used to check the accuracy of the analysis. Another summation test in inorganic analysis is the equality of cation and anion constituents, each expressed in terms of chemical equivalents. For example, a sample consisting of $MgSO_4$, KNO_3, and $NaCl$ is electrically neutral, and the

[5] W. L. Gore, *op. cit.*, p. 3.
[6] W. J. Youden, *op. cit.*

sum of the equivalents of the cations Mg^{++}, K^+, and Na^+ must be equal to the sum of the equivalents of the anions SO_4^{--}, NO_3^-, and Cl^-. A poor ionic balance indicates either an error in the analysis or the presence of other ions for which analysis was not made.

Blank determinations, in which all conditions (vessels, amounts of reagents and volumes of solution, temperature, etc.) are virtually identical with those employed in the analysis, are used to obtain corrections to be applied to the measurements of the unknowns.

Control analyses consist in performing the analytical operations that are used for the unknown, but with a sample containing a known amount of the desired constituent. The control sample should be as nearly as possible of the same composition as the unknown sample. The error of the control analysis is applied as a correction to the analysis of the unknown. **Standard samples** are samples that have been analyzed by several different methods and by several skilled analysts, and the results weighted and averaged. Standard samples of many varieties may be purchased from the National Bureau of Standards in Washington; they are much used for checking the accuracy of new methods of analysis.

Changing the conditions, or even the method of analysis, may be used to improve the accuracy of analysis. These changes may reveal the sources of errors previously considered to be indeterminate and lead to means of eliminating or correcting for them. It is highly improbable that errors of the same magnitude and sign would occur in widely different methods of analysis.

CALCULATIONS

The reliability of the operations of arithmetic in quantitative analysis must be included in this discussion, because they are involved in arriving at a result, that is, a number expressing the amount of constituent in the sample analyzed. Careless mistakes in arithmetic are inexcusable, of course. But the analyst must know and appreciate the significance of the figures or numbers that constitute the experimental data and represent the calculated results, so that the result will truly reflect the reliability of the analysis. The calculated result must not imply a reliability greater than justified by the measurement from which it is derived, and certainly the reliability must never be decreased by the computations made from experimental data.

Significant Figures

A quantity is expressed by a **number**, which is composed of figures or digits $(0, 1, 2, 3, \cdots, 9)$ used singly or in combination. A significant figure denotes the quantity in the place in which it stands (units, tens, hundreds, tenths, thousandths, etc.). The significant figures in a number are the digits in that number that are needed to express the precision of measurement from which the number was obtained; they include *all the certain figures and the first uncertain or doubtful figure* of the number. Unless the uncertainty of the doubtful figure is stated, it is generally understood to be ±1 in the last digit. For example, the number 33.07 is understood to mean that the quantity is nearer 33.07 than it is 33.06 or 33.08. However, if the number were written 33.07 ± 0.04, this would indicate that the quantity is between the limits 33.03 and 33.11.

The digit zero is a significant figure, except when it is the first figure in a number. Thus 358 has three significant figures, 0.358 has three, 0.00358 has three, 0.003582 has four, and so on; the zeros are not significant figures, but merely show the magnitude of the number, that is, the position of the decimal point. In any other position, zero is a significant figure; 305.8 has four significant figures, 305.80 has five, 0.0305080 has six. Terminal zeros are often used carelessly. A statement that the distance from the earth to the sun is 93,000,000 miles implies that this distance is known to a precision of ±1 mile, which is not the case. If the distance were known only to the nearest ten thousand miles, it should be written 9300×10^4 miles, or 93.00 million miles. The Avogadro number (number of molecules in a gram-mole) is 6.023×10^{23}, which properly expresses the precision with which the number is known; it would be not only inconvenient but entirely incorrect to write it 602,300,000,000,000,000,000,000. When terminal zeros are written, the reader has the right to assume that they are significant; if they are not significant, they must not be written.

Rules for Use of Significant Figures

1. In data and computations, retain as many significant figures as will give one uncertain figure; except that in derived values that are the basis of further computations, it may be permissible to retain one figure beyond the first uncertain figure.

2. In applying Rule 1, superfluous figures are rejected by the following rules:

a. When a figure next beyond the last one to be retained is less than 5, the last figure is retained unchanged. If 5.4323 is to be rounded to four significant figures, it becomes 5.432.

b. When the figure next beyond the last one to be retained is greater than 5, increase the last figure by 1. Thus, if 5.4327 is to be rounded to four figures, it becomes 5.433.

c. When the figure next beyond the last one to be retained is 5 and there is no figure or there are only zeros beyond the 5, the figure in the last place to be retained is increased by 1 if it is odd, and left unchanged if it is even. Thus, 1.235 or 1.2350 becomes 1.24 if three figures are to be retained; 1.245 or 1.2450 becomes 1.24. The logic of this rule is that odd and even numbers are equally probable.

d. When the figure next beyond the last one to be retained is 5 and there are figures other than zero beyond the 5, the last figure to be retained is increased by 1, whether it is odd or even. Thus, 1.2453 becomes 1.25 when only three figures are to be retained.

3. In addition and subtraction, retain figures in each number and in the sum or difference only to the decimal place corresponding to the term having the fewest number of decimal places. Thus,

$$
\begin{array}{ccc}
65.43 & \text{becomes} & 65.43 \\
1.245 & & 1.24 \\
0.4652 & & 0.47 \\
\hline
? & & 67.14
\end{array}
$$

Because the number 65.43 is known only to the hundredths place, any figure beyond the hundredths place in any term and in the sum is of no significance.

4. In multiplication and division, retain in each term and in the result only sufficient figures to express a relative precision as great as that of the least precisely known quantity. For example

$$0.092 \times 22.4 \times 6.023 = 12.4191 \cdots$$

becomes

$$0.092 \times 22.4 \times 6.02 = 12.4$$

Assuming the last digit in each term to be uncertain by 1 unit, the relative precisions of the original numbers are, respectively, 1/92, 1/224, and 1/6023. The first number has the smallest relative precision (largest relative uncertainty), hence it determines the number of figures to be retained in the other terms and in the product; the third term cannot be rounded to 6.0, for it would then have a precision of only 1/60. The operation

$$0.0923 \times 22.41 \times 6.0235 = 12.4537 \cdots$$

becomes

$$0.0923 \times 22.41 \times 6.024 = 12.45$$

In this case the relative precisions are, respectively, 1/923, 1/2241, and 1/60235. The third term is rounded to 6.024; it cannot be rounded to 6.02 because it would then have a precision of only 1/602, which is a smaller precision than that of the first term, which was formerly the least precise. For the same reason the second term, 22.41, and the product, 12.45, cannot be further rounded. *The precision must not be decreased by the computation.* It should be emphasized that the relative precision of the numbers, and not the number of significant figures in them, is the determining factor in applying this rule.

In addition and/or subtraction, the rounding off is based on the term having the smallest *absolute* precision; in multiplication and/or division, the rounding off is based on the term having the smallest *relative* precision. In combinations, addition and/or subtraction is considered before multiplication and/or division; thus

$$\frac{273(750 - 12.54)}{42.86(29.51 + 3.782)} = \frac{273(750 - 13)}{42.86(29.51 + 3.78)} = \frac{273 \times 737}{42.9 \times 33.3} = 140.9$$

5. In using logarithms for multiplication and division, retain in the *mantissa* of the logarithm of each term as many figures as are properly retained in the term itself, according to Rule 4. Remember that the characteristic of a logarithm is *not* a significant figure; it expresses magnitude only.

6. In all mathematical operations, superfluous figures should be discarded, according to the above rules, at each stage of the computations.

7. In stating the final results of multiplicate analyses, the agreement among the samples must be taken into account. For example, the average of 45.02, 45.34, and 45.18 (representing percent of a constituent in a sample) should be reported as 45.2 and, not as 45.18, because even the third figure is uncertain from the analytical results. However, the average of 45.12, 45.18, and 45.16 should be reported as 45.15; the third figure is certain in each case and only the fourth figure is uncertain.

8. When several steps are involved in calculating a result, strict adherence to the foregoing rules may result in an accumulation of digits that are not significant. *Judgment* must also be exercised by remembering that no result can be more precise than the least precise item of original data from which the result is derived.

In solving the problems in this book, the student should apply the rules for use of significant figures. When slide rule computations are made and the required number of significant figures cannot be read from the scale, the answer may be extended by the use of x's to show the required number of figures. For example, if the data showed that four significant figures should be carried in the answer, but the fourth figure cannot be read from the scale, it might be written 23.5x. In a problem, when a quantity is written as a word, rather than as a figure, it may be assumed that the figure can be extended by terminal zeros to a precision consistent with the precision with which other values in the problem are given. For example, if a "two-gram" sample is given and other data indicate that four significant figures should be carried in the sample weight, it may be used as 2.000 g.

PROBLEMS

8-1 How many significant figures are there in each of the following numbers?

(a) 107.870	(d) 96,500	(g) 0.0010	(j) 1.780×10^5
(b) 1.0080	(e) 169.880	(h) 100	(k) 1.780×10^{-5}
(c) 22,400	(f) 1020.3	(i) 1000.027	(l) 6.023×10^{23}

Ans. (a) 6.   (b) 5.

8-2 Rewrite each of the numbers in Problem 8-1 (1) to three significant figures; (2) to express a precision at least as great as 1‰ but no greater than 0.1‰.

8-3 To what precision, in parts per thousand (‰), or in parts per million (ppm) if more convenient, is each of the following measurements made?

(a) A 0.5-g sample weighed to the nearest 0.2 mg.   *Ans.* 0.4‰.

(b) Two meters measured to the nearest 5 mm.   *Ans.* 2.5‰.

(c) Five hours measured to the nearest minute.

(d) One mile measured to the nearest yard.

(e) A four-gram sample measured to the nearest 10 mg.

(f) Thirty minutes measured to the nearest second.

(g) One yard measured to the nearest $\frac{1}{8}$ inch.

(h) One meter measured to the nearest 0.5 mm.

(i) Two liters measured to the nearest 0.5 ml.

(j) Fifty milliliters measured to the nearest 0.02 ml.

8-4 In each part, rewrite the numerical value so as to indicate the stated precision.

(a) The velocity of light, 186,000 miles per second, measured to the nearest 100 miles per second.

(b) The mean distance from the earth to the moon, 238,857 miles, assuming it is known to the nearest 10 miles.

(c) The density of oxygen at 0°C, 1.428965 g/liter, measured to the nearest 0.030 mg/liter.

(d) The mass of the proton, 1.66089×10^{-24} g, assuming it is known to the nearest 12 ppm.

(e) The value of pi, 3.14159265, to the nearest 1 ppm.

8-5 Calculate the formula weight of the compound to the precision justified by the atomic weights of the elements involved.

(a) $IrBr_4$	(d) KIO_3	(g) $H_2C_4H_4O_6$	(j) NaBr
(b) H_2O	(e) H_2PdCl_4	(h) BaO_2	(k) $CaCO_3$
(c) $AgNO_3$	(f) Pu_2O_3	(i) PCl_5	(l) Au_2S_3

Ans. (a) 511.8.   (b) 18.0153.

8-6 Rewrite the following additions and subtractions (use a vertical column format), expressing each number, including the sum or difference, according to the rules for use of significant figures.

(a) $2.50 + 0.0850 + 40.255 + 0.1254 =$?   *Ans.* 42.97.

(b) $27.40 + 5.735 + 6.8164 + 0.565 =$?   *Ans.* 40.52.

(c) $16.6 + 0.06018 + 7.015 + 0.14245 =$?   *Ans.* 23.8.

(d) $646 + 6.46 + 64.6 + 0.646 =$?

(e) $40.3 + 0.150 + 1.254 - 25.05 =$?

(f) $1.439 + 0.3333 + 70.1 - 6.0 =$?

(g) $6.9897 + 321.04 + 2.971 + 0.225 =$?

(h) $0.654 + 6.54 + 65.4 + 654 =$?

(i) $(1.357 \times 10^4) + (3.5 \times 10^6) + (6.95 \times 10^5) + (2.712 \times 10^6) =$?

(j) $(4.28 \times 10^{-4}) + (1.57 \times 10^{-5}) + (6 \times 10^{-5}) + (9 \times 10^{-5}) =$?

8-7 Carry out the indicated multiplication and division; express each number, including the result, according to the rules for use of significant figures.

(a) $\dfrac{2.50 \times 0.1254}{40.255 \times 0.0850} =$?

(b) $\dfrac{5.735 \times 0.565}{27.40 \times 6.8164} =$?

$(c)\ \dfrac{16.6 \times 0.06018}{7.015 \times 0.14245} = \ ?$

$(g)\ \dfrac{6.9897 \times 321.04}{2.971 \times 0.225} = \ ?$

$(d)\ \dfrac{646 \times 0.646}{64.6 \times 6.46} = \ ?$

$(h)\ \dfrac{0.654 \times 6.54}{65.4 \times 654} = \ ?$

$(e)\ \dfrac{40.3 \times 0.150}{1.254 \times 25.050} = \ ?$

$(i)\ \dfrac{(1.35 \times 10^4)(3.5 \times 10^6)}{(6.95 \times 10^4)(2.712 \times 10^6)} = \ ?$

$(f)\ \dfrac{6.0 \times 0.3333}{1.429 \times 70.1} = \ ?$

$(j)\ \dfrac{(2.240 \times 10^4)(9.8 \times 10^{10})}{(6.023 \times 10^{23})(1.86 \times 10^{-5})} = \ ?$

Ans. (a) 0.0916.   (b) 0.01735.   (c) 1.000.

8-8   Perform the following arithmetic operations according to the rules for use of significant figures.

$(a)\ \dfrac{6.488 - 6.012}{1.250} = \ ?$

$(c)\ \dfrac{(80.68)(35.46 - 1.293)(0.076)}{(3.033 - 0.0456)} = \ ?$

$(b)\ \dfrac{6.488 + 6.012}{1.250} = \ ?$

$(d)\ \dfrac{(0.0953)(79.97 - 35.46)}{(1.8754)(119.02)} = \ ?$

8-9   From the data given in each lettered part below, (1) calculate the mean [*Note:* apply the rejection rule]; (2) calculate the relative average deviation of a single measurement, in ‰; (3) calculate the relative standard deviation of a single measurement, in ‰; (4) calculate the relative average deviation of the mean, in ‰; (5) calculate the relative standard deviation of the mean, in ‰; (6) calculate the relative error in ‰; (7) do you judge the results to be precise? accurate? Explain.

(a) % Cl, found: 25.21, 25.46, 25.66, 25.32; true: 25.47.
(b) % Fe, found: 15.24, 14.84, 15.02, 14.90; true: 15.30.
(c) % SO$_3$, found: 30.44, 30.30, 30.60, 30.37; true: 30.60.
(d) % S, found: 5.067, 5.050, 5.094, 5.082; true: 5.083.
(e) % Cl, found: 22.21, 22.38, 22.25, 22.43, 22.37, true: 22.47.
(f) % Ca, found: 40.14, 39.86, 40.02, 39.92, 40.35; true: 39.86.
(g) % Mn, found: 6.050, 6.048, 6.068, 6.054, 6.056; true: 6.064.
(h) % S, found: 15.15, 15.00, 15.27, 15.21, 15.30, true: 15.25.

Ans. (a) 25.41; 6; 8; 3; 4; −2.4.

8-10   In each part of Problem 8-9, what is the largest and what is the smallest value an additional result can have without being rejected?

8-11   Evaluate the data in each lettered part, as follows: (1) what is the median value? the mode value? (2) Calculate the mean (test for rejection). (3) Calculate the relative average deviation of a single measurement, in ‰. (4) Calculate the relative standard deviation of a single measurement, in ‰. (5) Calculate the relative average deviation of the mean, in ‰. (6) Calculate the relative standard deviation of the mean, in ‰.

(a) The following results were obtained in the analysis of multiplicates of a limestone for percentage of CaO: 32.25, 32.07, 32.46, 32.33, 31.92, 31.98, 31.74, 32.33, 32.19.

(b) The following results were obtained for the normality of a hydrochloric acid solution: 0.1207, 0.1225, 0.1246, 0.1233, 0.1192, 0.1198, 0.1174, 0.1215, 0.1233, 0.1219.

9

PREPARATION OF THE SAMPLE FOR ANALYSIS

Reliable analytical methods have been developed by careful consideration of the properties of the materials involved, painstaking attention to details of many aspects of the problem, and the analysis of many and varied samples to test the reliability of the procedures. Consideration must be given to the collection of the sample, the reagents required to attack it in preparation for analysis, the choice of laboratory ware to be used, the separations required before a desired constituent can be measured, the choice of analytical method to be employed, and an evaluation of the reliability of the results.

SAMPLING

If the analysis is to have any significance, the analysis sample must be not only homogeneous, but also truly representative of the bulk material for which the analysis is desired. The method of obtaining the sample should be as reliable as the analysis methods applied to it. Analyses based upon different samples should be in as good agreement as the analysis of multiplicates of one sample. Differences in composition, density, and hardness of solid materials, variations in particle size, segregation of impurities in alloys, suspension of solids in liquids, and other variables complicate the sampling problem to the extent that each material may require a somewhat different treatment. For certain classes of materials, rigid sampling procedures, based upon exhaustive testing, have been established by organizations such as the American Society for Testing Materials, the American Public Health Association, and the Association of Official Agricultural Chemists.

In order to be representative of the entire material, the sample must be taken by a systematic procedure. Detailed procedures for sampling various types of materials, including solids, liquids, and gases, may be found in reference books.[1,2]

Sampling of Solids

The Sampling Unit. The sampling unit of a solid material is a portion of the bulk material of such an amount that there is a high probability that it contains the same particle size distribution as the entire material being sampled. The amount of material required to fulfill this condition varies with the characteristics of the material.

The Gross Sample. The gross sample is obtained by combining a number of sampling units that have been collected systematically. The larger the number of sampling units, the more closely the gross sample will represent the bulk material. There is, of course, a practical limit beyond which the expenditure of time, effort, and expense in collecting and handling larger amounts of material does not lead to any significant improvement in the quality of the sample. The number of sampling units required for the gross sample depends upon particle size and uniformity of composition more than upon the total amount of material to be sampled.

Solids are most conveniently sampled during loading or unloading in shipment. Sampling units may be taken systematically in time, such as a scoopful every nth minute while the solid is discharging from a chute; or systematically in space, such as by taking a scoopful from every 10th or 20th or nth bag or barrel of packaged solid, or even the entire contents of every nth container. Materials of small particle size and fairly uniform composition at rest in a car, barge, or pile, may be taken with a sampling thief, which is a tube that can be driven into and filled with the material, then closed and withdrawn.

Reduction of Gross Sample. The gross sample is reduced in both particle size and in quantity by systematic crushing and grinding, and successive divisions by one-half, by coning and quartering and by the use of a riffle ("sample splitter"). Introduction of foreign matter from grinding equipment is minimized by using very hard materials; heat produced may cause loss of moisture from the sample, decomposition of unstable substances, and oxidation of easily oxidized substances. Small quantity grinding is done with an agate mortar and pestle. The final sample for analysis should pass a 100- or 200-mesh sieve.

Storage of Samples. Samples must be stored so as to minimize any changes that might occur before the analysis is performed, such as loss of water by hydrates, adsorption of water from the air, absorption of carbon dioxide by

[1] F. J. Welcher, *Standard Methods of Chemical Analysis*, 6th ed., Princeton, N. J., Van Nostrand, 1963, vol. IIA, chap. 2; vol. IIB, chap. 35.

[2] Chemists of U. S. Steel Corp., *Sampling and Analysis of Carbon and Alloy Steels*, New York, Reinhold, 1938.

alkaline substances, and air oxidation. Sometimes moisture is determined on the largest sample received by the laboratory (before reduction to analysis size), and the later analysis for other components is calculated to the as-received basis.

Drying of Samples.   Adsorbed moisture in samples varies with particle size, humidity, and nature of the sample. Most solids are analyzed after oven drying at about 110°C. Until ready for weighing, the sample is stored in a desiccator, which maintains an atmosphere of low, reproducible humidity.

Sampling of Metals

Detailed procedures for the sampling of metals such as ingots, billets, bars, sheets, and wire, have been published.[3] The principal considerations are based upon inhomogeneities resulting from segregation of impurities during cooling of melts, rolling, drawing, during welding operations, and so on. In general, drillings, sawings, or millings are taken systematically from the formed metals. Metal samples should not be oven dried, but may need to be washed with volatile organic solvents if cutting oils have been used in drilling or machining to obtain the sample.

Sampling of Liquids

If the liquid is homogeneous and at rest in a container, a "grab sample" is removed for analysis. Liquids flowing through pipes can be sampled by removal, through small sampling valves, of small increments on a regular time schedule. Liquids containing suspended solids, or mixtures of immiscible liquids, may be sampled at various depths by means of a sampling thief; if practical on the basis of composition and bulk of material, grab samples may be taken after thorough mixing.

Sampling of Gases

The procedures for sampling of gases vary considerably, depending upon the composition, location, and pressure of the gas to be sampled. Flue and stack gases often require quite elaborate sampling devices. Grab samples of a gas at atmospheric pressure may be taken by displacement of a liquid such as mercury or water previously saturated with the gas to be sampled.

LABORATORY WARE

Possible contamination of the sample by components of the vessels in which chemical work-up is performed must be given special attention when the

[3] *Ibid.*

analysis is to be made for small amounts of substances that are also present in common laboratory ware.

Various types of vitreous utensils (glass, porcelain) are high-silica materials, and are attacked by alkaline (and even by neutral) solutions much more than by acidic solutions. Porcelain is less attacked than glass, but the aluminosilicate glaze may introduce some aluminum. Soft, or soda-lime, glass, used principally as bottles for reagent storage, is not much attacked by mineral acids, but alkaline attack is extensive. Borosilicate glass (Pyrex, Kimax), principally SiO_2 and B_2O_3, is quite resistant to chemical attack as well as to thermal shock, but it can introduce traces of boron. Vycor (Corning trade name), which is about 96% SiO_2, is even more resistant to chemical attack and thermal shock. Fused quartz is very resistant to chemical action except by caustic alkalies and hydrofluoric acid (the latter attacks *all* silicate materials), and is used for stills to prepare conductivity water and for distillation of mineral acids for high purification.

Plastics of the polyethylene type have come into use for containers for hydrofluoric acid, caustic alkalies, and, indeed, for the common laboratory acids and ammonia.

Platinum ware is less attacked by many substances than is glass or porcelain. It is commonly used for sodium carbonate fusions and for evaporations with hydrofluoric acid to volatilize silica. However, it must *not* be used (1) for ignitions or fusions of hydroxides, nitrates, or cyanides of the alkali metals; (2) for compounds easily reducible to metals, such as AgCl, $PbSO_4$, SnO_2; (3) for ignition or fusions of sulfides, or compounds easily reduced to sulfides; (4) with mixtures that give free halogens; (5) with phosphides or arsenides. Heating of platinum must always be made with a nonluminous flame, and the inner cone of the flame must not touch the crucible.

Fusions with caustic alkalies are usually made in crucibles of silver, gold, iron, or nickel.

DECOMPOSITION OF SAMPLES

Owing to the complexity and variability of samples that must be analyzed, a set procedure for attack, applicable to all samples, is not possible. A knowledge of the qualitative composition of the sample is valuable in selecting the method of attack. However, it must be remembered that the behavior of a substance may be modified by its previous history and by the presence of other substances. For example, freshly precipitated hydrous oxides are much more readily dissolved in acids than are native or strongly ignited oxides; certain alloys are much more resistant to attack than are the individual metals of which the alloy is composed.

The solubility of the sample should be determined by testing small amounts with various reagents used in succession, generally in the order water, dilute and concentrated hydrochloric acid, dilute and concentrated nitric acid, and aqua regia. Usually, any residue that remains after these tests would require fusion to render it attackable. If the sample contains a relatively large amount of component requiring fusion, it is often advantageous to make the fusion on the original sample. The melt is then extracted with water and the water-insoluble fraction is decomposed with acids. Consideration must also be given to removal of excess reagent if necessary to avoid its possible interference in subsequent steps of the analysis.

Solution Reagents for Attack

1. *Water.* Many inorganic salts are soluble in water; see the simple solubility rules, p. 31. Very active metals *react* with water, with evolution of hydrogen.

2. *Hydrochloric acid* dissolves oxide and carbonate ores, and metals more active than hydrogen; see the activity series of the metals, p. 528. Concentrated hydrochloric acid is a mild reducing agent, and dissolves the higher oxides of lead and manganese; for example,

$$MnO_2 + 4H^+ + 2Cl^- \rightarrow Mn^{++} + Cl_2 + 2H_2O$$

Excess hydrochloric acid or chloride ion can be removed by evaporating with sulfuric acid until it fumes strongly.

3. *Nitric acid* is used primarily for its strong oxidizing action, to attack substances not decomposed by hydrochloric acid. It attacks metals slightly below hydrogen in the activity series (mercury, silver, copper, antimony); tin, antimony, and tungsten are converted to their insoluble oxides or acids, SnO_2, Sb_2O_5, and H_2WO_4. Some metals, notably iron and aluminum, are often rendered "passive" by nitric acid. It is used for attacking inactive metals, alloys, and insoluble sulfides such as CuS and PbS. Excess nitric acid can be removed by displacement with sulfuric acid, or by chemical destruction with hydrochloric acid.

4. *Aqua regia* (a mixture of hydrochloric and nitric acids) attacks alloy steels, very insoluble sulfides such as HgS, and the inactive metals gold and platinum.

5. *Sulfuric acid*, because of its high boiling point, is used to displace more volatile acids when they must be removed. It is applied for the dissolution of oxide ores of aluminum and titanium. It is also a good dehydrating agent.

6. *Perchloric acid*, $HClO_4$, is a very versatile reagent. When dilute, or when concentrated and cold, it is a strong acid only; most of its salts are soluble in water and also in many organic solvents. When it is both concentrated and hot, it is a very potent oxidizing agent and a good dehydrating agent. Destruction of its oxidizing action, after use, is effected merely by cooling and/or diluting. It is nonvolatile, and will therefore displace nitric and hydrochloric acids; with the latter it also reacts, by oxidation of the chloride ion. Perchloric acid is an excellent reagent for the finish oxidation of organic matter after most of the latter has been oxidized with nitric acid; easily oxidizable organic matter must *not* be treated first with perchloric acid, because of danger of explosion. In steel

analysis, perchloric acid is used advantageously for the attack, especially in the case of chrome steels.

7. *Hydroiodic acid* has special applications for attacking substances that are quite resistant to attack by other reagents. Mercury(II) sulfide, HgS, is dissolved with evolution of hydrogen sulfide; tin(IV) oxide, SnO_2, is volatilized as its iodide, SnI_4. Hydroiodic acid dissolves the halides of silver, calcium fluoride, and the insoluble sulfates (barium, strontium, lead).

8. *Sodium hydroxide* solution is used chiefly for dissolution of aluminum and its alloys, which react vigorously:

$$2Al + 2OH^- + 2H_2O \rightarrow 3H_2 + 2AlO_2^-$$

Oxides and hydroxides of aluminum, chromium(III), zinc, lead, and tin(IV) are amphoteric, and dissolve by reaction with alkali:

$$Al_2O_3 + 2OH^- \rightarrow 2AlO_2^- + H_2O$$

However, oxide ores of these elements are usually attacked by alkaline fusion.

9. *Selective reagents.* Several reagents have important, although selective, application.

a. Hydrofluoric acid has a specific action on silica and metal silicates:

$$SiO_2 + 4HF \rightarrow 2H_2O + SiF_4 \text{ (volatile)}$$

$$MSiO_3 + 6HF \rightarrow 3H_2O + MF_2 + SiF_4 \text{ (M = metal}^{2+})$$

Reactions with hydrofluoric acid must be conducted in platinum vessels. An excellent solvent for tin—antimony alloys is a solution containing 2 to 3% each of hydrofluoric acid and nitric acid.

b. Ammonium acetate dissolves lead sulfate (but not barium sulfate) by forming weakly ionized lead acetate.

c. Ammonium hydroxide dissolves silver chloride and silver bromide (but not silver iodide) by forming the complex $Ag(NH_3)_2^+$.

d. Ammonium sulfide dissolves the higher sulfides of arsenic, antimony, and tin (but not the sulfides of copper, lead, bismuth, and others) by forming the thio-anions, AsS_4^{---}, SbS_4^{---}, and SnS_3^{--}.

e. Potassium cyanide dissolves many "insoluble" compounds of silver, copper, cadmium, cobalt, and nickel, by forming the cyano-complexes, e.g., $Ag(CN)_2^-$, $Cd(CN)_4^{--}$, etc.

f. Sodium thiosulfate dissolves the halides of silver by forming the complex $Ag(S_2O_3)_2^{---}$.

Reagents for Fusion Attack

The sample, in a suitable crucible, is mixed with 10 to 20 times its own weight of **flux** (reagent) and heated above the melting point until the fusion is quiet and the melt is clear and homogeneous. After cooling, the solid mass is extracted with water and filtered. If the water-insoluble portion is to be analyzed, it can be dissolved in acid.

When the material to be transposed by fusion is predominantly acidic, such as silica and most silicates, the higher oxides and/or sulfides of tin, arsenic, antimony, molybdenum, and vanadium, an alkaline flux is used. If the material to be transposed is basic (oxides of many metals), an acidic flux is used.

1. *Sodium carbonate*, or a mixture of sodium and potassium carbonates (why?), is almost universally used for fusion attack of silicates and for transposition of insoluble sulfates and the halides of silver. For example,

$$MSiO_3 + Na_2CO_3 \rightarrow MCO_3 + Na_2SiO_3$$

$$BaSO_4 + Na_2CO_3 \rightarrow BaCO_3 + Na_2SO_4$$

2. *Sodium hydroxide* is used for fusions of oxide and/or sulfide ores of antimony, tin, zinc, chromium, and zirconium. Crucibles of iron, nickel, or silver are used.

3. *Alkaline oxidizing attack* is often required. Sodium peroxide is generally used for ores of antimony, arsenic, tin, and molybdenum, and for chromite (chrome iron ore):

$$2Fe(CrO_2)_2 + 7Na_2O_2 \rightarrow Fe_2O_3 + 4Na_2CrO_4 + 3Na_2O$$

Sodium peroxide is sometimes used for attacking chrome steels for chromium analysis. Highly insoluble sulfides are fused with sodium carbonate and an oxidizing agent, usually potassium chlorate or nitrate:

$$2FeS_2 + 4Na_2CO_3 + 5KClO_3 \rightarrow Fe_2O_3 + 4Na_2SO_4 + 5KCl + 4CO_2$$

Crucibles of metals *other than platinum* should be used with alkaline oxidizing fluxes.

4. *Potassium acid sulfate* or pyrosulfate ($2KHSO_4 \rightarrow H_2O + K_2S_2O_7$) is used as a flux for basic oxides, such as the oxide ores of cobalt, nickel, chromium, titanium, and iron:

$$Fe_2O_3 + 3K_2S_2O_7 \rightarrow Fe_2(SO_4)_3 + 3K_2SO_4$$

Certain steels containing chromium, molybdenum, vanadium, and tungsten are also attacked and rendered soluble. Vitreous-ware crucibles can be used if silica is not to be determined.

QUESTIONS

9-1 State briefly how to obtain the gross sample for analysis from the following.
(*a*) A 6-inch I-beam 12 ft long.
(*b*) A carload of cement shipped in 80-lb bags.
(*c*) A carload of mine run coal.
(*d*) Wheat being unloaded from a lake barge by a mechanical conveyor discharging into a grain elevator.

(*e*) Crude oil from a 10,000-gallon storage tank.

(*f*) Soil from a 10-acre field of farm land.

(*g*) Uranium ore as it comes from a mine in ore cars.

(*h*) Glassmaking sand from an open top railroad car, without unloading the sand.

(*i*) Air at an altitude of 20,000 feet.

(*j*) A liquid containing much suspended matter, from a 30-gallon shipping drum.

9-2 What reagent will dissolve one, but not the other, of the pair of substances given? Write ionic equations for all reactions that occur.

(*a*) Cu, Au   (*g*) $Al(OH)_3$, $Fe(OH)_3$

(*b*) Zn, Sn   (*h*) ZnS, CuS

(*c*) Mo, W   (*i*) SnO_2, SiO_2

(*d*) AgCl, Ag_2CO_3 (*j*) Bi_2S_3, As_2S_5

(*e*) AgCl, AgI   (*k*) CaC_2O_4, $CaCO_3$

(*f*) $BaSO_4$, $PbSO_4$ (*l*) $BaSO_4$, $BaCrO_4$

9-3 Formulate a scheme for complete decomposition (dissolution) of the sample given. In stepwise treatment with two or more reagents, show the composition of the soluble and of the insoluble fraction at each step. Write equations for all reactions.

(*a*) An alloy of tin, lead, and antimony.

(*b*) A mixture of lead sulfate and silver chloride.

(*c*) A mixture of CuS, SiO_2, and Fe_2O_3.

(*d*) A mixture of $Fe(CrO_2)_2$ and $MgSiO_3$.

(*e*) A mixture of BaO and $MgSO_4$.

(*f*) Limestone containing $CaCO_3$, $MgCO_3$, Fe_2O_3, and $KAlSi_3O_8$.

(*g*) A rock sample containing $Mg_2Al_4Si_5O_{18}$, CaF_2, LiCl, $BaSO_4$, and SiO_2.

9-4 What reagent(s) would be used to decompose a sample the essential constituent of which is the following? Write equations for all reactions.

(*a*) TiO_2 (*d*) Cassiterite, SnO_2

(*b*) Al_2SiO_5 (*e*) Magnetite, Fe_3O_4

(*c*) $SrSO_4$ (*f*) Corundum, Al_2O_3

10

ANALYTICAL SEPARATIONS: PRECIPITATION METHODS

Although only eight of the elements (oxygen, silicon, aluminum, iron, calcium, sodium, potassium, and magnesium) make up approximately 98% of the earth's crust, water areas, and atmosphere, many of the remaining elements are of much greater commercial importance; furthermore, some of the elements that were of only minor importance several years ago have now come into considerable commercial importance. The fact that the elements can combine with one another in various ways increases greatly the complexity of materials, both natural and manufactured, that may need to be analyzed. The known natural and synthetic organic (carbon) compounds number a few hundred thousand; naturally occurring inorganic materials (minerals) number about two thousand. Most of the minerals are of relatively few types: native metals (silver, gold, the platinum elements, mercury, copper), silicates, carbonates, oxides, and sulfides, with lesser numbers of sulfates, phosphates, and chlorides. However, few minerals are pure, and the isolation of the desired constituent often requires more effort than just its measurement after separation; the same considerations apply to many manufactured products.

Separations may be accomplished in a variety of ways, such as by precipitation, volatilization, extraction, electrolytic deposition, complexation, and adsorption. In most of these methods a new phase (gas, liquid, or solid) is formed; depending upon the nature of the sample, the desired constituent may be in either the new phase formed (e.g., precipitate), or in the original phase. The separation form should contain all of the desired constituent and no substances that would interfere with its subsequent measurement; or, if these conditions cannot be met, any departure from them should be capable of estimation so that corrections can be applied. Several techniques have accomplished some remark-

140

able separations; examples are the separation of mixtures of many amino acids by paper chromatography; the separation of isotopes by gaseous diffusion and by mass spectrometry; the separation of closely similar organic compounds by gas-liquid chromatography; the reduction of impurities to about one part per hundred billion (10^{11}) in transistor elements by zone melting. Often an ingenious utilization of a variety of methods is necessary in order to effect the required separation. Several separation methods are discussed briefly in Chaps. 10 through 13. Detailed treatment of various separation methods has been given by Berg.[1]

One of the most widely used general methods of separation is precipitation. The formation and properties of precipitates are discussed in Chaps. 14. The precipitate may contain the desired constituent or some substance chemically related to it, in which case the precipitate is further processed for measurement; or the precipitate may contain the interfering substances, in which case it is discarded and the filtrate used for completing the analysis.

FRACTIONAL PRECIPITATION BY CONTROLLED pH

Compounds frequently formed for precipitation separations of the cations are the hydroxides (hydrous oxides), sulfides, oxalates, phosphates, and carbonates. All of these anions are the anions of weak acids. Consequently, the concentration of hydrogen ion in solution controls the concentration of the anion in solution. If the solubilities of the various metal hydroxides, sulfides, oxalates, etc., are sufficiently different, they may be fractionally precipitated by proper regulation of the pH of the solution. By making use of the values of the solubility product constants of the insoluble compounds and of the ionization constants of the weak ionogen involved, it is possible to calculate which separations are possible. Experimental test is always required, however, because in some cases the solubility product constant is not known with much certainty, and because many substances behave quite differently when present in an environment of other substances than when present alone.

Hydroxides (Hydrous Oxides)

The "hydroxides" of most of the elements that separate by precipitation from solution are more properly called *hydrous oxides*, in which an indefinite, usually large, amount of water is associated with the oxide, e.g., $Fe_2O_3 \cdot xH_2O$. However, for convenience in writing equations and in making calculations from solubility product constants, these compounds will be considered as true hydroxides.

There are two reasons why the separation of the elements as their hydroxides is so widely applicable in analytical chemistry.

[1] E. W. Berg, *Physical and Chemical Methods of Separation*, New York, McGraw-Hill, 1963.

1. There is an enormous difference in the solubilities of the metal hydroxides.

2. The hydrogen ion or hydroxyl ion concentration in aqueous solution can be varied over a wide range. Furthermore, by the use of buffers the pH of the solution can be *adjusted to and maintained at a predetermined level*, in order to effect the desired separation.

Suppose it is desired to effect a precipitation separation of iron(III) as its hydroxide. K_{sp} of $Fe(OH)_3 = 4.5 \times 10^{-37}$. Assuming the original solution to be 0.010 M in Fe^{+++} and that precipitation is considered to be complete when no more than 0.10 mg of iron is left in 100 ml of solution, at what pH will precipitation start and at what pH will it be complete?

Calculation of pH to start precipitation. Given: $[Fe^{+++}] = 0.010$. Then

$$[OH^-] = \sqrt[3]{(4.5 \times 10^{-37})/(1.0 \times 10^{-2})} = 3.6 \times 10^{-12}$$

$$[H^+] = (1.0 \times 10^{-14})/(6.7 \times 10^{-12}) = 2.8 \times 10^{-3}$$

and

$$pH = 2.55.$$

Calculation of pH for complete precipitation. 0.10 mg of Fe^{+++} per 100 ml = 0.0010 g per liter. Atomic weight of $Fe = 56$; molar concentration of Fe^{+++} left in solution $= 0.0010/56 = 1.8 \times 10^{-5}$.

$$[OH^-] = \sqrt[3]{(4.5 \times 10^{-37})/(1.8 \times 10^{-5})} = 2.9 \times 10^{-11}$$

and

$$pH = 3.47.$$

Iron(III) hydroxide should therefore be completely precipitated in fairly acidic solution. The complete precipitation of iron(III) hydroxide at a pH between 3 and 4 is verified experimentally. Obviously, any other hydroxide that is less soluble than or has the same solubility as iron(III) hydroxide will also precipitate at this pH.

When the elements are arranged in the order of their precipitation pH, a continuous or overlapping series results, so that a sharp separation of adjacent elements in the series cannot be made. The pH at which precipitation starts is dependent upon the concentration of the cation entering the reaction; whether or not two given ions can be separated may be strongly dependent upon their relative concentrations in solution. Elements for which the precipitation pH differs by as much as 3 pH units should be quite satisfactorily separated unless their relative concentrations are unfavorable. Table 10-1 lists several common elements and their hydroxide precipitation pH values; these values may be shifted considerably by such factors as temperature changes and formation of stable colloidal systems, as well as by the presence of substances that may form stable complex ions and thus decrease the effective concentration of the ions to be precipitated.

Table 10-1   Approximate pH of Precipitation of Hydroxides[a]

Element	pH	Reagents
Si(IV), W(VI)	<1	Concentrated mineral acids
Sn(IV), Sb(V)	<1	Concentrated $HClO_4$ or HNO_3 but not HCl
Pb(IV), Mn(IV)	<1	Concentrated oxidizing acids, or anodic deposition from acid solution
Ce(IV), Ti(IV)	2–3	
Sb(III), Bi(III)[b]	2–3	
		Buffers:
Th(IV), Fe(III), Sn(II), Hg(I), Hg(II)[c]	3–4	pH 3–5: acetic acid–acetate benzoic acid–benzoate
Al(III), Be(II), Cr(III) Cu(II), Pb(II), Fe(II)	5–6	pH 6–8: suspensions of ZnO, HgO, $CdCO_3$, $CaCO_3$, $BaCO_3$
Cd(II), Co(II), Ni(II), Zn(II) Mn(II), Ag(I)	7–8	pH 8–10: ammonium hydroxide–ammonium salt (except for silver); suspension of MgO.
Mg(II)	11	NaOH; incomplete by NH_4OH
Ca(II), Sr(II), Ba(II)	>12	Incomplete precipitation by NaOH

[a] H. T. S. Britton, *J. Chem. Soc.*, **127(2)**, 2110–2159 (1925).
[b] Precipitated as basic salts, e.g., SbOCl, BiOCl.
[c] In chloride solution, precipitation of Hg(II) occurs at pH 8-9.

Silicon and the higher oxidation states of tungsten, tin, antimony, manganese, and lead are predominantly nonmetallic in character; their oxides and hydroxides are *acidic*, and they are precipitated from strongly acidic medium. The metallic elements, the oxides and hydroxides of which are *bases*, show a trend in the relation of oxidation number to solubility of their hydroxides, and therefore to the precipitation pH; the higher valent cations form the more insoluble hydroxides and therefore precipitate at the lower pH values. Hydroxides of aluminum, chromium(III), tin(II), and zinc, being amphoteric, dissolve in an excess of alkali. At pH 7 to 8, for example, both chromium(III) and nickel(II) hydroxides are precipitated; addition of strong alkali will redissolve the chromium(III) hydroxide but not the nickel hydroxide. Although separations based on amphoterism are used in qualitative analysis, they are not much used in quantitative analysis because redissolution of the amphoteric hydroxide from the mixture is likely to be incomplete.

Nonmetals such as arsenic, phosphorus, and sulfur, and the elements chromium(VI), vanadium(V), and manganese(VII), which in these high oxidation states are predominantly acidic, are not precipitated in either strongly alkaline or strongly acidic solution.

Complex Formation in Hydroxide Precipitation. By complex formation, the concentration of simple metal ions may be decreased and thus require a higher concentration of anion to exceed the solubility product constant of the compound formed by their union. Indeed, if the complex is very stable, precipitation of the cation may be completely prevented. For example, in the presence of tartrate or citrate, the precipitation of iron(III), aluminum, and certain other cations as their hydrous oxides is prevented. Ammonium hydroxide (principally dissolved ammonia, and only a low concentration of hydroxide ion) forms ammonia complexes with several cations, notably silver, copper, cadmium, zinc, cobalt, and nickel, and thus prevents their precipitation as hydrous oxides while allowing the precipitation of iron(III), titanium(IV), bismuth, aluminum, and many other cations. Many other examples of masking by complex formation could be cited.

Oxidation State for Separation. The properties of the elements in solutions of their compounds are dependent upon their oxidation states. Table 10-1 shows several cases of an element in two different oxidation states. In each case, except for the ions of mercury, the precipitation pH is considerably different for the hydroxides of the two different oxidation numbers. Sometimes it is possible to effect separations that otherwise would be unsatisfactory or impossible, by changing the oxidation state of one of the elements. Aluminum cannot be separated from chromium(III) by hydroxide precipitation; but if the chromium(III) is oxidized to chromium(VI), that is, chromate ion, aluminum can be precipitated as hydroxide and the chromium, being predominantly non-metallic in the $+6$ state, is not precipitated. Silver and mercury(I) cannot be separated by chloride precipitation, but if the mercury(I) is oxidized to mercury(II), addition of chloride ion precipitates only the silver as chloride.

Sulfides

Separation of the cations by sulfide precipitation is based upon the same principles as separation as hydroxides.

1. There is an enormous difference in the solubilities of sulfides, ranging from the water-soluble alkali and alkaline earth sulfides down to mercury(II) sulfide, for which the K_{sp} is about 10^{-54}.

2. The hydrogen sulfide equilibrium,

$$H_2S \leftrightarrows 2H^+ + S^{--}$$

is markedly influenced by the hydrogen ion concentration of the solution; the sulfide ion concentration can be varied over a range of about 10^{20} in going from 1 M hydrochloric acid to 1 M sodium hydroxide. The precipitation of sulfides can therefore be controlled by adjustment of the pH of the solution. In sulfide, as in hydroxide precipitation, changes in cation concentration by formation of complexes with ammonia, cyanide ion, etc., are also utilized in effecting separations.

Oxalates, Phosphates

Relatively few analytical separations are effected by fractional precipitation of metal oxalates or metal phosphates, because these salts of the different cations are not widely different in solubility. The principal application of oxalate precipitation is for the separation of calcium from magnesium and the alkalies, after all the heavy metals have been removed. Phosphate precipitation is used for separation of magnesium (as $MgNH_4PO_4$) from the alkali cations after removal of heavy metal and alkaline earth cations; the determination is completed by ignition of $MgNH_4PO_4$ to $Mg_2P_2O_7$ for weighing. The same method can be applied to the precipitation and gravimetric determination of zinc, cadmium, manganese, cobalt, and nickel when only one of these cations is present in solution. In the absence of interfering ions, precipitation of the normal phosphate can be used for the separation of aluminum, zirconium, or hafnium from many other cations.

ORGANIC PRECIPITANTS

The use of organic compounds as reagents for inorganic analysis has developed into a very important part of analytical chemistry, and an extensive literature exists on the subject.[2] Many organic compounds are used as complexing agents, precipitants, and reagents for colorimetric determination of inorganic ions. The present discussion is only a brief, elementary treatment of the use of organic precipitants.

Precipitation of Normal Salts

Two classes of organic compounds used as precipitants are the organic acids and bases, which form insoluble salts with certain cations and anions, respectively. A few examples in each category are given in Table 10-2.

Chelate Precipitants

The discovery by Tschugaeff[3] in 1905 that dimethylglyoxime formed a precipitate with nickel ion was the origin of the rapid development of a new phase of gravimetric precipitation analysis, both qualitative and quantitative. Subse-

---

[2] F. J. Welcher, *Organic Analytical Reagents*, Princeton, N. J., Van Nostrand, 1947–48, vols. I–IV.

[3] L. Tschugaeff, *Ber.*, **38**, 2520 (1905); *Z. anorg. Chem.*, **46**, 144 (1905).

Table 10-2 Normal Salt Precipitants

Reagent	Use
For Cations	
1. Oxalic acid, $O=C-O-H$ | $O=C-O-H$	Precipitates most cations. Used for separation of Ca^{++} from Mg^{++} after removal of heavy-metal cations.
2. Phenylarsonic acid, $C_6H_5-As=O$ with $O-H$, $O-H$	From strongly acidic solution, precipitates tetravalent cations: Ti, Th, Zr, Hf, Sn, Ce.
3. Picric acid (1, 3, 5-trinitrophenol), $C_6H_2(NO_2)_3OH$	Precipitates K^+ (also NH_4^+, Rb^+, Cs^+) but not Na^+. Most heavy metal ions also precipitate and must be removed.

4. Dipicrylamine (hexanitrodiphenyl-amine),
$(NO_2)_3-C_6H_2-N-C_6H_2-(NO_2)_3$
               |
              H
	Same as for picric acid.

5. Sodium tetraphenylboron, $NaB(C_6H_5)_4$	Best precipitant for K^+. Determination can be finished by gravimetric or titrimetric methods.
6. Thiocyanate plus certain nitrogen bases, e.g., pyridine, benzidine	Bases form coordination complexes with Cu^{++}, Cd^{++}, Zn^{++}, Ag^+, etc., which precipitate with CNS^-; example: $[Cu(pyr)_4](CNS)_2$.
For Anions	
1. Benzidine, $H_2N-C_6H_4-C_6H_4-NH_2$	Precipitant for SO_4^{--}; solubility about 100 mg/liter. Also precipitates PO_4^{---} and WO_4^{--}.
2. 4, 4'—Diaminotolane, [a] $H_2N-C_6H_4-C\equiv C-C_6H_4-NH_2$	Precipitant for SO_4^{--}; solubility 59 mg/liter.
3. 4-Chloro-4'-aminodiphenyl, (" CAD "),[b] $Cl-C_6H_4-C_6H_4-NH_2$	Precipitant for SO_4^{--}; solubility, 15 mg/liter.
4. " Nitron "	Precipitant for NO_3^-. Also precipitates NO_2^-, ClO_4^-, ClO_3^-, CrO_4^{--}, and Br^-.
5. Tetraphenylarsonium chloride, $(C_6H_5)_4AsCl$	Precipitant for ClO_4^-, IO_4^-, MnO_4^-, MoO_4^{--}, I^-, CNS^-. Also precipitates chlorocomplexes of Cd, Zn, Hg(II), Sn(IV); e.g., $[(C_6H_5)_4As]_2CdCl_4$.

[a] R. Belcher, M. Kapel, and A. J. Nutten, *Anal. Chim. Acta*, **8**, 122 (1953).
[b] R. Belcher, A. J. Nutten, and W. I. Stephen, *J. Chem. Soc.*, **1953**, 1334.

quent investigations have led to a considerable understanding of the nature of the chemical bonds involved in the reactions, and the relation of the functional groups to the structure of the organo-metallic compounds formed. These **chelate compounds** are derived from organic compounds containing two kinds of functional groups, so arranged in the organic molecule that the metallic ion can form a part of a ring structure.

Requisites for Chelate Compound Formation. In order to form a chelate compound, certain requirements must be met by both the organic reagent and the metallic ion.

1. The organic reagent must contain both an **acidic group** (i.e., hydrogen replaceable by a metal valence bond) and a **coordinating group** (i.e., an atom with an unshared pair of electrons that can serve as an electron pair donor). Following are some of the groups of each kind in organic chelating agents; note that the oxime group appears in both categories.

Acidic Groups		Coordinating Groups	
—COOH	carboxyl	—NH₂	amino
—OH	hydroxyl, especially aromatic	＼N／	cyclic nitrogen, as in pyridine
=NH	imine	—NO₂	nitro
=NO—OH	nitroxyl	—NO	nitroso
=N—OH	oxime	=N—OH	oxime
—SO₃H	sulfonic	=O	carbonyl oxygen

2. The acidic group and the coordinating group must be located in the organic compound in such positions that the entrance of the metal ion forms a 5- or a 6-membered ring, including the metal as one member of the ring.

3. In order to form a chelate with a given organic reagent, the metal ion must be of appropriate size, oxidation number, and coordination number.

Properties of Chelate Compounds. The chelate compounds of importance in gravimetric separations and determinations are the chelate nonelectrolytes or **inner complex salts.** Their properties, summarized below, differ markedly from normal salts.

1. Many inner complex salts are insoluble in water, which makes possible many separations that are impossible or unsatisfactory by inorganic reagents.

2. They are usually soluble in nonpolar solvents such as benzene and carbon tetrachloride; this property permits application of extraction procedures for effecting separations in many cases.

3. The reactions of chelating agents with inorganic ions are sometimes specific, or at least selective.

4. Chelating agents are weak acids; in forming the insoluble complex salts, the usual equilibrium principles apply. The overall reaction can be represented thus:

$$n\text{Hchel} + M^{n+} \rightleftharpoons n\text{H}^+ + M(\text{chel})_n$$

Precipitation of the chelate salts should be considerably influenced by pH; experimentally, this has been found to be the case in many instances. For example, the selectivity of 8-quinolinol and salicylaldoxime in precipitating cations is controlled by pH in much the same way as for fractional precipitation of hydroxides and sulfides of the metals.

5. Many chelate compounds are highly colored, making them especially useful for confirmatory tests in qualitative analysis (e.g., the pink color of nickel dimethylglyoximate). Even though a metal chelate is soluble, it may be useful analytically if it is highly colored, for then it may be applied in a colorimetric method. Iron(II) forms with 1,10-phenanthroline a soluble complex of intense red color, which is used for colorimetric determination of iron in the range of a few parts per million of solution; it is also a useful indicator in redox titrimetry. Organic reagents are widely used in photometric methods of analysis for inorganic ions.

6. In many cases the precipitates are suitable weighing forms for gravimetric analysis. When this is the case, the gravimetric factor for calculation to the metal is very favorable, because the metal constitutes only a small part of a heavy molecule. If the precipitate is not a suitable weighing form, it can be ignited to the metal oxide for weighing.

Separations by Chelating Reagents. Very many organic chelating reagents have been applied to the separation and determination of inorganic cations. Some systems, especially the precipitates formed by 8-quinolinol and by salicylaldoxime, have been studied extensively. Examples of a few commonly used reagents are given in Table 10-3.

Table 10-3 Chelate Precipitants

Reagent	Use
1. Dimethylglyoxime (diacetyldioxime), $H_3C—C=N$ —O—H $\quad\quad\quad\mid$ $H_3C—C=N$ —O—H	Precipitates nickel as $Ni(DMG)_2$, at pH 5–9; tartrate prevents precipitation of Fe^{+++}, Al^{+++}, Cr^{+++}. At pH 1, precipitates $Pd(DMG)_2$ but not Ni. Other 1,2-dioximes react similarly.

Table 10-3 (con't)

Reagent	Use
2. 8-Quinolinol (8-hydroxy-quinoline, or "oxine"),	Precipitates most cations; separations obtained by pH control, complexation with tartrate, etc. Precipitates are often weighed as such, or after ignition to metal oxide. Especially good for precipitation of Al^{+++} (pH 4–10) and Mg^{++} (pH 8–13), and for separation of Al^{+++} from PO_4^{---}.
3. 1-Nitroso-2-naphthol,	Precipitates Co^{++}, Cu^{++}, Pd^{++}, Fe^{+++}. Used mainly for separation of Co^{++} from Ni^{++}; reagent oxidizes Co^{++} to Co^{+++}, then precipitates the latter. Co determined by ignition to Co_3O_4.
4. Ammonium phenylnitroso-hydroxylamine ("cupferron"),	Precipitates Zr(IV), Ti(IV), Sn(IV), Ce(IV), U(VI), Fe(III) from 5–10% HCl or H_2SO_4; at lower acidity, precipitates Cu(II), Hg(II), Bi(III). Often used for removal of iron interference in analysis for other cations, such as Al^{+++}.
5. Ammonium naphthylnitroso-hydroxylamine ("neocupferron")	Same uses as for "cupferron"; gives less soluble precipitates.

Table 10-3 (con't)

Reagent	Use
6. α-Benzoinoxime ("cupron"), 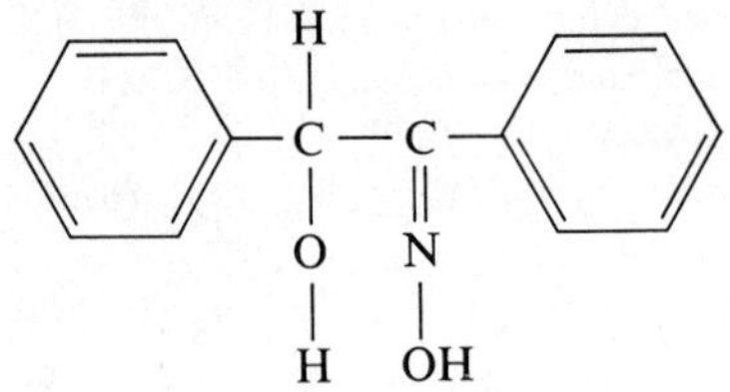	Highly selective for precipitation of Cu^{++} from ammoniacal tartrate solution and for Mo(VI) from mineral acid solulution (ignite and weigh as MoO_3).

Reagent	Use
7. Salicylaldoxime, 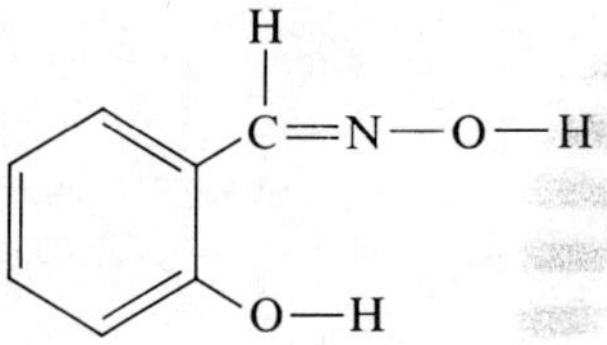	Precipitates many cations; separations attained by pH control: Cu^{++} (pH 3), Ni^{++} ($pH > 3.5$), Bi^{+++} (pH 7–9), Pb^{++} ($pH > 9$). Very good for separation of Cu^{++} from Cd^{++} and Zn^{++}, Pb^{++}, Fe^{++}, and many other cations.

QUESTIONS

10-1 What *inorganic* reagent will form a precipitate with one but not with the other of the pair of ions given? Write ionic equations for reactions that occur, state the conditions required (pH, additives, etc.), and designate the insoluble product.

(a) Sn^{4+}, Zn^{++}

(b) Fe^{++}, Fe^{+++}

(c) Fe^{+++}, Cr^{+++}

(d) Fe^{++}, Cu^{++}

(e) Hg^{++}, Hg_2^{++}

(f) Mg^{++}, Mn^{++}

(g) Cd^{++}, Zn^{++}

(h) SO_4^{--}, CO_3^{--}

(i) Cl^-, SO_4^{--}

(j) I^-, NO_3^-

(k) AsO_4^{---}, PO_4^{---}

(l) AsO_4^{---}, AsO_2^-

10-2 What *organic* reagent will form a precipitate with one, but not with the other, of the pair of ions given? State the conditions required. Write the graphic formula of the precipitate formed, and state whether it is a normal salt or a chelate nonelectrolyte (inner complex salt).

(a) Mg^{++}, Ca^{++}

(b) Fe^{+++}, Ti^{4+}

(c) Na^+, K^+ (3 methods)

(d) SO_4^{--}, NO_3^- (2 methods)

(e) ClO_3^-, ClO_4^-

(f) Ni^{++}, Fe^{+++} (2 methods)

(g) Ni^{++}, Co^{++} (2 methods)

(h) Al^{+++}, Mg^{++}

(i) Fe^{++}, Fe^{+++}

(j) Cu^{++}, Zn^{++} (2 methods)

11

SEPARATION
BY VOLATILIZATION

Separation by volatilization is effected by a change of physical state resulting in the formation of a gas or vapor. The method may be used merely to expel a volatile material, which is not recovered, in order to leave the desired constituent(s) as a residue, either solid or fluid; examples are the expulsion of moisture to dry a sample, or the ignition of a residue for expulsion of ammonium salts, or boiling a solution to expel dissolved oxygen, carbon dioxide, etc. In other instances the method involves recovery of the desired volatile material by absorption of the gas or vapor in a suitable absorbent, or the condensation of the vapor back to liquid or solid state. Examples are the volatilization of ammonia in the distillation step of the Kjeldahl method for determining nitrogen, the purification of iodine by sublimation, the distillation of arsenic(III) chloride to separate it from antimony and tin, and the separation of many organic compounds by fractional distillation.

The general method includes also treatments or reagents to give volatile reaction products, as illustrated below. In many cases the method is a step in the determination of a component, although the completion for determination is given here for only a few cases.

1. Thermal Decomposition. Many substances are unstable toward heat; the temperature required for decomposition varies over wide limits.

a. Hydrates vary widely in stability; some are decomposed at relatively low temperatures (even at room temperature), others may require quite high temperatures. In the Penfield method for water in silicate rocks, water is separated by strong ignition of the sample:

$$MSiO_3 \cdot xH_2O \rightarrow MSiO_3 + xH_2O \qquad (M = \text{a metal})$$

and the condensed water is determined by direct weighing.

b. Carbonates, except those of the alkali metals, are unstable toward heat:

$$MCO_3 \rightarrow MO + CO_2$$

The carbon dioxide can be determined either directly or indirectly. Sulfites behave similarly; however, they are not usually separated or determined in this way.

c. Ammonium salts are often removed by evaporation to dryness and ignition of the residue:

$$NH_4Cl \xrightarrow{\text{heat}} NH_3 + HCl \xrightarrow{\text{cool}} NH_4Cl \quad \text{(sublimation)}$$

Ammonium nitrate is decomposed as its solution is evaporated to near dryness:

$$NH_4NO_3 \rightarrow 2H_2O + N_2O$$

2. Displacement of Volatile Acids (or Anhydrides) from Their Salts.
a. Carbonates, sulfites, and acid-soluble sulfides react with strong acids:

$$CaCO_3 + 2H^+ \rightarrow Ca^{++} + H_2O + CO_2$$

$$Na_2SO_3 + 2H^+ \rightarrow 2Na^+ + H_2O + SO_2$$

$$FeS + 2H^+ \rightarrow Fe^{++} + H_2S$$

b. Anions of mineral acids such as hydrochloric and nitric, frequently used as reagents in preparing solutions for analysis, often interfere with subsequent steps in the analysis; they are removed by evaporation with concentrated sulfuric acid. These acids are also volatilized by treating their solid salts with concentrated sulfuric acid.

3. Oxidation. This is accomplished by atmospheric oxygen or by reagent chemicals, usually at elevated temperatures.
a. Sulfides are air-oxidized when heated strongly in air:

$$4FeS_2 + 11O_2 \rightarrow 2Fe_2O_3 + 8SO_2$$

b. Organic compounds burned in air or oxygen are completely converted to volatile products (unless some metallic constituent is also present):

$$C_{10}H_8 + 12O_2 \rightarrow 10CO_2 + 4H_2O$$

Thermal decomposition of many organic compounds gives a multiplicity of products not conveniently represented by a single equation; *complete* combustion of a carbon-hydrogen, or of a carbon-hydrogen-oxygen compound gives only carbon dioxide and water. The method is used for the removal of organic interferences in inorganic analysis, as well as for the determination of carbon and hydrogen in organic compounds.

4. Formation of Volatile, Nonpolar Compounds.   Examples are silicon tetra-fluoride and arsenic(III) chloride:

$$SiO_2 + 4HF \rightarrow 2H_2O + SiF_4 \quad \text{(volatile)}$$

$$As_2O_3 + 6HCl \rightarrow 3H_2O + 2AsCl_3 \quad \text{(volatile)}$$

5. Reduction by Hydrogen.   Oxides of inactive metals are easily reduced by hydrogen. The method is used in the analysis of platinum metals to get a satisfactory weighing form (pure metal):

$$PtO_2 + 2H_2 \rightarrow 2H_2O + Pt$$

Determination Methods

Determinations based on volatilization processes may be either of two types.

1. *Direct methods* involve the recovery of the volatile component for subsequent measurement. The determination of carbon and hydrogen in organic compounds is routinely made by absorption, in suitable absorbents, of carbon dioxide and water formed by combustion of the compound.

2. *Indirect methods* of determination are essentially loss in weight methods. The desired constituent may be the volatile matter determined by difference in weight of sample before and again after treatment, as in the determination of adsorbed moisture by loss in weight on oven drying, or loss on ignition of a limestone sample. Alternatively, the desired constituent may be the remaining residue, as in the determination of nonvolatile solids in water by evaporating the water and weighing the residue.

Applications

The following is a brief description of how some of the elements may be volatilized to effect a separation. In a few cases, mention is also made of the method of completing the determination.

1. *Hydrogen* is separated as water; adsorbed moisture is volatilized from most substances at 105 to 110°C (oven drying). Higher temperature is required to volatilize water of constitution or essential water, as in a hydrate. Hydrogen in organic compounds is volatilized and determined by combustion to water.

2. *Carbon* is volatilized and also determined as carbon dioxide, by heating carbonates, or by treating them with acids, or by combustion of organic compounds.

3. *Nitrogen* may be separated and determined as ammonia, by the Kjeldahl method. From certain organic compounds nitrogen is separated and determined as gaseous nitrogen (Dumas method).

4. *Oxygen* may be separated and determined as water from some compounds. It can be determined directly in organic compounds by vaporizing the sample

in a stream of dry nitrogen or helium and passing it over carbon heated to about 1200°C. The oxygen forms carbon monoxide, which is passed over iodine pentoxide:

$$5CO + I_2O_5 \rightarrow 5CO_2 + I_2$$

The iodine vapor is absorbed in alkali and titrated with sodium thiosulfate.

5. *Sulfur* can be volatilized as hydrogen sulfide from certain sulfides, as sulfur dioxide by roasting of sulfides in air, and as sulfur dioxide by treating sulfites with strong acids. Determinations may be finished titrimetrically, or finished by oxidation to sulfate and precipitation as $BaSO_4$, which is weighed.

6. *Halogens* can be separated as their hydrides or hydroacids, HF, HCl, HBr, and HI, by displacement with a nonvolatile acid. Volatilization as the free elements requires an oxidative treatment of the halides, and is sometimes applied to bromide and iodide separations from the other halides by expelling bromine and iodine. Halogens in organic compounds are volatilized by oxidation with dichromate and sulfuric acid; the free halogen element may be absorbed in alkali and determined titrimetrically. Fluoride may be separated from many substances that would interfere with its determination, by distillation with sulfuric acid or perchloric acid in the presence of silica (silicon dioxide). The fluorine is volatilized as hexafluosilicic acid, H_2SiF_6, which can be determined titrimetrically. Fluorides also react with borates in acid medium, forming volatile boron trifluoride, BF_3.

7. *Silicon* is volatilized as its tetrafluoride by treating silica with hydrofluoric acid (see p. 153). The method is routinely used to determine silica in the silica and insolubles residue in analysis of limestone, silicate rocks, etc.

8. *Boron* can be volatilized as boron trifluoride (item 6 above); obviously, the fluoride method will not separate boron from silicon. When this separation is required the boron, in the form of a borate or boric acid, is heated with methanol (or ethanol) and sulfuric acid:

$$Na_2B_4O_7 + H_2SO_4 + 5H_2O \rightarrow Na_2SO_4 + 4H_3BO_3$$

$$3CH_3OH + H_3BO_3 \rightarrow 3H_2O + (CH_3)_3BO_3$$

The methyl borate is distilled off; it can be absorbed in alkali and determined titrimetrically.

9. *Arsenic(III), antimony(III,) and tin(IV)* can be distilled as their halides (usually chlorides) and separated from many substances and also from each other. The mixture containing $AsCl_3$, $SbCl_3$, $SnCl_4$, and hydrochloric acid is distilled while a current of carbon dioxide is passed through the mixture; arsenic(III) chloride passes over first (bp 130°C). Phosphoric acid is added to the residual liquid in the still to complex the tin(IV) and prevent its volatilization, and antimony(III) chloride is distilled off (bp 155°C). Hydrobromic acid is added to the residue, and the tin is distilled over as tin(IV) bromide (bp 140°C).

Arsenic is sometimes volatilized as its hydride arsine, AsH_3, by treatment with zinc and acid:

$$As_2O_3 + 6Zn + 12H^+ \rightarrow 3H_2O + 6Zn^{++} + 2AsH_3$$

Antimony compounds are also reduced to SbH_3. Removal of antimony is not complete by this method, and obviously the method will not separate arsenic from antimony.

10. *Mercury* is very easily volatilized as the metal and thus separated from other metals. Mercury compounds are easily reduced to the metal for vaporization of the latter. The separation of silver chloride from mercury(I) chloride can be effected by ignition to expel the latter. Mercury(II) chloride can be volatilized by distilling in a stream of hydrogen chloride or chlorine.

11. *Chromium* is volatilized as chromyl chloride, CrO_2Cl_2. Because the chromium must first be in oxidation state $+6$, oxidative treatment with hot perchloric acid is generally used; metallic chromium or chromium(III) is oxidized to dichromate:

$$14Cr + 12ClO_4^- + H_2O \rightarrow 6Cl_2 + 2H^+ + 7Cr_2O_7^{--}$$
$$14Cr^{+++} + 6ClO_4^- + 25H_2O \rightarrow 3Cl_2 + 50H^+ + 7Cr_2O_7^{--}$$

An excess of chloride ion, either as hydrochloric acid or as sodium chloride, is added and the chromyl chloride is distilled:

$$Cr_2O_7^{--} + 4Cl^- + 6H^+ \rightarrow 3H_2O + 2CrO_2Cl_2$$

If the chromium to be separated is already in the form of chromate or dichromate, sodium chloride and sulfuric acid are used for the distillation of chromyl chloride.

This method is especially suited to application in steel analysis for the separation of chromium from iron, manganese, nickel, vanadium, etc. The chromium can be determined by absorption of the chromyl chloride in alkali:

$$CrO_2Cl_2 + 4OH^- \rightarrow 2Cl^- + 2H_2O + CrO_4^{--}$$

The chromate solution is then acidified and titrated with a standard reductant such as iron(II) solution.

12. *Osmium and ruthenium* can be separated from the other platinum elements (and from most other elements), as well as from each other, by volatilization of their tetroxides. Distillation from nitric acid solution volatilizes OsO_4; sulfuric acid and potassium bromate are added, and RuO_4 is distilled off. The volatile oxides can be absorbed in suitable solutions for subsequent determination.

Gas Absorption Methods

The absorption of gases in suitable solvents or on suitable solid absorbents is, in a sense, the converse of volatilization. Mixtures of gases can be separated and determined by a systematic procedure involving several absorbents used in

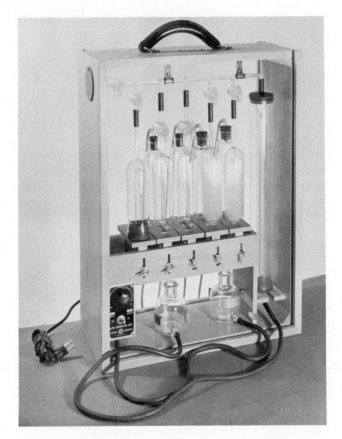

Fig. 11-1   Orsat-type gas analysis apparatus. (Courtesy of Fisher Scientific Co.)

succession. By starting with a measured volume of gas sample, the decrease in volume by the use of each absorbent represents the desired constituent that was absorbed.

Gas volumetric absorption methods are employed for the analysis of the components of industrial fuel gases, which contain small amounts of oxygen, nitrogen, carbon dioxide, and unsaturated hydrocarbons, and relatively large amounts of carbon monoxide, hydrogen, and methane. One type of commercial apparatus used in gas analysis is shown in Fig. 11-1. The essential parts are a gas measuring buret and several Orsat type absorption pipets connected to a common manifold. The separate pipets can be isolated and the gas passed back and forth by appropriate manipulation of the stopcocks and the leveling bulb attached to the gas buret. The outline below shows the order in which the various components of a fuel gas are determined by the absorbents.

1. *Carbon dioxide* is absorbed in concentrated potassium hydroxide solution.

2. *Heavy hydrocarbons and illuminants* consist of unsaturated hydrocarbons such as benzene (C_6H_6), ethylene (C_2H_4), and acetylene (C_2H_2). These compounds can be absorbed in fuming sulfuric acid containing 20 to 25% excess sulfur trioxide.

3. *Oxygen* can be absorbed in alkaline pyrogallol solution, or by moist sticks of white phosphorus, or in sodium hyposulfite ($Na_2S_2O_4$) in alkaline solution, or in an alkaline solution of anthrahydroquinone sulfonate containing also some sodium hyposulfite to regenerate the reagent after use.

4. *Carbon monoxide* is absorbed by a solution of copper(I) chloride, which may be either ammoniacal, or acidic with hydrochloric acid. Carbon monoxide forms a complex with copper(I) chloride, having the composition $Cu_2Cl_2 \cdot 2CO$. Because the copper(I) chloride solution also absorbs unsaturated hydrocarbons, the latter must be removed (step 2) before absorbing carbon monoxide.

5. *Hydrogen and methane* are often determined together by combustion. A known volume of oxygen is introduced into the gas mixture, which is passed slowly over a heated platinum wire in a combustion pipet. After combustion is complete the volume of gas remaining is measured, then passed into the potassium hydroxide for absorption of the carbon dioxide formed. The equations for the reactions are:

$$2H_2 + O_2 \rightarrow 2H_2O$$
2 vols. 1 vol. 0 vol.

$$CH_4 + 2O_2 \rightarrow CO_2 + 2H_2O$$
1 vol. 2 vols. 1 vol.   0 vol.

At room temperature, the water formed occupies negligible volume relative to the volumes of the gases used and produced in the reaction. The equations show that for hydrogen, three volumes of gas disappear in the reaction, and the volume of hydrogen is therefore two thirds of the contraction due to its combustion. In the combustion of methane, three volumes of reactants give one volume of product; the volume of carbon dioxide formed is equal to the volume of methane burned; the contraction due to the combustion of methane is twice the volume of methane. By measuring the volume of gas before addition of oxygen, the volume of oxygen added, the volume of residual gases, and the volume of carbon dioxide formed, the volume of methane and of hydrogen are obtained:

Volume of CH_4 = volume of CO_2 formed
Volume of H_2 = $\frac{2}{3}$ (total contraction − contraction for CH_4)
= $\frac{2}{3}$ [total contraction − (2 × volume of CO_2)]

6. *Nitrogen* is determined by difference, either by summing the percentages of the other components and subtracting from 100%, or by absorbing the excess oxygen remaining after the combustion and measuring the residual gas.

QUESTIONS AND PROBLEMS

11-1 What reagent or treatment will form a volatile product with one, but not with the other, of the given pair? Write equations for all chemical reactions that occur, state the conditions required, and identify the volatile product formed.

(a) $BaCO_3$, K_2CO_3.

(b) NH_4Cl, KCl (2 methods)

(c) $ZnCO_3$, $ZnSO_4$

(d) ZnS, CuS

(e) $CaSO_4$, $CaSO_3$

(f) $K_2Cr_2O_7$, $Ce(SO_4)_2$

(g) $CaCO_3$, CaC_2O_4

(h) SnO_2, SiO_2

(i) Bi_2O_3, B_2O_3

(j) $Na_2B_4O_7$, Na_3PO_4

(k) As_2O_3, Al_2O_3

(l) $SbCl_3$, $SnCl_4$

(m) $PbCl_2$, $HgCl_2$

11-2 50.0 ml of gas mixture consisting of hydrogen, methane, and nitrogen is mixed with 50.0 ml of oxygen, and the mixture is passed over a heated platinum wire in a combustion pipet to burn the hydrogen and methane. The residual gas, measuring 65.0 ml, is passed through KOH solution (to absorb the CO_2), after which the residual gas measures 60.0 ml. All volume measurements are at the same room temperature and pressure. Calculate the volume percentage of each component of the original mixture.

11-3 25.0 ml of a mixture of hydrogen, ethane (C_2H_6), and nitrogen is mixed with 25.0 ml of oxygen, and the mixture is burned. The residual gas measures 28.75 ml. After absorption of CO_2 in KOH, the residual gas measures 23.75. Calculate the volume percentage of hydrogen and of ethane in the original gas sample.

12

SEPARATION
BY EXTRACTION

The process whereby a material in one phase is transferred to another phase is referred to as **partition**. Although there are several types of partition methods, the discussion here will be limited to partition of a solute between two liquid phases, commonly called **extraction**, and a brief mention of extraction from the solid state.

The Distribution Law

The distribution law, also known as the law of heterogeneous equilibrium, may be stated as follows: At a given temperature, the ratio of the equilibrium concentrations (more exactly, the activities) of a substance distributed between two immiscible solvents in contact is a constant. The constant is called the **distribution constant**, or the **distribution coefficient**, or the **partition coefficient**. Expressed mathematically, the law is simply $C_2/C_1 = K$, where C_1 and C_2 are the equilibrium concentrations of the solute in solvents 1 and 2. Although the law has some restrictions, such as nonassociation or nondissociation of the solute, the discussion here will assume absence of deviations.

If a given amount of solute, in one solvent, is equilibrated with a second solvent immiscible with the first, the solute distributes itself between the two solvents in the ratio of its solubility in each solvent. The total amount of solute found in each phase will therefore depend upon its solubility in each solvent and upon the volume of each phase. The use of successive extractions in effecting a separation can best be illustrated by an example. The assumed conditions are as follows: 1.0 g of solute, dissolved in 50 ml of solvent 1, and extracted with 50 ml of solvent 2; solute is nine times as soluble in solvent 2 as in solvent 1.

After equilibration, the second solvent (and its solute) is separated from the first, which is then extracted with another 50-ml portion of pure solvent 2, and so on. After the first extraction, 0.9 g of solute will be found in solvent 2, leaving 0.1 g of solute in solvent 1. The second extraction removes another 0.09 g of solute in phase 2, leaving 0.01 g in phase 1, and so on. After the fourth extraction the first solvent contains only 0.0001 g, or 0.1 mg, of the original solute. When the volumes of the two solvents are not identical, account must be taken of their relative volumes in calculating the weight of solute in each solvent.

The progression 1.0, 0.1, 0.01, etc., is an exponential series; a general formulation can be made relating the weights of solute, the volumes of solvents, and the number of extractive steps:

$$W_1 = W_0 \left(\frac{V_1}{KV_2 + V_1} \right)^n$$

where W_0 = weight of original solute

W_1 = weight of solute remaining in solvent 1 after n extractions

V_1 = volume of solvent 1

V_2 = volume of solvent 2 used in each extraction

K = distribution constant of the solute

n = number of extractions

Suppose, for example, that 40 mg of iodine dissolved in 100 ml of water is extracted with successive 25-ml portions of carbon disulfide at a temperature at which the distribution constant for iodine between carbon disulfide and water is 150; what weight of iodine remains in the water solution after two extractions with 25 ml of carbon disulfide?

$$W_1 = 40 \left(\frac{100}{(150 \times 25) + 100} \right)^2 = 40 \left(\frac{100}{3850} \right)^2 = 0.027 \text{ mg}$$

The exponential nature of the extraction formula shows that a more complete transfer of solute from phase 1 into phase 2 can be effected by the use of a given volume of the extracting solvent if it is used in several small portions than if it is used all at once. Suppose that in the above example the 50 ml of carbon disulfide were used for a single extraction; then

$$W_1 = 40 \left(\frac{100}{(150 \times 50) + 100} \right) = 40 \left(\frac{100}{7600} \right) = 0.53 \text{ mg}$$

Two extractions of 25 ml each are 20 times as effective as a single extraction of 50 ml.

Methods and Applications

Extraction may be carried out either for the removal of a solute (exhaustive extraction) or for the separation of components of a complex mixture (selective extraction). For the removal of a solute, the method is rapid and the apparatus required can be very simple. If the solute has a large distribution coefficient, a batch extraction using a single equilibration in a separatory funnel effects a good separation; the operation may be repeated with fresh portions of immiscible solvent, as necessary, to effect a quantitative removal. Extraction methods are adaptable to continuous operation, the apparatus design depending upon whether the second solvent is more dense or less dense than the first; continuous counter-current extraction is a common industrial operation. For the separation of a mixture of components differing only slightly in distribution coefficients, multiple extractions by a countercurrent distribution technique are applied, in apparatus that makes the transfers of liquid phases automatically.[1]

Extraction techniques are widely used for the separation and purification of organic compounds. Several features of solvent extraction make the method also attractive for inorganic separations.

1. Even when the distribution constant of the solute is not large, several successive extractions can be made in order to diminish the unextracted solute to a negligible amount.

2. The process is applicable in two ways: interfering substances are extracted, leaving the desired constituent in the first solvent; or the desired constituent is extracted, leaving the impurities in the first solvent.

3. Extraction methods may sometimes be used to avoid coprecipitation and/or postprecipitation phenomena that would be present in a precipitation separation of the same constituents.

4. Solutes present in very small concentration may be gathered by extraction into a small volume of a second solvent when the distribution constant is large.

Extractive Separation of Metals

The use of diethyl ether for extraction of iron(III) from many other substances was introduced in 1892. The extraction is made from the chlorides of the metals in hydrochloric acid solution. The extractability is highly dependent upon the concentration of the hydrochloric acid, the optimum concentration being about 6 M. Under these conditions a single pass with an equal volume of ether extracts about 99 % of the iron present. The graph in Fig. 12-1 shows the way in which the extraction of iron(III) chloride varies with the concentration of hydrochloric acid in the solution. Below 3 M and above 9 M hydrochloric acid, extraction is very slight.

The chlorides that are highly soluble in ether are those that exhibit considerable covalent character, and they probably form complexes with the acid. In the case of iron(III), the substance extracted into the ether appears to be $HFeCl_4$. Table 12-1 lists the extent to which many of the elements, as their chlorides in

---

[1] L. C. Craig and O. Post, *Anal. Chem.*, **21**, 500 (1949).

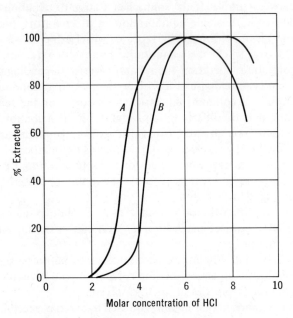

Fig. 12-1   Extraction of iron(III) chloride. *A*, by
ethyl ether. *B*, by isopropyl ether.

hydrochloric acid, are extracted with ether. Although isopropyl ether requires
a higher acid concentration for optimum extraction of iron(III) chloride, there
is a somewhat wider range of acidity over which extraction is virtually complete;
see curve *B* in Fig. 12-1. Isopropyl ether, being less volatile than ethyl ether, is
easier to confine and presents less fire hazard. Water and isopropyl ether are

Table 12-1   Extractability of Chlorides from 6 *M* HCl by Ether

Chloride Extracted (%)	Elements
90 to 100	Fe(III), 99%; Sb(V), 99%; Ga(III), 97%; Tl(III), 95%; Au(III), 95%; Mo(VI), 80–90%
10 to 90	Mo(VI), 80–90%; As(III), 80%; Ge(IV), 40–60%; Te(IV), 35%; Sn(II), 15–30%; Sn(IV), 17%
1 to 10	Ir(IV), 5%; Sb(III), 3%
<1 >0	As(V), Cu(II), In(III), Hg(II), Pt(IV), V(IV,V), Zn(II)
0	Most others

less soluble in each other than are water and ethyl ether; extractive separations are therefore sharper.

An even better extraction solvent for the separation of iron(III) from many other elements is a 1:1 or a 2:1 mixture of methyl isobutyl ketone and amyl acetate.[2] Extraction is made from solution which is 7–9 M in hydrochloric acid. The solvent mixture is much less volatile than isopropyl ether, and the partition coefficient of iron(III) is much larger than in the ethers. Extraction of other common metals, such as aluminum, chromium, lead, manganese, nickel, and titanium is less than 0.01 %. Recovery of the iron(III) is easily made by back extraction into water.

Ether extraction of nitric acid solution of the nitrates is used to separate uranium nitrate (extracted) from many other elements, notably lead and thorium. Gold chloride can be extracted into amyl acetate.

Extraction of metal chelates, e.g., cupferrates, dithizonates, etc., into non-polar solvents such as chloroform or benzene, offers attractive means for separation of cations.

Mixtures of solids of different solubilities are often separated by extracting the soluble solid(s) by treatment with a suitable solvent. Fractional dissolution by chemical reaction is, of course, a widely used procedure in many analyses. The present discussion is limited to cases in which no chemical reaction is involved.

The familiar examples in analytical chemistry are the separations of the alkali metals from each other, and the separations of the alkaline earths from one another. The solid compounds are obtained by evaporation of their solutions to dryness, and the solid residue is treated with an organic solvent to dissolve one (or more) compound, leaving the other(s) as solid residue. The following separations are made in this way.

1. *Alkali perchlorates.* Sodium perchlorate, $NaClO_4$, is soluble in *n*-butanol or a mixture of *n*-butanol and ethyl acetate; potassium perchlorate, $KClO_4$, is insoluble. If present, lithium and magnesium perchlorates follow the sodium, and rubidium, cesium, and ammonium perchlorates follow the potassium in the separation.

2. *Alkali chloroplatinates.* Sodium hexachloroplatinate(IV), Na_2PtCl_6, is soluble in 80 % ethanol, whereas the corresponding potassium salt, K_2PtCl_6, is insoluble. Lithium follows the sodium, and rubidium, cesium, and ammonium follow the potassium in the separation.

3. *Alkali chlorides.* Lithium chloride, LiCl, is soluble in dioxane or in pyridine; the other alkali chlorides are insoluble in these solvents.

4. *Alkaline earth nitrates.* Calcium nitrate is soluble in butyl cellosolve; strontium and barium nitrates are insoluble.

5. *Alkaline earth chlorides.* A mixture of equal volumes of ethanol and ethyl ether dissolves calcium chloride, but not strontium nor barium chloride.

---

[2] A. Classen and L. Bastings, *Z. anal. Chem.*, **160**, 403 (1958).

PROBLEMS

12-1 The partition coefficient of $GaCl_3$ between diethyl ether and 6 M HCl is 32.0. A certain solution contains 1.000 g of $GaCl_3$ in 100.0 ml of 6 M HCl. Calculate the weight of $GaCl_3$ remaining in the acid layer after extraction with a total of 60.0 ml of diethyl ether, used (*a*) all at once; (*b*) in two equal portions; (*c*) in four equal portions; (*d*) in six equal portions.   *Ans.* (*a*) 0.0495 g.

12-2 The partition coefficient of $SnCl_4$ between diethyl ether and 6 M HCl is 0.200. If the $GaCl_3$ solution in Problem 12-1 also contained 0.500 g of $SnCl_4$, what *total* weight of the latter is *extracted* with the $GaCl_3$ by each treatment, (*a*) through (*d*), of Problem 12-1?

12-3 The aqueous solution described in columns (1) and (2) contains a solute the partition coefficient of which, between an immiscible organic solvent and water, is given in column (3). Calculate the number of successive extractions, with the volume of organic solvent given in column (4), required so that the solute remaining in the aqueous solution does not exceed the weight given in column (5).

	(1) ml of aqueous solution	(2) g of solute	(3) Partition coefficient	(4) ml of organic solvent	(5) mg of solute remaining
(*a*)	100	0.25	10	20	0.20
(*b*)	50	0.20	6	25	0.10
(*c*)	50	0.30	20	10	0.10
(*d*)	50	0.50	30	15	0.05
(*e*)	100	0.20	5	25	0.20
(*f*)	100	0.20	4	20	0.10
(*g*)	100	0.50	2	5	1.0
(*h*)	100	2.0	80	25	0.50

Ans. (*a*) 7.   (*b*) 6.

12-4 What is the partition coefficient of a solute between CCl_4 and water if 99% of the solute originally present in 100 ml of water is removed by three successive extractions with 10 ml of CCl_4?

12-5 100 ml of solution contain 1.00 g of solute that is 20 times more soluble in benzene than it is in water. After five successive extractions with the same volume of benzene each time, the solute in the aqueous phase is only 0.010 mg. What volume of benzene was used for each extraction?

13

SEPARATION BY CHROMATOGRAPHY AND ION EXCHANGE

Only a brief outline of the principles and methods of chromatography and ion exchange is given here; for detailed treatment, many reference works are available. [1-7]

Adsorption Chromatography

The separation of substances by preferential adsorption was introduced in 1906 by Tswett,[8] who separated several pigments (chlorophylls, xanthophylls, carotenes) of green leaves by passing a petroleum ether extract of the leaves through a column of calcium carbonate powder. The various colored components were retained (adsorbed) in bands at different positions on the column, which was then called a **chromatogram**. The separated components were recovered by extruding the adsorbent, cutting it into sections, and extracting the adsorbed compounds. Since about 1930, separations based upon preferential adsorption have come into prominence in analytical methodology.

There are several steps in a chromatographic analysis:

1. Adsorption of substances to be separated, usually from solution in very nonpolar solvents such as petroleum ether.

[1] H. H. Strain, *Chromatographic Adsorption Analysis*, New York, Interscience, 1942. See also review articles in *Analytical Chemistry* since 1949.

[2] H. G. Cassidy, *Fundamentals of Chromatography* in A. Weissberger, ed., *Technique of Organic Chemistry*, New York, Interscience, 1957, vol. X.

[3] E. Lederer and M. Lederer, *Chromatography*, 2nd ed., New York, Elsevier, 1957.

[4] V. J. Coates, ed., *Gas Chromatography*, New York, Academic Press, 1958.

[5] R. L. Pecsok, ed., *Principles and Practice of Gas Chromatography*, New York, Wiley, 1959.

[6] R. Kunin, *Ion Exchange Resins*, 2nd ed., New York, Wiley, 1958.

[7] O. Samuelson, *Ion Exchange in Analytical Chemistry*, New York, Wiley, 1953.

[8] M. Tswett, *Ber. deut. botan. Ges.*, **24**, 384 (1906).

2. Development, in which the adsorbed materials are spread out by continuing the flow of solution or pure solvent.

3. Recovery of the separated components, usually accomplished by eluting the adsorbed material by use of a more polar solvent, or several solvents in turn, which differentially remove the desired material.

4. Identification and measurement of the individual substances by various means, such as by color reactions, ultraviolet fluorescence, adsorption spectrophotometry, etc.

The efficiency of the separations depends upon such factors as the chemical nature of the components to be separated, the solvent, and the adsorbent; the geometry of the column; the flow rate of the solution and of the developing solvent.

Columnar Chromatography

The adsorbent is placed in a long narrow tube fitted at the bottom with a stopcock (a buret will serve), the exit of which is attached to a suction flask. Various adsorbents, such as calcium carbonate, magnesium oxide, aluminum oxide, starch, and silica gel, can be used, depending upon the nature of the substances to be separated. The sample solution is poured on the top of the column and allowed to pass slowly through it. The least strongly adsorbed component appears first in the effluent, followed by other components in turn, in order of increasing adsorbability on the column material.

Frontal Analysis. In this procedure, the sample solution is added continuously at the top of the column. The first portions of effluent are pure solvent, followed after a time by the solution of the least adsorbed component (*A*); when the next to least adsorbed component (*B*) appears, the effluent contains mixture of the two (*A* and *B*), and so on, until finally the most adsorbed component appears after the column has become saturated with it. The composition of the effluent then corresponds to that of the original sample solution. A plot of concentration of solute against volume of solution passed through the column is a step diagram such as represented in Fig. 13-1. The method is useful in determining the *number* of components in a mixture; it is not applicable to the resolution of complex mixtures, because only a limited amount of the least adsorbed component can be recovered before the next component breaks through the column.

Elution Analysis. This procedure is the most widely used method of columnar chromatography. A *small* amount of sample solution is put on the top of the column, which has been previously saturated with pure solvent. The solutes are adsorbed in a narrow band at the top of the adsorbent column. Pure solvent is then added continuously to the column. By a series of stepwise desorptions and adsorptions the components move down the column at different rates

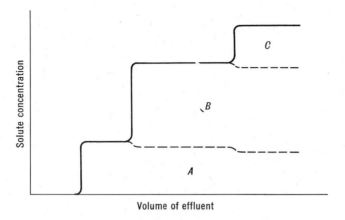

Fig. 13-1   Frontal analysis chromatogram.

(depending upon their adsorbabilities), spread out into zones, and ultimately emerge from the column. An elution curve of a three component mixture (component *A* is least adsorbed) is represented in Fig. 13-2. Ideally, a component gives a narrow Gaussian curve (as for *A*), but various factors may cause "tailing" of the elution band, skewing of the elution curve, and/or overlapping of curves of two components. The area under a component's curve represents the amount of that component in the sample. By gradually changing the composition of the eluting solvent (by addition of increasing amounts of a second more polar solvent), tailing and overlapping of elution curves may often be minimized, resulting in sharper separations. This technique is called *gradient elution*.

Displacement Analysis.   A *small* amount of sample solution is placed on the column, and the chromatogram is developed by washing the column with

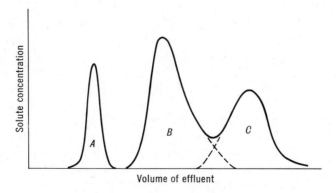

Fig. 13-2   Elution analysis chromatogram.

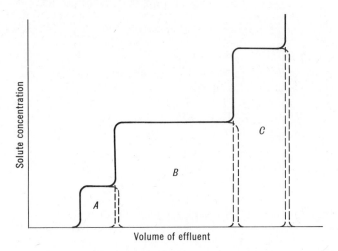

Fig. 13-3   Displacement analysis chromatogram.

solvent containing a solute more strongly adsorbed on the column than is any component of the sample mixture. The added solute displaces all the sample solutes, which in turn displace one another, and the components emerge step-wise in turn, from least to most strongly adsorbed. The chromatogram obtained is represented in Fig. 13-3. The step *height* is characteristic of the particular solute, and the *length* of the step is directly proportional to the amount of solute in the sample solution. By appropriate calibration of the column with known solutes, the method can give both qualitative and quantitative informa-tion about the sample solution, provided reversible adsorption and equilibrium conditions are attained.

Paper Chromatography

A small amount of sample solution is evaporated near the edge or corner of a strip of filter paper. The chromatogram is developed by dipping the edge of the filter paper into a tray of developing solvent, which is drawn into the paper by capillary action. During development, the paper strip is suspended vertically, and, along with the developing solvent, is placed in an air-tight jar, so the enclosed space is saturated with solvent vapor. In ascending paper chromato-graphy the sample spot is placed on the bottom edge of the paper, which dips into the developing solvent in the bottom of the jar; in descending paper chroma-tography the sample spot is near the top edge of the paper, which is passed over the side of the developing tray (supported in the top of the jar) into the solvent. As the solvent moves through the paper the sample components spread out into zones on the basis of their different adsorbabilities on the cellulose fibers. The separated components are often identified by spraying the paper with color-developing reagents; if desired, the paper can be cut into pieces containing the individual components for further analysis.

Better resolution can be obtained by *two-dimensional* paper chromatography. The sample is placed on the corner of a sheet of filter paper and developed in one direction; the paper is then turned 90° and again developed, often with a different solvent. By this technique mixtures of some twenty amino acids have been resolved, identified, and the quantities estimated.

Thin Layer Chromatography (TLC)

The use of thin layers of adsorbent on glass plates for effecting separations was first described in 1938, but most of the development of this technique took place in the 1950s.[9] The method is becoming one of the most useful means for the separation, identification, and assay of many substances. Much of the work has been concerned with biochemical materials, natural products, pharmaceutical preparations, and clinical chemistry (where speed is an important factor). Compared to paper chromatography, thin layer chromatography gives faster and sharper separations, and requires only a minute amount of sample solution. The method can also be used for preparative work up to about a gram of substance. Quantitative reliability of about 3 to 5% can be realized.

A slurry of the desired adsorbent, along with a binder of starch or plaster of Paris, is spread in a uniform thin layer (0.15–2.0 mm, depending on the particular situation) on a glass slide, 5 × 20 cm, or plate, 20 × 20 cm. The slurry is allowed to dry for 30 minutes or longer, to allow the binder to set. The layer is activated by heating, usually in a vertical position, at 100–110°C for various lengths of time (one to several hours); the plates are then stored in a desiccator or dry box until ready for use. Materials for making TLC slides and plates are available commercially. The adsorbents commonly used are silica gel, aluminum oxide, and cellulose. Glass microfiber support sheets impregnated with an adsorbent medium of silica gel, alumina gel, or potassium silicate, and packaged ready for use, are now available (Gelman Instrument Co.).

For diagnostic work, a few microliters of solution containing 10–100 micrograms of solutes is spotted near the end of the prepared slide or plate; for preparative work, up to several hundred milligrams of solute may be used. Ascending, descending, horizontal, two-dimensional, and circular development methods have been used. Multiple pass development with the same solvent (with drying between passes), and stepwise development with different solvents, have advantages in particular cases. Separated components can be recovered by elution (continuous development) off the end of the slide. Identification and quantification of the separated components involve much the same methods as with paper chromatography.

[9] J. M. Bobbitt, *Thin-Layer Chromatography*, New York, Reinhold, 1963.

Electrophoresis

Chromatographic separations, whether by column, paper, or thin layer, can be made more rapidly by application of a voltage across the system. The migration of the solute under the influence of the potential gradient is called **electrophoresis**. In paper or in thin layer work, the chromatogram is sometimes developed in one direction in the usual way, then developed in the second direction by electrophoresis.

PARTITION CHROMATOGRAPHY

In partition chromatography the **stationary phase** is a liquid strongly adsorbed on an inert supporting material in a column; the second **mobile phase**, which may be a solution or a gas or vapor, is caused to move through the column. The solutes are partitioned between the mobile and the stationary phase and are spread out into bands which move at different rates depending upon the partition coefficients between the two phases. The separated components are identified and/or measured as they emerge stepwise from the column.

Liquid-Liquid Partition Chromatography

This method was introduced in 1941 by Martin and Synge[10] for the separation of amino acids in chloroform-butanol solution by partitioning with water on silica gel.

The solutes, which pass through the column more slowly than the pure solvent, move at characteristic rates (under a given set of conditions), and are identified by their R_f values:

$$R_f = \frac{\text{rate of solute migration}}{\text{rate of solvent migration}}$$

In developing the theory of liquid-liquid partition chromatography, Martin and co-workers showed that

$$R_f = \frac{A_M}{A_M + P A_S}$$

where A_M = cross-sectional area of mobile phase

A_S = cross-sectional area of stationary phase

P = partition coefficient of solute between the two phases = C_S/C_M

The apparatus and operating procedures are essentially identical with those used in columnar adsorption chromatography. Supporting materials include silica gel, starch, cellulose, diatomaceous earth, Celite, etc.; water and aqueous

[10] A. J. P. Martin and R. L. M. Synge, *Biochem. J.*, **35**, 1358 (1941).

solutions, as well as organic liquids, have been used for the stationary phase; the mobile phase is usually an organic liquid. The method has been applied widely, for the separation of both organic and inorganic substances.

Gas-Liquid Partition Chromatography

It was also Martin who suggested that in partition chromatography the mobile phase need not be a liquid, but might also be a gas or vapor, and he predicted that gas-liquid chromatography would be a powerful tool for the separation of components of complex mixtures. It was not until 1951 that Martin himself returned to this idea for experimental exploration.[11] Since that time the development of excellent instrumentation and the superior advantages of the method have led to the very wide use of gas-liquid partition chromatography (GLPC, or merely GLC, also called vapor phase chromatography, VPC) for the separation of a wide variety of substances, in both academic and industrial laboratories.

The mixture to be analyzed, which must be volatile at the temperature of operation, is injected into the end of a narrow column packed with an inert supporting material such as crushed fire brick or Celite, on which has been deposited a coating of nonvolatile liquid (the stationary or immobile phase) such as silicone oil, dioctylphthalate, or squalene. The sample components partition between a gas phase in the pore space of the column and a liquid phase absorbed in the nonvolatile liquid coating. The mobile (gas) phase is eluted from the column with an inert carrier gas such as helium or nitrogen. On the basis of differences in partition coefficient the various sample components are spread out into bands and move along the column at different but characteristic rates, and finally emerge from the column where they are detected by a change in some property such as thermal conductivity or flame ionization. Detection is usually on a differential basis; some of the pure carrier gas is passed through one detector and the sample plus carrier gas through a second identical detector; the two detector elements are made two arms of a bridge circuit, the unbalance of which is registered on a strip-chart recorder, with time as the other variable.

A block diagram of the GLC apparatus is shown in Fig. 13-4, and a typical chromatogram is shown in Fig. 13-5. Retention time in a given column and with given experimental conditions is characteristic of the particular component; the quantitative feature of the analysis is the area under the curve. Infrared and/or mass spectrometry is often used as an adjunct method of identification of the components.

The method is rapid and extraordinarily selective and uses only very small samples (microliter range). For larger scale preparative separations larger

[11] A. T. James and A. J. P. Martin, *Biochem. J.*, **50**, 679 (1951).

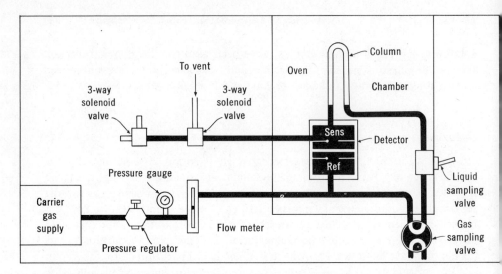

Fig. 13-4 Schematic diagram of gas chromatograph. Carrier gas is regulated and metered. Liquids are vaporized and carried by the gas onto the column. Components of mixture go through column at different speeds and arrive separately at column exit. (Courtesy of Perkin-Elmer Corp.)

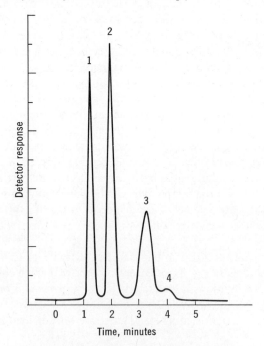

Fig. 13-5 Gas-liquid chromatogram showing separation of aromatic hydrocarbons. 1, benzene; 2, toluene; 3, xylene; 4, trace of impurity. Sample, 10 μl, injected at zero time. (Courtesy of Tracor, Inc.)

columns, often used in parallel, and automatic sample injection and fraction collection are used. In practice, GLC has largely replaced fractional distillation as a separation technique.

ION EXCHANGE

The fact that certain materials can exchange one ion for another has been known for a long time. The science of ion exchange methods dates from 1850–54, when two English agricultural chemists, Thompson and Way, made an extensive study of ion exchange in soils. They found that aluminosilicates were responsible for the exchange reactions, and they were able to synthesize exchange materials from alum and soluble silicates. The exchange studies involved principally sodium, potassium, ammonium, and calcium ions. In the early 1900s ion exchange methods were introduced on an industrial scale for water softening. Natural and artificial zeolites (sodium aluminum silicates) came into wide use for water softening, both on a small scale for home installations, and on a large industrial scale. In use, the calcium and magnesium ions of hard water exchange with the sodium ions of the zeolite; regeneration is effected by treatment with sodium chloride solution, followed by flushing to remove the calcium and magnesium salts.

In 1935, Adams and Holmes[12] found that certain synthetic sulfonic acid resins could exchange cations, and polyamide resins could exchange anions. Since that time many different synthetic ion exchange resins have become available commercially, and have been put to a variety of uses in both research and industrial applications.

The ion exchange resins are complex organic polymers with cross-linking between various units of the polymer; by varying the degree of cross-linking and the functional (acidic or basic) groups, the properties of the resin can be modified with respect to rate of exchange, exchange capacity, and selectivity.

Cation Exchange Resins

The cation exchange resins contain polar groups held firmly in the resin structure, while the cation is diffusible or exchangeable. Most of the cation exchange resins contain anions of sulfonic or carboxylic acid. If the resin is in its acid (H^+) form, the hydrogen ion is exchanged for other cations from a solution in contact with the resin. The sulfonic acid resins are stronger acids than the carboxylic acid resins. The sulfonic acid type therefore exchanges its hydrogen ion for other cations more easily than does the carboxylic acid type. It follows, also, that the conversion back to the hydrogen form is more difficult in the case of the sulfonic acid type. Also, sodium ions in a sulfonic acid type resin are somewhat more difficult to replace by calcium or magnesium ions than the sodium ions of a carboxylic acid type resin.

[12] B. A. Adams and E. L. Holmes, *J. Soc. Chem. Ind.*, **54**, 1T (1935).

The exchange reactions can be illustrated by the following scheme, in which " Res- " represents all the resin except the acidic group.

$$Res-SO_3^- \cdot H^+ + Na^+ \rightleftarrows Res-SO_3^- \cdot Na^+ + H^+$$

$$Res-COO^- \cdot H^+ + Na^+ \rightleftarrows Res-COO^- \cdot Na^+ + H^+$$

$$2Res-COO^- \cdot Na^+ + Ca^{++} \rightleftarrows (Res-COO^-)_2 \cdot Ca^{++} + 2Na^+$$

The exchange affinity or exchange potential of the cations for the resins is in general the same as their adsorbability in the lyotropic series in colloidal systems, which also parallels the order of increasing degree of hydration with increasing ionic charge and decreasing crystallographic radius. For example, at low temperature, the exchange affinity increases with increasing ionic charge $(Na^+ < Ca^{++} < Al^{+++} < Th^{4+})$; for constant charge, the exchange affinity increases with increasing atomic number $(Li^+ < Na^+ < K^+ < Rb^+ < Cs^+)$. The exchange affinity of hydrogen ion varies with the strength of the acid formed between hydrogen ion and the functional group of the resin; the stronger the acid, the lower the exchange affinity of hydrogen ion. In nonaqueous media, at high concentration and at high temperature, the differences in exchange affinity with ionic charge and atomic number become smaller or may even be reversed in order.

Anion Exchange Resins

The functional groups in anion exchange resins are substituted amines or quaternary ammonium compounds, which are organic bases. The exchange reactions can be represented by analogy with the behavior of primary amines which, in aqueous solution, react to form the hydroxyl compound:

$$Res-NH_2 + H_2O \rightleftarrows Res-NH_3^+ \cdot OH^-$$

The hydroxyl ion can then be exchanged with other anions:

$$Res-NH_3^+ \cdot OH^- + Cl^- \rightleftarrows Res-NH_3^+ \cdot Cl^- + OH^-$$

Also, anions other than hydroxyl can exchange with one another:

$$2\ Res-NH_3^+ \cdot Cl^- + SO_4^{--} \rightleftarrows (Res-NH_3^+)_2 \cdot SO_4^{--} + 2Cl^-$$

If the material to be exchanged with a hydroxyl-form resin is an acid, the hydroxyl ion, which is displaced by the anion, is neutralized by the hydrogen ion of the acid; the stronger the acid, the more complete the removal of OH^- from the resin and its exchange by anions. The hydroxyl form of the resin can be regenerated by treatment with sodium hydroxide.

The exchange affinity of anions is somewhat dependent upon ionic charge (e.g., $Cl^- < SO_4^{--}$), although there appear to be anomalies with certain of the oxy anions ($PO_4^{---} < NO_3^- < SO_4^{--}$). In the halide group, the exchange affinity increases with atomic number ($F^- < Cl^- < Br^- < I^-$). The position of hydroxyl ion in the exchange series depends upon the basic strength of the functional group of the anion resin; hydroxyl ion has a high exchange affinity for weak base resins and a low exchange affinity for strong base resins.

Applications of Ion Exchange

The applications of ion exchange separations are many and varied; detailed discussion of ion exchangers can be found in reference books[13,14] and in an extensive journal literature. A few general types of applications, with examples, are given here.

1. Exchange of Ionic Constituents. Total salt content of a solution can be determined by passing the solution through the hydrogen form of a strong acid (sulfonic type) resin; the displaced hydrogen ion from the resin is titrated with standard alkali. Conversion of sulfates to chlorides, or of either of these to hydroxides (or the reverse changes) can be made with anion exchange resins.

2. Fractionation of Electrolytes. Two ionic species of opposite charge can be separated by either a cation or an anion exchanger. Ions of the same charge may be separated, if of sufficiently different exchange affinities, by using a resin that exchanges only one of them. For example, two anions of acids of different strength may be separated by use of an anion exchanger of a basic strength that will neutralize only one of them. Bases of different strength can be separated by use of a carboxylic type cation exchanger. When the exchange potentials of the different ions are not sufficiently different to permit exchange of only one of them, they may all be put onto the exchanger, then desorbed and eluted chromatographically. The latter method has been used for separation of the rare earths from one another, for separation of the isotopes of certain elements, and for many other separations of closely similar species where classical methods of separation have not been satisfactory.

3. Removal of Interfering Ions in Analysis. Ions that interfere in many analytical procedures may be removed by ion exchangers. Phosphate, which interferes in the analysis for barium and calcium, is removed with an anion exchanger. Interference from iron(III) and aluminum in the determination of sulfate as barium sulfate, is eliminated by removal of the iron and aluminum with a cation exchanger.

4. Concentration of Trace Constituents. Ions present in very small amounts can be collected by passing a large volume of the solution through the resin column, followed by elution with a small volume of reagent. The method has been used for analysis of traces of sodium and copper in milk and milk products, magnesium in sea water, and many other metals in the microgram range in

---

[13] R. Kunin, *op. cit.*
[14] O. Samuelson, *op. cit.*

samples. Recovery of valuable chemicals, such as platinum, silver, and uranium from reagents used in analysis, can be effected by ion exchangers, often in a form for re-use or for easy conversion to usable reagents.

5. Water Treatment. Cations that constitute hardness in water (mainly Ca^{++} and Mg^{++}) can be exchanged for an equivalent amount of sodium ion from a zeolite (e.g., Permutit water softener). The raw waters in about 75% of continental United States are high in bicarbonate alkalinity, which is objectionable for many applications. A recently developed weakly acidic cation exchange resin, Amberlite IRC-84, can "split" bicarbonates, including sodium bicarbonate; the resin has high regeneration efficiency.[15] De-ionized water is prepared by removal of both cations and anions, by passing the raw water through a cation exchanger (hydrogen form), then an anion exchanger (hydroxyl form) in succession, or through a mixture of the two types of resin. The hydrogen ion liberated by cation exchange is exactly equivalent to the hydroxyl ion liberated in anion exchange. Water prepared in this way has a much higher purity than the distilled water ordinarily available, and it is free from carbonate and silica. Large scale de-ionization of water may use a mixture of the two kinds of resins, one of greater density than the other; when the resins have become saturated with the ions removed from the water, the two types of resins are separated by a flotation process and then regenerated separately with acid and alkali. The desalting of sea water to make it potable for emergency use is accomplished by briquettes of high capacity resins in the silver ion form; the reaction with sodium chloride is

$$Res^- \cdot Ag^+ + Na^+ + Cl^- \rightarrow Res^- \cdot Na^+ + AgCl$$

The magnesium and sulfate ions of the sea water are removed by barium hydroxide incorporated in the resin material:

$$Ba^{++} + 2OH^- + Mg^{++} + SO_4^{--} \rightarrow BaSO_4 + Mg(OH)_2$$

The precipitated $AgCl$, $BaSO_4$, and $Mg(OH)_2$, and the sodium resin are filtered off.

6. Miscellaneous Applications. Liquid exchangers can be used in counter-current extraction operations. Ion exchange membranes, and fabrics impregnated with ion exchangers, are finding industrial applications. A nitrated polystyrene resin has high affinity for potassium ion, and might be useful for extraction of potassium from sea water.

Electron Exchange Resins

A polymerized vinylhydroquinone can serve to exchange electrons, in a manner analogous to the quinone-hydroquinone reaction. This type of resin has the special advantage of effecting oxidation or reduction without introducing an oxidizing agent or a reducing agent into the solution.

[15] Rohm and Haas, *Reporter*, **XXIII** (4), 14 (1965).

14

PRECIPITATION PHENOMENA

In gravimetric precipitation methods of analysis the constituent sought is separated as an insoluble substance, which is weighed directly or converted quantitatively to another substance for weighing.

Requisites of Gravimetric Precipitation Analysis

Several requisites and/or desirable properties of the **precipitation form** and of the **weighing form** influence the success of the analysis. Departures from these requirements lead to errors in the analysis.

Precipitation Form. Ideally the precipitation form should fulfill the following requirements.

1. The precipitate should be so insoluble that any of the desired constituent left in solution is below the limit of weighing with the analytical balance (about 0.1 mg).

2. Other constituents present in the solution should neither be precipitated by the reagent nor prevent precipitation of the desired constituent.

3. The precipitation form should not be contaminated with soluble substances present in the solution. Often this requirement is not easily attained, although contamination may be minimized by proper choice of conditions of precipitation (see p. 184).

4. In preparation for weighing, the precipitation form should be easily filtered and washed free from soluble impurities. In some instances the separation form is not suitable for weighing, and it is dissolved and then precipitated in another form or ignited to another form before weighing.

Weighing Form. If the precipitation form is also a suitable weighing form and, after washing, is merely wet with water or easily volatile solutes, it may be oven dried (e.g., silver chloride). Ignition may sometimes be primarily for burning off filter paper (e.g., $BaSO_4$); in other instances ignition may be required to convert the precipitation form to another substance suitable for weighing (e.g., $MgNH_4PO_4 \rightarrow Mg_2P_2O_7$). In other cases the precipitation form may be of indefinite composition but converted to a material of definite composition by ignition (e.g., metal hydrous oxides converted to metal oxides).

The requisites and desirable qualities of the weighing form are as follows:

1. It must be of definite, known composition.

2. It should be obtained from the precipitation form at relatively low temperatures, but must be stable at higher temperatures.

3. The dried or ignited residue should not absorb or react with the components of air.

4. A small gravimetric factor for the constituent sought is desirable. This feature is particularly important when the sample contains only a small amount of the desired constituent.

Solubility

When a solid solute is placed in contact with a liquid in which it is soluble, solute molecules or ions leave the solid phase and pass into the solvent, forming a solution. If an excess of solid is used (at constant temperature), eventually there will be no net change in the amount of solid phase in contact with the solution, which is said to be **saturated**, that is, it **contains the equilibrium amount of solute at the given temperature**.

Most solid solutes are more soluble at high temperature than at low temperature. A curve constructed by plotting solubility against temperature, as in Fig. 14-1, represents the saturation amount of solute at any temperature and can be used to interpret changes that occur in one function when the other is changed. Suppose, for example, that a quantity of solute represented by Q is placed in contact with solvent at temperature T; only the amount of solute, represented by S, on the solubility curve, will go into solution, and excess solute represented by $Q - S$ will remain undissolved. (The student should deduce the composition of the system when the temperature is changed successively from T to T_1, to T_2, to T_3.) Under certain conditions solids fail to separate from a solution; the solution is then **supersaturated**, that is, **it contains more than the equilibrium amount of solute**. This metastable condition, which in some cases may persist indefinitely, is relieved by adding a minute amount of the solid solute to induce crystallyzation until the equilibrium condition is reached.

Many inorganic compounds consist of ionic solids, in which the ions are held by electrostatic forces in a regular geometric pattern or crystal lattice. In solutions of ionogens in water it is thought that the ions of the solute are surrounded

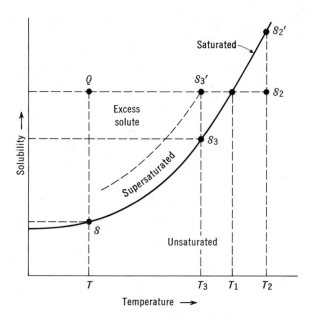

Fig. 14-1   Solubility diagram.

by water molecules acting as dipoles oriented about the ions. In many cases well-defined ion hydrates are known, for example $[Cu(H_2O)_4]^{++}$, in which the water is bound to the central ion by coordinate covalent bonds.

Formation of Nuclei and Growth of Crystals

If the amounts of cation and anion brought together exceed the solubility of the ionic compound formed by their union, the system is unstable from the viewpoint of equilibrium, and unless supersaturation occurs, a precipitate will form until the remaining solution is just saturated. Thus, if the original concentration of ions brought together corresponds to the point Q in Fig. 14-1, precipitation occurs until the solution has the composition S, the solubility at the given temperature. The amount of precipitate formed corresponds to $Q - S$.

In a solution containing silver ion and chloride ion of such low concentrations that the solubility of silver chloride is not exceeded, the ions of Ag^+ and Cl^-, each with its shell of water molecules, may be considered as being so far apart and/or so well shielded by the water dipoles that the attractive forces of the opposite charges are negligible. With increasing concentration of the ions, they are brought closer together; the chance of collision is thereby increased, and a "nucleus" of silver chloride may be formed. There is then a chance that either Ag^+ or Cl^- will collide with or approach close enough to this nucleus for the ion to be drawn into its correct lattice position, forming $AgCl \cdot Ag^+$ or

$Cl^- \cdot AgCl$. Because of the charge of the three-atom nucleus the chance of adding another ion of opposite charge is increased, and a second "molecule" of silver chloride is thus added to the first. So long as the solution is supersaturated, this process may continue, the nuclei growing at the expense of the ions in the solution. If the solution has relatively high supersaturation, many primary particles (nuclei) may form initially and leave in solution very few ions to grow onto the nuclei. Also, if many nuclei are formed, their collisions may be so frequent that they will form aggregates without assuming the correct lattice positions for the ions, and an **amorphous** precipitate may result.

The relation between particle size and relative supersaturation was recognized in 1913 by von Weimarn, who found that

$$\frac{\text{rate of precipitation}}{\text{or number of nuclei}} = K \frac{Q - S}{S}$$

where Q is the total amount of substance of solubility S, and K is a proportionality constant. The term $(Q - S)/S$ is the **relative supersaturation** of the solution. When a precipitate is formed under conditions of high relative supersaturation, precipitation of much of the material may occur as primary particles, which cannot grow appreciably because there is little dissolved solute in excess of the solubility. Conversely, if the relative supersaturation at any moment is small, few nuclei are formed; these can grow from ions in the solution, and the final precipitate consists of relatively large, well-formed crystals.

The precipitation of any substance from solution involves at first the formation of very small particles—few or many, depending upon the relative supersaturation—and it is in this condition that much of the contamination of precipitates occurs. It is important, therefore, to consider the properties of matter in the form of fine suspensions.

The Colloidal Condition

A substance that is dispersed in another in such a way that the dispersed particles are of the order of 1 to 100 or 200 mμ [1 millimicron (mμ) = 10^{-6} mm] is said to be in the **colloidal condition**. The dispersed particles are so small that they do not settle under the influence of gravity. Examples are emulsions, smokes, fogs or "aerosols," and many chemical systems such as colloidal hydrous ferric oxide.

Methods of Formation. The colloidal condition represents a certain range of particle sizes, consequently this condition may be approached either by **condensation** of smaller particles, or by **dispersion** of larger particles. The former method is of interest in precipitation reactions, where ions form "molecules" that coalesce to give solid particles of colloidal dimensions, dispersed in the aqueous solution. Dispersion of larger particles may occur in the peptization of coagulated colloids during washing.

Properties of Colloids. Among the properties of colloids, the following are of importance in precipitation methods of analysis.

1. The particles are so small that they pass through the usual filter media.

2. A solid dispersed into particles of colloidal dimensions has an enormous specific surface; **adsorption** by colloidal particles is therefore very pronounced, and coagulation to give precipitates may result in considerable contamination by the adsorbed substances.

3. Colloidal particles are electrically charged; all particles in the same system have the same charge, either positive or negative. The repelling action of the like charges keeps the particles from coalescing and is a major factor in the stability of colloidal dispersions. A diagrammatic representation of colloidal particles of silver chloride is shown in Fig. 14-2. When silver chloride is formed in the presence of excess silver ion, the colloidal particles are stabilized by the **primary adsorption** of silver ions, as in Fig. 14-2(*a*). The system as a whole is electrically neutral; anions (NO_3^-) which are attracted toward the positive particle, are called **counter ions.** When nearly the equivalent amount of chloride ion has been added, the concentration of the primary adsorbed ion (Ag^+) becomes so small that the colloid is no longer stable; the particles **coagulate** or **flocculate** and settle out as a precipitate.

If silver nitrate solution is added to sodium chloride solution, the colloidal silver chloride first formed is negatively charged by primary adsorption of chloride ion, and cations (Na^+) form the counter ion layer, as in Fig. 14-2(*b*).

4. Colloidal particles are coagulated or flocculated by the addition of electrolytes. Anions are the effective ions for flocculation of positive colloids, and cations are the effective ions for flocculation of negative colloids. During flocculation, counter ions are carried down with the precipitate and constitute contamination; their removal by washing is difficult. Electrolytes used to aid in

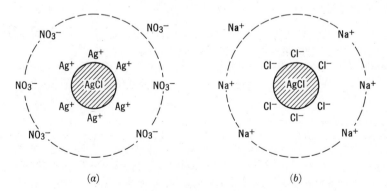

Fig. 14-2 Diagrammatic representation of colloidal silver chloride. (*a*) Precipitated in the presence of excess silver ion. (*b*) Precipitated in the presence of excess chloride ion.

the flocculation of colloids should be easily volatile substances, so that they may be expelled when the precipitate is dried or ignited.

5. Precipitates that consist of flocculated colloids are often redispersed, or **peptized**, by washing out the electrolyte that caused flocculation. Peptization of the precipitate is prevented by using a dilute electrolyte solution for washing.

6. Colloids in which there is considerable affinity between the phases may be quite viscous or even semisolid in the form of a **gel**; these **hydrophilic** colloids can be troublesome in quantitative analysis. Hydrous silica precipitated from solution forms a very stable, highly hydrophilic colloid that cannot be coagulated sufficiently to be filtered off except by dehydration at temperatures above 100°C. In general, coagulated hydrophilic colloids are easily peptized during washing, unless an electrolyte is present in the wash solution.

Solubility of Small Particles

Studies of certain slightly soluble substances have shown that when the particle size is less than about one micron, the solubility increases with decreasing particle size.[1,2] The saturated solution around the very small, more soluble particles is supersaturated with respect to larger crystals, and solute crystallizes out on the larger particles. This process disturbs the solubility equilibrium of the very small particles; eventually the very small crystals will have disappeared, and the solid phase consists of relatively large, well-formed crystals of precipitate. This process, known as **Ostwald ripening**, is a secondary process, distinct from the growth of crystals during precipitation under conditions of low relative supersaturation.

It appears likely that the magnitude of the increased solubility with decreasing particle size has been overestimated, and that factors other than Ostwald ripening play a large part in the digestion process. It has been observed[3,4] that barium sulfate, not retained by a filter when freshly precipitated, gave an easily filtered precipitate by aging at room temperature or by hot digestion, although there was no significant change in particle size. Kolthoff and Noponen[5] concluded that the perfection of barium sulfate crystals during digestion was due predominantly to recrystallization in the liquid film around the particles, resulting in a decrease of surface by cementing primary particles together.

Aging of Precipitates

When precipitation conditions are such that many nuclei and particles of colloidal dimensions are formed, flocculation of the colloid may take place very

[1] R. A. Gortner, *Outlines of Biochemistry*, New York, Wiley, 1938, p. 188.
[2] M. L. Dundon and E. Mack, *J. Am. Chem. Soc.*, **45**, 2479 (1923).
[3] M. L. Dundon, *J. Am. Chem. Soc.*, **45**, 2658 (1923).
[4] H. M. Trimble, *J. Phys. Chem.*, **31**, 601 (1927).
[5] I. M. Kolthoff and G. E. Noponen, *J. Am. Chem. Soc.*, **60**, 197, 499, 505 (1938).

rapidly and result in the formation of agglomerates that are far from perfect crystals. However, in the saturated solution the dynamic equilibrium involves dissolution of the solute and its recrystallization from solution. This process results not only in the formation of more perfect crystals, but also in purification from foreign substances with which the particles are contaminated. Both recrystallization and Ostwald ripening are important in order to obtain large, well-formed particles free from contamination.

CONTAMINATION OF PRECIPITATES

Coprecipitation

Soluble substances, in the reaction mixture, that are carried down with a precipitate are said to be **coprecipitated**. The amount of contamination by coprecipitated substances depends upon the conditions of precipitation, the nature of the precipitate, and the kind and concentration of the ions in the solution from which precipitation is made. Different kinds of coprecipitation can occur.

Adsorption is a process by which foreign atoms, molecules, or ions are held on surfaces. Gelatinous and amorphous precipitates resulting from the flocculation of colloids are likely to be much contaminated by adsorption, on account of the high specific surface of the colloidal material. It is a general rule that **an ion of the crystal lattice of a precipitate is very strongly adsorbed**. For example, if barium sulfate is precipitated in the presence of excess sulfate ion, barium ions at the surface of the crystal strongly attract sulfate ions; conversely, if barium ions are present in excess in the solution, they are strongly adsorbed by the sulfate ions of the crystal surface.

If the solution contains no ions in common with the precipitate, ionic adsorption can be predicted by the **Paneth-Fajans-Hahn rule: The ion most strongly adsorbed is the one that forms the least soluble compound with an ion of the precipitate**. For example, barium sulfate precipitate adsorbs calcium ion more than it does magnesium ion, because calcium sulfate is less soluble than magnesium sulfate.

Occlusion is the process in which foreign substances become incorporated in the precipitate during its formation. If a foreign ion is of appropriate size and can form a compound with an ion of the precipitate that has the same crystal structure as the precipitate (i.e., is **isomorphous** with it), the foreign ion may deposit in a lattice position normally occupied by an ion of the precipitate, and **mixed crystals** or solid solutions are formed. For example, lead ion can occupy lattice positions normally occupied by barium ion in barium sulfate, and can be coprecipitated by occlusion even though the lead ion concentration is so small that lead sulfate would not form a primary precipitate. There are many other cases of occlusion by isomorphism. During recrystallization in the aging process the foreign ion that forms mixed crystals with the precipitate tends toward an equilibrium distribution between solid phase and solution, and little or no purification can be realized.

Even though isomorphous replacement does not occur, foreign ions can be incorporated as imperfections in the crystal lattice of the precipitate. Perfection of the crystals by recrystallization during aging leaves the foreign ions in the solution and results in a purer precipitate.

Postprecipitation

Postprecipitation is the separation of a second solid phase after the formation of another precipitate. The phenomenon occurs because the second substance crystallizes slowly from the supersaturated solution. In the separation of calcium from magnesium by oxalate the precipitated calcium oxalate should be filtered off after only a short digestion period, otherwise it may be much contaminated by magnesium oxalate, which is postprecipitated. Magnesium oxalate readily forms a quite stable supersaturated solution, and even after some solid phase has formed, crystallization from the solution is quite slow.

Optimum Conditions for Precipitation

In general, large particles and relatively pure particles result from the same conditions, namely, precipitation from solution of small relative supersaturation. The following conditions tend to give large particles and minimum contamination. Where applicable, the student should deduce the reason for the stated condition, in terms of Q and S of the von Weimarn expression (p. 180).

1. *Use of Dilute Solution of Reactants.* There is, of course, a practical limit to which dilution can be used, determined by larger solubility loss of precipitate and by difficulties in handling a larger volume of solution.

2. *Slow Addition of Reagent, with Good Stirring.*

3. *Precipitation from Hot Solution.*

4. *Precipitation in the Presence of a Reagent That Increases the Solubility of the Precipitate.* The precipitation of calcium oxalate is a good example of this effect. In acid solution, the oxalate ion concentration is small, because the second ionization of oxalic acid is weak. Therefore, if the calcium ion solution contains enough hydrochloric acid, no precipitate is formed when the oxalate reagent is added. Slow neutralization of the acid produces a slow increase in the oxalate ion concentration, resulting in the formation of large particles of pure precipitate.

5. *Precipitation from Homogeneous Solution.*[6] In this technique the precipitant is formed by a slow reaction within the solution, rather than by direct

[6] L. Gordon, M. L. Salutsky, and H. H. Willard, *Precipitation from Homogeneous Solution*, New York, Wiley, 1959.

addition of the reagent. The principal requirements are that the chemical used must not cause any reaction during its addition to the system, and that it can then be made to form the precipitant by a *slow* reaction, often hydrolysis. Several of the applications involve homogeneous removal of hydrogen ion in order to increase the concentration of an anion acting as the precipitant for acid-soluble compounds. For example, urea scarcely reacts with cold water, but near the boiling point it hydrolyzes slowly:

$$CO(NH_2)_2 + H_2O \rightarrow CO_2 + 2NH_3$$

The ammonia generated homogeneously in the solution neutralizes the hydrogen ion of acidic solutions. The method was first applied by Willard and Tang[7] to the precipitation of calcium oxalate, starting with an acidic solution of calcium ion and ammonium oxalate; an easily filtered precipitate, quite free from contamination, is produced. The general method is also advantageous for precipitation of hydroxides (hydrous oxides) of cations that are easily hydrolyzed; for example,

$$Al^{+++} + 3H_2O \rightarrow Al(OH)_3 + 3H^+$$

This **hydrolytic precipitation** is favored by removal of the hydrogen ion, which may be accomplished in several ways.

  a. Hydrolysis of urea, generating ammonia, as above.
  b. Hydrolysis of hexamethylenetetramine:

$$(CH_2)_6N_4 + 6H_2O \rightarrow 6HCHO + 4NH_3$$

  c. Reaction of a nitrite and boiling:

$$3NO_2^- + 3H^+ \rightarrow 3HNO_2 \xrightarrow{\text{boil}} 2NO + NO_3^- + H^+ + H_2O$$

  d. Reaction with thiosulfate and boiling:

$$S_2O_3^{--} + 2H^+ \rightarrow H_2S_2O_3 \rightarrow S + H_2SO_3 \xrightarrow{\text{boil}} H_2O + SO_2$$

Homogeneous precipitation of sulfates, oxalates, or phosphates can be made by adding the alkyl ester and boiling to hydrolyze the ester to form the anion. For example, hydrolysis of dimethylsulfate

$$(CH_3)_2SO_4 + 2H_2O \rightarrow 2CH_3OH + 2H^+ + SO_4^{--}$$

can be used for precipitation of barium ion as sulfate. Homogeneous generation of chloride ion results from the hydrolysis of ethylene chlorohydrin $CH_2Cl \cdot CH_2OH$; hydrolysis of trichloracetic acid, CCl_3COOH, produces carbonate ion. A unique method has been devised by Gordon[8] for the precipitation

---

[7] H. H. Willard and N. K. Tang, *J. Am. Chem. Soc.*, **59**, 1190 (1937); *Ind. Eng. Chem., Anal. Ed.*, **9**, 357 (1937).
[8] L. Gordon, *J. Chem. Ed.*, **38**, 16 (1961).

of nickel ion by dimethylglyoxime generated homogeneously by reaction of biacetyl with hydroxylamine:

$$CH_3—C\!=\!O \atop CH_3—C\!=\!0 \quad \xrightarrow{NH_2OH} \quad {CH_3—C\!=\!N—OH \atop CH_3—C\!=\!O} \quad \xrightarrow{NH_2OH} \quad {CH_3—C\!=\!N—OH \atop CH_3—C\!=\!N—OH}$$

The nickel dimethylglyoximate precipitates in long needle-like crystals that are very easily filtered and washed.

6. *Multiple Precipitation.*   When contamination cannot be avoided, the first precipitate is separated and washed, then dissolved in a suitable reagent, and reprecipitated. The second precipitate is formed from a solution containing only the amount of contaminant carried down by the first precipitate. Because the amount of contamination is a function of the concentration of foreign ion in the solution, the second precipitate is less contaminated than the first.

7. *Choice of pH.*   The *kind* of foreign ion carried down by a precipitate is markedly dependent upon the sign of the charge of primary adsorbed ions; this charge can be influenced by pH. Hydrogen ion is strongly adsorbed on precipitates formed in an acidic medium, and anions form the counter ion layer. The flocculated precipitate is contaminated with anions. When formed in an alkaline medium, precipitates may adsorb hydroxyl ion, and cations of the counter ion layer are carried down with the precipitate. The pH to be used in the precipitation is therefore often dependent upon the separation desired, that is, whether the desired constituent is to be separated from anions or from cations.

8. *Adjustment of Oxidation State of Foreign Ions.*   A precipitate of barium sulfate formed in the presence of iron(III) is likely to be badly contaminated by the latter; contamination by iron can be diminished by reduction of iron(III) to iron(II), which is not much coprecipitated. (A safer procedure, when very accurate results are desired, is to remove the iron before precipitating barium sulfate.) Chlorate, which is much coprecipitated with barium sulfate, can be reduced to chloride, which is not much coprecipitated.

9. *Digestion.*   The digestion of most precipitates results in their purification as the impurities are left in the solution during the recrystallization process. Hydrous oxides of the metals are usually digested for only a short time to aid in coagulation of the colloidal particles. Longer digestion accomplishes little in the way of purification and often results in a slimy precipitate that is more difficult to filter.

10. *Washing.*   In some instances washing of the precipitate can effect purification. Whether washing is very effective depends upon the nature of the precipitate and the conditions under which it was formed. Occluded contaminants are not affected, but adsorbed contaminants may sometimes be washed out, at least partially. The requisites of a wash liquid are summarized below.

a. The wash solution must be without chemical action on the precipitate, and ordinary solubility losses must be negligible.

b. The wash solution must not contain any substance that can form insoluble products with any component of the mother liquor.

c. Precipitates that are easily peptized must be washed with an electrolyte solution to replace the counter ions that are washed out.

d. In some cases the wash solution contains a reagent to prevent hydrolysis of heavy metal ions in the mother liquor.

e. The wash solution often contains an ion in common with the precipitate, to decrease the solubility of the latter. If the precipitate is very insoluble, application of the common ion effect is unnecessary.

f. Solutes of the wash solution must leave no weighable residue when the precipitate is dried or ignited. It is for this reason that volatile acids (hydrochloric, nitric) and ammonium salts are commonly used as electrolytes in wash solutions.

A precipitate is more effectively washed by using several successive small portions of wash liquid than by using the same total volume in a few large portions. Each portion of wash liquid should be separated, by decantation or by drainage through the filter, as completely as possible from the precipitate before the next portion of wash liquid is added.

THERMOGRAVIMETRIC ANALYSIS

The process of bringing a precipitate to constant weight by oven drying or by ignition, followed by cooling in a desiccator, weighing, reheating, cooling, weighing, etc., until constant weight is attained is tedious, to say the least. The temperatures used in the past were often determined merely by use of the equipment at hand, such as a drying oven at 130°C, or a muffle furnace at 1000°C, or by ignition with a Meker burner. The invention of a recording thermobalance by Chevanard[9] made it possible to follow the weight changes while the precipitate was being heated in the furnace. The record obtained is a **thermogram** or **pyrolysis curve** in which the weight is plotted against temperature. By proper calibration, temperatures accurate to 1°C over the range from room temperature to 1000°C, and weights accurate to a relative error of 0.01 %, are attainable. Stable species are indicated by a horizontal or plateau in the pyrolysis curve, and weight changes are easily correlated with the chemical changes that occur.

Duval[10] and co-workers have examined nearly a thousand gravimetric procedures by determining the pyrolysis curves of the precipitates. It was found that in only about 200 of the cases was the method originally proposed completely satisfactory. In most cases in the past, precipitates have been heated too long and at too high a temperature. As a result of Duval's work, new methods have

[9] P. Chevanard, X. Waché, and R. de la Tullaye, *Bull. Soc. Chim.*, [5], **11**, 41 (1944).
[10] C. Duval, *Inorganic Thermogravimetric Analysis*, Amsterdam, Elsevier, 1953; *Anal. Chem.*, **23**, 1271 (1951). See also articles by W. W. Wendlandt in *Anal. Chem.* and *Anal. Chim. Acta* since 1956.

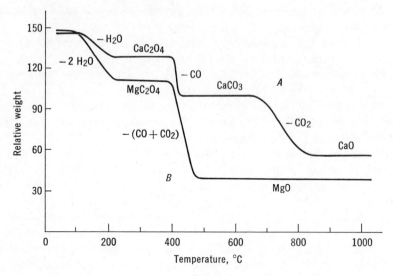

Fig. 14-3 Pyrolysis curves. *A*, calcium oxalate; *B*, magnesium oxalate.

been developed (sulfate determined by weighing benzidinium sulfate), and new compounds (U_3O_7) and new methods of preparation (HBO_2) have been discovered.

The pyrolysis curve of calcium oxalate is shown in curve A of Fig. 14-3. The curve shows the following features.

a. After losing adhering water, the compound $CaC_2O_4 \cdot H_2O$ is stable to about 100°C.

b. Between 100 and 226°C the monohydrate loses its water of hydration; from 226 to 398°C the anhydrous CaC_2O_4 is stable.

c. Abruptly at 420°C the oxalate loses carbon monoxide:

$$CaC_2O_4 \rightarrow CaCO_3 + CO$$

The $CaCO_3$ is stable to 660°C.

d. The dissociation of calcium carbonate starts at 660°C:

$$CaCO_3 \rightleftarrows CaO + CO_2$$

With free escape of carbon dioxide, the reaction is complete at 840°C above which CaO is stable to $>1000°C$.

Comparison with the pyrolysis curve of magnesium oxalate, curve B in Fig. 14-3, shows the following:

a. Magnesium oxalate dihydrate loses water from <100 to 233°C; the anhydrous salt is stable from 233 to 397°C.

b. At 400°C the oxalate loses carbon monoxide and carbon dioxide simultaneously and rapidly:

$$MgC_2O_4 \rightarrow MgO + CO + CO_2$$

There is no plateau corresponding to $MgCO_3$.

c. The oxide is stable from 480 to $>1000°C$.

The continuous recording of weight during heating provides exact knowledge of the various weighing forms and their temperature range of stability; also, it automatically "ignites to constant weight" without attention of the analyst. The weight loss by the precipitate at the various temperatures is directly proportional to the weight of volatile product. For example, if the weight of $CaC_2O_4 \cdot H_2O$ (mol. wt., 146.1) taken were 146.1 mg, then the weight loss between 100 and 226°C would be 18.0 mg (due to H_2O), between 390 and 420°C the loss would be 28.0 mg (due to CO), and between 660 and 840°C the loss would be 44.0 mg (due to CO_2).

The difference in behavior of calcium oxalate and magnesium oxalate on heating makes possible the determination of both calcium and magnesium in a mixture of their oxalates. Heating to about 500° results in a residue consisting of $CaCO_3$ and MgO; at 900°, the residue is CaO and MgO. The weights of the original mixture and of the residue at 500 and at 900°C provide the data for calculation of the individual components by the usual change-in-weight type of calculations (see p. 195).

A similar analysis of the binary mixture $AgNO_3$ and $Cu(NO_3)_2 \cdot 6H_2O$ can be made from the weight of residue at temperatures in the range 300 to 500°C ($AgNO_3$ and CuO), and the weight of residue above 700°C (Ag and CuO).

A check on the atomic weight of carbon can be made from the pyrolysis data of CaC_2O_4, in which the weight loss due to CO (x) and the weight loss due to CO_2 (y) are measured. The atomic weight of carbon is calculated from the relation

$$\frac{C + 16}{C + 32} = \frac{x}{y}$$

Part II □ Gravimetric Methods

15

CALCULATIONS OF GRAVIMETRIC ANALYSIS

In gravimetric methods of analysis the weight of some constituent, or of a substance derived from some constituent, of the sample is measured. The calculations make use of atomic and molecular (formula) weights and are based upon the constancy of composition of pure substances and the weight relations (stoichiometry) of chemical change.

A soluble chloride, such as sodium chloride, treated with a soluble silver salt gives a precipitate of silver chloride, which can be filtered off, washed, dried, and weighed. The chemical change that occurs may be represented by the "molecular" equation

$$NaCl + AgNO_3 \rightarrow NaNO_3 + AgCl \text{ (solid)}$$

$$(58.443) \quad (169.874) \quad (84.994) \quad (143.323)$$

which shows that 143.323 parts by weight of silver chloride are produced from 58.443 parts by weight of sodium chloride; therefore, *any* given weight of silver chloride is produced from sodium chloride in this same weight ratio.

EXAMPLE 1

What weight of NaCl will produce 0.5000 g of AgCl?
Solution:

$$g \text{ NaCl} = 0.5000 \text{ g AgCl} \times \frac{58.44 \text{ g NaCl}}{143.32 \text{ g AgCl}}$$

$$= 0.20388$$

Note the use of the labels associated with the numbers, and the way the labels are handled mathematically; note also the proper use of significant figures. The **gravimetric factor**, NaCl/AgCl, is the ratio of the formula weight of the substance *sought,* NaCl, to the substance *weighed,* AgCl; multiplication by this factor will convert any given weight of AgCl to the weight of NaCl which produced it. In general terms

$$\text{g substance sought} = \text{g substance weighed} \times \frac{a(\text{F.W. substance sought})}{b(\text{F.W. substance weighed})} \quad (15\text{-}1)$$

where a and b are coefficients required to represent the stoichiometry of the substances concerned in the chemical change which occurs. In the example given, $a = b = 1$.

EXAMPLE 2

Calculate the weight of $BaCl_2$ required to produce 0.5000 g of AgCl.

Solution: Each mole of $BaCl_2$ gives 2 moles of AgCl:

$$BaCl_2 \rightarrow 2AgCl$$
$$(208.25) \quad (2 \times 143.32)$$

The gravimetric factor in this case is $BaCl_2/2AgCl$; hence,

$$\text{g } BaCl_2 = 0.5000 \text{ g AgCl} \times \frac{208.25 \text{ g } BaCl_2}{286.64 \text{ g AgCl}} = 0.36325$$

EXAMPLE 3

A 0.4000–g sample containing chloride gave a precipitate of silver chloride weighing 0.2500 g; calculate the percentage of chlorine in the sample.

Solution: The weight of chlorine in the sample is given by

$$\text{g Cl} = \text{g AgCl} \times \text{Cl/AgCl}$$

$$= 0.2500 \times 35.45/143.32 = 0.06184$$

This weight of chlorine was contained in 0.4000 g of sample; the percentage of chlorine (fractional part of 100) is then given by

$$\% \text{Cl} = \frac{0.06184}{0.4000} \times 100 = 15.460$$

Generalizing, we can write

$$\% X \text{ in sample} = \frac{\text{g } Y \text{ weighed} \times (aX/bY) \times 100}{\text{g sample}} \quad (15\text{-}2)$$

where X is the substance sought, Y is the substance weighed, and a and b are coefficients of X and Y, respectively, required to express the correct stoichiometry between them.

Gravimetric Factors

Gravimetric factors are formulated according to the following rules.

1. The gravimetric factor is *always* represented by the **atomic or formula weight of the substance sought in the numerator and of the substance weighed in the denominator.**

2. If a series of reactions is involved in converting the substance sought to the substance weighed, only these two substances are involved in the factor; all intermediate substances are ignored, *except as provided by Rule* 3.

3. The number of atomic or formula weights of the substances, in numerator and denominator of the factor, *must represent the stoichiometry of the chemical changes that occur.*

In the sequence of reactions represented by

$$As_2S_3 \rightarrow 2H_3AsO_4 \rightarrow 2Ag_3AsO_4 \rightarrow 6Ag^+ \rightarrow 6AgCl$$
(sought)   (weighed)

the gravimetric factor is $As_2S_3/6AgCl$. The numerator and the denominator have no element in common, but the factor represents the stoichiometry of the chemical changes that occur. The intermediate steps are ignored except in preserving the stoichiometry from initial reactant to final product.

Gravimetric factors are of great convenience in making calculations, especially in repetitive analysis for a given constituent. For example, the factor $Cl/AgCl = 35.453/143.233 = 0.24737$ is the same for *all* determinations of chlorine weighed as silver chloride, regardless of the origin of the chlorine precipitated as silver chloride.

Change-in-Weight Factors.   Loss in weight or gain in weight can be used in gravimetric factors in the same way as any other weight, provided the change is due to a single reaction of definite stoichiometry.

EXAMPLE 4

A 1.0000-g sample of impure Fe_2O_3 was strongly ignited, after which the residue weighed 0.9834 g. Assuming the loss to be due solely to oxygen from Fe_2O_3, what is the percentage of Fe_2O_3 in the sample?

Solution: The reaction is $6Fe_2O_3 \rightarrow 4Fe_3O_4 + O_2$; the loss in weight is due to oxygen expelled. The substance weighed is oxygen ($1.0000 - 0.9834 = 0.0166$ g), and the factor is $6Fe_2O_3/O_2$.

$$\% Fe_2O_3 = \frac{g\ O_2 \times \dfrac{6Fe_2O_3}{O_2} \times 100}{g\ sample}$$

$$= \frac{0.0166 \times 958 \times 100}{1.000 \times 32.0} = 49.7$$

(Note the application of rules for use of significant figures.)

EXAMPLE 5

A bromide sample weighing 0.4500 g gave a precipitate of silver bromide that lost 0.1425 g in weight when heated in chlorine. Calculate the percent bromine in the sample.

Solution: The reaction of silver bromide with chlorine is

$$2AgBr + Cl_2 \rightarrow 2AgCl + Br_2$$

The loss in weight is due to the difference in weight between silver bromide and silver chloride, and the substance weighed is the loss represented by the difference in their formula weights, that is, $AgBr - AgCl$. Since silver is common to the two formulas, it is simpler to write merely $Br - Cl$; that is, the loss in weight is due to replacement of a heavy element, bromine, by a lighter element, chlorine. When bromine is sought, the factor is therefore $Br/(Br - Cl)$.

$$\% \, Br = \frac{g \, loss \times \dfrac{Br}{Br - Cl} \times 100}{g \, sample}$$

$$= \frac{0.1425 \times 79.91 \times 100}{0.4500 \times (79.91 - 35.45)} = 56.92$$

Factor-Weight Samples

In the general expression (15-2), any term can be found if the remaining terms are known. In industrial laboratories, where many repetitive samples are analyzed by technicians, there is an advantage in setting up the analytical routine so that a simple relationship exists between the amount of substance weighed and the percentage of the constituent sought. The time then required to make the calculations from the analytical data is negligible.

EXAMPLE 6

What weight of sample must be taken for analysis so that each 10.00 mg of silver chloride precipitate obtained represents 1.000% chlorine in the sample?

Solution: Factor $= Cl/AgCl = 0.2474$

$$1.000 \, \% \, Cl = \frac{0.01000 \, g \, AgCl \times 0.2474 \times 100}{g \, sample}$$

$$g \, sample = \frac{0.01000 \times 0.2474 \times 100}{1.000} = 0.2474$$

When 0.2474 g of any sample containing chlorine is taken, the weight of silver chloride in milligrams divided by 10, or its weight in grams multiplied by 100, gives the percentage of chlorine in the sample. It is observed in this case that the sample weight in grams is identical with the gravimetric factor; this identity of the two numbers was due to a fortuitous combination of stipulations of the required relation between weight of silver chloride and the percentage of chlorine. However, for any specified ratio between these terms, there will be the same ratio between the sample weight and the gravimetric factor.

Calculations to Dry Basis

For samples that tend to lose or gain moisture readily, analyses at different times and under different conditions of storage would not be concordant. Either of two procedures may be followed with "wet" samples: (1) the sample may be air dried until any further change in weight is negligible; (2) the sample may be oven dried at about 110°C (this is the usual procedure). The latter procedure may not remove all the water, but its content is reduced to a low, constant level so that concordant analytical results can be obtained. The constituents are therefore determined on the oven-dried basis, and then calculated back to the as-received basis from the oven-drying loss, determined separately. Because drying removes a constituent (water) of the sample, other constituents will be present in higher percentage in the dry sample than in the sample as received.

EXAMPLE 7

A sample of wheat flour loses 15.0% of its own weight on oven drying. The dry sample is found to contain 2.31% nitrogen. What is the percentage of nitrogen on the as-received basis?

Solution: The percentage of nitrogen in the as-received sample is smaller than its percentage in the oven-dried sample in the same ratio that the percentage residue from the oven-drying loss, that is, $100.0 - 15.0 = 85.0\%$, is smaller than 100%. Therefore

$$\% \text{ N, as received,} = 2.31 \times 85.0/100.0 = 1.96$$

The relations just illustrated can be formulated for the general case as follows:

$$\% \ Y_{a.r.} = \frac{\% \ Y_{o.d.} \times (100 - \% \text{o.d. loss})}{100} \qquad (15\text{--}3)$$

$$\% \ Y_{o.d.} = \frac{\% Y_{a.r.} \times 100}{(100 - \% \text{o.d. loss})} \qquad (15\text{--}4)$$

where Y is the constituent analyzed, and the abbreviations a.r. and o.d. refer to as-received and oven dried, respectively.

EXAMPLE 8

A sample of commercial Glauber's salt (impure $Na_2SO_4 \cdot 10H_2O$) contained 20.0% SO_3, as received. An exact 1-g sample was oven dried, leaving a residue weighing 0.520 g. (a) Calculate the percentage of water in the sample. (b) Calculate the percentage of SO_3 on the dry basis.

$$(a) \ \% \text{ water} = \frac{(1.000 - 0.520) \times 100}{1.000} = 48.0$$

$$(b) \ \% \ SO_3 \ _{o.d.} = \frac{20.0 \times 100}{100.0 - 48.0} = 38.4$$

Indirect Determinations

Certain pairs of substances that may be difficult to separate from each other can be determined indirectly if they fulfill the following conditions: (1) They can be obtained together in pure form for weighing; (2) they contain an element (ion) in common that can be converted to a single product for weighing, or they can be converted to a mixture of other pure compounds that can be weighed together. For example, sodium and potassium can be obtained together as their solid chlorides, NaCl and KCl, which are weighed. The mixed chlorides in solution are then converted to silver chloride, which is weighed. The calculations are as follows:

Let

$$Y = \text{g of NaCl} + \text{KCl}$$

and

$$X = \text{g of NaCl}$$

then

$$(Y - X) = \text{g of KCl}$$

By applying the appropriate gravimetric factors:

$$\text{g AgCl from NaCl} = X\left(\frac{\text{AgCl}}{\text{NaCl}}\right)$$

$$\text{g AgCl from KCl} = (Y - X)\left(\frac{\text{AgCl}}{\text{KCl}}\right)$$

$$\text{Total g AgCl} = X\left(\frac{\text{AgCl}}{\text{NaCl}}\right) + (Y - X)\left(\frac{\text{AgCl}}{\text{KCl}}\right)$$

Putting in the numerical values for the formula weights gives,

$$\text{g AgCl} = X\left(\frac{143.32}{58.44}\right) + (Y - X)\left(\frac{143.32}{74.56}\right)$$

$$= 2.4523\,X + 1.9223\,(Y - X)$$

The weight of AgCl and of the mixed chlorides, Y, being known, it remains merely to solve for X, the grams of NaCl in the mixture. Once the weights of sodium chloride and potassium chloride are known, other gravimetric calculations may be made in the usual way.

A weighed mixture of sodium chloride and potassium chloride can be treated with sulfuric acid, evaporated to dryness, and the mixed sulfates weighed. The calculations are made in the same way as illustrated for the previous case.

Let

$$Y = \text{g of mixed NaCl} + \text{KCl}$$

$$X = \text{g of NaCl}$$

$$(Y - X) = \text{g of KCl}$$

$$\text{g Na}_2\text{SO}_4 \text{ from NaCl} = X\,\frac{\text{Na}_2\text{SO}_4}{2\text{NaCl}}$$

$$\text{g } K_2SO_4 \text{ from KCl} = (Y - X)\frac{K_2SO_4}{2KCl}$$

$$\text{g mixed sulfates} = X\frac{Na_2SO_4}{2NaCl} + (Y - X)\frac{K_2SO_4}{2KCl}$$

The formula weights are introduced into the factors, and the known weights of mixed chlorides and mixed sulfates are then used to solve for the value of X, the grams of sodium chloride in the mixed chlorides.

It is possible to combine gravimetric and titrimetric methods in indirect analysis. For example, a known weight of mixed halides, such as NaCl and KCl, or NaCl and NaBr, or NaBr and KCl, could be dissolved and titrated with standard silver nitrate solution, and the composition of the mixed halides calculated. The method is illustrated under titrimetric calculations in Chap. 22.

The indirect method of analysis should not be applied to the determination of a constituent that is present in very small amounts, because even a slight error in the determination of one constituent is automatically reflected as a large error of opposite sign in the other constituent.

PROBLEMS

Additional problems on gravimetric analysis are given in Chapters 16–19.

15-1 Calculate* the gravimetric factor for the following.

Sought	Weighed		Sought	Weighed
(a) MgO	$Mg_2P_2O_7$		(e) Fe_2O_3	Fe_3O_4
(b) FeS_2	$BaSO_4$		(f) KCl	K_2PtCl_6
(c) K_2O	$KClO_4$		(g) $Fe(CrO_2)_2$	Fe_2O_3
(d) P_2O_5	$Mg_2P_2O_7$		(h) $Al_2(SO_4)_3$	$BaSO_4$

Ans. (a) 0.36223.   *(b)* 0.25700.

15-2 Calculate* the gravimetric factor for the following.

Sought		Transformations		Weighed
(a) Sb_2S_3	$\rightarrow$	$H_2S \rightarrow H_2SO_4$	$\rightarrow$	$BaSO_4$
(b) P_2O_5	$\rightarrow$	$H_3PO_4 \rightarrow Ag_3PO_4 \rightarrow Ag^+$	$\rightarrow$	AgBr
(c) $NaNO_3$	$\rightarrow$	$NH_3 \rightarrow (NH_4)_2PtCl_6$	$\rightarrow$	Pt
(d) $H_2C_2O_4$	$\rightarrow$	$CaC_2O_4 \rightarrow CaCO_3$	$\rightarrow$	CaF_2
(e) NaN_3	$\rightarrow$	$NH_3 \rightarrow (NH_4)_2PdCl_4$	$\rightarrow$	PdO_2
(f) $Na_2B_4O_7$	$\rightarrow$	$H_3BO_3 \rightarrow BF_3$	$\rightarrow$	$KB(C_6H_5)_4$
(g) $(P_4H_2)_3$	$\rightarrow$	$(NH_4)_3P(Mo_3O_{10})_4 \rightarrow MoO_4^{--}$	$\rightarrow$	$PbMoO_4$
(h) Cr_3Si_2	$\rightarrow$	$H_2CrO_4 \rightarrow Ag_2CrO_4 \rightarrow Ag^+$	$\rightarrow$	AgCl
(i) $Al_2Si_3O_8$	$\rightarrow$	$SiO_2 \rightarrow SiF_4$	$\rightarrow$	PbF_2
(j) K_3PO_4	$\rightarrow$	$K^+ \rightarrow K_2NaCo(NO_2)_6$	$\rightarrow$	Co_3O_4

Ans. (a) 0.48514.   *(b)* 0.12599.

* The instructor may wish to require only the formulation of the gravimetric factor in terms of the formula weights as represented by formulas, without calculation of the numerical value of the factor.

15-3 What weight of silver halide precipitate can be obtained from 1.2500 g of mixture that contains 35.50% $BaCl_2 \cdot 2H_2O$, 48.70% NaBr, and 10.80% KI, the remainder of the sample being inert?   *Ans.* 1.823 g.

15-4 A sample weighing 0.8000 g and containing only $KClO_3$ and inert matter is ignited to KCl, after which the residue weighs 0.5655 g.

(*a*) Calculate the percentage of $KClO_3$ in the sample.

(*b*) If the ignited residue is dissolved and then precipitated as AgCl, what weight of the latter will be formed?   *Ans.* (*a*) 74.84. (*b*) 0.7002 g.

15-5 A sample of pure $KClO_x$ weighing 0.2800 g is reduced to KCl, then is precipitated with silver nitrate, giving 0.2900 g of AgCl. What is the value of x in the formula $KClO_x$?   *Ans.* 4.

15-6 In what weight ratio must $BaCO_3$ and $CaCO_3$ be mixed so that the mixture will contain the same percentage of CO_2 as is present in pure $SrCO_3$?

Ans. $BaCO_3/CaCO_3 = 1.885/1.000.$

15-7 A sample containing only $CaBr_2$ and NaBr, and weighing 0.4050 g, gives 0.7500 g of AgBr precipitate.

(*a*) Calculate the percentage of NaBr in the sample.

(*b*) Calculate the calcium content in terms of the percentage of CaO.

Ans. (*a*) 50.03. (*b*) 14.02.

15-8 What weight of silicate rock sample should be taken for analysis so that:

(*a*) each 5.00 mg of $KClO_4$ obtained will represent 0.200% K_2O in the sample?

Ans. 0.850 g.

(*b*) each 10.0 mg of K_2PtCl_6 obtained will represent 0.0500% K_2O in the sample?

Ans. 3.88 g.

(*c*) the percentage of K_2O is one-fifth of the weight in milligrams of platinum obtained from K_2PtCl_6?   *Ans.* 0.241 g.

15-9 A sample of clay contains 8.80% moisture and 13.46% Al_2O_3 as received. What is the percentage of Al_2O_3 in an air-dried sample of the clay that contains 2.10% moisture?   *Ans.* 14.45.

15-10 A 0.5250-g sample containing iron pyrite, FeS_2, is oxidized and the sulfate is precipitated as $BaSO_4$, which weighs 0.4200 g.

(*a*) Calculate the percentage of FeS_2 in the sample.

(*b*) What weight of Fe_2O_3 could be obtained from a 1.000-g sample of the pyrite? (Assume no other iron compound is present in the sample.)

15-11 In what weight ratio (grams) must NaBr and RbBr be mixed so that the mixture will contain the same percent bromine as pure KBr?

15-12 A sample of ferric alum, $Fe_2(SO_4)_3 \cdot (NH_4)_2SO_4 \cdot 24H_2O$, containing only inert impurities, is analyzed by several different methods as indicated below. Calculate the percentage purity of the sample.

(*a*) A 0.5000-g sample loses 0.2223 g when dehydrated.

(*b*) A 0.4000-g sample gives 0.3834 g of $BaSO_4$.

(*c*) A 2.000-g sample gives 0.3300 g of Fe_2O_3.

(*d*) A 1.5000-g sample is converted to $(NH_4)_2PtCl_6$ which, on ignition, leaves a residue of 0.3015 g of platinum metal.

(*e*) What is the average percentage purity by the above four methods?

15-13 A sample weighing 0.7500 g and containing only $KClO_4$ and inert impurities is ignited to KCl, after which the residue weighs 0.4296 g.

(a) Calculate the percentage of $KClO_4$ in the sample.

(b) If the ignited residue is dissolved and then precipitated as $AgCl$, what weight of the latter is obtained?

15-14 A sample of pure KIO_x weighing 0.4000 g is reduced to KI, then precipitated as AgI, which weighs 0.4388 g. What is the value of x in the formula KIO_x?

15-15 A 0.2000-g sample of Na_2S_x is oxidized to sulfate and the latter is precipitated as $BaSO_4$, which weighs 1.0842 g. What is the value of x in the formula Na_2S_x?

15-16 The ratio of the weight of neptunium(III) chloride, $NpCl_3$, to the equivalent amount of AgCl is 0.79875. Using $Ag = 107.870$ and $Cl = 35.453$, calculate the atomic weight of neptunium to five significant figures.

15-17 In what weight ratio (grams) must $SrCO_3$ and $MgCO_3$ be mixed so that the mixture will contain the same percentage of CO_2 as pure $CaCO_3$?

15-18 A mixture of KCl and KBr contains chlorine and bromine in a weight (gram) ratio of $1:2$. What is the percentage of potassium in the mixture?

15-19 How many grams of Li_2SO_4 must be mixed with 1.000 g of K_2SO_4 so that the mixture will contain 25.00% sulfur?

15-20 A mixture containing only $CaCO_3$, $CaSO_4$, and $BaCO_3$ contains 28.5% calcium and 32.0% carbon dioxide. Calculate the percentage of $CaCO_3$, of $CaSO_4$, and of $BaCO_3$ in the sample.

15-21 What weight of clay sample (containing potassium aluminum silicate) should be taken for analysis so that:

(a) each 10.0 mg of $KClO_4$ obtained will represent 0.100% K_2O?

(b) each milligram of K_2PtCl_6 will represent 0.0200% K_2O?

(c) the percentage of aluminum is one-fifth the weight in milligrams of Al_2O_3 obtained?

(d) the percentage of Si is obtained by multiplying the grams of SiO_2 by 100.

15-22 How many kilograms of uranium metal can be obtained from one metric ton of pitchblende ore that assays 1.25% U_3O_8?

15-23 A limestone sample weighing 0.8000 g gives an ignited residue of mixed oxides, Al_2O_3, Fe_2O_3, and TiO_2, weighing 0.0780 g. By separate analyses the oxides residue is found to contain 5.00% Ti, and the original sample is found to contain 2.50% Fe. Calculate the percentage of Al in the sample.

15-24 A mixture of AgCl and AgBr, when heated in a current of chlorine, loses 5.00% of its own weight. Calculate the percentage of Cl in the original mixture.

15-25 A sample containing PbS and silica (inert) gains 20.00% of its own weight on conversion of the PbS to $PbSO_4$. Calculate the percentage of S in the original sample.

15-26 0.5000-g of mixture containing only LiCl and KCl is converted to a mixture of Li_2SO_4 and K_2SO_4; the mixed sulfates weigh 0.6227 g. Calculate the percentage of Cl in the original sample.

15-27 A sample of pure hydrated magnesium oxalate loses 24.30% of its weight on oven drying at 150°C, leaving the anhydrous salt as a residue. In the hydrate, how many moles of water are in combination with one mole of magnesium oxalate?

15-28 A sample of wheat flour loses 8.00% of its own weight on oven drying. The dried sample contains 1.25% nitrogen. Calculate the percentage of nitrogen on the as-received basis.

15-29 A sample of impure hydrated sodium sulfate contains 11.0% sulfur and 47.0% moisture as received.

(*a*) Calculate the percentage of S in an air-dried sample which contains 7.50% moisture.

(*b*) Calculate the percentage of S in an oven-dried sample (assume all water is expelled).

15-30 A sample weighing 0.6800 g gives a residue, presumably $CaCO_3$, weighing 0.2202 g. It is suspected that the residue is not pure $CaCO_3$, and analysis of the residue shows it to contain 2.10% magnesium, present as $MgCO_3$. Calculate the true percentage of CaO in the sample.

15-31 MgC_2O_4, heated at 500°C, loses CO and CO_2 simultaneously, leaving a residue of MgO. CaC_2O_4, heated at 500°C, loses CO, leaving a residue of $CaCO_3$; upon heating at 900°C, $CaCO_3$ loses CO_2, leaving a residue of CaO. A 2.0000-g sample containing MgC_2O_4, CaC_2O_4, and SiO_2 (stable) on heating at 500°C leaves a residue weighing 1.3966 g; after further heating to 900°C, the residue weighs 1.0530 g. Calculate the percentages of MgC_2O_4 and CaC_2O_4 in the original sample.

15-32 A sample of pure CaC_2O_4 weighing 0.3200 g is heated at 500°C, which results in loss of CO and leaves a residue weighing 0.2500 g. On heating to 900°C, CO_2 is lost and a residue weighing 0.1400 g remains. Using the atomic weight of oxygen as 16.000, calculate the atomic weight of carbon to four significant figures, using *only* the weight losses. (Do *not* use molecular weights of any of the calcium compounds.)

15-33 Copper(II) nitrate hexahydrate and silver nitrate undergo pyrolysis as indicated by the following transitions at the temperatures shown:

$$3Cu(NO_3)_2 \cdot 6H_2O \rightarrow Cu(NO_3)_2 \cdot 2Cu(OH)_2 \quad (60–150°C)$$

$$Cu(NO_3)_2 \cdot 2Cu(OH)_2 \rightarrow 3CuO \quad (200–278°C)$$

$$AgNO_3 \rightarrow Ag \quad (350–608°C)$$

One gram of an alloy containing copper and silver (and possibly inert matter) is dissolved in nitric acid. The solution is evaporated to dryness and then baked at 135°C; the residue weighs 1.6336 g. The residue is heated at 250°; the resulting solids weigh 1.2558 g. Heating to 550°C gives further loss in weight and a residue that weighs 1.0259 g. Calculate the percentages of Cu and Ag in the alloy.

15-34 Given the following pyrolysis transitions:

$$H_3BO_3 \rightarrow H_2O + HBO_2 \quad (55–135°C; HBO_2 \text{ stable to } 168°C)$$

$$2HBO_2 \rightarrow H_2O + B_2O_3 \quad (168–443°C; B_2O_3 \text{ stable to } 1000°C)$$

$$KBF_4 \rightarrow KF + BF_3 \text{ (gas)} \quad (400–850°C; KF \text{ stable to } 1000°C)$$

A 1-g sample containing H_3BO_3, KBF_4, and silica (inert) loses 0.0800 g between 55 and 135°C, and loses an additional 0.3200 g between 600 and 900°C. Calculate the percentages of H_3BO_3 and KBF_4 in the sample.

16

DETERMINATION OF WATER, HYDROGEN, AND CARBON

DETERMINATION OF WATER

Water, or the elements of water, may be found in a wide variety of materials. The importance of analysis for water and the method to be used will be governed to some extent by the state in which water exists in the sample.

Nonessential Water

Water that is held by means other than chemical forces is called nonessential water. It is commonly referred to as "moisture" in the sample, and its presence affects the percentage of other constituents found by analysis (see p. 197).

Hygroscopic water is adsorbed on the surface of particles; it is usually determined by oven drying at about 110°C, although this treatment is no guarantee that all surface moisture has been expelled; furthermore, some substances, notably certain hydrates, may lose essential water at temperatures below 100°C. Oven drying is commonly used to decrease the moisture content of samples to a low, controlled level prior to weighing the samples for analysis.

Included water (sometimes called "occluded" water) is often present in minerals and in precipitates that have been formed by crystallization from aqueous solution. Water in this condition is not removed by heating at 100°C. Much higher temperature is required, and strong ignition may be used to advantage if the stability of the sample permits. On heating crystals containing cavities of water, volatilization of the latter causes bursting of the crystals ("decrepitation"), and precaution must be taken to prevent mechanical loss of material when this occurs.

Essential Water

Water, or the elements from which water is obtained, that exists as part of the definite stoichiometric composition of compounds is called essential water. Hydrogen and oxygen need not necessarily be present in the 2 : 1 ratio to form water.

Water of Hydration. Water in hydrates is bound by coordinate covalent forces that are usually weaker than electrovalent or primary covalent forces; consequently, hydrate water is relatively easily removed by heating. Various hydrates differ widely in stability; each hydrate is characterized by a definite aqueous tension and a definite transition temperature to a lower hydrate, if one exists, or to the anhydrous substance. If water can be removed completely (e.g., by oven drying) without decomposition of the anhydrous material, water may be determined indirectly by loss in weight; otherwise, a direct method must be used.

Water of Constitution. Hydrogen and oxygen (or hydroxyl), bound in the compound by primary valence forces, often may be converted to water by decomposition of the compound. For example,

$$2NaHCO_3 \rightarrow Na_2CO_3 + H_2O + CO_2$$
$$2MgHPO_4 \rightarrow Mg_2P_2O_7 + H_2O$$
$$Ca(OH)_2 \rightarrow CaO + H_2O$$

The hydroxides of the metals are *not* hydrates; the elements of water are much more firmly bound than in hydrates. Sodium bicarbonate and magnesium acid phosphate may be said to contain essential acidic hydrogen, and calcium hydroxide to contain essential basic (hydroxyl) hydrogen. The hydroxides of the alkali metals and barium are very stable and do not lose water except at very high temperature, and then incompletely.

Carbohydrates such as sucrose, $C_{12}H_{22}O_{11}$, decompose on heating, to yield water and many other substances. By heating such compounds in excess air or oxygen, all the hydrogen can be obtained as water (and the carbon as carbon dioxide). Virtually all carbon-hydrogen-oxygen compounds can be burned to carbon dioxide and water in the same way, and it may be a matter of opinion whether or not to designate the product as "water of constitution." Hydrocarbons can also be burned in oxygen to give carbon dioxide and water; clearly, a compound containing only carbon and hydrogen cannot be said to "contain" water of constitution. However, combustion analysis is almost invariably used for the determination of hydrogen (as water) and carbon (as carbon dioxide) in organic compounds.

Total water (nonessential and essential) may be determined by expulsion at high temperature. Whether or not nonessential water (moisture) can be determined separately depends upon whether it is adsorbed or included water, and upon the stability of the substance containing essential water.

Methods of Determination

Indirect Method.   Water is determined by loss in weight of the sample when it is subjected to conditions that remove the type of water desired—essential, nonessential, or both. The indirect method is valid only if the loss in weight is due solely to water that is expelled.

The following are some of the techniques used for removal of water for indirect determination.

1. *Heat only.*   The temperature appropriate to the nature of the sample is provided by an electric oven, or an air bath, or by direct heating over a flame.

2. *Heat and reduced pressure.*   The sample is heated in a vacuum oven, at 50 to 100 mm of mercury and at about 100°C, or at a lower temperature if the sample is unstable at 100°C. The method is widely used for determination of moisture in fruits, vegetables, grain, and other food and agricultural products. Vacuum oven drying gives more concordant results in multiplicate analysis than when heating alone is used.

3. *Use of desiccants.*   Samples in contact with dry air in a desiccator may lose nonessential water and possibly essential water also. Different low pressures of water vapor can be provided by use of different dehydrants, such as magnesium perchlorate, barium oxide, phosphorus pentoxide, fresh concentrated sulfuric acid, and other substances. After most of the water has been lost by the sample, the last remaining amounts may be withdrawn very slowly. The analyst should always keep in mind that every time the desiccator is opened, moist air enters and considerable time may be required for moisture in the confined air to reach equilibrium with the desiccant.

4. *Vacuum desiccation.*   Desiccation over fresh concentrated sulfuric acid at reduced pressure, for example, 10 mm of mercury, is useful for determining water in samples that would decompose or volatilize if heated.

Direct Method.   The water expelled from the sample may be collected and measured by weight or by volume, or by some chemical property of water. In some cases the water is not separated, and its amount is measured by alteration of some physical property of the sample.

1. *Absorption.*   The weighed sample, in a combustion boat, is placed in a combustion tube which is heated, usually by an electric furnace, while dry air is drawn through the apparatus. The exit end of the combustion tube is connected to one or more drying tubes containing a desiccant to fix the water. The difference in weight of the absorption tube(s) after and before the experiment is due to water expelled from the sample.

2. *Distillation* (*Bidwell-Sterling*) *method.*   The apparatus is shown in Fig. 16-1. The weighed sample is placed in the flask and covered with toluene (bp 110°C). Upon boiling, water is volatilized with the toluene; the condensate drips into the collection tube. Water and toluene are immiscible; the water, being more dense than toluene, settles into the narrow graduated portion of the

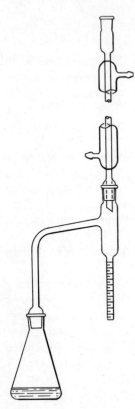

Fig. 16-1   Apparatus for determination of water by the distillation method.

tube; the less dense toluene overflows out the side tube back into the distillation flask. When no more water distills over, the volume of water is read in the graduated tube. The method is used for determination of water in organic materials such as oils, fats, and food products; it is more rapid than oven-drying methods, and the distillation temperature is low enough to prevent decomposition of the sample.

3. *Calcium carbide method.*   The method is based upon the reaction of water with calcium carbide to form acetylene gas:

$$2H_2O + CaC_2 \rightarrow Ca(OH)_2 + C_2H_2$$

The amount of acetylene can be measured (*a*) by loss in weight, (*b*) by collection and measurement of its volume, or (*c*) by measuring the pressure increase in a closed system. The determination is rapid, and has been applied to the determination of water in soap, butter, leather, flour, fruit juices, and many other organic substances.

4. *Electrical methods.*   Certain electrical properties of materials are altered by the presence of water, and serve as the basis for the rapid estimation of

moisture in materials such as flour, starch, wheat, and corn. Instruments have been devised for making rapid determinations (approximately one minute). The electrical properties that have been used are the dielectric constant, which is 80 for water but less than 10 for starches and proteins found in cereal grains; and the conductivity (or resistivity), which decreases (resistance increases) rapidly with decreasing water content. The meters used for the measurement are calibrated by the use of samples of known moisture content.

5. *Other physical methods.* Refractive index and density as a measure of water content are other methods applicable to certain materials. These methods are often used for sugar and for alcohol solutions. Various handbooks contain tables showing the water contents corresponding to measured refractive index and/or density.

6. *Titrimetric (Karl Fischer) method.* This method, developed in 1935, has come into wide use for the determination of water in a variety of materials. The method is described on p. 417.

DETERMINATION OF CARBON

Carbon is determined as carbon dioxide. Carbon in organic compounds is converted to carbon dioxide by complete combustion, which also converts hydrogen to water; both carbon and hydrogen are determined directly by absorbing the carbon dioxide and the water in separate weighed absorbers. Carbon dioxide in carbonates is liberated by treatment with dilute acid (perchloric acid is preferred), and may be determined directly by increase in weight of an absorber, or indirectly by loss in weight. An estimate of the carbon dioxide content of carbonate minerals can be made by loss in weight on thermal decomposition, as in the "loss on ignition" of limestone.

Absorbers for Carbon Dioxide

1. *Potassium hydroxide solution* was formerly much used to absorb carbon dioxide in combustion analysis; it has the disadvantage that the solution froths so much that rapid gas flow cannot be used, and the solution gives up more water to the gas stream than do the solid absorbers.

2. *Soda lime* is made from a solution of sodium hydroxide and calcium hydroxide by evaporation to dryness and ignition to redness. For effective absorption of carbon dioxide, the solid should contain about 2% water. During absorption of carbon dioxide, soda lime gives up water to dry air, hence must be followed by a desiccant weighed with the soda lime.

3. *Soda asbestos* or *ascarite* is asbestos that has been impregnated with sodium hydroxide and heated to about 180°C for several hours. It can absorb about 20% of its own weight of carbon dioxide, and can be used at relatively high

flow rates. The fresh material is gray; a change to white when carbon dioxide is absorbed serves as a self-indicator for exhaustion.

4. *Barium hydroxide solution* is sometimes used to absorb carbon dioxide. The determination can be finished in several ways. (*a*) The barium carbonate can be filtered off, washed, dried, and weighed. (*b*) The washed precipitate of barium carbonate is dissolved in a known volume of standard acid, the excess of which is titrated with standard alkali to the methyl orange end point. (*c*) A standard solution of barium hydroxide is used; after absorption of carbon dioxide the excess barium hydroxide is titrated with standard acid to the phenolphthalein end point.

Direct Method

The carbon dioxide is absorbed in an alkaline absorber, usually soda asbestos. The carbon dioxide must be quantitatively swept into the absorber. In the analysis of carbonates, this is done by a stream of carbon dioxide-free air drawn through the reaction train; in combustion analysis, a stream of oxygen is used.

Other acidic gases, such as hydrogen chloride, hydrogen sulfide, sulfur dioxide, and chlorine, that would react with the alkaline absorber, must be absent. An absorption tube containing anhydrous copper sulfate is used for this purpose.

The gas stream must not introduce nor remove moisture; the gas stream is passed through a desiccant before going through the carbon dioxide absorber. Soda asbestos (and other absorbers) give up moisture when carbon dioxide is absorbed; a drying tube is always placed after the soda asbestos tube and is weighed with it. When air is used to sweep the gas through the train, the air inlet is provided with a soda asbestos tube to remove carbon dioxide from the entering air.

1. Analysis of Carbonates. Evolution of carbon dioxide, by treating the carbonate sample with dilute perchloric acid, is carried out in a flask-dropper-condenser assembly (Knorr alkalimeter) the exit of which is connected to a train of absorption tubes for removing moisture and then absorbing the carbon dioxide. The tube for absorbing carbon dioxide is usually about two-thirds filled (on the entrance side) with soda asbestos and one-third filled with magnesium perchlorate to fix moisture given up when the soda asbestos absorbs carbon dioxide. Increase in weight of this absorption tube represents carbon dioxide from the sample.

2. Combustion of Organic Compounds. Decomposition is carried out by heating the sample in a silica or Vycor tube part of the length of which contains granular copper oxide held in place by rolls of copper gauze, while oxygen is passed through the combustion tube. The exit end of the combustion tube is connected to absorption tubes for absorbing, in turn, water vapor, then carbon dioxide. Both hydrogen (as water) and carbon (as carbon dioxide) are determined. If the sample also contains halogen or sulfur, lead chromate is substituted for copper oxide in the tube packing.

A direct determination of oxygen in organic compounds can be made by heating the sample, as in a combustion analysis, while passing an inert gas such as helium through the tube. Oxygen is quantitatively converted to carbon monoxide, which is passed through iodine pentoxide:

$$5CO + I_2O_5 \rightarrow 5CO_2 + I_2$$

The liberated iodine is titrated with sodium thiosulfate solution.

Most combustion analyses are now done on a semimicro or micro scale, using milligram-weight samples and diminutive equipment.

Indirect Method

The indirect determination of carbon dioxide in carbonates is made in an alkalimeter of the form shown in Fig. 16-2; the entire apparatus is about 12–15 cm tall. The trap on the left is half-filled with concentrated sulfuric acid to prevent escape of water vapor; dilute perchloric acid is placed in the dropper bulb. The weighed sample is introduced through the side tube of the reaction chamber, and covered with a few milliliters of water. The entire apparatus, charged ready for use, is weighed against a suitable tare. The acid is added slowly to the sample to effect decomposition of the carbonate. The alkalimeter is then heated to about 80–90°C to expel carbon dioxide from the solution, while a current of air is drawn through the alkalimeter by connecting the exit tube of the sulfuric acid trap to an aspirator. When the apparatus has cooled to room temperature, it is weighed again. The loss in weight represents carbon dioxide.

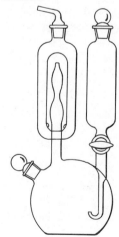

Fig. 16-2 Schroedter alkalimeter for indirect determination of carbon dioxide in carbonates.

PROBLEMS

16-1 An ignited residue containing Fe_2O_3 and silica weighs 0.2680 g. Upon reduction of the iron oxide with hydrogen, 0.0817 g of water is formed. Calculate the percentage of Fe_2O_3 in the sample.   *Ans.* 90.1.

16-2 What weight of water and what weight of carbon dioxide is formed by complete combustion of the organic compound given?

(a) 0.4200 g of toluene, $C_6H_5CH_3$.

(b) 0.8000 g of sucrose, $C_{12}H_{22}O_{11}$.

(c) 0.8800 g of benzoic acid, C_6H_5COOH.

(d) 0.4000 g of phthalic acid, $C_6H_4(COOH)_2$.

(e) 0.4500 g of naphthalene, $C_{10}H_8$.

(f) 0.5000 g of glycerol, $C_3H_5(OH)_3$.   *Ans.* (a) 0.32845 g H_2O, 1.4043 g CO_2.

16-3 The water formed by combustion of 0.5450 g of a pure organic compound is absorbed in a tube containing magnesium perchlorate desiccant; weight of tube before absorption, 21.4335 g; weight of tube after absorption, 21.6736 g. A 0.2200-g sample of the same compound gives 0.5560 g of carbon dioxide. Assume the remainder of the compound (besides carbon and hydrogen) to be oxygen. Calculate the empirical formula of the compound.   *Ans.* $C_7H_6O_2$.

16-4 A 1.2500-g sample containing 75.00% $CaCO_3$, 20.00% $FeCO_3$, and 5.00% SiO_2 is ignited to convert $CaCO_3$ to CaO and $FeCO_3$ to Fe_2O_3. What is the weight of the ignited residue?   *Ans.* 0.7601 g.

16-5 A sample of limestone weighing 0.9800 g is strongly ignited, leaving a residue weighing 0.6800 g. Assuming all the loss on ignition to be due to carbon dioxide, calculate the percentage of CO_2 in the sample.

16-6 Washing soda, $Na_2CO_3 \cdot 10H_2O$, readily loses water of hydration on exposure to air. A sample of washing soda was found to have an air-drying loss of 56.0%. An air-dried sample lost 5.0% of its weight when oven dried at 110°C. The oven-dried sample contained 87.5% Na_2CO_3.

(a) Calculate the percentage of Na_2CO_3 (anhydrous) in the sample as received.

(b) Calculate the percentage of Na_2CO_3 in the air-dried sample.

(c) If the price of the decahydrate is 55.0% of the price of the air-dried material, (1) which form is more economical in terms of Na_2CO_3? (2) What is the percent saving in cost by buying one form rather than the other?

16-7 Combustion of 0.4240 g of a pure organic compound gives 0.6906 g of CO_2 and 0.2355 g of H_2O.

(a) Calculate % C in the compound.

(b) Calculate % H in the compound.

(c) Assuming the remainder of the compound to be oxygen, calculate the empirical formula of the organic compound.

16-8 Combustion of 0.5000 g of a pure organic compound gives 1.221 g of CO_2 and 0.3332 g of H_2O.

(a) Calculate % C and % H in the compound.

(b) The remainder of the compound is nitrogen; calculate the empirical formula of the compound.

(c) The molecular weight of the compound is approximately 100. What is the molecular formula of the compound?

16-9   Moisture in an organic liquid is determined by the calcium carbide method; a 1-g sample gives 18.0 ml of gas measured at 750 mm mercury pressure and 30°C. Calculate percent water in the sample.

16-10   Water is determined in a 10-g sample of mayonnaise by the Bidwell-Sterling (distillation) method. The water collected measured 3.45 ml at 25°C; the density of water at this temperature is 0.997. Calculate the percentage of water in the sample.

16-11   An organic compound containing C, H, N, and O gives the following results on analysis: Combustion of a 0.2000-g sample gives 0.4290 g of CO_2. Combustion of a 0.5000-g sample gives 0.1830 g of H_2O. A 0.4000-g sample gives 40.92 ml of nitrogen gas measured at 30°C and 750 mm. Oxygen is calculated by difference. Derive the empirical formula of the compound.

17

GRAVIMETRIC DETERMINATION OF CHLORIDE (SILVER)

Chloride ion in solution is determined by precipitation with silver nitrate from a solution slightly acidic with nitric acid. After a suitable digestion period the silver chloride is filtered on an inert filter, washed, and dried to constant weight. When proper procedure is followed, practically all sources of error can be eliminated, and the method is one of the most exact of all gravimetric determinations. The following discussion includes some of the possible sources of error, and methods whereby they may be avoided or eliminated.

Interfering Substances

In almost any gravimetric separation and determination, interfering substances can be classified into three categories: (1) substances that contaminate the precipitate by forming an insoluble product with the reagent, or by being coprecipitated; (2) substances that prevent complete precipitation of the desired constituent; (3) substances that react with the precipitation and/or the weighing form of the desired constituent. In any of these categories there may be different modes of action that result in the main effect stated above. Specific interferences in the determination of chloride are mentioned below.

1. Other Anions Precipitated by Silver Ion in Acid Solution. The silver salts of the anions bromide, iodide, thiocyanate, cyanide, and sulfide are insoluble in dilute nitric acid. If any of these anions are present in the sample for chloride analysis, their separation is required before precipitating chloride.

2. Anions Forming Silver Salts Soluble in Nitric Acid. In neutral solution silver ion forms insoluble compounds with many common anions, namely,

212

carbonate, phosphate, arsenate, arsenite, chromate, oxalate, and hydroxide. Although silver compounds of these anions are soluble in dilute nitric acid, coprecipitation of these anions is a possible source of error.

3. Heavy Metal Ions Having Insoluble Chlorides. Mercury(I) chloride, Hg_2Cl_2, is insoluble in water and dilute nitric acid. Lead chloride is also somewhat insoluble, although it will transpose to the less soluble silver chloride when excess silver ion is added. Removal of mercury(I), and in fact most heavy metal ions, can be effected by fusion with sodium carbonate or by boiling with concentrated sodium carbonate solution.

4. Heavy Metal Ions Giving Insoluble Hydrolysis Products. Compounds of antimony(III), bismuth(III), and tin(IV) hydrolyze extensively to give insoluble products SbOCl, BiOCl, and $SnO_2 \cdot xH_2O$, respectively.

5. Cations Forming Stable Chloro Complexes. Certain cations, notably mercury(II) and chromium(III), form chloro complexes (e.g., $HgCl_4^{--}$) that are so stable that not all the chloride content can be precipitated by silver ion.

6. Reducing Agents. Substances that can reduce silver ion or silver chloride to elemental silver must be absent. Tin(II), hypophosphites, and many organic compounds such as formaldehyde, hydroquinone, and cellulose, reduce silver compounds. Organic matter is removed, prior to analysis, by strong ignition of the sample.

Precipitation and Digestion

The precipitation is made from dilute solution of the chloride, corresponding to 0.2 to 0.5 g of sample in 150 ml of water. If the sample solution is alkaline, it is first neutralized with nitric acid, then an excess of 1 ml of 6 M nitric acid is added; this gives a solution about 0.04 M in nitric acid. From this point on, the sample must be worked in subdued light, for reasons given later in this chapter. To the solution 0.1 M silver nitrate solution is added to complete precipitation and to provide a slight excess of silver ion. Precipitation is always made from cold solution. If the solution is hot, or if too much nitric acid is present, chloride ion may be oxidized by the nitric acid.

The solubility of silver chloride is so slight that solubility loss is negligible except for the most exacting analysis. The solubility is increased by high temperature and by high concentration of nitric acid. A *slight* excess of silver ion decreases the solubility by common ion effect. The solubility of silver chloride in various solutions is shown in Table 17-1.

Silver chloride precipitated from solution always forms a colloidal system, by rapid agglomeration of the many small nuclei formed. The colloid has minimum stability at the stoichiometric point of the reaction; as this point is approached by the addition of silver nitrate reagent, the colloidal particles coagulate

Table 17-1   Solubility of Silver Chloride

Solvent	Solubility, mg/liter
Water, at 25°	1.9
Water, at 100°	21
HNO_3, 0.04 M, at 25°	2.3
HNO_3, 1 M, at 25°	3.3
$AgNO_3$, 0.001 M, at 25°	0.06

to a considerable extent. The mixture is digested just under the boiling point and then set aside for the precipitate to settle. When properly coagulated, the precipitate should settle rapidly after stirring, leaving a clear supernatant solution. Nitric acid in the solution aids in the coagulation; the displacement of adsorbed silver ions by hydrogen ions is also important in minimizing coprecipitation of silver nitrate.

Filtration and Washing

Silver chloride, and also the excess silver ion in solution, is easily reduced by organic matter, especially at elevated temperature; for this reason filter paper, which would have to be burned off later, cannot be used. Filtration is made through filter crucibles of sintered glass, porous porcelain, or asbestos (Gooch filter). The precipitate, being a flocculated colloid, will easily peptize and run through the filter as the coagulating electrolyte is washed away. The wash water must therefore contain a little nitric acid to prevent peptization. Washing must be continued until the washings are free from silver ion as shown by a negative test with chloride.

Drying

Silver chloride is usually oven dried at 110–130°C, which removes all but a trace of water. Silver chloride is stable well above its melting point (455°C), and can be fused for removal of the last trace of moisture if the situation demands it. At high temperature, dust and other organic matter must be scrupulously excluded; reduction by these substances is rapid and extensive.

Photochemical Decomposition

The silver halides are sensitive to light (this property is the basis of photography). The photochemical action is very pronounced by light of the shorter wavelengths. While working with silver chloride, precautions must be taken to protect the precipitate from exposure to direct sunlight or to strong artificial light, especially of the blue or daylight variety. Even when working in subdued light, the silver chloride is seldom pure white but a gray-purple color. The change is usually superficial and does not represent a significant weight change for ordinary analysis.

For simplicity, the photochemical decomposition of silver chloride may be represented as

$$2AgCl \rightarrow 2Ag + Cl_2$$

Any decomposition leads to low results if it occurs *after* the filtration and washing, or at any time during the determination of silver ion by the converse reaction. However, before filtration in the determination of chloride, the chlorine undergoes disproportionation in the solution:

$$3Cl_2 + 3H_2O \rightarrow 6H^+ + ClO_3^- + 5Cl^-$$

and the chloride ion reacts with the excess silver ion in the solution to form silver chloride. Therefore, if photochemical decomposition of silver chloride occurs before filtration in a chloride determination, the results are too high. (The student should justify this conclusion by considering the over-all stoichiometry.)

Additional Applications

1. Standardization of Hydrochloric Acid. Hydrochloric acid for use in acidimetry can be standardized by weighing the silver chloride obtained from an accurately measured volume of the acid. Obviously, the method is indirect for hydrogen ion.

2. Other Anions Precipitated in Nitric Acid Solution. The anions bromide, iodide, and thiocyanate can be precipitated and weighed as the silver salt. There are other superior methods of analysis for iodide and thiocyanate, so the gravimetric method is seldom used for these anions.

3. Mixture of Two Halides. Two halides in the same sample, for example, chloride and bromide, can be precipitated and weighed together as their silver salts, which are then reduced by hydrogen at elevated temperature, and the residue of metallic silver is weighed. Alternatively, the mixed silver salts can be heated in chlorine, and the loss in weight determined.

4. Oxidized Forms of Chlorine. Any of the oxidized forms of chlorine (i.e., Cl_2, ClO^-, ClO_2^-, ClO_3^-, ClO_4^-) can be determined by reduction to chloride ion which is then precipitated and weighed as silver chloride. Sulfur dioxide or sulfite ion will reduce all of them except perchlorate; nitrite ion reduces them all.

For example,

$$Cl_2 + 2H_2O + SO_2 \rightarrow 4H^+ + SO_4^{--} + 2Cl^-$$

$$ClO_3^- + 3SO_3^{--} \rightarrow 3SO_4^{--} + Cl^-$$

$$ClO_4^- + 4NO_2^- \rightarrow 4NO_3^- + Cl^-$$

"Chlorine water" is reduced by warm ammonium hydroxide:

$$3Cl_2 + 8NH_4OH \rightarrow N_2 + 8H_2O + 6NH_4^+ + 6Cl^-$$

The solution is then acidified with nitric acid and the chloride is precipitated in the usual way.

5. Organic Halogen Compounds. Halogens in organic compounds can be converted to inorganic halide by (*a*) fusion with sodium peroxide, or (*b*) heating under pressure (in a closed tube) with fuming nitric acid (method of Carius). The halide is then determined in the usual way.

6. Anions Having Acid-Soluble Silver Salts. Anions such as chromate, phosphate, arsenate, and carbonate form silver salts insoluble in water but soluble in nitric acid. In order to determine one of these ions, it is precipitated with silver nitrate in neutral solution, and filtered and washed. The precipitate is dissolved quantitatively from the filter with nitric acid, and the solution containing the silver ion is precipitated with chloride ion, and silver chloride is weighed. The method is therefore an application of the determination of silver ion and, indirectly, of the anion first precipitated.

DETERMINATION OF SILVER

The same general conditions and possible sources of error as in the chloride determination prevail also in the determination of silver by chloride. The precipitant is hydrochloric acid, the hydrogen ion of which serves the same function as the nitric acid in the chloride determination, in preventing precipitation of silver salts of anions of weak acids, in helping coagulate the precipitate, and in preventing its peptization during washing. A *slight* excess of hydrochloric acid is desirable to decrease the solubility of silver chloride by common ion effect. A large excess is to be avoided because of the increased solubility of the precipitate through formation of soluble chloro-complexes of silver:

$$AgCl + Cl^- \rightarrow AgCl_2^- \quad (AgCl_3^{--}, \text{ etc.})$$

Table 17-2 shows the solubility of silver chloride in hydrochloric acid solution and in sodium chloride solution of various concentrations; the solubility in water is included for comparison.

Table 17-2   Solubility of Silver Chloride in Chloride Solutions at 25°C

HCl Concentration mole/liter	Solubility of AgCl, mg/liter	NaCl Concentration, mole/liter	Solubility of AgCl mg/liter
(Water)	1.9	(Water)	1.9
0.01	0.002	0.004	0.10
0.05	0.003	0.036	0.27
0.10	55	0.50	4.0
		1.93	56

PROBLEMS

(For other problems on halogens, see Chapter 15, problems 3, 4, 5, 11, 13, 14, 18, 24, 26.)

17-1   A sample weighing 0.3550 g gives a silver chloride precipitate that weighs 0.4545 g. Calculate (*a*) the percentage of Cl; (*b*) the percentage of NaCl.

Ans. (*a*) 31.67.   (*b*) 52.20.

17-2   What must be the percentage of KCl in a sample so that the weight of AgCl obtained is equal to the weight of sample taken?   *Ans.* 52.04.

17-3   A sample of impure trisodium phosphate weighing 0.8000 g is just neutralized with nitric acid. An excess of silver nitrate is added to precipitate Ag_3PO_4, which is filtered off and washed free from excess silver ion. The precipitate is dissolved in nitric acid, and the silver ion is precipitated as AgCl, which weighs 1.2580 g. Calculate the phosphate content of the sample as percentages of (*a*) Na_3PO_4; (*b*) P_2O_5.

Ans. (*a*) 59.96.   (*b*) 25.96.

17-4   A sample of mixed AgCl and AgBr weighing 0.8000 g loses 0.1066 g when heated in chlorine. Calculate the weight of AgCl and of AgBr in the mixture.

Ans. 0.3497 g AgCl, 0.4503 g AgBr.

17-5   What weight of sample of impure KBr should be taken for analysis so that when the silver bromide is heated in chlorine, the percentage of KBr is represented by one-half the weight loss in milligrams?

17-6   What weight of silver halide precipitate can be obtained from 1.2000 g of mixture that contains 45.50% $BaCl_2 \cdot 2H_2O$, 43.70% KBr, and 5.80% NaI, the remainder of the sample being inert?

17-7   A 0.4500-g sample containing only $BaCl_2$ and KCl gives 0.7755 g of AgCl.

(*a*) Calculate the percentage of KCl in the sample.

(*b*) Calculate the barium content as percentage of BaO.

17-8   0.6500 g of mixture containing only AgBr and AgI is reduced in hydrogen, yielding a residue of metallic silver weighing 0.3274 g. Calculate the percentage of Br in the mixture.

17-9   A 0.5000-g mixture of AgCl, AgBr, and AgI is heated in an atmosphere of bromine, after which the residue weighs 0.4500 g. This residue is heated in chlorine, after which the residue weighs 0.3557 g.

(*a*) Calculate the grams of AgCl, AgBr, and AgI in the original mixture.

(*b*) Calculate the weight of residue that would remain after reduction to metallic silver.

17-10   A sample of chromite ore weighing 0.8000 g is fused with sodium peroxide. The melt is leached with water, boiled, and filtered to remove iron as its hydrous oxide. The filtrate containing chromate is neutralized, and the chromium is precipitated as Ag_2CrO_4. The washed precipitate is dissolved in nitric acid, and the silver ion is precipitated as AgCl, which weighs 0.3264 g. Calculate the percentages of (a) Cr, and (b) Cr_2O_3 in the sample.

17-11   An 0.8000-g mixture containing only LiCl and KCl is converted to the mixed sulfates, Li_2SO_4 and K_2SO_4, which weigh 0.9606 g. Calculate the percentages of LiCl and KCl in the mixture.

17-12   Calculate the weight of AgCl that could be obtained from the mixed chlorides of Problem 17-11.

17-13   A 0.4000-g sample of a pure organic bromine compound is decomposed to convert the bromine content to bromide, which yields 0.7440 g of AgBr.

(a) Calculate the percentage of Br in the compound.

(b) If the compound contains 17.99% C and 3.02% H, what is the empirical formula of the compound?

17-14   A certain sample contains $KClO_3$, $KClO_4$, and possibly inert matter. An 0.8000-g sample of the material is reduced with sulfite, and the chloride is precipitated as AgCl, which weighs 0.5862 g. A 0.6000-g sample is reduced with nitrite, and the chloride is precipitated as AgCl, which weighs 0.5172 g. Calculate the percentages of $KClO_3$ and $KClO_4$ in the sample.

17-15   In what ratio (grams) must LiBr and KBr be mixed so that the mixture contains the same percentage of bromine as pure NaBr?

17-16   A 0.4500-g sample of silver alloy is dissolved in nitric acid, and the silver ion is precipitated as AgCl, which weighs 0.2392 g. Calculate the percentage of Ag in the alloy.

18

DETERMINATION OF
SULFATE (BARIUM)

Sulfate ion in solution is determined by precipitation with barium chloride from a hot solution slightly acidified with hydrochloric acid: $SO_4^{--} + Ba^{++} \rightarrow BaSO_4$. The precipitate is digested and filtered hot, washed, ignited, and weighed as $BaSO_4$.

The determination of sulfate as barium sulfate is fraught with difficulties due to coprecipitation of other substances. Quantitatively exact determinations are obtained only from solution of sulfuric acid or sodium sulfate under well-defined conditions; even then, significant errors may occur.

Interfering Substances

1. Anions of Weak Acids.   Barium sulfate is the only common water-insoluble barium salt that is also insoluble in strong acid. Precipitation of other water-insoluble barium salts (e.g., carbonate, phosphate, chromate, etc.) is prevented by hydrochloric acid in the solution from which sulfate is precipitated.

2. Cations Forming Insoluble Sulfates.   Barium, strontium, and lead sulfates are insoluble, and calcium sulfate is sparingly soluble, in water and acids. If these cations are present along with sulfate, as in some minerals, the sample is fused with sodium carbonate; the melt is extracted with water and the insoluble carbonates are filtered off. After acidifying the solution with hydrochloric acid and boiling out carbon dioxide, sulfate is precipitated in the usual way.

3. Heavy Metal Ions.   Almost all cations are more or less coprecipitated with barium sulfate. In general, the higher the oxidation number of the cation, the greater the coprecipitation. Hydrolysis of certain high-valent cations may result in precipitation of their basic sulfates. Sodium carbonate fusion will remove most of the heavy metals, and also the alkaline earths and magnesium. If iron-(III) is the principal cation interference and it is not feasible to remove it, reduction to iron(II) with metallic zinc or iron is advantageous; iron(II) is coprecipitated much less than is iron(III). The presence of chromium(III) in the solution may prevent complete precipitation of barium sulfate on account of the great stability of sulfato complexes of chromium. Transposition of the sulfato complex to the acetato complex displaces the sulfate ion so it can be precipitated.

4. Nitrate and Chlorate. These anions are coprecipitated, as their barium salts, to such an extent as to introduce very large errors. Nitrate and/or chlorate in the original sample can be removed by repeated evaporation with hydrochloric acid:

$$2NO_3^- + 6Cl^- + 8H^+ \rightarrow 2NO + 3Cl_2 + 4H_2O$$

$$ClO_3^- + 5Cl^- + 6H^+ \rightarrow 3Cl_2 + 3H_2O$$

Precipitation and Digestion

When barium sulfate is formed slowly from dilute solutions, relatively large crystalline particles are formed. The solubility of barium sulfate at 100°C is about 50% greater than at room temperature. The second ionization of sulfuric acid is slightly weak; hence, hydrogen ion lowers the sulfate ion concentration to some extent and thus increases the solubility of barium sulfate:

$$BaSO_4 + H^+ \rightarrow Ba^{++} + HSO_4^-$$

By precipitating barium sulfate in hot solution and in the presence of some hydrochloric acid, the relative supersaturation is decreased somewhat and a better precipitate is obtained.

Table 18-1 shows the solubility of barium sulfate in water at different temperatures, and in hydrochloric acid and in nitric acid of different concentrations. In addition to increased solubility by formation of HSO_4^-, the solubility at high concentration of acids is also increased on account of the high ionic strength of the solution.

If sulfuric acid is being analyzed, no hydrochloric acid is added. If a solid sample is insoluble in water but soluble in acid, or if the sample is soluble to give an alkaline solution, hydrochloric acid is added dropwise just to dissolve the sample or neutralize the solution, plus an excess of acid to make the solution approximately 0.06 *M* in hydrochloric acid. The solution is heated to incipient boiling, and precipitated by the addition of a slight excess of barium chloride solution. The precipitate is digested for an hour or more (overnight is preferable) at a temperature somewhat below the boiling point, to age and purify the precipitate.

Table 18-1   Solubility of Barium Sulfate[a]
(Solubility in milligrams of $BaSO_4$ per liter)

Temp., °C.	Solubility in Water	Molarity of Acid	Solubility in HCl	Solubility in HNO_3
0	1.2	0.05	—	14
10	2.0	0.10	10	26
20	2.4	0.30	29	76
30	2.8	0.50	47	123
50	3.4	1.0	87	237
100	3.9	2.0	146	393

[a] Values taken from A. Seidell, *Solubilities of Inorganic and Metal Organic Compounds*, 3rd ed., Princeton, N. J., Van Nostrand, 1940, vol. I. The solubility of barium sulfate determined under different conditions by various workers varies widely. The solubility of very small particles of freshly precipitated barium sulfate is considerably greater than that of the larger particles of well-aged precipitate. Literature values for the solubility may vary several-fold, depending upon the precipitation and digestion conditions.

Filtration and Washing

A filter medium of high retentivity (fine porosity) is required. The barium sulfate is filtered hot, by decantation, and washed with hot water until the washings are free from chloride ion.

Ignition

The paper containing the barium sulfate is dried, charred at low temperature, and the carbon is burned off at higher temperature with good access of air to the crucible. If oxidizing conditions do not prevail, the barium sulfate may be reduced to barium sulfide by carbon or carbon monoxide from the paper, or by reducing gases from the flame, and results are too low. The sulfide can be brought back to sulfate either by heating with good access of air or by metathesis with one or two drops of concentrated sulfuric acid followed by *careful* volatilization of the excess sulfuric acid using a radiator or air bath.

Coprecipitated Substances

Barium sulfate is not sufficiently soluble in any reagent to permit dissolution and reprecipitation as a means of decreasing contamination. The behavior on ignition of substances that may be coprecipitated with barium sulfate and their influence on the results of analysis for sulfate are shown in Table 18-2. Errors

Table 18-2 Effect of Contaminants on Sulfate Determination (as $BaSO_4$)

Contaminant	Ignition Products	Error
$BaCl_2$	Only slightly volatile	Positive
H_2SO_4	H_2O, SO_3	Negative
Na_2SO_4, K_2SO_4	Stable	Negative
$NaHSO_4$, $KHSO_4$	Na_2SO_4 or K_2SO_4, H_2O, SO_3	Large negative
$(NH_4)_2SO_4$	NH_3, H_2O, SO_3	Large negative
Heavy metal sulfates	MO (M_2O_3, etc.), SO_3	Variable[a]
$Ba(NO_3)_2$	BaO, NO_2, O_2	Positive
$Ba(ClO_3)_2$	$BaCl_2$, O_2	Positive

[a] Sign and magnitude of the error depends upon relative weights of SO_3 volatilized and metal oxide residue; the error is usually negative.

due to nitrate, chlorate, and ammonium ions are so serious that their removal is mandatory before precipitating barium sulfate. Nitrate and chlorate ions are removed as shown earlier. Ammonium ion is removed by evaporation with nitric acid:

$$NH_4^+ + NO_3^- \rightarrow N_2O + 2H_2O$$

followed by removal of excess nitric acid with hydrochloric acid.

Other Applications

Any form of sulfur can be determined by conversion to sulfate ion for precipitation as barium sulfate. Sulfur, sulfides, and sulfites are oxidized to sulfate, and peroxydisulfates (persulfates), e.g., $K_2S_2O_8$, are reduced to sulfate. (For the reactions indicated in this section, the student should write the ionic equations, using the ion-electron half-reaction method where applicable.) A common application is the analysis of sulfide ores and minerals.

1. *Sulfides.* The treatment to be used depends primarily upon the solubility of the sulfide.

a. Water-soluble sulfides. Hydrogen sulfide gas is absorbed in ammoniacal hydrogen peroxide solution. Ammonium ion is removed (for the reason and by the method given earlier), and the sulfate is determined in the usual way. Alkali metal sulfides are oxidized with hydrogen peroxide (without ammonia) or with bromine water.

b. Acid-soluble sulfides, such as those of zinc, manganese, iron, and cadmium, may be treated with hydrochloric acid, and the hydrogen sulfide absorbed quantitatively in ammoniacal hydrogen peroxide, as in (*a*).

c. Acid-insoluble sulfides, such as HgS, FeS_2 (pyrites), and CuS, and many mixed sulfide or double sulfide minerals require more drastic means for their decomposition.

(1) *Wet oxidation.* The oxidizing agents commonly used are aqua regia, followed by potassium chlorate if any free sulfur remains, or bromine dissolved in carbon tetrachloride, followed by concentrated nitric acid. Heavy metal ions are removed by precipitation, the solution is repeatedly evaporated with hydrochloric acid to decompose nitrate ion, and the sulfate is determined in the usual way.

(2) *Fusion.* The sample is fused with an alkaline oxidizing flux. The fluxes most commonly used are sodium peroxide, or sodium carbonate plus potassium nitrate, or sodium carbonate plus potassium chlorate. After extracting the melt with water, insolubles (heavy metal hydrous oxides or carbonates) are filtered off. The solution is evaporated with hydrochloric acid, usually with the addition of some bromine water to complete the oxidation of any sulfide or sulfite that may still be present, and the sulfate is determined as usual.

2. *Sulfur in organic material.*

a. Wet oxidation is effected by heating with fuming nitric acid under pressure in a sealed tube (Carius method); oxidation to sulfate (sulfuric acid) occurs, and subsequent treatment is the same as for inorganic samples.

b. Fusion with a mixture of potassium hydroxide and potassium nitrate (in a silver crucible) converts the sulfur to sulfate; analysis is continued in the usual way.

3. *Sulfite.* Sulfur dioxide, sulfurous acid, and sulfites are easily oxidized to sulfate ion; hydrogen peroxide or bromine water is generally used.

4. *Peroxydisulfate.* For gravimetric analysis, the peroxydisulfate solution is acidified and boiled for about ten minutes:

$$S_2O_8^{--} + 2H_2O \rightarrow 2SO_4^{--} + 2H^+ + H_2O_2$$

$$2H_2O_2 \rightarrow 2H_2O + O_2$$

Sulfate is then determined in the usual way.

DETERMINATION OF BARIUM, LEAD, AND STRONTIUM

Barium

The gravimetric determination of barium as barium sulfate is quite obviously subject to many of the same difficulties as the determination of sulfate. A moderate excess of sulfuric acid, used as the precipitant, decreases the solubility of barium sulfate by common ion effect, but other acids should not be present in high concentration on account of their effect in increasing the solubility of barium sulfate.

Interfering Substances. When barium is to be analyzed in a sample that also contains lead, strontium, or calcium, separation of the cations is required. Lead may be separated with hydrogen sulfide, or by electrolytic deposition of lead dioxide on the anode. Barium is separated from strontium and calcium by double precipitation as barium chromate from hot solution buffered with ammonium acetate. The barium chromate precipitate can be ignited and weighed as such, although this method for the determination of barium is not used except when separation from strontium and/or calcium is required.

Coprecipitation. Precipitation of barium sulfate for the determination of barium is subject to contamination with the same substances as in the determination of sulfate. The student should refer to Table 18-2 and deduce the nature of the error, keeping in mind that *barium* is being determined.

Lead

The precipitation of lead ion from solution is made by double evaporation with sulfuric acid to copious fumes of sulfur trioxide. After the solution has cooled, it is diluted with water, using 100 ml for each 0.1 g of lead present. An equal volume of 95% ethanol is added, and the mixture is allowed to stand at least one hour (overnight is better). The precipitate is filtered in a filter crucible; paper would partially reduce the lead sulfate during ignition. The precipitate is washed with 2% sulfuric acid, and ignited to 500–600°C (in a muffle furnace or radiator) to constant weight. At much higher temperatures, the lead sulfate may lose some sulfur trioxide. Some solubility data for lead sulfate are shown in Table 18-3.

Table 18-3 Solubility of Lead Sulfate (Milligrams of $PbSO_4$ per liter).

| Water | | H_2SO_4 (25°C) | | Ethanol (25°C) | |
Temperature	Solubility	Molar Concentration	Solubility	Volume Percent	Solubility
0°	33	0.00	45	0	45.
10°	38	0.01	5	10	11
20°	43	0.10	2.2	20	4
30°	48	0.50	2.0	30	1.5
40°	53	1.0	1.6	40	0.5
50°	57	2.0	0.5	50	0.3
		7.0	1.2	60	0.2

Strontium

The solubility of strontium sulfate in water at 25°C is about 135 mg per liter. For the determination of strontium as sulfate, sulfuric acid is added in tenfold excess over the amount of strontium present, and alcohol equal to the volume of the solution is added to decrease the solubility. Washing with 50% alcohol containing some sulfuric acid, and finally with 95% alcohol (to displace the acid) is required. The precipitate is ignited, and weighed as $SrSO_4$.

PROBLEMS

(For other problems on sulfate, see Chapter 15, Problems 10, 12, 15, 19, 25.)

18-1 A bottle labeled merely "anhydrous iron ammonium sulfate" could contain either $Fe_2(SO_4)_3 \cdot (NH_4)_2SO_4$ or $FeSO_4 \cdot (NH_4)_2SO_4$. A 0.5000-g sample of the solid gives 0.8783 g of $BaSO_4$. Which iron salt is it? Prove by appropriate calculations.

Ans. Ferric.

18-2 A sample of impure As_2S_3 weighing 0.4400 g is quantitatively oxidized to sulfate. If the sample contains 44.45% As_2S_3, what weight of $BaSO_4$ is obtained?

Ans. 0.5566 g.

18-3 What weight of pure Li_2SO_4 should be mixed with 1.0000 g of pure K_2SO_4 so that the mixture contains the same percent of sulfate as pure Na_2SO_4?

Ans. 0.6333 g.

18-4 A 0.5000-g sample containing sulfate and some perchlorate, and possibly inert matter, is precipitated with barium ion and gives a precipitate weighing 0.5159 g. It is suspected that some perchlorate coprecipitated with the barium sulfate. The precipitate is fused with sodium carbonate, leached with water, filtered, and the filtrate is reduced with nitrite; addition of silver nitrate to the acidified solution gives 25.0 mg of AgCl.

(*a*) Calculate the percentage of K_2SO_4 in the sample, based on the weight of the first precipitate.

(*b*) Calculate the percentage of K_2SO_4 in the sample, assuming the coprecipitated material to be $Ba(ClO_4)_2$.

(*c*) Calculate the true percentage of K_2SO_4 in the sample if the coprecipitated barium perchlorate is converted to barium chloride during ignition of the precipitate.

(*d*) What is the percent relative error on the K_2SO_4 content if the correction for impurity is not made?

18-5 A one-liter sample of water from a sulfur spring is boiled to expel the sulfur compounds, which are trapped in ammoniacal hydrogen peroxide to oxidize them to sulfate. After acidification of the solution, barium chloride is added, yielding 0.4567 g of $BaSO_4$. Calculate the milligrams of sulfur per liter.

18-6 Calculate the milligrams of precipitate that would be lost by washing a precipitate of $SrSO_4$ with 100 ml of water.

18-7 A 0.2750-g sample of pure sulfide of antimony, Sb_xS_y, is oxidized to sulfate, which yields 0.7951 g of $BaSO_4$. In a separate analysis for antimony content, a 0.5000–g sample of the antimony sulfide yields 0.3808 g of Sb_2O_4. Calculate the formula for the antimony sulfide.

18-8 0.7800 g of mixture containing only K_2SO_4 and $(NH_4)_2SO_4$ yields 1.1943 g of $BaSO_4$. Calculate the percentage of N in the mixture.

18-9 A 0.3428-g sample of a pure oxide of lead yields 0.4550 g of $PbSO_4$. Calculate the formula of the lead oxide.

18-10 White lead, used as a paint base, is a basic lead carbonate, $(PbCO_3)_2 \cdot Pb(OH)_2 \cdot$ A 0.4000-g sample of white lead is dissolved in acid, and precipitated as $PbSO_4$ which weighs 0.4321 g. Assuming that no other lead compound is present in the sample, calculate the percent purity of the white lead.

18-11 A chrome ore weighing 0.6500 g is oxidized to chromate and is precipitated as $PbCrO_4$, which is dissolved in acid and precipitated as $PbSO_4$, which weighs 0.6227 g. Calculate the percentage of Cr_2O_3 in the ore.

18-12 A mixture containing only $BaSO_4$ and $SrSO_4$ weighs 0.6000 g and contains 15.00% sulfur. Calculate the percentage of Ba and Sr in the mixture.

19

OTHER COMMON GRAVIMETRIC DETERMINATIONS

I. DETERMINATION OF SILICON

Silicon, the second most abundant element in the outer portion of the earth, is never found free in nature. Silica (silicon dioxide) occurs in varying degrees of purity, and silica or silicates will be found in notable amounts in all important rocks except the carbonates. Silicon is added to iron and copper alloys to make them corrosion resistant.

Decomposition of Silica and Silicate Samples

Silica is resistant to chemical attack by all mineral acids except hydrofluoric acid. When silicon is a minor constituent, as with many ores and minerals, the sample is attacked by acid (HCl or $HClO_4$), the silica remaining insoluble. The residue, or the original sample if it contains a large fraction of acid insolubles, is transposed by sodium carbonate fusion:

$$MSiO_3 + Na_2CO_3 \rightarrow MO + CO_2 + Na_2SiO_3$$

In limestone analysis, ignition prior to acid attack transposes silica to an acid-soluble silicate:

$$SiO_2 + CaCO_3 \rightarrow CO_2 + CaSiO_3$$

After carbonate fusion the melt is treated directly with hydrochloric acid.

Separation

Silicic acid (hydrous silica) is one of the weakest of all inorganic acids, and when formed by metathesis it is one of the most hydrophilic of inorganic colloids.

227

In order to separate silica, the hydrochloric acid containing the colloidal hydrous silica is evaporated to dryness and the residue is baked at 110–120°C for about an hour, to give a granular product approximating the composition $SiO_2 \cdot \frac{1}{2}H_2O$, which can be retained by a filter. Alternatively, the silica can be dehydrated by evaporation of the solution to strong fuming with sulfuric or perchloric acid. The silica residue is taken up with concentrated hydrochloric acid, then diluted and boiled. The hot solution is filtered through paper, and washed with very dilute hydrochloric acid to prevent peptization of the silica and hydrolysis of heavy metal cations. Some silica almost invariably passes into the filtrate, and a second evaporation and baking is required for its recovery.

Ignition

The paper is burned off and the silica is ignited finally at the full temperature of a Meker burner. The ignited residue seldom consists of pure silica; it is reported, therefore, as "uncorrected silica" or as "silica and insolubles."

Corrected Silica.   The residue from above is evaporated with hydrofluoric acid and sulfuric acid in a platinum crucible, in order to volatilize silicon tetrafluoride. The equations below illustrate the changes that occur; assume the residue of SiO_2 to be contaminated with Fe_2O_3 and $Fe_2(SiO_3)_3$ (i.e., $Fe_2O_3 \cdot 3SiO_2$).

$$SiO_2 + 4HF \rightarrow 2H_2O + SiF_4$$

$$Fe_2O_3 + 6HF \rightarrow 2FeF_3 + 3H_2O$$

$$Fe_2(SiO_3)_3 + 18HF \rightarrow 2FeF_3 + 9H_2O + 3SiF_4$$

$$2FeF_3 + 3H_2SO_4 \rightarrow Fe_2(SO_4)_3 + 6HF$$

$$Fe_2(SO_4)_3 \rightarrow Fe_2O_3 + 3SO_3$$

The iron impurity is then in the same form, Fe_2O_3, as in the original residue, and the loss in weight therefore represents SiO_2, "corrected silica."

Errors Due to Boron and Fluoride

Boron in the sample is always carried down as boric acid with the hydrous silica. The boric oxide formed on ignition is also volatilized in the hydrofluoric acid treatment:

$$2H_3BO_3 \rightarrow 3H_2O + B_2O_3$$

$$B_2O_3 + 6HF \rightarrow 3H_2O + 2BF_3$$

and this loss in weight would be counted with the silica. Separation of boron may be made on the silica before its dehydration, by treatment of the nearly dry residue with methanol, to volatilize trimethyl borate:

$$H_3BO_3 + 3CH_3OH \rightarrow 3H_2O + (CH_3)_3BO_3$$

Fluorides present in more than traces result in loss of silicon as silicon tetra-fluoride in the original acid treatment of the sample and evaporation for separation of silica. If fluorides are present, platinum ware must be used for de-composition of the sample, and most of the loss of silicon can be prevented by covering the dish with a platinum cover to keep the atmosphere in the dish saturated with water vapor. Hydrolysis of the silicon fluoride occurs:

$$SiF_4 + 2H_2O \rightarrow SiO_2 + 4HF$$

and the hydrogen fluoride is volatilized by the use of perchloric acid heated to copious fuming.

II. DETERMINATION OF IRON

Iron, the second most abundant metallic element, occurs principally in the form of oxides, carbonates, sulfides, and mixed sulfides. In trace amounts it is very widely distributed in nature. Ferrous metals such as iron and steel are important industrial materials; usually they are not analyzed for iron content, but for alloying constituents such as chromium, manganese, cobalt, vanadium, molybdenum, and tungsten.

Decomposition of Ores

Iron ores are always dissolved in hydrochloric acid, or are attacked by fusion with alkali bisulfate (pyrosulfate). The ores are almost unattacked by nitric or sulfuric acid, or by alkaline fusion. Minerals, especially the sulfides, in which iron is not a major constituent are often attacked by nitric acid, aqua regia, or alkaline oxidizing fusions.

Precipitation

Iron(II) hydroxide is sufficiently soluble (K_{sp} about 10^{-15}) that it cannot be completely precipitated except in moderately alkaline solution. On the other hand, iron(III) hydroxide[1] is very insoluble (K_{sp} about 10^{-37}) and can be precipitated quantitatively even from solution of pH 4. For gravimetric separa-tion, iron is therefore always brought to the $+3$ state by oxidation of any iron(II) with nitric acid, bromine water, or hydrogen peroxide.

Owing to its very small solubility, relative supersaturation of iron(III) hydroxide during precipitation is very great (except when precipitated from homogeneous solution), and the precipitate is a flocculated colloid likely to be

---

[1] The freshly precipitated material is not a true hydroxide of definite Fe : OH ratio of 1 : 3 but rather a hydrous oxide of indefinite composition. In discussion and in writing formulas and equations, however, it is more convenient to represent the precipitate as Fe(OH)$_3$. The same comment applies to other hydrous oxides.

considerably contaminated by adsorbed ions. Ordinarily, the acid solution containing the dilute iron(III) is heated to near boiling, and 1:1 ammonium hydroxide is added until, after good stirring of the solution and blowing away the fumes, the solution smells faintly of ammonia. The ammonium ion formed in the neutralization tends to displace other cations from the counter ion layer, and also prevents the precipitation of magnesium. The mixture is allowed to stand for a short time for the precipitate to settle and is then filtered promptly and washed. The precipitate is dissolved from the filter by hot dilute hydrochloric acid, and the paper is washed well with hot water. The solution containing the iron is reprecipitated with ammonia and is filtered through the same paper.

Interfering Substances. Several other cations precipitate under the same conditions as iron, and certain substances prevent precipitation.

1. *Cations* commonly associated with iron and also precipitated as their hydrous oxides include aluminum, chromium(III), titanium(IV), and manganese. Although manganese(II) is not quantitatively precipitated by ammonia, it is oxidized along with iron(II) if bromine is used as the oxidizing agent, and in any event it is quite easily air-oxidized and precipitated as manganese(IV) hydrous oxide in alkaline solution.

2. *Orthophosphate* forms insoluble $FePO_4$, which would be found as such in the ignited precipitate. Prior to iron analysis, phosphate is removed as ammonium molybdiphosphate (see p. 239). Alternatively, the iron precipitate, after weighing, may be dissolved and analyzed for phosphate, and corrected to iron oxide. Arsenate and vanadate also form insoluble iron(III) salts in ammoniacal solution.

3. *Fluoride* and *pyrophosphate* ions form stable complexes with iron(III), for example FeF_6^{---} and $FeP_2O_7^-$, from which iron(III) hydroxide cannot be precipitated.

4. *Organic hydroxy compounds*, notably tartrate, citrate, glycerol, and sugars, form stable complexes with iron(III), from which the hydroxide is not precipitated. Organic matter is destroyed by ignition of the original sample, or by wet oxidation with nitric acid or aqua regia.

5. *Silica*, which in small amounts escapes prior separation, is carried down with the hydrous iron oxide; silica may also be introduced with the ammonium hydroxide reagent, on account of long storage in glass bottles. If silica contamination of the precipitate is significant, it can be corrected by volatilization with hydrofluoric and sulfuric acids (see p. 228).

Filtration and Washing

Hydrous iron oxide (or *any* gelatinous precipitate) is always filtered on paper of coarse porosity; filtration and first washings should be done by decantation. The solubility of iron(III) hydroxide is so small (about 0.05 mg per liter) that relatively large amounts of hot wash liquid can be used without significant solubility loss. A hot 1% solution of ammonium nitrate is generally used, the electrolyte serving to prevent peptization; washing is continued until the filtrate is free from chloride ion.

Ignition

All the usual precautions regarding ignition in paper should be observed. The final ignition temperature should be about 1000°C. Above about 1100°C some of the iron(III) oxide may be reduced to the magnetic oxide:

$$6Fe_2O_3 \rightarrow O_2 + 4Fe_3O_4$$

Good access of air is required during ignition to prevent reduction of Fe_2O_3 to Fe_3O_4, or even to metallic iron by hot carbon or carbon monoxide from the paper or by reducing gases from the flame.

Any aluminum, chromium, titanium, or manganese in the ammonia precipitate will be present in the ignited residue as Al_2O_3, Cr_2O_3, TiO_2, and Mn_3O_4, respectively. In some analyses, the residue is reported as "mixed oxides" or "R_2O_3," rather than as iron.

Other Applications

The general method for iron applies also to the determination of aluminum, chromium(III), titanium(IV), and manganese(IV) when any one of these elements is present alone. Other methods for the analysis of chromium and manganese are available, hence the ammonia precipitation method is seldom used for these elements. When present with iron in the R_2O_3 precipitate, titanium, manganese, and chromium can be determined spectrophotometrically after dissolution of the precipitate in acid.

Iron is also determined by titrimetric oxidation of iron(II) to iron(III) by potassium permanganate, potassium dichromate, or cerium(IV); these methods are discussed in Chaps. 28 and 30.

III. DETERMINATION OF ALUMINUM

Aluminum is the third most abundant element and the most abundant metallic element. The principal ore is bauxite, $Al_2O_3 \cdot 3H_2O$, from which the metal is obtained by electrolysis in the molten mineral cryolite, Na_3AlF_6. Many silicates containing aluminum are found in nature, some of which (the clays) are widely used in the manufacture of ceramic materials. Aluminum and its alloys are usually analyzed only for the alloying elements or trace components.

Decomposition of Samples

Oxide ores and minerals of aluminum are best decomposed by a mixture of sulfuric, nitric, and hydrofluoric acids. By this treatment silica is volatilized as its tetrafluoride. Excess hydrofluoric acid must be expelled completely, otherwise it would complex the aluminum and prevent its complete precipitation. Aluminosilicate minerals and refractories are decomposed by sodium carbonate fusion. Metallic aluminum is readily dissolved in dilute hydrochloric or sulfuric acid; it is very little attacked by concentrated nitric acid, by which the metal is rendered *passive*. The metal and its alloys are often prepared for analysis by dissolution in sodium hydroxide solution:

$$2Al + 2OH^- + 2H_2O \rightarrow 2AlO_2^- + 3H_2$$

Precipitation

The amphoteric character of aluminum hydroxide,

$$Al(OH)_3 \rightleftarrows Al^{+++} + 3OH^-$$

$$H_3AlO_3 \rightleftarrows H^+ + H_2AlO_3^- \text{ (or } AlO_2^- + H_2O)$$

limits the pH range over which it can be precipitated completely. Precipitation begins at about pH 3 and is complete near the neutral point, but the precipitate starts to redissolve as the pH is further increased. By the use of the base and the acid ionization constants of $Al(OH)_3$, namely, $K_b = 2 \times 10^{-32}$ and $K_a = 4 \times 10^{-13}$, and noting that at minimum solubility $[Al^{+++}] = [H_2AlO_3^-]$, the pH of minimum solubility is calculated to be 5.4. The solubility in acid increases as the third power of the hydrogen ion concentration, whereas the solubility in alkali increases as the first power of the hydroxyl ion concentration.

In actual practice, aluminum hydroxide is usually precipitated by adding ammonium hydroxide to an acidic solution containing the aluminum ion, either in the presence of methyl red indicator (color change between pH 6 and 7), or only to *faint* alkaline reaction followed by boiling for a short time to expel excess ammonia. Presence of considerable ammonium ion in the solution suppresses the ionization of ammonium hydroxide, and also aids in coagulation of the precipitate. The precipitate is filtered by decantation and washed with hot dilute ammonium nitrate solution which has been made neutral to methyl red indicator by addition of a small amount of ammonium hydroxide.

Ignition

Ignition for a few minutes at 1100–1150°C is sufficient to expel moisture from hydrous aluminum oxide; however, the aluminum oxide formed at this temperature is very hygroscopic and troublesome to weigh. Ignition at temperatures above 1200°C converts the aluminum oxide to a different crystal form (corundum), which is not hygroscopic.

Determination of Aluminum with 8-Quinolinol

Aluminum is precipitated quantitatively by 8-quinolinol from acetic acid—acetate buffer solution:

$$Al^{+++} + 3C_9H_7ON \rightarrow Al(C_9H_6ON)_3 + 3H^+$$

The crystalline precipitate is easy to filter and wash; it is weighed after oven drying at 130°C, and is not hygroscopic; it has a favorable gravimetric factor for aluminum. If desired, the determination can be finished titrimetrically (see p. 431). Use of 8-quinolinol is the only good method for the separation of aluminum from beryllium and from phosphate.

Mixed Oxides in Limestone Analysis

In limestone analysis the acidic filtrate from the silica separation contains iron, aluminum, calcium, and magnesium ions, and possible trace constituents. After precipitation by adding ammonium hydroxide, the mixture is boiled to expel excess ammonia and to coagulate the precipitate. The hydrous oxide precipitate in limestone analysis is likely to be badly contaminated with magnesium (why?); therefore a double precipitation of the hydrous oxides is always made.

Prompt filtration is especially important in limestone analysis; absorption of carbon dioxide by the ammoniacal solution forms carbonate ion and may result in premature precipitation of the alkaline earths or magnesium as their carbonates, along with the hydrous oxides. The filtrate from the hydrous oxide separation should be acidified at once. The mixed oxide or "R_2O_3" precipitate of most limestones is due principally to iron and/or aluminum, although traces of titanium and manganese may be present.

IV. DETERMINATION OF CALCIUM

Calcium compounds are abundant in nature. The carbonate exists in many varieties. Other common ores and minerals are $CaCO_3 \cdot MgCO_3$ (dolomite), $CaSO_4 \cdot 2H_2O$ (gypsum), CaF_2 (fluorspar), $Ca_3(PO_4)_2$ (phosphate rock), and CaF_2 or $CaCl_2 \cdot 3Ca_3(PO_4)_2$ (apatite). In natural water, calcium may be present as $Ca(HCO_3)_2$ (temporary hardness) or as $CaSO_4$ (permanent hardness). Calcium compounds have wide industrial uses. Calcium oxide (quicklime) or hydroxide (slaked lime) is the cheapest strong base.

Decomposition of Samples

Most calcium compounds are readily soluble in hydrochloric acid. Calcium sulfate is sparingly soluble in water (about 2 g per liter), but more soluble in hydrochloric acid; it is best attacked by sodium carbonate fusion.

Interfering Substances

The gravimetric determination of calcium by separation as oxalate requires prior removal of all other cations except magnesium and the alkalies. In systematic analysis (e.g., limestone) any fluoride or phosphate in the original solution is precipitated as calcium salt along with the hydrous oxides when the solution is made ammoniacal. The oxalates of barium and strontium are almost as insoluble as calcium oxalate; small amounts of these ions can be tolerated if double precipitation of calcium oxalate is made.

Precipitation and Digestion

Magnesium oxalate forms supersaturated solutions from which it separates only slowly; its solubility is increased by addition of excess oxalate ion, due to formation of a complex, $Mg(C_2O_4)_2^{--}$. The precipitation of calcium oxalate from solution containing also magnesium ion involves several equilibria:

$$HC_2O_4^- \rightleftarrows H^+ + C_2O_4^{--} \begin{cases} + Ca^{++} \rightarrow CaC_2O_4 \\ + Mg^{++} \rightleftarrows MgC_2O_4 \xrightarrow{+C_2O_4^{--}} Mg(C_2O_4)_2^{--} \end{cases}$$

The second ionization of oxalic acid is somewhat weak, consequently calcium oxalate is soluble in strong acids; but the solubility of calcium oxalate in a solution of pH 5 or even 4 is only slightly greater than in neutral solution; the solubility is, of course, decreased by common ion effect of excess oxalate. The precipitation conditions for calcium are therefore excess oxalate to complex the magnesium and decrease the solubility of calcium oxalate, hot solution, less acidic than pH 4, and a short digestion period (one hour). Longer standing, especially if warm, may result in considerable postprecipitation of magnesium oxalate, which is isomorphous with calcium oxalate. A second precipitation is often required to get a sharp separation from magnesium. By precipitation from homogeneous solution, in which the acid is neutralized by hydrolysis of urea (see p. 185), a single precipitation gives a clean separation from magnesium.

Filtration and Washing

If the determination is to be finished by weighing as the carbonate, a filtering crucible is recommended; if the sulfate or fluoride weighing form is to be used, collection on filter paper is required.

The precipitate is washed with cold 0.1% solution of ammonium oxalate until the washings are free from chloride ion. If a titrimetric finish with permanganate is to be used (see p. 402), the preliminary washing with ammonium oxalate must be followed by washing with cold water until the washings give a negative test for oxalate ion.

Weighing Forms

When calcium oxalate precipitate, $CaC_2O_4 \cdot H_2O$, is heated, it undergoes stepwise decomposition at the approximate temperatures indicated:

$$CaC_2O_4 \cdot H_2O \xrightarrow{100-226°C} H_2O + CaC_2O_4 \xrightarrow{420°C}$$

$$CO + CaCO_3 \xrightarrow{660-840°C} CO_2 + CaO$$

Various weighing forms have been proposed, as follows.

1. $CaC_2O_4 \cdot H_2O$ is satisfactory only for rapid determination where moderate error can be tolerated.

2. $CaCO_3$, obtained by heating the oxalate in a muffle furnace at about 500°C.

3. CaO, obtained by strong ignition of the oxalate in a platinum crucible. Cooling in a tightly covered crucible over a good desiccant and rapid weighing as soon as cooled is required.

4. $CaSO_4$, obtained by treating the oxide with sulfuric acid, then evaporating and igniting at about 1200°C.

5. CaF_2, formed by treating the oxide with hydrofluoric acid (platinum crucible), followed by evaporation and ignition of the residue.

Effect of Coprecipitated Substances

Any magnesium or alkali metal oxalates coprecipitated with calcium oxalate lead to positive error in all the gravimetric methods and in the permanganate titration method of finishing the determination. Coprecipitated oxalic acid and ammonium oxalate give positive error in the titrimetric finish, but these compounds are completely volatilized at temperatures used for obtaining any of the recommended weighing forms.

Any sulfate present in the solution from which calcium oxalate is precipitated is likely to be strongly coprecipitated (why?). When weighed as carbonate, oxide, or fluoride, coprecipitated sulfate gives high results, but no error when weighed as calcium sulfate. Coprecipitated calcium sulfate gives low results in the permanganate titration method.

Other Applications

Practically all the cations except magnesium and the alkalies form oxalates that are insoluble in neutral or ammoniacal solution. Theoretically, any of these cations could be determined as oxalate. In practice, other methods are used for most of the cations, but precipitation of oxalates is frequently used for the separation of zirconium, thorium, and the rare earths from other elements of the ammonia precipitate.

V. DETERMINATION OF MAGNESIUM

Important magnesium minerals are $MgCO_3$ (magnesite), $MgSO_4 \cdot 7H_2O$ (epsomite), $MgCl_2 \cdot KCl \cdot 6H_2O$ (carnallite), $H_2Mg_3(SiO_3)_4$ (talc or soapstone), and $CaMg_3(SiO_3)_4$ (asbestos). Magnesium chloride is present in certain salt wells and in small amounts in sea water; magnesium metal is obtained commercially from these sources. The metal and its alloys are important articles of commerce.

Decomposition of Samples

The carbonate minerals, as well as the metal and its alloys, are readily soluble in dilute mineral acids. The silicates are usually attacked by sodium carbonate fusion.

Interfering Substances

Following the separation of calcium oxalate, excess oxalate ion must be removed, to destroy the oxalato complex of magnesium; excess ammonium ion is also removed, so that a controlled amount can be provided for precipitation of magnesium as $MgNH_4PO_4$. Addition of concentrated nitric acid and evaporation to dryness removes both oxalate and ammonium ions:

$$C_2O_4^{--} + 2NO_3^- + 4H^+ \rightarrow 2CO_2 + 2NO_2 + 2H_2O$$

$$NH_4^+ + NO_3^- \rightarrow 2H_2O + N_2O$$

Precipitation and Digestion

The system from which magnesium ammonium phosphate is precipitated involves several equilibria, some of which are represented as follows:

$$Mg^{++} + NH_4^+ + PO_4^{---} \rightleftharpoons MgNH_4PO_4$$
$$+ \qquad +$$
$$OH^- + H^+ \qquad \rightleftharpoons H_2O$$
$$\updownarrow \qquad \updownarrow$$
$$NH_4OH \quad HPO_4^{--}$$

The principal controlling equilibrium is the third ionization of phosphoric acid,

$$HPO_4^{--} \rightleftharpoons H^+ + PO_4^{---}, \qquad K_3 = 4.7 \times 10^{-13}$$

Addition of ammonium hydroxide (to remove H^+) increases the concentration of phosphate ion; however, the buffer action of ammonium ion limits the effect of ammonium hydroxide in increasing the *p*H. In nearly neutral solution, hydrolysis of both phosphate ion (extensive) and ammonium ion (slight) would operate to decrease the concentration of these ions; these hydrolyses are suppressed by making the solution alkaline.

Precipitation is made from magnesium ion solution containing 5 ml of concentrated hydrochloric acid in about 150 ml of solution. A liberal excess of diammonium hydrogen phosphate is added, followed by ammonium hydroxide with good stirring, using 5 ml beyond the amount required to change the color of methyl red indicator. Magnesium ammonium phosphate readily forms supersaturated solutions, and even when some solid phase is present, solubility equilibrium is attained only slowly. The precipitation mixture should stand at least four hours (preferably overnight) in the cold before filtering.

Filtration and Washing

The high ignition temperature of the precipitate precludes the use of sintered glass filtering crucibles, although an alundum (Monroe) crucible may be used. Generally, the precipitate is filtered on paper. The filtration mixture must be cold, and the precipitate is washed with cold, dilute (1:20) ammonium hydroxide until the washings are free or nearly so from chloride ion. Good scrubbing of the glass is necessary to free all the precipitate, which adheres especially tenaciously to any scratches on the glass.

The first precipitate is usually so much contaminated that it cannot be used for ignition. After being washed, the precipitate is dissolved in a small amount of hydrochloric acid; a small amount of $(NH_4)_2HPO_4$ is added, and reprecipitation is made by adding ammonium hydroxide as before. The second precipitate is nearly free from contamination.

Ignition

The filter paper must be dried, charred, and burned off at the *lowest possible temperature*, otherwise some of the carbon may be fireproofed. Final ignition at 1000–1100°C converts the precipitate to magnesium pyrophosphate for weighing:

$$2MgNH_4PO_4 \rightarrow 2NH_3 + H_2O + Mg_2P_2O_7$$

Effect of Coprecipitated Substances

The influence of various possible contaminants on the final result in magnesium analysis is shown in Table 19-1. The student should justify the nature of the error, bearing in mind that the correct weighing form is $Mg_2P_2O_7$ and that the analysis is for *magnesium*.

Table 19-1   Effect of Contaminants on Magnesium
Determination (as $Mg_2P_2O_7$)

Contaminant	Ignition Products	Error
$MgHPO_4$	$Mg_2P_2O_7$, H_2O	None
$Mg(H_2PO_4)_2$	$Mg(PO_3)_2$, H_2O	Positive
$Mg_3(PO_4)_2$	Stable	Negative
$NH_4H_2PO_4$ $(NH_4)_2HPO_4$ $(NH_4)_3PO_4$	P_2O_5, HPO_3, NH_3, H_2O	Positive
$Mg(OH)_2$	MgO, H_2O	Negative
$MgCl_2$	MgO, HCl	Negative
NH_4Cl	NH_3, HCl	None

Other Applications

The method can be used for the cations Mn^{++}, Zn^{++}, Cd^{++}, Ni^{++}, and Co^{++}, all of which form metal ammonium phosphates that ignite to the corresponding pyrophosphate. All these ions except Mn^{++} form stable complexes with ammonia, as a result of which their metal ammonium phosphates are soluble in excess ammonium hydroxide; precipitation must therefore be made in nearly neutral solution, and washing is done with cold water.

Determination of Magnesium with 8-Quinolinol

The determination of magnesium by precipitation with 8-quinolinol offers a number of advantages over the phosphate method.

1. The precipitate forms rapidly from hot acidic solution containing the reagent, by adding ammonium hydroxide to distinct alkalinity. Sufficient ammonium salts must be present to prevent the precipitation of magnesium hydroxide.

2. Contamination by coprecipitation of other inorganic components of the solution is negligible; some of the reagent may be coprecipitated.

3. Weighing can be made as the dihydrate, $Mg(C_9H_6ON)_2 \cdot 2H_2O$, after oven drying at 105°C. It is usually better to dry at about 140°C and weigh as the anhydrous salt. The higher temperature serves to volatilize any coprecipitated reagent.

4. The method can be applied to the filtrate from calcium separation without the necessity of removing oxalate ion.

5. In a continuing analysis, the filtrate from the magnesium separation can be used for analysis for the alkali cations. The excess 8-quinolinol is easily volatilized in the process of obtaining the alkali salts.

Applied to original samples, precipitation of magnesium with 8-quinolinol requires absence of all other cations except the alkalies, although small amounts of calcium can be tolerated if a double precipitation of magnesium is made. The reagent is especially suitable for the analysis of aluminum-magnesium alloys. Aluminum can be precipitated with 8-quinolinol from acetic acid—acetate buffer mixture, leaving magnesium in solution. From solution containing alkali tartrate to complex the aluminum, magnesium is precipitated as the quinolinolate from sodium hydroxide solution.

VI. DETERMINATION OF PHOSPHATE

Phosphate and arsenate give similar analytical reactions. When these ions are present together, arsenate is first removed by reduction to arsenic(III) followed by distillation as arsenic trichloride from hydrochloric acid solution or by precipitation as the sulfide from acid solution. It is customary to make a preliminary separation of phosphate by precipitation as ammonium molybdiphosphate.

The hot nitric acid solution containing the phosphate (and no arsenate) is treated with excess ammonium molybdate to form the "yellow precipitate," $(NH_4)_3P(Mo_3O_{10})_4 \cdot 2HNO_3 \cdot H_2O$. Weighing as $(NH_4)_3P(Mo_3O_{10})_4$ after heating at 300°C, or as $P_2O_5 \cdot 24MoO_3$ after heating at 400°C has been proposed, but the usual procedure is to dissolve the yellow precipitate in ammonium hydroxide and precipitate the phosphate as $MgNH_4PO_4$, which is ignited to $Mg_2P_2O_7$ for weighing, exactly as in the magnesium determination. Phosphorus is usually reported as the percentage of P_2O_5. Several of the same substances that are coprecipitated in the magnesium determination are likely to be contaminants in the phosphate determination. The student should refer to Table 19-1 and consider the effect of these contaminants on the results when phosphate is being determined.

In a titrimetric method for phosphate the yellow precipitate is dissolved in a measured excess of standard sodium hydroxide:

$$(NH_4)_3P(Mo_3O_{10})_4 \cdot 2HNO_3 \cdot H_2O + 25OH^- \rightarrow$$
$$3NH_4^+ + HPO_4^{--} + 12MoO_4^{--} + 2NO_3^- + 14H_2O$$

and the excess alkali is back titrated with standard acid.

VII. DETERMINATION OF SODIUM AND POTASSIUM

The principal sources of sodium compounds are the chloride, carbonate, and borate (borax); potassium minerals of importance are the simple chloride, and double chlorides and/or sulfates with magnesium. Both sodium and potassium chlorides are found in natural waters. Many silicate rocks contain sodium or potassium, often associated with aluminum, as in the feldspars. Natural and manufactured compounds of sodium and potassium are widely used in commerce, and their analysis is frequently required.

Collection of Mixed Chlorides

In the general case, sodium and potassium are obtained together as their solid chlorides, after removal of all other cations. Silicate rocks are decomposed and the alkali chlorides are obtained by the J. Lawrence Smith method,[2] in which the sample is mixed with ammonium chloride and a large excess of alkali-free calcium carbonate, and the mixture heated until the mass just begins to sinter. The following reactions occur, using $KAlSi_3O_8$ for illustration.

$$CaCO_3 \rightarrow CaO + CO_2$$

$$CaO + 2NH_4Cl \rightarrow 2NH_3 + H_2O + CaCl_2$$

$$2KAlSi_3O_8 + CaCl_2 + 6CaCO_3 \rightarrow 6CaSiO_3 + Ca(AlO_2)_2 + 6CO_2 + 2KCl$$

The sintered mass is leached repeatedly with hot water to dissolve the alkali chlorides and excess reagents. Heavy metals and magnesium are precipitated as hydrous oxides by the excess calcium oxide. From the water extract, calcium is removed by precipitation with ammonium carbonate and ammonium oxalate. The filtrate is evaporated to dryness and strongly ignited to decompose ammonium salts and oxalate. The residue, moistened with hydrochloric acid, is again ignited, then cooled and weighed as $NaCl + KCl$.

The analysis may be completed gravimetrically in one of three ways: (1) an indirect method, in which the weighed chlorides are converted to mixed sulfates which are weighed, or to silver chloride which is weighed; (2) direct determination of either sodium or potassium, and calculation of the other by difference from the mixed chlorides; (3) direct determination of both sodium and potassium.

Indirect Determination

The weighed mixed chlorides are treated with sulfuric acid, the excess acid is fumed off, and the residue is ignited at 400–800°C; the residue is weighed as $Na_2SO_4 + K_2SO_4$. Alternatively, the mixed chlorides are dissolved and precipitated as silver chloride, which is handled in the usual way. The arithmetic of indirect determinations is given in Chap. 15.

Determination of Potassium

1. Chloroplatinate Method. To the mixed chlorides dissolved in a small amount of water, chloroplatinic acid, H_2PtCl_6, is added in excess of the amount to convert *both* of the chlorides to the hexachloroplatinate compounds, K_2PtCl_6 and Na_2PtCl_6. The mixture is evaporated until it solidifies on cooling. The mixed solid chloroplatinates are treated with 80% ethanol, which extracts the sodium compound and leaves the potassium compound. The residual solid is dried at 100–130°C, and weighed as K_2PtCl_6.

[2] J. L. Smith, *Amer. J. Sci.*, **50**, 269 (1871).

2. Perchlorate Method. The mixed chlorides are dissolved in a small volume of water, perchloric acid (70–72%) is added, and the mixture is evaporated to dryness on a hot plate. The solid perchlorates are extracted with a 1:1 mixture of *n*-butanol and ethyl acetate, which dissolves only the sodium perchlorate. The potassium perchlorate is separated on a filtering crucible (NOT on paper!), washed with the organic solvent mixture, dried for a few minutes in an oven, then heated for 15 minutes in a 350°C muffle. The residue is weighed as $KClO_4$.

3. Tetraphenylboron Method. Sodium tetraphenylboron, $NaB(C_6H_5)_4$, is soluble in water and in dilute acids, but the potassium compound is insoluble.[3] The reagent has been thoroughly investigated as a reagent for potassium[4] and the method has several desirable features.

a. The solubility of $KB(C_6H_5)_4$ is much smaller than that of K_2PtCl_6 or $KClO_4$.

b. The only common cation offering interference appears to be mercury(II).

c. The precipitate can be dried easily at 100–120°C.

d. The small gravimetric factor for potassium makes the compound particularly suited to micro methods.

e. Titrimetric methods for finishing the determination have been developed.[5]

Determination of Sodium

1. Triple Acetate Method. Sodium ion forms triple acetate salts of the general formula $NaC_2H_3O_2 \cdot M(C_2H_3O_2)_2 \cdot 3UO_2(C_2H_3O_2)_2 \cdot 6H_2O$, where M may be certain dipositive ions, usually Zn^{++} or Mg^{++}. The reagent is a mixture of concentrated solutions of zinc (or magnesium) acetate, uranyl acetate, and acetic acid, saturated with the sodium salt. The sodium sample should be in small volume; the reagent is added in generous excess, and the mixture is allowed to stand in the cold for an hour or longer. The precipitate is brought onto a filtering crucible, washed with ethanol saturated with the triple salt, and finally with ether or acetone. The precipitate is dried by drawing air through the crucible, and is weighed as the triple acetate hexahydrate.

A volumetric method of measuring the precipitate consists in settling it into the narrow graduated stem of a special centrifuge bulb and measuring the volume of the compact precipitate. The method is calibrated by the same procedure with known amounts of sodium.

2. After Chloroplatinate Method for Potassium. The alcoholic solution from the potassium separation is evaporated in a flask to remove most of the alcohol.

[3] G. Wittig, G. Keicher, A. Rückert, and P. Raff, *Ann.*, **563**, 110, 126 (1949); G. Wittig, *Angew. Chem.*, **62A**, 231 (1950); G. Wittig and P. Raff, *Ann.*, **573**, 195 (1951).

[4] P. Raff and W. Brotz, *Z. anal. Chem.*, **133**, 241 (1951); M. Kohler, *ibid.*, **138**, 9 (1953).

[5] H. W. Spier, *Biochem. Z.*, **322**, 467 (1952); H. Flaschka et al., *Z. anal. Chem.*, **138**, 161, 241 1953); **144**, 415 (1955); W. Rüdorff and H. Zannier, *Angew. Chem.*, **66**, 638 (1954).

The flask is fitted with a stopper carrying inlet and exit tubes, and after air has been displaced with hydrogen gas the exit tube is closed to maintain a slight pressure of hydrogen gas over the solution. The flask is kept warm, with occasional shaking, until the chloroplatinate has been completely reduced to metallic platinum:

$$PtCl_6^{--} + 2H_2 \rightarrow Pt + 4H^+ + 6Cl^-$$

The platinum is filtered off, the filtrate is evaporated carefully to dryness, and the residue, after igniting at about 800°C, is weighed as NaCl.

3. After Perchlorate Method for Potassium. The filtrate containing the sodium perchlorate is evaporated to less than 40% of its original volume, to volatilize ethyl acetate. An excess of 20% solution of hydrogen chloride gas in *n*-butanol is added and the mixture is cooled to room temperature. The precipitated sodium chloride is collected on a filtering crucible, washed with dilute hydrogen chloride–butanol solution, and after drying briefly at 100°C is heated for a short time at about 600°C. The residue is weighed as NaCl. Any lithium in the original sample is in the filtrate from this separation.

In all the methods of precipitating potassium, the heavier alkali elements rubidium and cesium, and also ammonium, follow the potassium in being precipitated. Ammonium salts are easily removed by ignition prior to precipitation of potassium. Determination of rubidium and cesium requires involved procedures when these elements are present with potassium; fortunately, they are rarely encountered.

Spectrophotometric Determination

Sodium and potassium (as well as many other elements) can be determined quickly and accurately by flame (emission) photometry or by atomic absorption spectrophotometry. In flame photometry the sample in solution, usually as chlorides because of their higher volatility, is atomized into an oxyhydrogen or oxyacetylene flame. The radiant energy from the flame is passed through a spectrophotometer with its monochromator set at the wavelength of the characteristic emission line of the element in question: sodium, 589 mμ, or potassium, 767 mμ. The intensity of the radiant energy is measured photoelectrically. The method is calibrated with known amounts of the element to be analyzed. In atomic absorption spectrophotometry, the source of radiation is a hollow cathode tube containing the element to be analyzed, and it produces radiant energy of wavelength characteristic of that element. The sample is atomized in a flame, where the atoms of the vaporized element absorb the characteristic radiation of the source; the decrease in intensity of the source radiation, due to absorption by the sample, is measured. Calibration is made with known amounts of the element under investigation.

PROBLEMS

SILICON

19-1 A limestone sample weighing 2.500 g is ignited, then decomposed with acid, and the silica separated in the usual way. The ignited silica residue weighs 0.0880 g. The residue is evaporated with hydrofluoric and sulfuric acids and again ignited; the residue weighs 8.0 mg.

(*a*) Calculate the percentage of uncorrected silica.

(*b*) Calculate the percentage of corrected silica.

(*c*) What is the percent relative error on the silica analysis if reported as un-corrected silica? *Ans.* (*a*) 3.512. (*b*) 3.200. (*c*) +10%.

19-2 A 0.5680-g sample of silicate mineral gives an " insolubles " residue weighing 0.1840 g. The residue from the $HF-H_2SO_4$ treatment weighs 6.6 mg. Later it is found that the original sample contains 1.5% of boron, which carries into the insolubles residue as B_2O_3 and volatilizes as BF_3. Calculate the percentage of SiO_2 in the mineral.

19-3 A magnesium calcium silicate, $(MgO)_x(CaO)_y(SiO_2)_z$, is found to contain 17.48% magnesium, 9.60% calcium, and 57.68% silica. Calculate the formula of the compound.

19-4 The mineral beryl has the composition $Be_3Al_2(SiO_3)_6$. Calculate the percentage of Be, Al, and SiO_2 in the mineral.

19-5 A silicate mineral weighing 0.6500 g gives an insoluble residue of SiO_2 and Fe_2O_3 weighing 0.1550 g. Analysis of the residue shows it to contain 5.00% iron. Calculate the percentage of SiO_2 in the sample.

19-6 (*a*) What volume (STP) of SiF_4 gas can be obtained by treating 0.5000 g of pure SiO_2 with excess hydrofluoric acid?

(*b*) If the SiF_4 of part (*a*) is hydrolyzed:

$$3SiF_4 + 2H_2O \rightarrow 2H_2SiF_6 + SiO_2$$

what weight of H_2SiF_6 is obtained?

IRON AND ALUMINUM

19-7 A sample of Mohr's salt, $FeSO_4 \cdot (NH_4)_2SO_4 \cdot 6H_2O$, is assayed for use as a primary standard for iron; a 1.500-g sample gave an ignited residue of Fe_2O_3 weighing 0.3016 g.

(*a*) Calculate the percent purity of the sample. *Ans.* 98.75.

(*b*) Calculate the percentage of Fe in the sample. *Ans.* 14.064.

(*c*) What conclusion could be drawn if the analysis results calculate to more than 100% purity?

19-8 A 0.7500-g sample containing aluminum gave a dried precipitate of aluminum 8-quinolinolate, $Al(C_9H_6ON)_3$, weighing 0.0304 g. Calculate the percentage of Al_2O_3 in the sample. *Ans.* 0.450.

19-9 Calculate the weight of iron ore sample that should be taken for analysis so that

(*a*) each 5.00 mg of Fe_2O_3 obtained represents 1.00% iron.

(*b*) one-fifth of the number of milligrams of Fe_2O_3 represents the percentage of Fe_2O_3 in the sample.

(*c*) the percentage of Fe_3O_4 is half the number of milligrams of Fe_2O_3 obtained.

19-10   A 0.5000-g sample of iron ore gave an ignited iron oxide residue weighing 0.1700 g. It is suspected that the oxide residue may have been at least partially reduced to Fe_3O_4 during ignition; the precipitate was therefore reduced to metallic iron, which weighed 0.1225 g.

   (*a*) Calculate the apparent percentage of Fe in the sample, based on the weight of the oxide residue.

   (*b*) Calculate the true percentage of Fe in the sample. What is the percent relative error between the two results?

   (*c*) Calculate the weight of Fe_3O_4 that was present in the oxide residue. Was the reduction of Fe_3O_4 slight, or extensive?

19-11   A 1-g sample of iron ore gives an ignited R_2O_3 residue weighing 0.2500 g. Analysis of this residue shows it to contain 5.00% Al and 1.25% Ti. Calculate the percentages of Fe, Al, and Ti in the original sample.

19-12   A mixture of pure $Al_2(SO_4)_3$ and $Fe_2(SO_4)_3$ weighing 0.5000 g is strongly ignited to expel SO_3; the residue of Al_2O_3 and Fe_2O_3 weighs 0.1845 g. Calculate the percentages of Al and Fe in the original mixture.

CALCIUM AND MAGNESIUM

19-13   A sample weighing 0.6800 g gives a residue of $CaCO_3$ weighing 0.2202 g. Analysis of the residue shows it to contain 2.10% of magnesium, present as $MgCO_3$. Calculate the true percentage of CaO in the sample.   *Ans.* 16.82.

19-14   A 1-g sample of steel is analyzed for phosphorus through the yellow precipitate; 0.0639 g of $P_2O_5 \cdot 24MoO_3$ is obtained. Calculate the percentages of (*a*) phosphorus; (*b*) P_2O_5.   *Ans.* (*a*) 0.110.   (*b*) 0.252.

19-15   A certain mineral contains 22.70% calcium. If the calcium is determined in a sample weighing 0.6300 g, what weight of residue is obtained if the calcium is weighed as (*a*) $CaCO_3$, (*b*) CaO, (*c*) $CaSO_4$, (*d*) CaF_2?

19-16   A sample consisting only of silica and dolomite ($CaCO_3 \cdot MgCO_3$) loses 30.0% of its weight on strong ignition. Calculate the percentages of CaO, MgO, and SiO_2 in the sample.

19-17   A mixture weighing 0.4800 g and containing only $CaCO_3$ and $MgCO_3$ is ignited strongly; the residue weighs 0.2599 g. Calculate the percentages of Ca and Mg in the original mixture.

19-18   A sample of Epsom salt, $MgSO_4 \cdot 7H_2O$, weighing 0.5255 g is analyzed for magnesium, and forms 0.2337 g of $Mg_2P_2O_7$. Calculate the results as (*a*) percent purity; (*b*) percentage of Mg; (*c*) percentage of MgO.

19-19   The magnesium from a 1.2145-g sample of limestone gives a precipitate of $Mg(C_9H_6ON)_2$ weighing 0.0723 g. Calculate the percentage of MgO.

19-20   A phosphatic mineral weighing 0.8000 g is dissolved in acid; the phosphorus is separated as the "yellow precipitate," which is reprecipitated as $MgNH_4PO_4$ and ignited to $Mg_2P_2O_7$; the latter weighs 0.2550 g.

   (*a*) Calculate the percentage of P_2O_5 in the sample.

   (*b*) If the yellow precipitate were ignited to $P_2O_5 \cdot 24MoO_3$, what weight of the latter would be obtained?

19-21   (*a*) A 1-g sample of Dowmetal yields 0.1512 g of Al_2O_3; a 0.2000-g sample yields 0.8330 g of $Mg_2P_2O_7$. Calculate the percentages of Al and Mg in the sample.

(*b*) If the remainder of the alloy is manganese, what weight of Mn_3O_4 would be obtained from a 5-g sample?

19-22 A phosphor bronze sample is analyzed for phosphorus, which is weighed as $Mg_2P_2O_7$. What weight of $Mg_2P_2O_7$ can be obtained from a 3-g sample of bronze which contains 0.200% phosphorus?

19-23 Calculate the percent of each metal in a silver solder, given the following data: A 1.0000-g sample yields 0.1398 g of $Zn_2P_2O_7$; a 0.7600-g sample yields 0.4040 g of $AgCl$; a 0.4000-g sample yields 0.2031 g of SnO_2; a 0.6500-g sample deposits 0.0910 g of copper on a cathode.

SODIUM AND POTASSIUM

19-24 An increase in weight of 0.2000 g is observed when a sample of pure NaCl is transposed to Na_2SO_4. What weight of NaCl is used?   *Ans.* 0.9290 g.

19-25 A 2.250-g sample of silicate rock, analyzed by the J. Lawrence Smith method, gave 0.2468 g of $KClO_4$. Calculate the percentage of K_2O in the sample.

Ans. 3.729.

19-26 What weight of feldspar sample containing 6.6% K_2O is required to give a precipitate of $KClO_4$ weighing 0.4100 g?

19-27 The potassium ion from a 2.500-g sample of rock is separated as K_2PtCl_6, which upon ignition yields a residue of metallic platinum weighing 0.1035g. Calculate the percentage of K_2O in the sample.

19-28 What weight of silicate rock must be taken for analysis so that
(*a*) each 5.0 mg of $KClO_4$ obtained will represent 0.100% K_2O.
(*b*) each 10.0 mg of K_2PtCl_6 obtained will represent 0.025% K_2O.
(*c*) the percentage of K_2O is one-fifth of the weight in milligrams of the metallic platinum obtained from K_2PtCl_6.

19-29 In what weight ratio must pure KCl and pure K_2SO_4 be mixed so that the mixture will contain 50.00% potassium?

19-30 A 1.5600-g sample containing potassium and sodium gives a residue of $KCl + NaCl$ weighing 0.4545 g. The mixed chlorides are converted to $K_2SO_4 + Na_2SO_4$, which weighs 0.5382 g. Calculate the percentages of K_2O and Na_2O in the sample.

19-31 In what weight ratio must pure NaCl and pure RbCl be mixed so that the mixture will contain the same percentage of chlorine as pure KCl?

19-32 What weight of $KB(C_6H_5)_4$ can be obtained from 0.7500 g of a feldspar which contains 2.45% K_2O?

Part III □ Titrimetric Methods

20

THE MEASUREMENT
OF VOLUME

The unit of volume is the **liter**, which is the volume occupied by one kilogram of water at one atmosphere pressure and at its temperature of maximum density (3.98°C). In establishing the metric standards it was intended that the kilogram represent the mass of one cubic decimeter (1000 cubic centimeters) of water so that there would be a simple relation between the standard of mass and the standard of length (the meter). Because of slight errors in the experimental measurements this simple relation was not realized, and a kilogram of water at its temperature of maximum density occupies 1.000028 cubic decimeters, or 1000.028 cc. The milliliter, which is one thousandth part of a liter, is therefore not identical with the cubic centimeter, although the difference of only about three parts per hundred thousand is not significant in ordinary analytical work.

The concentration of a solution is usually expressed as a weight-volume relation. A titrimetric method of analysis involves the measurement of the volume of solution of known concentration to complete a certain reaction. Liquid or solution samples are often measured by volume. The accurate measurement of volume is therefore an important operation in quantitative analysis.

Volumetric Ware

The laboratory ware used for accurate measurement of liquid volumes consists of volumetric flasks, pipets, and burets. All these devices are designed so that a relatively large change in level of the liquid is produced by a small change in the contained volume. The inside surface of ware used for *delivering* a measured volume of liquid (burets and pipets, rarely volumetric flasks) must be scrupulously clean so that the film of liquid on the glass never breaks when the liquid is withdrawn; a warm (*not* hot) soap or detergent solution is usually effective for cleaning.

Soda-lime glass is satisfactory for the construction of volumetric ware. Ordinarily solutions are not allowed to remain in them for long periods of time, hence contamination by chemical attack of the glass is not serious. Volumetric flasks and burets of borosilicate glass may be obtained, if required for resistance to chemical attack.

All volumetric ware is calibrated for use at a specified temperature, 20°C, and also for use in a specified manner. Owing to the change in volume of liquids and solutions, and also of the glass, with change in temperature, recalibration must be made if the apparatus is to be used at temperatures much different from the standard calibration temperature. The manufacturer's calibration should not be assumed to be infallible, but should be tested to make sure the graduation is within the tolerance required for the work at hand. Although the manufacturers take great care in the calibration, a human element is involved and mistakes can be made.[1]

The construction and calibration of volumetric apparatus is described in this chapter. Details of the technique of use are given in Chap. 33.

VOLUMETRIC FLASKS

Construction

Volumetric flasks (see Fig. 20-1) most commonly used have capacities of 25, 50, 100, 250, 500, and 1000 ml. They are calibrated to *contain* (rarely also to deliver) the specified volume of liquid at 20°C when filled so the bottom of the meniscus is at the mark on the neck. The National Bureau of Standards has published specifications for the different kinds of volumetric ware,[2] which designate construction, shapes, dimension, position of calibration marks, flow rates, etc. For volumetric flasks, the minimum and maximum diameter of the neck, and the limits of location of the graduation mark on the neck are specified as is also the tolerance for the indicated capacity.

Calibration

Volumetric flasks may be calibrated by the weight of water contained or by the use of Morse-Blalock calibrating bulbs. The former method is more con-

---

[1] A case is on record of a buret which had only four graduation divisions between the 33.0- and 33.5-ml marks, and six divisions between the 37.0- and 37.5-ml marks. Whenever the volume delivered was less than 33.4 or more than 37.5 ml, no error was made in measuring the delivered volume; but when the meniscus position was between these values, the volume delivered was too small by 0.1 ml. The author has in his possession a thermometer on which the etched numbers of consecutive ten-degree intervals read 0, 10, 20, 40, 50, etc., and also a 100-ml volumetric flask that contains only 99 ml when filled to the graduation mark.

[2] *Testing of Glass Volumetric Apparatus*, National Bureau of Standards Circular 434 (1941).

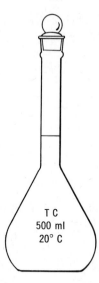

Fig. 20-1   Volumetric flask.

venient if only one or a few flasks are to be calibrated; the latter method is more rapid when a number of flasks are to be calibrated. In a calibration by weight, either of two objectives may be considered: (1) to establish a graduation mark for the nominal capacity at the temperature of use or (2) to determine the capacity of the flask at its graduation mark. The former is preferable for use in volumetric calculations; the latter would require application of a correction for the actual volume of the solution or any aliquot of it.

Calibration by Weight.   The flask to be calibrated is weighed on a balance of adequate load capacity; additional weights equal to the calculated weight of water for the nominal capacity of the flask are then placed on the pan, and are exactly counterbalanced by adding distilled water to the flask. Care must be taken that no separate drops cling to the neck of the flask above the water surface.

The liter is the volume occupied by 1 kilogram (vacuum weight) of water at very nearly 4°C; volumetric ware is calibrated for 20°; but it may be desired to use the equipment at some other temperature, for example, 25 or 30°C. Experimentally, it is impossible to weigh water at 4°C in a flask at 20 or 25°C and in vacuum; but it is possible to calculate the weight of water, against brass weights, that should be taken at the calibration temperature so that its volume would be that occupied by 1 kilogram of water (or a given fraction or multiple thereof, corresponding to the nominal capacity of the flask) at 4°C and in vacuum. Three corrections are required.

1. *Correction for density of water.*   In Table 20-1, the second column gives the density of water, in grams (vacuum weight) per milliliter, for the temperature shown in the first column. For example, a 1-liter volumetric flask would require

Table 20-1   Weight of 1 Milliliter of Water
at Different Temperatures

Temp., °C	Vacuum Weight (Density), g	Apparent Weight in Air vs. Brass, g	Apparent Weight Corrected for Glass Expansion
4	1.00000		
10	0.99973	0.99868	0.99843
15	0.99913	0.99808	0.99795
16	0.99897	0.99792	0.99782
17	0.99880	0.99775	0.99767
18	0.99862	0.99757	0.99752
19	0.99843	0.99738	0.99736
20	0.99823	0.99718	0.99718
21	0.99802	0.99697	0.99700
22	0.99780	0.99675	0.99680
23	0.99756	0.99651	0.99659
24	0.99732	0.99627	0.99637
25	0.99707	0.99602	0.99615
26	0.99681	0.99576	0.99591
27	0.99654	0.99549	0.99567
28	0.99626	0.99521	0.99541
29	0.99597	0.99492	0.99515
30	0.99567	0.99462	0.99488
31	0.99537	0.99432	0.99460
32	0.99505	0.99400	0.99430
33	0.99473	0.99368	0.99401
34	0.99440	0.99335	0.99370
35	0.99406	0.99301	0.99338

$1000 \times 0.99707 = 997.07$ g (vacuum weight) of water for calibration at 25°C, if there were no other corrections.

2. *Correction for buoyancy.*   The water is to be weighed in air against brass weights, and the buoyant effect of air is different for water (density about 1) and for brass (density 8.4) and depends also upon the density of air, which itself varies with temperature, pressure, and relative humidity. An average value, for the density of air, of 0.0012 g per ml is sufficiently accurate for all but the most refined work. The air weight of 1 ml of water at 25°C is given by

$$0.99707 = W_{air}\left[1 + 0.0012\left(\frac{1}{0.997} - \frac{1}{8.4}\right)\right]$$

$$= W_{air} \times 1.00106$$

$$W_{air} = 0.99707/1.00106 = 0.99602$$

The buoyancy effect in weighing water in air against brass weights accounts for $0.99707 - 0.99602 = 0.00105$ g per ml, the air weight being smaller than the vacuum weight. Although the density of air changes slightly with temperature, this change is not significant with respect to other factors in the buoyancy correction, and the air weight per milliliter of water is given by subtracting 0.00105 from the density (vacuum weight) at each temperature. These *apparent weights* of 1 ml of water are shown in column three of Table 20-1.

3. *Correction for expansion of glass.*   When the working temperature of the volumetric ware is different from the standard calibration temperature of 20°C, correction must be made for the expansion of glass with temperature. An average value for the coefficient of cubical expansion of glass is 0.000025 per degree. For each degree below 20°C this correction must be subtracted, and for each degree above 20°C it must be added, to give the apparent weight of water at the given temperature that would occupy 1 ml at 20°C. These values are given in the last column of Table 20-1.

In order to calibrate a volumetric flask it is now merely necessary to note the working temperature and have available distilled water at that temperature. The appropriate figure in the last column of Table 20-1 is multiplied by the nominal capacity of the flask, and that weight of water is added to the flask. For example, a 100-ml flask at 25°C requires $100 \times 0.99615 = 99.615$ g of water; a 500-ml flask at 30°C requires $500 \times 0.99488 = 497.435$ g. Actually, weights to the nearest 10 mg (approximately 0.01 ml of water) are sufficiently exact. If the level of the meniscus does not coincide with the manufacturer's mark on the neck, a narrow strip of gummed paper can be affixed so that its upper edge indicates the new graduation mark. If desired, a more permanent mark may be made by scratching with a glass marking stylus, or by etching with hydrofluoric acid.

Another method of calibration is the determination of the volume at the graduation mark, even when the temperature is different from the standard calibration temperature of 20°C. This method is applied as illustrated by the following calculations. Suppose a 1-liter volumetric flask is properly graduated to hold exactly 1000.00 ml at 20°C. Owing to the expansion of the glass, the flask at 30°C will hold $1000.00[1 + 10(0.000025)] = 1000.25$ ml. Referring to the third column of Table 20-1, the apparent weight of this volume of water is found to be $1000.25 \times 0.99462 = 994.88$ g. The difference between the volume 1000.00 and this weight is 5.12. If, therefore, the number 5.12 is added to the weight of water at 30°C that is contained to the mark in a 1-liter volumetric flask, the exact volume, correct to 0.01 ml, is obtained. This method is valid if the graduation mark on the 1-liter flask is within 1 ml of the nominal volume. Similar values, calculated for other temperatures, are shown in Table 20-2; tabular values are numbers to be added to the weight of water in grams to get the actual volume in milliliters contained in a 1-liter flask at the graduation

Table 20-2 Numbers to Be Added
to Apparent Weight of 1 Liter of Water
to Give True Volume in Milliliters

Temp., °C	Add to Apparent Weight	Temp., °C	Add to Apparent Weight
10	1.60	25	3.84
15	2.07	26	4.08
16	2.18	27	4.33
17	2.32	28	4.59
18	2.47	29	4.85
19	2.64	30	5.12
20	2.82	31	5.40
21	3.02	32	5.70
22	3.21	33	6.00
23	3.41	34	6.32
24	3.62	35	6.62

mark. For volumetric flasks of other capacities, the proper proportional parts of the tabular values are used.

Suppose, for example, that a 1-liter flask contains 994.58 g of 30°C water when filled to the mark; its volume is 994.58 + 5.12 = 999.70 ml. If 498.21 g of water at 25°C fills a 500-ml flask to the mark, the actual volume is 498.21 + 3.84/2 = 500.13 ml.

It should be emphasized that this method is a *test* of the manufacturer's graduation mark. If it should be significantly in error, the *correct* volume, rather than the nominal volume, would be used in all computations based on concentration, and would also have to be applied in taking aliquots by pipet. It is better, therefore, to calibrate for the nominal volume at the working temperature.

Calibration by Morse-Blalock Bulbs. Some varieties of Morse-Blalock bulbs are shown in Fig. 20-2; by use of multiple bulbs in the same piece of equipment, a wide range of capacities of flasks may be calibrated. [The bulb shown in Fig. 20-2 (c) is used mainly for calibrating burets.] The bottom stem of the bulb is fitted with a three-way stopcock, the side arm of which leads to a reservoir of distilled water in an elevated position. Each bulb and each stem section is calibrated separately by weighing the water delivered, and converting weight to volume (Table 20-1, column 3). A *dry* flask is then calibrated by delivering into it the correct volume from bulb and stem, and marking the meniscus level. Morse-Blalock bulbs are a great convenience when several flasks are to be calibrated, even over a long peiod of time. Calibration of the bulb at one temperature serves for other temperatures, because changes in density of water and expansion of the glass are the same for the bulb as for the flasks to be calibrated.

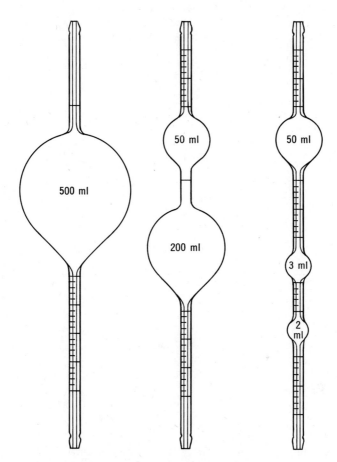

Fig. 20-2   Morse-Blalock calibrating bulbs.

PIPETS

Construction

The two types of pipet commonly used in analytical chemistry are shown in Fig. 20-3. The transfer pipets most frequently used in student laboratories are of capacity 5, 10, 25, and 50 ml. For standard series work in colorimetry and spectrophotometry, additional pipets of capacities 1, 2, 3, and 4 ml are a great convenience. The National Bureau of Standards specifications[3] for transfer pipets stipulate various dimensions of length and diameter, the position of the graduation mark, the shape of the tip, and the maximum delivery time. For

[3] *Ibid.*

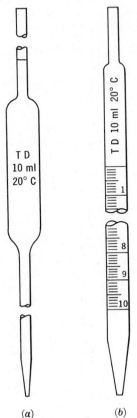

(a)   (b)   **Fig. 20-3**   (a) Transfer pipet. (b) Mohr (measuring) pipet.

measurement of the extremely small volumes of samples used in mass spectrometry, in gas liquid chromatography, and in microchemical analysis, "lambda" pipets are used; 1 μl (microliter) = 1 λ (lambda).

The Mohr or graduated pipets most commonly used are of capacity 1, 2, 5, and 10 ml, although other sizes are available if required. Small capacity Mohr pipets are straight bore to the mouthpiece, and often are graduated to read directly to 0.01 ml and can be estimated to about 0.002 ml. Mohr pipets are used when it is desired to add a volume of reagent that must be measured much more accurately than can be done with a graduated cylinder, or when the volume to be added is not an integral multiple of 1 ml (for which a transfer pipet could be used).

Calibration

Transfer pipets are tested by weight of water delivered. The clean pipet is filled to the mark with distilled water at known temperature. Any droplets adhering to the outside of the stem are wiped off with a clean towel or absorbent tissue, and the water is then allowed to flow freely from the vertical pipet into a previously weighed flask. When the water reaches the upper end of the delivery tube, the tip is touched to the wet surface of the receiving vessel and kept in contact with it until delivery is complete. *The water remaining in the tip must not be blown out.* From the weight of water and the appropriate fraction of the number in Table 20-2, the capacity of the pipet at the graduation mark can be calculated. Suppose a 10-ml pipet delivers water at 28°C, which weighs 9.951 g in air against brass weights; to this number add $4.59 \times 0.010 = 0.046$; the pipet delivery volume is $9.951 + 0.046 = 9.997$ ml, well within the tolerance of the calibration. If, however, the weight of water delivered is 9.905 g, the delivery volume at the mark is $9.905 + 0.046 = 9.951$ ml, an error of about 0.5%.

Reference to column 3 of Table 20-1 shows that the weight of water at 28°C that is delivered by a correctly marked 10-ml pipet is $10 \times 0.99541 = 9.954$ g. If the pipet is to be marked for delivery of exactly 10.00 ml at the working temperature of 28°C, one might use a trial and error method, delivering water from temporary marks placed by estimate from the first test. A quicker procedure is to affix a narrow strip of gummed paper along the axis of the tube adjacent to the graduation mark and rule off the paper in small divisions, say 1 mm. The weight of water delivered from a temporary mark (above or below the original mark, depending upon the results of the first test) is determined as before, and the new volume is computed. The difference between the second and the first volume is the volume of the stem between the temporary and the permanent mark. Assuming that the diameter of the tubing is constant, the final calibration position for the exact nominal volume is located by a linear measurement on the ruled strip of paper. A narrow strip of gummed paper can then be placed around the tube to designate the correct calibration.

BURETS

Construction

Burets are graduated for measuring the volume of liquid delivered through a capillary tip. A Geissler buret has a ground glass stopcock and delivery tip sealed onto the buret tube, as shown in Fig. 20-4(a). Because alkaline solutions, if allowed to remain in the buret for a considerable time, tend to cause the plug of the stopcock to "freeze" to the barrel, alkaline solutions are frequently used in a Mohr buret, the bottom of which is fitted with a delivery tip attached by rubber tubing. Outflow of liquid is controlled by a pinchcock, or, better, by a bead valve (glass bead inside the rubber tubing) as shown in Fig. 20-4(b). Other types of valves for control of liquid flow are used occasionally, and Teflon stopcocks are now available. A 50-ml buret, graduated to 0.1 ml, is used for most macro work in titrimetry; for micro work, 5-ml or smaller burets are used.

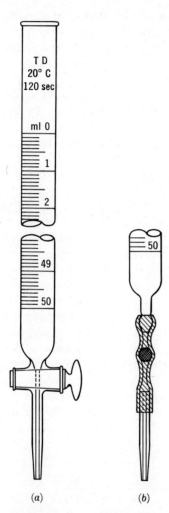

Fig. 20-4   (*a*) Geissler buret. (*b*) Bead valve for Mohr buret.

(*a*)   (*b*)

The National Bureau of Standards specifications[4] for burets include the following: Adjacent marks must have at least 1 mm clear space between them. All graduation marks must extend at least half way around, and every tenth mark must extend all the way around the circumference. (Many burets do not conform to some of these specifications.) The length of the graduated portion of the tube must not exceed 70 cm. The free outflow time must not exceed 3 minutes, nor be less than the following:

Graduated length, cm	20	30	40	50	60	70
Delivery time, sec	35	50	75	90	120	160

[4] *Op. cit.*

The calibration tolerances for 5-, 10-, 25-, and 50-ml burets are 0.01, 0.02, 0.03, and 0.05 ml, respectively.

Calibration

A buret may be calibrated by weight of water delivered at definite intervals, for example, each 5 ml, over the entire length. Some workers prefer to calibrate always from the zero mark to a definite graduation, such as 0 to 5, 0 to 10, 0 to 15, etc. The tedium of a weight calibration can be avoided by use of a Morse-Blalock bulb of the type shown in Fig. 20-2(c), connected with a three-way stopcock so that the buret serves as the reservoir for removal of water by increments that are the capacities of the small bulbs, namely 2, 3, or 5 ml.

A more convenient calibrator, adapted from the Morse-Blalock bulb and the Ostwald pipet, is shown in Fig. 20-5. Details of the calibration procedure, with illustrative calculations, are given by the manufacturer.[5]

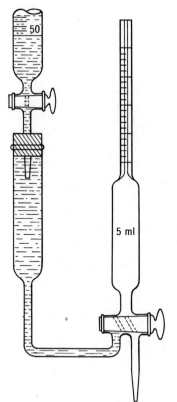

Fig. 20-5   Pipet for calibrating burets.

[5] Available from The Kauffman-Lattimer Co., 42 E. Chestnut Street, Columbus Ohio.

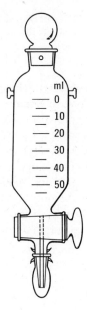

Fig. 20-6   Weight buret.

Weight Burets

Sometimes it is necessary to take liquid or solution samples with greater accuracy than is possible with a pipet or buret. For this purpose a weight buret is used. A volume of 50 ml can be measured in a buret to an accuracy of about 0.04 ml (reading and drainage errors), or one part in 1250. The same amount of liquid (assuming a density of 1.0000), even if weighed only to the nearest milligram, is accurate to one part in fifty thousand. Additional advantages are that no calibration is necessary, and the weight is independent of temperature. However, careful corrections for buoyancy must be made in order to attain the highest accuracy.

The Friedman-LaMer type of weight buret is shown in Fig. 20-6. The buret is suspended from the balance stirrup by a wire hook on the lugs; a cap held on the tip by rubber bands on the hooks prevents loss of liquid by evaporation. A weight buret is used for measuring liquid samples by mass; it is not volumetric equipment in the usual sense.

PROBLEMS

20-1   What apparent weight of water (i.e., weight in air against brass weights and corrected for expansion of glass) occupies the specified volume?

    (*a*) 500.0 ml at 28°C   (*d*) 100.0 ml at 22°C.

    (*b*) 250.0 ml at 18°C.   (*e*) 5.00 ml at 27°C.

    (*c*) 250.0 ml at 33°C.   *Ans.* (*a*) 497.7 g.

20-2 A volumetric flask of the nominal capacity stated contains the apparent weight of water given. What is the true capacity of the flask?

(a) A 100-ml flask: 99.90 g of water at 18°C.

(b) A 250-ml flask: 249.00 g of water at 28°C.

(c) A 500-ml flask: 497.95 g of water at 25°C.

(d) A one-liter flask: 995.15 g of water at 30°C.   *Ans.* (a) 100.15 ml.

20-3 Calculate the true capacity of a pipet from the apparent weight of water delivered at the temperature stated.

(a) 0.993 g at 30°C.   (d) 24.974 g at 18°C.

(b) 4.980 g at 24°C.   (e) 49.990 g at 15°C.

(c) 9.950 g at 25°C.   *Ans.* (a) 0.998 ml.

20-4 What apparent weight of water would be delivered by a correctly marked pipet at the temperature given?

(a) A 50-ml pipet at 17°C.   (d) A 5-ml pipet at 30°C.

(b) A 25-ml pipet at 26°C.   (e) A 1-ml pipet at 22°C.

(c) A 10-ml pipet at 35°C.

20-5 24.830 g of water (apparent weight, and corrected for glass expansion) at 25°C is delivered from the top to the bottom mark of a 25-ml buret. Is the calibration within the National Bureau of Standards tolerances?

21

FUNDAMENTALS OF
TITRIMETRIC ANALYSIS

In titrimetric analysis the amount of a substance in a sample is determined indirectly by measuring the volume of a solution of known concentration required for reaction with the desired constituent or with another substance chemically equivalent to the desired constituent. The process of bringing a measured volume of solution of known concentration into reaction with the desired constituent (or its equivalent of another substance) is called **titration**, hence the methods are called **titrimetric methods.**[1] A solution of accurately known concentration is a **standard solution**, which may be prepared either directly from, or by **standardization** by reaction with, a **primary standard**. The **end point** of a titration is marked by an abrupt change in some property of the reaction system, as shown by an **indicator**; ideally, this change should occur when chemically **equivalent** amounts of reactants are brought together, that is, at the **stoichiometric point** of the reaction.

Fundamental Requirements

In order to be suitable for application of the titrimetric method, a process must fulfill a number of requirements.

1. A *single* reaction must occur between the desired constituent and the titrant; the reaction serves as the basis for calculations.

---

[1] These methods are sometimes called "volumetric" methods; this is a general term referring to the measurement of volume by any means and for any purpose. For example, the measurement of the volume of carbon dioxide gas obtained by action of an acid on a carbonate is a volumetric method; it is not a titration, however. Volumetric analysis is a generic term, of which titrimetric is a specific kind.

262

2. The reaction must be *stoichiometric;* calculations from titrimetric data require a *definite* reaction.

3. The reaction must be *rapid*, so that little time is consumed in performing the titration. Most ionic reactions are so rapid as to be considered instantaneous; this is especially true of ionic metatheses. Some ionic redox reactions are slow, but can be made rapid by the addition of a catalyst. Examples are the reaction between arsenite and cerium(IV) catalyzed by osmium tetroxide or iodine monochloride; the oxidation of oxalate by permanganate, autocatalyzed by manganese(II).

4. The reaction must be *complete* when equivalent (stoichiometric) amounts of reactants have been brought together, so that the calculations are valid.

5. A suitable *standard solution* must be available as the titrant.

6. There must be an *indicator* to mark the end point of the titration.

7. Accurate measuring instruments (buret, pipet, balance, etc.) must be available.

Standard Solutions

Any solution the exact concentration of which is known is a standard solution. A standard solution may be prepared by either of two methods.

1. Direct Method. An exactly weighed amount of the solute, of definite and known composition, is dissolved and made up to known volume in a volumetric flask; from the known weight and volume, the concentration is calculated. The solute in this case must be a primary standard substance (see below). This method is especially convenient for the preparation of a standard solution of a predetermined concentration, such as a solution that is exactly 0.1000 *N*, or a solution that has an exact titer in terms of a specified desired constituent that is to be determined, e.g., an iron titer of 5.00 mg per milliliter.

2. Indirect Method. Many of the solutes required as titrants are not available as primary standards, so these solutions cannot be prepared by the direct method. A solution of the approximate concentration is made with only rough measurements of weight and volume; the solution is then **standardized** by measuring accurately the volume of this solution required to titrate an exactly weighed amount of primary standard. The exact concentration is then calculated from the volume of solution used, the weight of the primary standard, and its equivalent weight in the titration reaction.

Primary Standards

A primary standard substance must meet certain requirements.

1. It must be either of absolute (100.00%) purity, or of a known purity (e.g., 98.55%) in the active component. Primary standard chemicals are available from chemical supply houses and from the National Bureau of Standards.

2. If the material is of other than absolute purity, any impurities must be inert with respect to the substances with which it is to be brought into reaction. For example, sodium carbonate known to contain 98.25% Na_2CO_3 and 1.75% NaCl would be entirely satisfactory for the standardization of an acid, with which only the carbonate reacts.

3. The primary standard should be capable of being tested for possible "interfering" impurities by simple, reliable tests of known sensitivity.

4. It should be stable at the oven temperatures used for drying. For this reason, hydrated substances are seldom used, because of the difficulty of removing adsorbed moisture without causing some decomposition of the hydrate that would result in a material of unknown composition.

5. The standard should be unaltered by contact with air during weighing, that is, it must not be hygroscopic, nor react with oxygen or carbon dioxide at room temperature.

6. It must enter into reaction with the solution to be standardized according to all the requirements previously given for a titrimetric method. Many of these requirements are summarized by specifying that the reaction must be "quantitative," indicating a single, rapid, complete, stoichiometric reaction.

7. A high equivalent weight is desirable, in order to keep weighing errors below the usual buret reading and drainage errors.

8. A primary standard should be readily available, preferably at a reasonable cost. When used for standardization of a solution of another substance, the amount of primary standard is insignificant. However, if it is used for the preparation of large volumes of standard solution by the direct method, cost might be of considerable importance.

When circumstances permit, there is an advantage in standardizing a titrant solution against a primary standard of the same substance that is to be determined by the titrant, or against a standard sample of the same desired constituent and of about the same composition as the unknown samples to be analyzed. In this way certain errors inherent in the analytical method, including indicator errors, are largely cancelled. For example, if hydrochloric acid is to be used for the determination of the alkalinity of soda ash (impure sodium carbonate), the hydrochloric acid is standardized advantageously against primary standard sodium carbonate. If permanganate is to be used for the titrimetric determination of iron in iron ore, standardization of the permanganate against a standard sample of iron ore, carried through the same analytical steps as in the analysis, is advantageous.

Detection of End Point: Indicators

The end point of a titration is detected by an abrupt change in some property of the reaction mixture or of some substance added to it. Although indicator action is discussed in detail in connection with specific determinations, some of the principal methods of detecting end points are outlined below. Most end points are detected either by a visual observation of the change, or by measurement of some physical property of the titration system.

1. Visual Methods

a. The titrant serves as its own indicator.   Potassium permanganate, used in acid solution as a tritrimetric oxidant, is reduced to (almost) colorless manganese(II). When the redox reaction is complete, the next added small drop or fractional drop of permanganate imparts a pink color to the solution.

b. Acid-base indicators.   The acid-base indicators are themselves weak acids or weak bases, the anions or cations of which, respectively, are of different color from the undissociated forms. The indicators are weaker acids and bases than those titrated or used as titrants, hence the indicator does not react permanently with the titrant until the main reaction is complete. They must be selected to correspond closely to the end-point pH of the neutralization reaction.

c. Redox indicators.   These indicators are intensely colored substances capable of undergoing oxidation or reduction at characteristic potentials, and must be selected to correspond closely to the emf of the redox titration system at the stoichiometric point, so that the first slight excess of titrant reacts with the indicator.

d. Formation of a soluble product of distinctive color.   In the Volhard method for silver, a solution of a thiocyanate is used as the titrant, and a ferric salt is used as the indicator. When the silver ion is completely precipitated as AgCNS (white), the next drop of thiocyanate produces a red color,

$$Fe^{+++} + CNS^- \rightarrow Fe(CNS)^{++} \quad \text{(red solution)}$$

e. Disappearance of the color of the substance titrated.   In the determination of copper by titration of the ammoniacal copper solution with cyanide, the end point is indicated by the disappearance of the deep blue color of $Cu(NH_3)_4^{++}$; the reaction products are colorless. The reaction is

$$2Cu(NH_3)_4^{++} + 7CN^- + H_2O \rightarrow$$
$$2Cu(CN)_3^{--} + CNO^- + 6NH_3 + 2NH_4^+$$

f. Formation of a second precipitate of color different from the main precipitate. In the Mohr method for titrimetric determination of chloride, potassium chromate indicator is used. After precipitation of silver chloride (white) is complete, silver chromate is formed by the first slight excess of silver ion:

$$CrO_4^{--} + 2Ag^+ \rightarrow Ag_2CrO_4 \quad \text{(red-orange precipitate)}$$

g. Titration to first turbidity is illustrated by the Liebig method for titration of cyanide ion with silver ion:

$$2CN^- + Ag^+ \rightarrow Ag(CN)_2^- \quad \text{(soluble)}$$
$$Ag(CN)_2^- + Ag^+ \rightarrow AgAg(CN)_2 \quad \text{(or 2AgCN, white ppt.)}$$

The end point is the first detectable turbidity or opalescence in the titration mixture.

h. Completion of precipitation, or "clear point" method. If an insoluble product is formed that readily settles out leaving a clear supernatant liquid, the titrant may be added until an additional drop produces no more precipitate or turbidity in the supernatant solution. The method is quite tedious, but it has been applied satisfactorily in a number of cases, such as the titration of chloride by silver or the converse.

i. Adsorption indicators. These indicators are used in certain precipitation titrations. Depending upon the direction of titration and hence upon the ion of the precipitate that is primarily adsorbed before and after the stoichiometric point, adsorption or desorption of the indicator counter ions occurs immediately upon reversal of the charge of the adsorbed ion of the precipitate. The adsorption or desorption process is accompanied by a change in structure of the indicator, resulting in a change of color. Because the indicator action involves adsorption or desorption processes, the precipitate must be kept finely dispersed in the solution, with little or no coagulation near the stoichiometric point; for this reason protective colloids are often added before starting the titration. The method has been much used in the titrimetric precipitation of silver halides, using fluorescein and related compounds; see Fajans method for chloride, p. 338.

It is a general principle that if an indicator is to be used in the titration mixture (an internal indicator), the indicator must not react permanently with the substance being titrated nor with the localized excess of titrant where the latter is delivered into the solution. For example, in the Mohr determination of chloride, a localized slight excess of silver ion will produce some red-orange silver chromate precipitate; however, this precipitate disappears upon stirring, by reaction with chloride ion which is not yet precipitated:

$$Ag_2CrO_4 + 2Cl^- \rightarrow CrO_4^{--} + 2AgCl$$

The same principle applies to other indicator systems, including the acid-base and the redox indicators. The temporary appearance of the indicator product is an advantage in that it gives the analyst some warning of the approach of the end point, because the disappearance of the indicator product takes place more and more slowly as the amount of desired constituent decreases with the approaching stoichiometric point.

Many reactions are otherwise suitable for titrimetric use, except that no suitable indicator is known. In a few cases, external indicators can be used to test either for the first slight excess of titrant or for the disappearance of the substance being titrated. The use of external indicators is inconvenient and somewhat tedious, but for certain determinations the analyst has no choice until internal indicators may be discovered for the reaction used.

2. Electrical Methods. There are several methods of indicating the end point of titrations on the basis of changes in the electrical properties of the titration mixture. Electrometric titrations are discussed in detail in Chap. 32. It is sufficient here merely to give the basis of the end point detection, and to point out that most of these methods involve construction of a graph of an electric measurement against the amount of titrant added; the stoichiometric point is indicated by a rapid rate of change of the electrical property measured.

a. Potentiometric. The emf developed by suitable electrodes placed in the titration mixture is measured. Near the stoichiometric point the potential changes very rapidly on addition of small increments of titrant.

b. Conductometric. Removal of ions from solution by neutralization, precipitation, or complexation results in marked " breaks " in the rate of change of conductance with amount of titrant added near the stoichiometric point.

c. Amperometric. The current flowing in a polarographic cell (dropping mercury electrode or other indicating electrode) is measured during titration. A break in the rate of change of current with titration indicates the stoichiometric point. The graphs derived in amperometric titrations are similar to those from conductometric titration data, but the principles involved in the measurement are quite different.

d. Coulometric. These titrations measure the amount of electricity required to complete an electrolysis reaction or the electrolytic generation of a reagent serving as the titrant. A very exact measurement of current and of time is required to calculate the number of coulombs of electricity and hence the number of equivalents of reactant.

General Principles

In titrimetric analysis, whether for standardization of solutions or for analysis of unknowns, the following principles should be observed.

1. The sample taken should not be too small, so that the usual weighing errors, e.g., 0.2 mg, will be relatively small ($< 1\%_0$). For substances of low equivalent weight, such as KIO_3 in redox methods, a relatively large sample may be weighed and dissolved to known volume, and aliquots taken for titration. However, any accidental error in preparation of the solution is not detected by lack of precision in titrating aliquots.

2. The volume of titrant required should not be too small. Assuming buret reading errors of 0.02 ml and a drainage error of 0.02 ml, a total volume error of 0.04 ml will require the use of 40 ml of solution to keep the volumetric error within $1\%_0$.

3. The sample taken should not be so large that the buret used needs to be refilled in order to complete the titration. Refilling is not only inconvenient, but may also involve additional reading and drainage errors.

4. The concentration of the titrant should be chosen so as to permit fulfillment of the conditions in items 1 to 3. It is obvious that sample size, titrant concentration, and titrant volume are also related to the percent of active component in the sample being titrated.

5. In general, the titration should be made directly to the end point; over-running the end point and back titrating with another standard solution is not only inconvenient, but it also increases the possibility of error. However, there are some titrimetric methods in which use of an excess of standard solution is advantageous or even required, for one reason or another; back titration is then used.

6. Indicator blanks should be determined when possible, and the amount of the blank subtracted from the total volume of titrant used. However, if the titrant has been standardized by the same reaction as in the analysis of unknown samples, the indicator error largely cancels.

7. The standardization or the analysis should be based upon the results of at least three closely agreeing titrations, preferably with somewhat different amounts of sample so that prejudiced end points are avoided. For work of the highest accuracy, or for the statistical evaluation of the reliability of methods, many multiplicate samples are titrated.

Types of Reactions in Titrimetry

Many reactions fulfill the fundamental criteria for application of titrimetric methods. The following classification of reactions into three main categories is convenient, especially in relation to the definition of equivalency.

1. Neutralization Reactions.   The reaction of an acid with a base is called **neutralization**. The terms acid and base are to be considered in their broad sense; that is, **an acid is a proton donor**, and **a base is a proton acceptor**.

Titrimetric methods are often named by the class of reagent, or even by the reagent itself, which is used as the titrant. Thus, **acidimetry** is a reaction in neutralimetry in which the amount of a base in a sample is determined by titration with a standard acid; **alkalimetry** is the measurement of the amount of acid in a sample by titration with a standard alkali.

2. Formation of Precipitate, Weak Ionogen, or Complex Ion.   These reactions approach completeness because ions are extensively removed from solution. The following equations are illustrative:

$$Ag^+ + Cl^- \rightarrow AgCl \quad \text{(precipitate)}$$

$$2Cl^- + Hg^{++} \rightarrow HgCl_2 \quad \text{(weak ionogen)}$$

$$2CN^- + Ag^+ \rightarrow Ag(CN)_2{}^- \quad \text{(complex ion)}$$

$$Ca^{++} + H_2Y^{--} \text{ (EDTA)} \rightarrow 2H^+ + CaY^{--} \quad \text{(complex ion)}$$

Many reactions involving precipitation, complexation, or formation of weak ionogen satisfy most of the criteria for titrimetric analysis except that no internal indicator is available. In these cases an electrometric method may often be used to indicate the end point.

3. Oxidation-Reduction or Redox Reactions. Redox reactions involve the transfer of one or more electrons from the reducing agent (which is thereby oxidized) to the oxidizing agent (which is thereby reduced). The force (potential) representing the tendency of the substances to lose or gain electrons determines whether or not reaction will occur, and if so, to what extent. The electrochemical theory of redox reactions is treated in detail in Chap. 26. Practical redox titrations, which are very numerous, are discussed in Chaps. 28, 29, and 30.

22

CALCULATIONS OF
TITRIMETRIC ANALYSIS

The Concentration of Solutions. A solution concentration is designated by stating the amount of solute in a given amount of solvent or of solution. Concentrations expressed as weight percent or volume percent have little utility in quantitative analysis except in procedural directions where exact amounts of reagents are not critical. Concentrations on the molar basis find their principal application in calculations involving the mass law (K_{sp}, K_{ion}, etc.), but they are not convenient in titrimetry; for example, complete neutralization of one mole of a mono-, di-, or tribasic acid requires 1, 2, and 3 moles, respectively, of sodium hydroxide.

The most rational basis for expressing concentration of solutions in titrimetric analysis is **normality. A one normal solution contains one gram-equivalent weight of solute, for a given type of reaction, per liter of solution.** The normality of a solution is then a number designating the number of equivalents or fraction of an equivalent of the solute per liter of solution; for example, 2.0 N sodium hydroxide; 0.1000 N sulfuric acid. The definition of a normal solution obviously requires a definition of equivalent weight, which will be given presently. The advantage of concentrations based on the chemical equivalent is the simple 1:1 ratio involved in reactions of the same type. For example, one equivalent of sodium hydroxide reacts with one equivalent of hydrochloric acid, or with one equivalent of sulfuric acid, or with one equivalent of *any* acid, regardless of the number of "replaceable" hydrogen ions (protons) per molecule of the acid. This relation is obvious if the equations for the reactions are written in the ionic form. The equivalent weight of a substance in a given reaction bears a definite relation to the formula weight, hence the gram-equivalent weight is related in the same way to the gram-formula weight.

Equivalency

The equivalent weight is now defined and illustrated for the different types of reactions.

1. Neutralimetry. The equivalent weight of a substance in neutralimetry is the **weight of the substance that will furnish, or react with, or be chemically equivalent to one gram-atom of protons (H^+) in the reaction that occurs.** Thus, the equivalent weight of HCl is the same as the molecular weight; the equivalent weight of H_2SO_4 is one-half the molecular weight, or $H_2SO_4/2$. The equivalent weight of acetic acid, $HC_2H_3O_2$ or CH_3COOH, is the same as the molecular weight; the fact that acetic acid is somewhat weakly ionized has no bearing on the equivalence, for in reaction with a base, the acetic acid furnishes all of its proton content. The three stages of ionization of phosphoric acid, H_3PO_4, are represented by ionization constants K_1, K_2, and K_3, of approximately 10^{-3}, 10^{-8}, and 10^{-13}, respectively. Phosphoric acid can furnish protons (i.e., it can be neutralized) stepwise, each step according to a specific reaction to a characteristic end point. Phosphoric acid therefore has three different equivalent weights, represented by $H_3PO_4/1$, $H_3PO_4/2$, and $H_3PO_4/3$, depending on the neutralization of 1, 2, or 3 protons.[1] It is a universal principle that **the equivalent weight is determined by the reaction that occurs.**

The equivalent weight of a base is the weight of it that reacts with or accepts one gram-atom of protons. Thus, the equivalent weight of sodium hydroxide is $NaOH/1$; of barium hydroxide, $Ba(OH)_2/2$; of sodium carbonate, $Na_2CO_3/1$ for reaction to HCO_3^-, or $Na_2CO_3/2$ for reaction to H_2CO_3.

If phenylenediamine, $C_6H_4(NH_2)_2$, is determined by the Kjeldahl method, the $-NH_2$ groups are converted to NH_4^+, which is distilled from sodium hydroxide solution as NH_3; the ammonia is collected in standard acid: $NH_3 + H^+ \rightarrow NH_4^+$. The equivalent weight of phenylenediamine is therefore $C_6H_4(NH_2)_2/2$, because one mole of the compound furnishes two moles of NH_3, each of which combines with one mole of protons. This example illustrates the part of the definition that states "... or is chemically equivalent to one proton." It also illustrates another universal principle in titrimetry, namely, **in a sequence or series of reactions, the equivalent weight of the desired constituent is based upon the reaction in which a standard substance is used.** After deducing the equivalent of the substance brought into reaction with the standard substance, it is then simply a matter of correct stoichiometry between the desired constituent and the substance that reacts with the standard.

2. Formation of Precipitate, Complex, or Weak Ionogen. In this type of titrimetry, the equivalent weight of a substance is **that weight which will furnish, react with, or be chemically equivalent to one gram-atom of a univalent cation in**

---

[1] The third proton of phosphoric acid can be neutralized if some cation, e.g., Ca^{++}, is present to precipitate the phosphate ion.

the precipitate, complex, or weak ionogen formed. In the titrimetric precipitation of silver chloride, one mole of $AgNO_3$ is also one equivalent, because it is the amount that furnishes one gram-atom of Ag^+, a univalent cation, in the precipitate. In the same reaction, the equivalent weight of KCl is the molecular weight, because it furnishes the amount of chloride ion that reacts with a gram-atom of the univalent cation Ag^+. For precipitation as AgCl, the equivalent weight of barium chloride is $BaCl_2/2$ (why?). For precipitation as $BaCrO_4$ the equivalent weight of potassium chromate is $K_2CrO_4/2$, because one-half the molecular weight furnishes an amount of chromate ion that reacts with one-half a gram-atom of the divalent cation Ba^{++} to form the precipitate $BaCrO_4$. One-half gram-atom of a divalent cation is equivalent ("equi-valent") to one gram-atom of a univalent cation.

In the reaction $2CN^- + Ag^+ \rightarrow Ag(CN)_2^-$, the equivalent of potassium cyanide is 2KCN, because $2CN^-$ are required to react with one gram-atom of the univalent cation Ag^+ in forming the complex. Note that the equivalency of KCN is based upon the *reaction* with Ag^+, and not on the potassium ion of the KCN; K^+ plays no role in the reaction. In fact, equivalency based on the univalency of K^+ would lead to an erroneous conclusion. In the formation of the weak ionogen $HgCl_2$, the equivalent of NaCl is the same as the molecular weight; but in the formation of the complex $HgCl_4^{--}$, the equivalent is 2NaCl. It cannot be overemphasized that the **equivalent is determined by the reaction that occurs.**

3. Redoximetry. In redox titrimetry, the equivalent weight of a substance is **that weight which will furnish, accept** (react with), **or be chemically equivalent to one mole of electrons transferred in the reaction that occurs.** The best way to deduce the equivalent of a substance is to write the ion-electron half-reaction equation and note the number of electrons required per mole of the substance concerned. Just as polyprotic acids can have several different equivalent weights, so substances that can undergo several different electron changes have different equivalent weights. For example, the equivalent weight of potassium permanganate is the molecular weight divided by 5, 4, 3, or 1, depending upon its reduction to Mn^{++}, MnF_5^{--}, MnO_2, or MnO_4^{--}, respectively. (The student should confirm these equivalencies by writing the half-reaction equations.)

In the half reaction

$$Cr_2O_7^{--} + 14H^+ + 6e \rightleftarrows 2Cr^{+++} + 7H_2O$$

the equivalent of potassium dichromate as an oxidizing agent is $K_2Cr_2O_7/6$; in the oxidation of chromium(III) chloride to dichromate the equivalent weight is $CrCl_3/3$. In a series of reactions in which KIO_3 is treated with excess iodide and acid,

$$IO_3^- + 5I^- + 6H^+ \rightarrow 3H_2O + 3I_2$$

and the iodine is titrated with sodium thiosulfate,

$$I_2 + 2S_2O_3^{--} \rightarrow 2I^- + S_4O_6^{--}$$

the equivalent weight of potassium iodate is $KIO_3/6$, because each mole of KIO_3 gives three moles of iodine, each of which is two equivalents *in the titration reaction* with sodium thiosulfate. The fact that each molecule of KIO_3 gains five electrons in the reaction with iodide and acid is irrelevant to the equivalence in the over-all process.

The importance of the *reaction* in titrimetry can be illustrated by reference to another example. Suppose the question is asked, "What is the equivalent weight of potassium acid oxalate, KHC_2O_4?" This question cannot be answered until or unless the type of reaction is specified, for KHC_2O_4 is both an acid and a reducing agent. As an acid, its equivalent is $KHC_2O_4/1$; but as a reducing agent (giving CO_2 as its oxidation product) its equivalent is $KHC_2O_4/2$.

One of the principal objectives of the study of titrimetric analysis, as a part of analytical chemistry, is for the student to acquire an understanding of the *reactions* by means of which it is possible to make a wide variety of determinations, including the performance of the necessary calculations.

Computations

The liter as a measure of volume or capacity is too large for convenience; it is customary to express volumes in titrimetry in terms of the milliliter (1 ml = 0.001 liter). A one normal solution contains one gram-*milli*equivalent weight of solute per *milli*liter of solution. The following mathematical relationships, which serve as the basis for computations in titrimetry, are derived directly from the definition of a normal solution.

1. The product of normality by volume in liters is the number of gram-equivalent weights of solute. Thus, 2 liters of a 1.5 N solution of a reagent contain a total of $2 \times 1.5 = 3$ gram-equivalent weights of solute. One-half liter of 0.2 N reagent contains $0.5 \times 0.2 = 0.10$ gram-equivalent weight of solute. With the smaller units of weight and volume, the product of *milli*liters by normality is the number of gram-*milli*equivalent (gme) weights of reagent represented. Thus, 50.0 ml of 0.120 N reagent contain $50.0 \times 0.120 = 6.00$ gram-milliequivalents (gme) of the reagent.

2. The product of milliliters by normality represents not only the number of gme weights of solute contained in the given solution, but also the number of gme weights of another substance that will *react* with the first, or that is chemically *equivalent* to the first, whether reaction occurs or not. These relations may be summarized by the following, where the subscripts A and B indicate different substances.

$$ml_A \times N_A = \text{number of gme weights of A}$$

$$ml_B \times N_B = \text{number of gme weights of B}$$

Because the equivalent, or its smaller unit the milliequivalent, is the reactive unit in titrimetry, the number of gme weights of A and B must be the same (in the same type of reaction). Therefore,

$$ml_A \times N_A = ml_B \times N_B$$

When any three of these terms are known, the fourth is readily calculated.

EXAMPLE 1

How many milliliters of 0.1200 N solution of an acid are required to neutralize exactly 32.00 ml of 0.1500 N solution of a base? It is not necessary to know what acid or what base is used, because the concentrations of the solutions are given in the normality (equivalent) system.

$$ml_A \times 0.1200 = 32.00 \times 0.1500$$

$$ml_A = 32.00 \times 0.1500/0.1200 = 40.00$$

EXAMPLE 2

50.00 ml of 0.1000 N acid are neutralized by 40.00 ml of base. What is the normality of the base?

$$50.00 \times 0.1000 = 40.00 \times N_B$$

$$N_B = 50.00 \times 0.1000/40.00 = 0.1250$$

EXAMPLE 3

What must be the normality of a solution of hydrochloric acid so that 40.00 ml of the solution will neutralize the same amount of base as can be neutralized by 36.00 ml of 0.1250 N sulfuric acid?

$$40.00 \times N_{HCl} = 36.00 \times 0.1250$$

$$N_{HCl} = 36.00 \times 0.1250/40.00 = 0.1125$$

From the foregoing, it should be obvious that for a given type of reaction or reagent, volumes are inversely proportional to normalities. It follows, also, that equal volumes of all solutions of the same normality, for a given type of reaction, contain the same number of gme weights of reactant. Thus, 50.00 ml of 0.1000 N solutions of HCl, H_2SO_4, $HC_2H_3O_2$, or any other acid, contain 5.000 gme weights of acid, and will therefore neutralize 5.000 gme weights of base.

Dilution problems are calculated on the basis of the number of gme weights of contained solute.

EXAMPLE 4

How many milliliters of water must be added to 250.0 ml of 0.0955 N acid to make it exactly 0.0900 N? By dilution of the acid, the number of gme of solute remains unchanged; the product of the new volume by its normality must equal the product of the original volume by its normality. Let $X =$ milliliters of water to be added.

$$250.0 \times 0.0955 = (250.0 + X) \times 0.0900$$

$$23.88 = 22.50 + 0.0900X$$

$$X = 1.38/0.0900 = 15.3$$

This problem may be solved also by calculating the final (new) volume. Let $Y =$ new volume in ml. Then

$$250.0 \times 0.0955 = Y \times 0.0900$$

$$Y = 265.3$$

ml of water to be added $= 265.3 - 250.0 = 15.3$

EXAMPLE 5

What is the normality of a solution of $KHC_8H_4O_4$ made by diluting 200.0 ml of 0.0575 N solution with 25.0 ml of water?

$$200.0 \times 0.0575 = (200.0 + 25.0) \times N$$

$$N = 200.0 \times 0.0575/225.0 = 0.0511$$

3. The number of gme weights of substances, for the same type of reaction, can be added or subtracted, because the gme is the reacting unit.

EXAMPLE 6

What is the normality, as an acid, of a solution made by mixing 25.00 ml of 0.0800 N HCl and 30.00 ml of 0.1100 N H_2SO_4? In solving this problem, it is assumed that no volume change occurs on mixing the solutions; this assumption is justified when the solutions are as dilute as those commonly employed in titrimetry.

$$\text{ml} \times \quad N \quad = \text{No. of gme weights}$$
$$25.00 \times 0.0800 = 2.000 \text{ gme of HCl}$$
$$30.00 \times 0.1100 = 3.300 \text{ gme of } H_2SO_4$$
$$\overline{55.00 \times \quad N_{\text{acid}} = 5.300 \text{ gme of acid}}$$
$$N_{\text{acid}} = 5.300/55.00 = 0.0963$$

EXAMPLE 7

The following solutions are mixed: 50.00 ml of 0.1450 N NaOH, 22.00 ml of 0.1050 N H_2SO_4, and 40.00 ml of 0.0950 N HCl. Is the resulting solution acidic, alkaline, or neutral? If not neutral, what is its normality as an acid or as a base?

$$\text{ml} \qquad N \quad = \text{No. of gme acid} \qquad \text{or No. of gme base}$$
$$50.00 \times 0.1450 = \qquad\qquad\qquad\qquad\qquad 7.250 \text{ NaOH}$$
$$22.00 \times 0.1050 = 2.310 \ H_2SO_4$$
$$40.00 \times 0.0950 = 3.800 \text{ HCl} \qquad\qquad\qquad\quad -6.110$$
$$\overline{112.00 \times N \quad = \text{No. of gme excess base} = 1.140}$$
$$N_{\text{base}} = 1.140/112.0 = 0.01018$$

4. The number of gme weights of a reagent multiplied by the weight, in grams, of 1 gme of the reagent or of any substance equivalent to it (whether the substances react or not), is the number of grams of the reagent (or any substance equivalent to it). Therefore

$$ml_A \times N_A \times \text{gme wt.}_A = \text{grams}_A$$

$$ml_A \times N_A \times \text{gme wt.}_B = \text{grams}_B$$

EXAMPLE 8

A certain solution contains 1.12 gme weights of sodium hydroxide. How many grams of sodium hydroxide does the solution contain? As a base (proton acceptor), the equivalent weight of NaOH is the same as its molecular weight, that is, 40.00, and its gme weight is $40.00/1000 = 0.04000$. Hence,

$$1.12 \text{ gme} \times 0.0400 \text{ g NaOH/gme} = 0.0448 \text{ g NaOH}$$

EXAMPLE 9

How many grams of sulfuric acid can be neutralized by 44.00 ml of 0.1100 N sodium hydroxide solution? The product ml $\times$ N is the number of gme of sodium hydroxide, which must equal the number of gme of sulfuric acid neutralized by it. Sulfuric acid furnishes two protons per molecule; its gme weight is therefore $H_2SO_4/2000 = 98.08/2000 = 0.04904$. Then

$$44.00 \times 0.1100 \times 0.04904 = 0.2375 \text{ g of } H_2SO_4$$

The problem of finding the weight of a given solute to prepare a given volume of solution of a stated normality is solved in exactly the same way as the above examples.

There is merit in setting up the calculations by the factor-label method; each term or factor has an appropriate label, and the labels are handled mathematically just as are the numbers. In the computation process the labels cancel out except for the appropriate label of the value to be calculated. In the last example, the label attached to the normality term is "gme/ml." Then

$$44.00 \text{ ml} \times 0.1100 \frac{\text{gme}}{\text{ml}} \times 0.04904 \frac{\text{g } H_2SO_4}{\text{gme}} = 0.2375 \text{ g } H_2SO_4$$

5. The grams of a substance divided by its gme weight gives the number of gme weights of that substance, or of any substance with which it reacts, or to which it is chemically equivalent, whether reaction occurs or not.

EXAMPLE 10

How many gme of base are represented by 0.5000 g of $Ba(OH)_2$? It is first necessary to establish the gme of $Ba(OH)_2$ as a base. One molecule of $Ba(OH)_2$ reacts with two protons, therefore the gme weight is $Ba(OH)_2/2000 = 171.36/2000 = 0.08568$. Then

$$\frac{0.5000 \text{ g of } Ba(OH)_2}{0.08568 \text{ g/gme}} = 5.836 \text{ gme of } Ba(OH)_2$$

The mathematical relation between grams, gme weight, and number of gme weights can also be deduced from the expressions given previously, to obtain

$$ml_A \times N_A = \text{No. gme}_A = \text{No. gme}_B = \frac{g \text{ of } B}{\text{gme wt.}_B}$$

EXAMPLE 11

What is the normality of an acid solution if 45.00 ml are required to titrate 0.5000 g of pure Na_2CO_3 to H_2CO_3? In the titration of Na_2CO_3, each molecule of sodium carbonate (carbonate ion) accepts two protons; the gme weight is therefore $Na_2CO_3/2000 = 105.99/2000 = 0.05300$. Then

$$N_{\text{acid}} \text{ (gme/ml)} = \frac{0.5000 \text{ g}}{45.00 \text{ ml} \times 0.05300 \text{ g/gme}} = 0.20964$$

EXAMPLE 12

How many grams of potassium acid phthalate, $KHC_8H_4O_4$, should be taken so that in standardizing a 0.1000 N alkali, more than 40 ml but less than 50 ml of the alkali will be used in the titration? As an acid, one molecule of $KHC_8H_4O_4$ furnishes one proton; one mole is therefore one equivalent, and gme weight is $KHC_8H_4O_4/1000 = 204.23/1000 = 0.20423$. The minimum weight of potassium acid phthalate to be taken is

$$40.00 \times 0.1000 \times 0.2042 = 0.8169 \text{ g}$$

and the maximum weight that could be used is

$$50.00 \times 0.1000 \times 0.2042 = 1.021 \text{ g}$$

From a practical standpoint, about 0.9 g of $KHC_8H_4O_4$ should be taken for the standardization of a base that is about one-tenth normal.

6. In item 4 it was shown that

$$ml_A \times N_A \times \text{gme wt.}_B = \text{grams}_B$$

The percent of B in a sample is then obtained by dividing by the sample weight in grams, and multiplying by 100. All the factors involved in the calculation of the percent of desired constituent in a sample from titration data can be put into one expression, namely,

$$\% B = \frac{ml_A \times N_A \times \text{gme wt.}_B \times 100}{\text{g sample}}$$

The subscripts A represent the standard solution used for the titration, and B represents the desired constituent, which reacts with the standard solution or is chemically equivalent to it, whether direct reaction occurs or not.

EXAMPLE 13

A sample of iron ore weighing 1.1255 g is dissolved, all the iron is reduced to Fe^{++}, and the solution is titrated with 0.1005 N $KMnO_4$ solution, requiring 42.50 ml. Calculate % Fe_2O_3 in the sample. In the titration reaction Fe^{++} is oxidized to Fe^{+++} by loss of one electron. Each atom of iron is one equivalent, so the gme of the desired constituent is $Fe_2O_3/2000 = 159.69/2000 = 0.07984$.

$$\% Fe_2O_3 = \frac{42.50 \times 0.1005 \times 0.07984 \times 100}{1.1255} = 30.31$$

The general expression given above can be used for the calculation of any one of the terms, or two terms that have a fixed numerical relation, if the other terms are known.

EXAMPLE 14

0.2270 g of a pure solid acid of molecular weight 126.1 requires 45.00 ml of 0.0800 N alkali for titration. How many protons per molecule does this acid furnish in the neutralization reaction? The unknown term in this case is the gme weight of the acid.

$$100.0 \% = \frac{45.00 \times 0.0800 \times \text{gme wt.} \times 100}{0.2270}$$

$$\text{gme wt.} = \frac{100.0 \times 0.2270}{45.00 \times 0.0800 \times 100} = 0.06306$$

The equivalent weight of the acid is therefore 63.06, and the number of equivalents (protons) per molecule is $126.1/63.06 = 2$.

The indirect method can be applied to compute the composition of a mixture of two components each of which reacts with a given titrant.

EXAMPLE 15

0.5000 g of a mixture of pure KCl and KBr requires 58.03 ml of 0.1000 N $AgNO_3$ for precipitation of the halides as AgCl and AgBr. Calculate the weight of each salt in the mixture. The weight in grams of KCl divided by its gme weight is the number of gme weights of KCl; similarly, the weight of KBr divided by its gme weight is the number of gme weights of KBr. The sum of the number of gme weights of the two halides must equal the number of gme weights of $AgNO_3$ for their titrimetric precipitation, which is given by ml × N of $AgNO_3$. The gme weights are: $KCl/1000 = 0.07456$; $KBr/1000 = 0.11901$.

Let X = g of KCl in the sample; then $0.5000 - X$ = g of KBr in the sample.

$$\frac{X}{0.07456} + \frac{(0.5000 - X)}{0.11901} = 58.03 \times 0.1000$$

from which $X = 0.3206$ = g KCl, and g KBr = $0.5000 - 0.3206 = 0.1794$.

Calculation by Titer. Calculations of titrimetry can be made also by means of the **titer** of the standard solution, which is the weight of a given substance that can be titrated by 1 milliliter of a given standard solution. Letting dc represent the desired constituent and T its titer, the following relations hold:

$$N_{std} \times \text{gme wt.}_{dc} = T_{dc} \text{ of the given standard solution}$$

$$T_{dc}/\text{gme wt.}_{dc} = N_{std}$$

EXAMPLE 16

What is the sodium hydroxide titer of 0.0500 N sulfuric acid? gme wt.$_{NaOH}$ = 0.04000.
NaOH titer of this sulfuric acid = 0.0500 × 0.04000 = 0.002000.

EXAMPLE 17

What is the normality of a sulfuric acid solution having a sodium hydroxide titer of
0.00600?

$$N_{H_2SO_4} = 0.00600/0.04000 = 0.1500.$$

The titer method of calculation is advantageous in cases involving possible
ambiguity in deducing the equivalent weight. For example, the titration of
ammoniacal copper(II) solution by cyanide,

$$2Cu(NH_3)_4^{++} + 7CN^- + H_2O \rightarrow 2Cu(CN)_3^{--} + CNO^- + 2NH_4^+ + 6NH_3$$

involves not only complex ion decomposition and formation, but also redox;
on which basis should equivalency of copper be deduced? (The question is
even more frustrating with regard to cyanide.) If the KCN titrant is standardized
against copper or a copper compound, the concentration of KCN can be
expressed in terms of its copper titer.

EXAMPLE 18

A 0.6000-g sample of copper ore, determined by the cyanide method, requires
32.25 ml of KCN which has a copper titer of 0.001500. Calculate the percentage of
copper in the sample.

$$\% \, Cu = \frac{32.25 \times 0.001500 \times 100}{0.6000} = 8.062$$

The normality method can still be used for this type of problem if the "normality" of the titrant is determined by the same reaction as used in the analysis;
any error in the assumed equivalent weight in the standardization is cancelled
when the same equivalent weight is assumed in the analysis.

PROBLEMS

22-1 What is the gram milliequivalent weight of the substance given, in the process
specified? Write appropriate ionic equations.
    (a) CaO for complete neutralization.   *Ans.* 0.028040.
    (b) $H_2C_2O_4 \cdot 2H_2O$ for complete neutralization.   *Ans.* 0.063035.
    (c) $K_2Cr_2O_7$ for reduction to Cr^{+++}.   *Ans.* 0.049033.
    (d) $Ca(OH)_2$ for complete neutralization.
    (e) $BaCO_3$ for complete neutralization.
    (f) H_3PO_4 for neutralization to Na_2HPO_4.
    (g) MgI_2 for precipitation by $AgNO_3$.
    (h) K_2HPO_4 for precipitation as Ag_3PO_4.
    (i) $K_2Cr_2O_7$ for conversion to K_2CrO_4.

(j) NH_3 in a neutralization reaction.

(k) KCN in the formation of $Ag(CN)_2{}^-$.

(l) $NiCl_2$ for conversion to $Ni(CN)_4{}^{--}$.

(m) $Na_2S_2O_3$ for oxidation to $Na_2S_4O_6$.

(n) HVO_3 for reduction to VO^{++}.

22-2 What weight of solute is required to prepare the solution specified?

(a) 100.0 ml of 0.5500 *N* H_2SO_4.   *Ans.* 2.697 g.

(b) 250.0 ml of 0.0865 *N* $AgNO_3$.   *Ans.* 3.674 g.

(c) One liter of 0.1000 *N* $K_2Cr_2O_7$ for use as an oxidant (reduced to Cr^{+++}).

                                                               Ans. 4.903 g.

(d) 500.0 ml of 0.0890 *N* $BaCl_2$, for precipitation as AgCl.

(e) 250.0 ml of 0.1000 *N* $Ba(CNS)_2$, for precipitation of AgCNS.

(f) 100.0 ml of 0.05000 *N* $NaHCO_3$, for reaction with HCl.

(g) One liter of 0.05000 *N* KCN, for formation of $Ag(CN)_2{}^-$.

(h) 600.0 ml of 0.1100 *N* $KMnO_4$, reduction product Mn^{++}.

(i) 200.0 ml of 0.0950 *N* $Ce(SO_4)_2$, reduction product Ce^{+++}.

(j) 150.0 ml of 0.1250 *N* $FeSO_4 \cdot 7H_2O$, oxidation product Fe^{+++}.

(k) One liter of 0.05000 *N* $KHC_2O_4 \cdot H_2C_2O_4 \cdot 2H_2O$, for complete neutralization.

(l) One liter of 0.05000 *N* $KHC_2O_4 \cdot H_2C_2O_4 \cdot 2H_2O$, for oxidation to CO_2.

(m) 400.0 ml of 0.08000 *N* KI, for oxidation to $IO_3{}^-$.

22-3 How many milliliters of 0.1100 *N* acid are required for the complete neutralization of the substance given?

(a) 32.50 ml of 0.1010 *N* NaOH.   *Ans.* 29.84.

(b) 43.75 ml of 0.1255 *N* $Ba(OH)_2$.   *Ans.* 49.91.

(c) 43.75 ml of 0.1255 *M* $Ba(OH)_2$.

(d) 44.02 ml of 0.0570 *N* NH_3.

(e) 25.00 ml of 0.1110 *M* Na_2CO_3.

22-4 What volume of water must be added to 225.0 ml of 0.1080 *N* acid to make it exactly 0.1000 *N*?   *Ans.* 18.0 ml.

22-5 What weight of sample of soda ash (impure Na_2CO_3) should be taken for analysis so that when completely neutralized by 0.1450 *N* acid, each milliliter of acid used will represent 1.000% of Na_2CO_3 in the sample?   *Ans.* 0.7685 g.

22-6 A sample of pure element, M, weighing 0.1358 g, is dissolved in acid to form M^{++}, which is titrated to $MO_3{}^-$ by 40.00 ml of 0.2000 *N* oxidizing agent. Calculate the atomic weight of the element M.   *Ans.* 50.92.

22-7 (a) 32.40 ml of 0.0880 *N* acid is mixed with 46.60 ml of 0.1100 *N* acid; what is the normality of the mixture? (b) If the solution in (a) is diluted to 100.0 ml with water, what is the acid normality of the solution?   *Ans.* (a) 0.1010.   (b) 0.07977.

22-8 35.20 ml of 0.0800 *N* acid and 44.80 ml of 0.1200 *N* acid are mixed and then diluted with water to 100.0 ml. What is the normality (a) of the solution before adding water, and (b) of the final solution?

22-9 35.00 ml of 0.1100 *N* NaOH and 50.00 ml of $Ba(OH)_2$ of unknown normality are mixed and diluted to 100.0 ml; the solution is exactly neutralized by 42.50 ml of 0.1800 *N* HCl. What is the normality

(a) of the alkali mixture before dilution?

(b) of the diluted alkali mixture?

(c) of the $Ba(OH)_2$ solution used?

22-10   What volume of 0.5000 N sulfuric acid must be added to 200.0 ml of 0.1500 N sulfuric acid so that after dilution to 500.0 ml the solution is exactly 0.1000 N?

22-11   What weight of sample of impure phosphoric acid should be taken for analysis so that when completely neutralized with 0.1250 N NaOH, each milliliter of alkali used will represent (*a*) 0.500% of H_3PO_4 in the sample; (*b*) 1.000% of P_2O_5 in the sample?

22-12   What must be the normality of a solution of silver nitrate so that in titrating 0.5000-g samples of impure sodium chloride, the percentage of NaCl is twice the number of milliliters of silver nitrate used?

22-13   What is the maximum weight of pure oxalic acid dihydrate that can be taken so that in standardizing 0.1050 N alkali, a 50-ml buret will not have to be refilled?

22-14   What weight of pure solid $Ba(OH)_2 \cdot 8H_2O$ must be added to 250.0 ml of 0.0900 N alkali to make it exactly one-tenth normal?

22-15   A sample of pure vanadium metal weighing 0.1612 g is dissolved in acid and brought to an intermediate oxidation state. The vanadium solution requires 42.20 ml of 0.1500 N oxidizing agent for titration to VO_3^-. What is the oxidation state of the vanadium before titration?

23

NEUTRALIZATION THEORY

Different acids and bases vary considerably in their extent of ionization, or the energy with which a proton can be donated to and accepted by the base; that is, they vary in acidic or basic *strength*, and therefore in the extent of their interaction. The student must have a thorough understanding of the equilibrium principles involved in neutralimetry in order to know what acid-base titrations are feasible, and in order to comprehend the change of *p*H during titration. The *p*H at the stoichiometric point is especially important in the selection of an appropriate indicator.

Because acids and bases vary considerably in strength, several different cases of neutralization titrations arise; these are treated in some detail below. The various mathematical formulations involved in calculating [H$^+$] and/or *p*H have been given in detail in Chapter 5, to which reference should be made in the study of the present chapter.

Titration of a Strong Acid with a Strong Base

This type of neutralization is illustrated by the titration of hydrochloric acid by sodium hydroxide solution. The reaction is simply

$$H^+ + OH^- \rightarrow H_2O$$

and as titration progresses, the hydrogen ion concentration is decreased (*p*H increased). Near the stoichiometric point the change becomes very rapid, and this rapid change in *p*H is the basis for detecting the end point of the titration. The change in *p*H during titration is conveniently represented by a graph or plot of *p*H against the volume of titrant. Experimentally, the *p*H is measured with a pH meter or a potentiometer during the course of the titration. Values for plotting a pH titration curve can be calculated as illustrated below.

EXAMPLE 1

50.00 ml of 0.1000 N HCl are titrated with 0.1000 N NaOH; calculate the pH at several stages during the titration.

a. Before any base is added, the pH corresponds to that of a 0.1000 N (which is also 0.1000 M) HCl solution. For all practical purposes, the HCl is completely ionized, therefore [H$^+$] $= 0.1000$, and $pH = 1.00$. (It is customary to give pH values only to two decimal figures.)

b. After 10.00 ml of 0.1000 N NaOH have been added, an equivalent amount of HCl has been neutralized, leaving the equivalent of 40.00 ml of the acid unneutralized; the total volume of the solution is now 60.00 ml. Hence, [H$^+$] $= 0.1000 \times 40.00/60.00 = 0.0667$, and $pH = 1.18$.

Similarly, after 20.00 ml of NaOH have been added, [H$^+$] $= 0.1000 \times 30.00/70.00 = 0.0427$, and $pH = 1.37$. Additional values for other points *up to, but not including, the stoichiometric point* are calculated in exactly the same way. Only when the concentration of unneutralized acid is less than about five times the [H$^+$] furnished by water (in this example, at 49.9995 ml of NaOH added, which is far beyond the measuring precision of the buret) is it necessary to use the rigorous calculation of equation (5-32). Even at $C_A = 5 \times 10^{-7}$, the difference between the approximate calculation ($pH = 6.30$) and the exact calculation ($pH = 6.28$) is of little significance.

c. At the stoichiometric point (50.00 ml of added NaOH) the system is merely an aqueous solution of sodium chloride; the pH is therefore that of water.

$$[H^+] = [OH^-] = \sqrt{K_w} = \sqrt{1.0 \times 10^{-14}} = 1.0 \times 10^{-7}$$

and $pH = 7.00$.

d. After the stoichiometric point has been passed, OH$^-$ is in excess, and the pH is calculated from [OH$^-$] and K_w. Only at an extremely small excess of base is there any difference between the approximate calculation and the exact calculation of equation (5-33). At 50.10 ml of added NaOH there is 0.10 ml of 0.1000 N NaOH in excess, and the total volume is 100.10 ml.

$$[OH^-] = 0.1000 \times 0.10/100.10 = 0.00010 = 1.0 \times 10^{-4}$$

$$[H^+] = K_w/[OH^-] = (1.0 \times 10^{-14})/(1.0 \times 10^{-4}) = 1.0 \times 10^{-10}$$

and $pH = 10.00$. Alternatively, [OH$^-$] $= 1.0 \times 10^{-4}$, $pOH = 4.00$, and $pH = 14.00 - 4.00 = 10.00$. Similar calculations are made for additional increments of NaOH beyond the stoichiometric point.

Calculations for this titration are summarized in Table 23-1. Curve A in Fig. 23-1 is a graph in which the pH is plotted against the volume of sodium hydroxide solution. From the point 0.10 ml before the stoichiometric point (49.90 ml of NaOH added) to a point 0.10 ml after the stoichiometric point (50.10 ml of NaOH added) the pH has changed from 4 to 10. This very rapid change of pH makes possible the determination of the end point of the titration, by the use of an indicator that changes color with the change in pH. The color

Table 23-1 Titration of 50.00 ml of 0.1000 N HCl with
0.1000 N NaOH

NaOH Added, ml	Equiv. ml of HCl Unneutralized	Total Volume of Solution, ml	[H$^+$]	pH
0.0	50.00	50.00	0.1000	1.00
10.00	40.00	60.00	0.0667	1.18
20.00	30.00	70.00	0.0427	1.37
30.00	20.00	80.00	0.0250	1.60
40.00	10.00	90.00	0.0111	1.96
45.00	5.00	95.00	0.0054	2.27
49.00	1.00	99.00	0.0010	3.00
49.90	0.10	99.90	0.00010	4.00
49.99	0.01	99.99	0.00001	5.00
50.00	0.00	100.00	1.0×10^{-7}	7.00
	Excess NaOH, ml		[OH$^-$]	
50.01	0.01	100.01	0.00001	9.00
50.10	0.10	100.10	0.00010	10.00
51.00	1.00	101.00	0.0010	11.00
55.00	5.00	105.00	0.0048	11.68
60.00	10.00	110.00	0.0091	11.96

change of most two-color indicators corresponds to a pH change of about 2 units. Because the stoichiometric point in this titration occurs when the solution has a pH of 7.00, an indicator such as bromthymol blue or phenol red, showing its color change near pH 7, would be appropriate, so that the end point (the experimentally determined point at which the indicator color change shows when to stop the titration) will coincide with the stoichiometric or equivalence point.

In actual practice, any indicator showing its color change in the region from about pH 4 to 10 would be satisfactory for this titration. For example, the midpoint of the color change interval for methyl orange is about pH 3.8. In this region the addition of one drop (about 0.05 ml or less) of the alkali is sufficient to change the pH by about 1.5 units and to cause methyl orange to change from its red to its yellow form. Similarly, just beyond the stoichiometric point, a single drop of dilute alkali will change the pH through the phenolphthalein color interval (midpoint at about pH 8.8) and change phenolphthalein from colorless to pink. In a total volume of 50 ml of titrant, an error of one drop represents only about one part per thousand, an error that can be tolerated for ordinary analytical purposes.

The calculations previously illustrated were very simple by reason of the fact that the acid being titrated and the alkali used as titrant were of the same

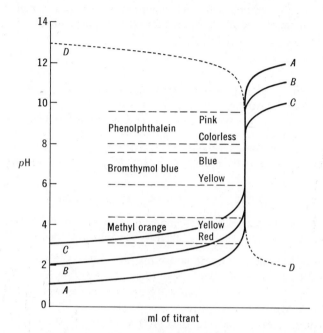

Fig. 23-1 Titration curves. Hydrochloric acid titrated with equivalent sodium hydroxide: *A*, 0.1 *N*; *B*, 0.01 *N*; *C*, 0.001 *N*. *D*, 0.1 *N* sodium hydroxide titrated with 0.1 *N* hydrochloric acid.

normality, hence reacted in a 1:1 volume ratio. When the first solution, after measurement of its volume, is diluted with water before starting the titration, or when the two solutions are of different normalities, or when a weighed amount of a solid acid is dissolved in water and titrated, the calculations are made most conveniently on the basis of the number of gme weights of acid remaining after each increment of added alkali and the total volume of the solution at that stage.

EXAMPLE 2

50.00 ml of 0.1000 *N* HCl, diluted to 100.0 ml, are titrated with 0.1250 *N* NaOH.

a. 50.00 ml of 0.1000 *N* HCl = 5.000 gme weights of HCl. By dilution of this solution to 100.0 ml its concentration is $5.000/100.0 = 0.05000$ *N*; $[H^+] = 0.05000$, and $pH = 1.30$.

b. Addition of 10.00 ml of the 0.1250 *N* NaOH is the addition of $10.00 \times 0.1250 = 1.250$ gme weights of NaOH, which neutralizes 1.250 gme weights of acid. The amount of acid remaining is therefore $5.000 - 1.250 = 3.750$ gme weights in 110.0 ml of solution; $[H^+] = 3.750/110.0 = 0.0341$, and $pH = 1.47$. Similar calculations are made for other points in the titration. The student should complete the calculations, tabulate the results, and plot the titration curve. An important point in this example is the calculation of the volume of the alkali required for exact neutralization, for location of the stoichiometric point.

EXAMPLE 3

0.4375 g of sulfamic acid, NH_2SO_3H, a monoprotic strong acid, is dissolved in 75.00 ml of water and titrated with 0.1100 N alkali.

a. Sulfamic acid is a monoprotic acid; its gme is $NH_2SO_3H/1000 = 97.09/1000 = 0.09709$. The weight of acid taken is $0.4375/0.09709 = 4.506$ gme, and the normality of the solution is $4.506/75.00 = 0.06000$. $[H^+] = 0.06000$, and $pH = 1.22$.

b. After addition of 10.00 ml of the 0.1100 N alkali the concentration of unneutralized acid is

$$[4.506 - (10.00 \times 0.1100)]/85.00 = 0.04007$$

and $pH = 1.40$. Similar calculations should be made by the student for other points in the titration, including the volume of alkali required for exact neutralization.

By means of the calculation methods illustrated above, it is of course possible to calculate the volume of alkali used when the solution has a specified pH. In Example 3, what volume of alkali will have been added when the solution has a pH of 2.70? A pH of 2.70 corresponds to $[H^+] = 0.0020$, the concentration of unneutralized acid. Let $X = $ ml of 0.1100 N alkali to give this pH in the titration; then

$$\frac{4.506 - (X \times 0.1100)}{75.00 + X} = 0.0020$$

from which $X = 38.90$ ml.

Feasibility of a Titration.   A titration is said to be **feasible** if the observed change, which marks the end point, occurs upon the addition of a volume of titrant that is within the error, relative to the total volume of titrant used, that is allowable for the purpose at hand. Because many indicators show a detectable color change when the pH of the solution changes by about two pH units, a neutralization titration is feasible if this change in pH results from the addition of a volume increment of titrant within the allowable error according to the requirements of the analysis. If this error is to be only about one part per thousand, the indicator color change should result from the addition of one small drop of titrant when a total volume of about 50 ml is used, as illustrated in Example 1. If an error of two parts per thousand can be tolerated, the use of about two drops of titrant to change the color of the indicator is permissible, and so on.

Effect of Concentration.   If 0.0100 N HCl is titrated with 0.0100 N NaOH, the initial pH is 2.00, and the titration curve of pH against volume of alkali lies one pH unit higher than that for Example 1, up to the stoichiometric point, and one pH unit lower beyond the stoichiometric point, as shown by curve B in Fig. 23-1; the stoichiometric point pH is still 7.00. In this case the pH change from 49.9 ml to 50.1 ml of base is from 5 to 9. For the titration of 0.0010 N solutions (curve C in Fig. 23-1) the same volume increment corresponds to a pH change from 6 to 8; in this case, methyl orange indicator would show its color change too early, and phenolphthalein too late in the titration, and it would be necessary to choose an indicator changing color very close to pH 7, such as bromthymol blue or phenol red, if reliable results are to be obtained. A concentration of 0.001 N strong acid and/or strong base is therefore about the lower concentration limit of feasibility for titration.

Titration of a Strong Base with a Strong Acid

This case is entirely analogous to the titration of a strong acid by a strong base, except for the direction of titration. At the start (alkaline solution) the solution has a high concentration of OH^- and therefore a high pH. The pH decreases gradually at first, then more rapidly in the vicinity of the stoichiometric point, and again gradually after the stoichiometric point has been passed.

EXAMPLE 4

50.00 ml of 0.1000 N NaOH solution are titrated with 0.1000 N HCl.

a. Before any acid is added, $[OH^-] = 0.1000$, pOH $= 1.00$, and pH $= 13.00$.

b. After addition of 10.00 ml of acid, $[OH^-] = 0.1000 \times 40.00/60.00 = 0.0667$; pOH $= 1.18$, and pH $= 12.82$. Similar calculations are used for the increments of added acid, up to but not including the stoichiometric point.

c. At the stoichiometric point, pH $= 7.00$.

d. Beyond the stoichiometric point, the $[H^+]$ is calculated from the amount of excess acid and the total volume of the solution. For example, when 51.00 ml of acid have been added, this is an excess of 1.00 ml of 0.1000 N acid in a total volume of 101.00 ml. $[H^+] = 0.1000 \times 1.00/101.00 = 0.00100$, and pH $= 3.00$.

The titration curve for this case is shown by curve D in Fig. 23-1. It will be noted that this curve is the reciprocal of the curve for titration of 0.1000 N strong acid by 0.1000 N strong base. All of the same considerations as in the strong acid–strong base titration apply in the matter of choice of indicator, effect of concentration, and feasibility of titration.

Titration of a Weak Acid with a Strong Base

This type of titration may be illustrated by the general equation

$$HA + OH^- \rightarrow H_2O + A^-$$

in which HA represents a weak monoprotic acid, and A^- is its anion (salt). This case differs from the strong acid–strong base titration in four important respects: (1) The hydrogen ion concentration at the start is considerably smaller (*p*H is larger) than for a strong acid. (2) In the early stages of titration the *p*H of the solution increases rather rapidly, because the ionization of the weak acid is suppressed by the common ion effect of the anion (highly ionized salt) formed by neutralization; see pp. 60–62. (3) For a considerable distance on either side of half-neutralization (i.e., from about 10 to 90% or about 20 to 80% titration, depending on K_a of the acid) the titration curve is approximately linear because this is a *buffer region* (see pp. 62 and 75). (4) The stoichiometric point does not occur at *p*H 7.00, because of the reverse reaction in which the anion A$^-$ (the conjugate base of HA) acquires some protons from water, leaving the solution somewhat alkaline.

EXAMPLE 5

50.00 ml of 0.1000 *N* acetic acid, HAc, are titrated with 0.1000 *N* NaOH solution; K_a of HAc $= 1.8 \times 10^{-5}$. Calculate the *p*H values for construction of the titration curve.

a. In the acetic acid solution, before any alkali is added, $[H^+] = [Ac^-]$, and $[HAc] = 0.1000$ (approximately); actually, $[HAc]$ is slightly less than 0.1000, but the slight amount of HAc that is ionized can be ignored without introducing appreciable error (see p. 58).

$$K_a = \frac{[H^+][Ac^-]}{[HAc]}$$

hence,

$$[H^+] = \sqrt{K_a[HAc]} = \sqrt{(1.8 \times 10^{-5})(0.100)}$$

$$= \sqrt{1.8 \times 10^{-6}} = 1.34 \times 10^{-3}$$

and *p*H $= 2.87$. For comparison, note that 0.100 *N* solution of HCl has a *p*H of 1.00.

b. As soon as some sodium hydroxide has been added, neutralizing an equivalent amount of acetic acid and forming an equivalent amount of acetate ion, the common ion effect comes into play, and the calculation of the hydrogen ion concentration must take this effect into account.

$$K_a = \frac{[H^+][Ac^-]}{[HAc]} \quad \text{and} \quad [H^+] = K_a \frac{[HAc]}{[Ac^-]}$$

Addition of 1.00 ml of 0.1000 *N* NaOH (i.e., 0.100 gme of NaOH) neutralizes 0.100 gme of HAc and leaves $5.000 - 0.100 = 4.900$ gme of HAc, and forms 0.100 gme of Ac$^-$, in a total volume of 51.00 ml.

$$[HAc] = 4.900/51.00 = 0.0961 \quad \text{and} \quad [Ac^-] = 0.100/51.00 = 0.00196$$

$$[H^+] = 1.8 \times 10^{-5} \times 0.096/0.00196 = 8.8 \times 10^{-4}$$

and *p*H $= 3.05$.

The above calculation using the Henderson equation (5-45) is an approximation that is valid in the buffer region of the titration. Near the start of the titration, where $[Ac^-] \ll [HAc]$, and near the stoichiometric point, where $[Ac^-] \gg [HAc]$, the exact method of equation (5-44) should be used. For the above example,

$$[H^+] = (1.8 \times 10^{-5})(0.096 - [H^+])/(0.00196 + [H^+])$$

Solving the quadratic equation, $[H^+] = 6.5 \times 10^{-4}$ and $pH = 3.19$, a value somewhat different from that calculated above. The closer the calculated point is to the initial point or to the stoichiometric point, and the smaller the value of K_a, the greater the difference between the approximate and the exact calculations.

Because the reacting solutions in this example are of the same concentration, and the acetic acid unneutralized and the acetate ion formed by neutralization are in the same solution, it is not necessary, in the approximate calculations, to use the actual molar concentrations of the substances. It is more convenient to use the "equivalent volumes" of HAc and Ac$^-$, which are, of course, in the same ratio as their molar concentrations; that is, the original concentration and the final volume would cancel in the calculation of $[H^+]$ from the K_a expression. For example, addition of 1.00 ml of 0.1000 N NaOH can be considered as neutralizing 1.00 ml of 0.1000 N HAc, leaving 49.00 ml of acid unneutralized, and forming the equivalent of 1.00 ml of 0.1000 N Ac$^-$. Hence,

$$[H^+] = 1.8 \times 10^{-5} \times 49.00/1.00 = 8.8 \times 10^{-4} \quad \text{and} \quad pH = 3.05$$

the same value that was calculated previously from the actual molar concentrations of HAc and Ac$^-$.

It will be noted in this example that addition of only 1 ml of NaOH solution changed the pH from 2.87 to 3.05, a change of 0.18 pH unit (or from 2.87 to 3.19, through 0.32 pH unit if the exact calculation is used). This is a greater change in pH than was produced by addition of 10 ml of alkali in the titration of 0.1000 N HCl (Example 1), and illustrates in a striking way the influence of even a small amount of acetate ion in suppressing the ionization of acetic acid. These calculations also illustrate the fact that the solution of acetic acid has relatively small buffer capacity.

When 10.00 ml of NaOH have been added,

$$[H^+] = 1.8 \times 10^{-5} \times 40.00/10.00 = 7.2 \times 10^{-5} \quad \text{and} \quad pH = 4.14$$

When 25.00 ml of alkali have been added,

$$[H^+] = 1.8 \times 10^{-5} \times 25.00/25.00 = 1.8 \times 10^{-5} \quad \text{and} \quad pH = 4.74$$

In all cases of weak monoprotic acids, at the half-neutralization point $[HA] = [A^-]$, hence $[H^+] = K_a$, and $pH = pK_a$.

Additional points up to the stoichiometric point are calculated in exactly the same way as illustrated above.

c. At the stoichiometric point the system is an aqueous solution of sodium acetate. The acetate ion is the conjugate base of acetic acid:

$$Ac^- + H_2O \rightleftharpoons HAc + OH^-$$

and the solution at this point is not neutral, but slightly alkaline. The hydroxyl ion concentration of the solution depends upon the K_a of acetic acid, the concentration of acetate ion, and K_w, and is calculated by equation (5-21) or (5-39) as derived in Chap. 5:

$$[OH^-] = \sqrt{\frac{K_w[Ac^-]}{K_a}}$$

By using the known numerical values for the three terms under the radical, $[OH^-]$ can be calculated, then converted to pH in the usual way through K_w or pK_w. Because the relations developed above for acetic acid apply generally to the conjugate bases of weak acids, and the pH of the solution, rather than $[OH^-]$, is usually the item desired for plotting and/or for the selection of an indicator, the conversion can be done once and for all, for the various cases, as follows.

$$[H^+] = \frac{K_w}{[OH^-]} = \frac{K_w}{\sqrt{K_w[A^-]/K_a}} = K_w\sqrt{\frac{K_a}{K_w[A^-]}} = \sqrt{\frac{K_w{}^2 K_a}{K_w[A^-]}} = \sqrt{\frac{K_w K_a}{[A^-]}}$$

Now take the logarithm of the expression, remembering that multiplication (division) of numbers is performed by adding (subtracting) their logarithms, and that the square root is taken by dividing the logarithm by 2.

$$\log [H^+] = \tfrac{1}{2}(\log K_w + \log K_a - \log [A^-])$$

Changing signs (i.e., multiplying the equation by -1):

$$-\log [H^+] = \tfrac{1}{2}(-\log K_w - \log K_a + \log [A^-])$$

Table 23-2   Titration of 50.00 ml of 0.1000 N Acetic Acid with 0.1000 N Sodium Hydroxide

NaOH Added, ml	Equiv. ml of HAc Unneutralized	Equiv. ml of Ac⁻ Formed	Total Volume, ml	$[H^+]$	pH
0.00	50.00	0.00	50.00	1.34×10^{-3}	2.87
1.00	49.00	1.00	51.00	8.8×10^{-4}	3.05
5.00	45.00	5.00	55.00	1.62×10^{-4}	3.79
10.00	40.00	10.00	60.00	7.2×10^{-5}	4.14
20.00	30.00	20.00	70.00	2.7×10^{-5}	4.57
25.00	25.00	25.00	75.00	1.8×10^{-5}	4.74
30.00	20.00	30.00	80.00	1.20×10^{-5}	4.92
40.00	10.00	40.00	90.00	4.5×10^{-6}	5.35
45.00	5.00	45.00	95.00	2.0×10^{-6}	5.70
49.00	1.00	49.00	99.00	3.7×10^{-7}	6.43
49.90	0.10	49.90	99.90	3.6×10^{-8}	7.44
49.99	0.01	49.99	99.99	3.6×10^{-9}	8.44
50.00	0.00	50.00	100.00	1.9×10^{-9}	8.72
	Excess NaOH, ml			$[OH^-]$	
50.01	0.01		100.01	1.0×10^{-5}	9.00
50.10	0.10		100.10	1.0×10^{-4}	10.00
51.00	1.00		101.00	1.0×10^{-3}	11.00
55.00	5.00		105.00	4.8×10^{-3}	11.68
60.00	10.00		110.00	9.1×10^{-3}	11.96

But $-\log [H^+] = pH$, $-\log K_w = pK_w$, and $-\log K_a = pK_a$. Therefore,

$$pH = \tfrac{1}{2}(pK_w + pK_a + \log [A^-])$$

$[A^-]$ is the anion (salt) concentration, in moles per liter, at the stoichiometric point; at 25°C, $pK_w = 14.00$.

In this example, $50.00 \times 0.1000 = 5.000$ gme of HAc are neutralized, and the volume at the stoichiometric point is 100.00 ml. Therefore, $[Ac^-] = 0.05000$, and $\log 0.050 = 0.70 - 2 = -1.30$. $K_a = 1.8 \times 10^{-5}$, and $pK_a = 4.74$. Then

$$pH = \tfrac{1}{2}(14.00 + 4.74 - 1.30) = 8.72$$

and the stoichiometric point of the titration occurs in slightly alkaline solution.

d. Beyond the stoichiometric point the pH is calculated from the amount of excess alkali and the total volume of the solution, exactly as in the case of the strong acid–strong base titration. The acetate ion present in the solution has no direct influence on the ionization of the strong base.

Table 23-2 shows the calculated pH values for several points in this titration, and the titration curve is shown in Fig. 23-2. The differences between the weak acid and the strong acid cases, given on pp. 287–288, are now obvious. The solution becomes neutral (pH 7.00) at about 49.7 ml of added NaOH, or about 0.6% before the stoichiometric point. Phenolphthalein has the midpoint of its color change interval at pH 8.8,

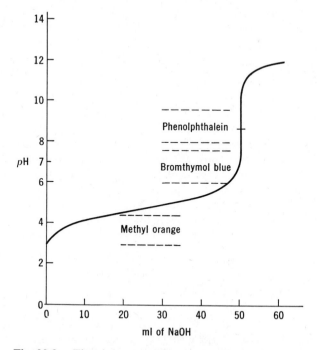

Fig. 23-2   Titration curve. 50.0 ml of 0.100 N acetic acid titrated with 0.100 N sodium hydroxide.

and is therefore a suitable indicator. Methyl orange, although suitable for use in the titration of 0.1 N HCl, is entirely unsuitable for the titration of acetic acid; methyl orange, with midpoint of its color change interval at pH 3.8, would change color very gradually, and would be mostly in its alkaline form when only about 10% of the acetic acid had been neutralized.

All the variations (dilution before titration, use of solutions of different normalities, or of weighed amounts of solid weak acids dissolved in a known volume of water for titration) previously illustrated for the titration of a strong acid, can be applied to the titration of weak acids by expressing the concentrations of HA and A⁻ in terms of millimoles (derived from milliequivalents) at each desired calculation point, and calculating [H⁺] and/or pH by the use of K_a of the acid being titrated.

EXAMPLE 6

50.0 ml of 0.100 N HAc are diluted to 75.0 ml and titrated with 0.125 N NaOH.

a. At the start, $50.0 \times 0.100 = 5.00$ gme (also millimoles) of HAc are contained in 75.0 ml of solution.

$$[HAc] = 5.00/75.0 = 0.0667$$

$$[H^+] = \sqrt{(1.8 \times 10^{-5})(0.067)} = 1.10 \times 10^{-3}$$

and $pH = 2.96$.

b. After addition of 1.0 ml of 0.125 N NaOH ($= 0.125$ gme), an equivalent amount of HAc is neutralized and an equivalent amount of Ac⁻ is formed, in a total volume of 76.0 ml.

$$[HAc] = (5.00 - 0.125)/76.0 = 0.0642$$

$$[Ac^-] = 0.125/76.0 = 0.00164$$

$$[H^+] = \frac{(1.8 \times 10^{-5})(6.4 \times 10^{-2})}{1.64 \times 10^{-3}} = 7.0 \times 10^{-4}$$

and $pH = 3.15$. Other points in the titration are calculated in the same way.

c. The volume of NaOH required to reach the stoichiometric point is $50.0 \times 0.100/0.125 = 40.0$ ml, and the total volume of solution is then 115.0 ml. This volume of solution contains 5.00 gme of Ac⁻, and $[Ac^-] = 5.00/115.0 = 0.0435$; log $0.0435 = -1.36$. $pH = \frac{1}{2}(14.00 + 4.74 - 1.36) = 8.69$.

d. Beyond the stoichiometric point, the pH is calculated from the amount of excess alkali added and the volume of the solution, exactly as in previous examples.

From the ionization constant of the weak acid being titrated, it is possible to calculate the error that would be produced if the titration were stopped at a pH other than the pH of the stoichiometric point.

EXAMPLE 7

Calculate the percent error that would result from the use of bromcresol purple indicator (pH interval 5.2–6.8) in the titration of 50.0 ml of 0.100 N HAc with 0.100 N NaOH. The midpoint of the indicator color change is at pH 6.0. Assume that titration is stopped at this pH, and calculate the ratio $[HAc]/[Ac^-]$ at this pH, which corresponds to $[H^+] = 1.0 \times 10^{-6}$.

$$\frac{[HAc]}{[Ac^-]} = \frac{[H^+]}{K_2} = \frac{1.0 \times 10^{-6}}{1.8 \times 10^{-5}} = 5.6 \times 10^{-2}$$

That is, there is 0.056 mole of unneutralized HAc for every 1.00 mole of Ac^- that has been formed or every mole of HAc that has been neutralized; stated in another way, if 1.056 moles of HAc were taken, then at pH 6.0, 1.00 mole has been titrated and 0.056 mole is not yet titrated.   Hence,

$$\% \text{ error} = \frac{0.056}{1.056} \times 100 = 5.3$$

an error so large as to be intolerable.

Effect of Concentration of Weak Acid.   If acetic acid of lower concentration, e.g., 0.010 N, is titrated with 0.010 N NaOH, the following conditions will prevail, compared to titration of more concentrated solutions: (1) the pH at the start and early in the titration will be *slightly* higher. (2) The pH at intermediate stages will be approximately the same, because $[H^+]$ is determined by the *ratio* $[HAc]/[Ac^-]$. (3) The pH at the stoichiometric point will be slightly lower, owing to the lower concentration of the anion. (4) The pH after the stoichiometric point will be significantly lower because of the lower concentration of excess alkali added. Because of conditions (3) and (4), the rate of change of pH with addition of titrant in the vicinity of the stoichiometric point is more gradual, and the end point, shown by color change of the indicator, will not be as sharp as when more concentrated solutions are used. The practical limit of feasibility for acetic acid titrations is about 0.010 N solution, unless errors of the order of one percent can be tolerated.

Effect of Acid Strength.   For a given normality of acid being titrated, the following effects will be noted as the acid becomes progressively weaker (smaller K_a): (1) The initial pH is higher, and the rate of change in early stages of titration is greater; indeed, when K_a is about 10^{-10} (e.g., boric acid) or less, the greatest rate of change of pH is at the start of the titration. (2) The rate of change of pH near the stoichiometric point is more gradual. (3) The reverse reaction is more extensive, hence the stoichiometric point pH is higher and the rate of change of pH with excess alkali is smaller. These factors, illustrated in Fig. 23-3, result in an indistinct end point (gradual change of color of the indicator), and the titration will not give reliable results. The situation just described is true for titration of 0.10 N solutions of acids for which K_a is less than about 10^{-7}.

Combining the effect of the concentration of solution and the K_a of the weak acid, it may be stated that if the product $K_a[HA]$ is less than about 10^{-8}, the titration is not feasible.

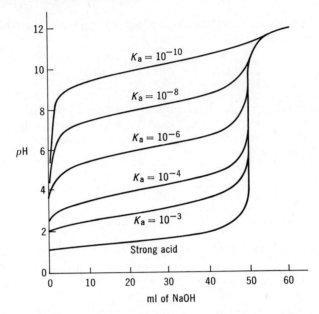

Fig. 23-3   Titration curves. 50.0 ml of 0.100 N HA of different strengths titrated with 0.100 N sodium hydroxide.

Titration of a Weak Base with a Strong Acid

All of the features of this type of titration are analogous in principle to the titration of a weak acid by a strong base.

EXAMPLE 8

Calculate the pH during titration of 50.0 ml of 0.100 N NH$_4$OH with 0.100 N HCl; $K_b = 1.8 \times 10^{-5}$.

a. At the start, [OH$^-$] = [NH$_4{}^+$], and [NH$_4$OH] = 0.100

$$[\text{OH}^-] = \sqrt{(1.8 \times 10^{-5})(0.100)} = 1.34 \times 10^{-3}$$

$$p\text{OH} = 2.87 \quad \text{and} \quad p\text{H} = 11.13$$

b. The titration reaction is

$$\text{NH}_4\text{OH} + \text{H}^+ \rightleftharpoons \text{NH}_4{}^+ + \text{H}_2\text{O}$$

During the titration, the NH$_4{}^+$ formed suppresses the ionization of NH$_4$OH, and

$$[\text{OH}^-] = K_b \frac{[\text{NH}_4\text{OH}]}{[\text{NH}_4{}^+]}$$

At 5.00 ml of HCl added,

$$[\text{OH}^-] = (1.8 \times 10^{-5}) \times 45.0/5.00 = 1.62 \times 10^{-4}$$

from which $pOH = 3.79$ and $pH = 10.21$. Other points are calculated similarly. At half titration,

$$[NH_4OH] = [NH_4{}^+], \quad [OH^-] = K_b, \quad \text{and} \quad pOH = pK_b$$

c. At the stoichiometric point the pH is that of a solution of 0.050 N NH$_4{}^+$, which reacts as shown by the reverse of the neutralization reaction, and the solution is therefore slightly acidic. The hydrogen ion concentration is calculated by equation (5-23), or by equation (5-36) if it is noted that K_a for the weak acid, NH$_4{}^+$, is identical with K_w/K_b, where K_b is the ionization constant of the weak base NH$_4$OH:

$$[H^+] = \sqrt{\frac{K_w[NH_4{}^+]}{K_b}}$$

Expressing this relation in terms of pH (by treatment analogous to that on pp. 290–291) gives

$$pH = \tfrac{1}{2}(pK_w - pK_b - \log[NH_4{}^+])$$

In the example illustrated, [NH$_4{}^+$] at the stoichiometric point is 0.050; log 0.050 = -1.30; therefore

$$pH = \tfrac{1}{2}(14.00 - 4.74 + 1.30) = 5.28$$

which occurs in the color change interval of methyl red indicator.

d. After the stoichiometric point, $[H^+]$ and pH are calculated from the amount of excess acid and the total volume of solution. For example, at 0.10 ml excess 0.100 N HCl, the total volume is 100.1 ml, $[H^+] = 1.0 \times 10^{-4}$, and $pH = 4.00$.

All the variations regarding dilution before titration, use of a titrant of different normality from the weak base being titrated, etc., are calculated by application of the same principles as illustrated previously. The effects of concentration and of magnitude of K_b, and the feasibility factors, are also analogous to those given for titration of weak acids.

Weak Acid–Weak Base Reaction

The titration of a weak acid by a weak base (or the reverse), using color indicators for end point detection, is not feasible. Near the equivalence point the rate of change of pH with addition of small increments of dilute titrant is very small and the color change of the indicator is therefore so gradual that a decision when to stop the titration can hardly be made with reliability, even by comparison with a reference solution containing the salt and indicator. The reason for the gradual change is apparent from the nature of the solution near (on either side of) the equivalence point. Consider, for example, the titration of HAc ($K_a = 1.8 \times 10^{-5}$) by NH$_4$OH ($K_b = 1.8 \times 10^{-5}$):

$$HAc + NH_4OH \rightleftarrows NH_4{}^+ + Ac^- + H_2O$$

The change of pH during titration, up to the equivalence point, is not different from the titration of HAc with NaOH. For example, in the titration of 50.0 ml of 0.100 N HAc with 0.100 N NH_4OH, when 49.0 ml of NH_4OH have been added, $[H^+] = 3.7 \times 10^{-7}$ and $pH = 6.43$. When 51.0 ml of NH_4OH have been added, the solution contains the equivalent of 50.0 ml of 0.100 N NH_4^+ and 1.0 ml of excess NH_4OH. $[OH^-] = (1.8 \times 10^{-5}) \times 1.0/50.0 = 3.6 \times 10^{-7}$, from which $pOH = 6.44$ and $pH = 7.56$. The addition of 2 ml of NH_4OH changed the pH by only about 1.1 units.[1] Even by the use of a pH meter, location of the end point would probably require use of a derivative plot of the data to determine the stoichiometric point.

At the equivalence point of reaction of a weak acid with a weak base,

$$HA + BOH \rightleftharpoons H_2O + B^+ + A^-$$

the reverse reaction is appreciable. For solutions of this type it can be shown that, as a close approximation,

$$pH = \tfrac{1}{2}(pK_w + pK_a - pK_b)$$

and the pH is independent of salt concentration. If $K_a > K_b$ the solution is acidic; if $K_a < K_b$ the solution is alkaline. Although the titration is not feasible, it is useful to be able to calculate the pH of solutions of salts of weak acids and weak bases.

Titration of Polyprotic Acids with a Strong Base

A polyprotic acid furnishes two or more protons per molecule. In all cases, the ionization of polyprotic acids occurs in successive steps, each reaction having a characteristic ionization constant. Thus, for the diprotic acid H_2A:[2]

$$H_2A \rightleftharpoons H^+ + HA^-, \qquad K_1 = \frac{[H^+][HA^-]}{[H_2A]} \tag{23-1}$$

$$HA^- \rightleftharpoons H^+ + A^{--}, \qquad K_2 = \frac{[H^+][A^{--}]}{[HA^-]} \tag{23-2}$$

K_2 is always smaller than K_1. The acid can be titrated stepwise with alkali provided that (1) K_1 and K_2 are large enough so that the product of K and the concentration of the acid is greater than about 10^{-8} (see p. 293); and (2) the ratio K_1/K_2 is at least as great as 10^4, so that well separated breaks in pH occur

---

[1] The calculations given are approximate only. The more exact calculations involve consideration of the extent of hydrolysis of the salt cation and anion near the equivalence point, and the influence of these hydrolyses on the pH. For the exact calculations see I. M. Kolthoff and V. A. Stenger, *Volumetric Analysis*, 2nd ed., New York, Interscience, 1942, vol. I, pp. 24–25.

[2] In this section the subscript a to designate an acid will be omitted for reasons of convenience in writing the constants of polyprotic acids.

as the titration progresses from one step to the other. If K_1/K_2 is less than 10^4 the inflections in the pH titration curve are smeared out, and only one sharp break is observed, corresponding to the neutralization of both protons.

At the start of the titration, the pH is calculated from the relation $[H^+] = \sqrt{K_1[H_2A]}$. During the titration according to the first reaction,

$$H_2A + OH^- \rightarrow H_2O + HA^- \qquad (23\text{-}3)$$

$[H^+] = K_1[H_2A]/[HA^-]$, exactly as in the case of any weak acid. At the stoichiometric point of the first reaction, the solution contains the alkali salt of HA^-. The anion HA^- is an ampholyte, and can furnish protons: $HA^- \rightarrow H^+ + A^{--}$, or react with protons: $HA^- + H^+ \rightarrow H_2A$. For such a solution, the hydrogen ion concentration is derived as shown in Chap. 5, equations (5-66) through (5-75). In the usual case,

$$[H^+] = \sqrt{K_1 K_2} \qquad \text{and} \qquad pH = \tfrac{1}{2}(pK_1 + pK_2) \qquad (23\text{-}4)$$

An indicator for the first neutralization step would be chosen to correspond to this pH.

During the second step of the titration, the reaction is

$$HA^- + OH^- \rightarrow H_2O + A^{--} \qquad (23\text{-}5)$$

and the pH during titration up to the second stoichiometric point is calculated in the usual way from K_2; i.e., $[H^+] = K_2[HA^-]/[A^{--}]$. At the second stoichiometric point the solution contains only the alkali salt of A^{--} and water. The pH is calculated as shown previously for the weak acid–strong base titration:

$$pH = \tfrac{1}{2}(pK_w + pK_2 + \log[A^{--}]) \qquad (23\text{-}6)$$

and an indicator is selected accordingly.

In the titration of a triprotic acid, H_3A, the first titration step is calculated, as before, from K_1, and the pH at the first stoichiometric point is given by equation (23-4). During the second titration step, the pH is calculated from K_2 in the usual way. By reasoning entirely analogous to that given in Chap. 5, it can be shown that at the second stoichiometric point,

$$pH = \tfrac{1}{2}(pK_2 + pK_3) \qquad (23\text{-}7)$$

The third ionization stage of a triprotic acid is often so slight (K_3 is so small) that the third proton cannot be titrated directly unless the anion, A^{---}, is removed by precipitation to prevent its extensive hydrolysis. This same principle applies also, of course, to diprotic and monoprotic acids if the ionization constant is very small. As K_a gets smaller, approaching the magnitude of K_w, the reverse reaction is more extensive, and the *equilibrium* point of the reaction is quite different from the *stoichiometric* point.

The following examples illustrate the above principles for polyprotic acids; end point detection is assumed to be by color indicators or by pH meter.

Sulfuric Acid.   Even the second ionization of sulfuric acid is extensive:

$$HSO_4^- \rightarrow H^+ + SO_4^{--}, \qquad K_2 = 1.0 \times 10^{-2}, \qquad pK_2 = 2.00$$

Sulfuric acid therefore titrates directly as a diprotic acid; it cannot be titrated stepwise.

Oxalic Acid.   The ionization steps and constants are:

$$H_2C_2O_4 \rightleftarrows H^+ + HC_2O_4^-, \qquad K_1 = 5.6 \times 10^{-2}, \qquad pK_1 = 1.25$$

$$HC_2O_4^- \rightleftarrows H^+ + C_2O_4^{--}, \qquad K_2 = 5.2 \times 10^{-5}, \qquad pK_2 = 4.28$$

Although the titration of the second proton is feasible, oxalic acid cannot be titrated stepwise because $K_1/K_2 = 1.1 \times 10^3$, which is less than the 10^4 required to give good separation of the breaks in pH. The pH titration curve of oxalic acid shows only a slight inflection at the first stoichiometric point.

Sulfurous Acid.   The ionization steps and constants are:

$$H_2SO_3 \rightleftarrows H^+ + HSO_3^-, \qquad K_1 = 1.3 \times 10^{-2}, \qquad pK_1 = 1.89$$

$$HSO_3^- \rightleftarrows H^+ + SO_3^{--}, \qquad K_2 = 6.3 \times 10^{-8}, \qquad pK_2 = 7.20$$

The second proton can be titrated, provided the acid concentration is about 0.2 M or higher, so that the product $K_2[HSO_3^-]$ is greater than 10^{-8}. The titration can be done stepwise, with good separation of the breaks in pH, because $K_1/K_2 > 10^4$. At the first stoichiometric point, pH $= \frac{1}{2}(1.89 + 7.20) = 4.55$. At the second stoichiometric point, assuming $[SO_3^{--}] = 0.10$, pH $= \frac{1}{2}(14.00 + 7.20 - 1.00) = 10.10$. The second end point is not very sharp because K_2 is about at the lower limit of feasibility.

Carbonic Acid.   The ionization steps and constants are:

$$H_2CO_3 \rightleftarrows H^+ + HCO_3^-, \qquad K_1 = 4.6 \times 10^{-7}, \qquad pK_1 = 6.34$$

$$HCO_3^- \rightleftarrows H^+ + CO_3^{--}, \qquad K_2 = 5.6 \times 10^{-11}, \qquad pK_2 = 10.25$$

The first proton can be titrated, provided the carbonic acid concentration is about 0.1 M or higher; the stoichiometric point occurs at pH $= \frac{1}{2}(6.34 + 10.25) = 8.30$. The end point is not sharp, because K_1 is not far from the lower limit of feasibility. The second proton cannot be titrated directly. However, if Ba^{++} is added to remove CO_3^{--} by precipitation as $BaCO_3$, the second proton is available for reaction. The titrimetric determination of H_2CO_3 and/or HCO_3^- is best made by addition of a known excess of standard barium hydroxide solution:

$$CO_3^{--} + Ba^{++} \rightarrow BaCO_3$$

$$HCO_3^- + Ba^{++} + OH^- \rightarrow BaCO_3 + H_2O$$

and back titration of the excess barium hydroxide (a strong base) with standard hydrochloric acid, using phenolphthalein indicator.

Phosphoric Acid.   The ionization steps and constants are:

$$H_3PO_4 \rightleftarrows H^+ + H_2PO_4^-, \qquad K_1 = 7.5 \times 10^{-3}, \qquad pK_1 = 2.12$$

$$H_2PO_4^- \rightleftarrows H^+ + HPO_4^{--}, \qquad K_2 = 6.2 \times 10^{-8}, \qquad pK_2 = 7.21$$

$$HPO_4^{--} \rightleftarrows H^+ + PO_4^{---}, \qquad K_3 = 4.7 \times 10^{-13}, \qquad pK_3 = 12.33$$

$K_1/K_2 > 10^4$, therefore stepwise titration is possible. The first stoichiometric point occurs at $pH = \frac{1}{2}(2.12 + 7.21) = 4.67$, and methyl orange or bromcresol green indicator would be suitable. The second titration step requires an acid $(H_2PO_4^-)$ concentration greater than about 0.2 M, and the stoichiometric point comes at $pH = \frac{1}{2}(7.21 + 12.33) = 9.77$; thymolphthalein indicator is suitable. The second end point is not very sharp, because K_2 is near the limit of feasibility, and the solution is moderately buffered by the HPO_4^{--} present. The third proton cannot be titrated directly, although it may be made available by removal of phosphate ion by precipitation with calcium ion. The two-step titration of phosphoric acid is represented by the titration curve in Fig. 23-4.

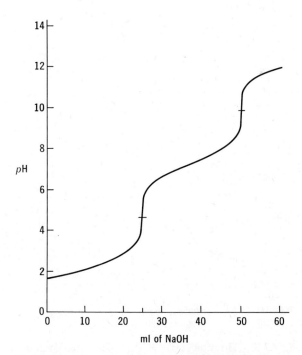

Fig. 23-4   Titration curve. 25.0 ml of 0.100 M phosphoric acid titrated with 0.100 M (N) sodium hydroxide.

Titration of a Mixture of Strong Acid and Weak Acid

This case is not essentially different from the titration of a diprotic acid in which K_1 and K_2 are of such magnitudes that stepwise titration of both protons is feasible. Such a diprotic acid reacts toward alkali just as if it were a mixture of two acids of different strength; the source of the protons is of no importance. For example, a mixture of hydrochloric acid (strong) and acetic acid (weak) can be titrated stepwise with sodium hydroxide solution. The hydrogen ion of the hydrochloric acid suppresses the ionization of acetic acid by the common ion effect, and the sodium hydroxide neutralizes the hydrochloric acid first. When this reaction is complete, the pH rises to that of the acetic acid solution, which is then titrated as illustrated previously. Figure 23-5 shows a titration curve for a mixture of hydrochloric acid and acetic acid titrated with sodium hydroxide. The change of pH at the first stoichiometric point is not very great, and the end point determined by a color indicator would not be very sharp. A differential graphical evaluation of data from a potentiometric titration (pp. 510–511) would give a more exact location of this stoichiometric point.

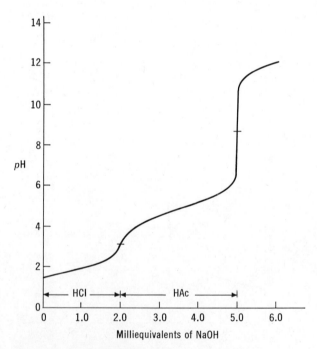

Fig. 23-5 Titration curve. 50.0 ml of solution containing 2.0 milliequivalents of hydrochloric acid (strong) and 3.0 milliequivalents of acetic acid (weak), titrated with sodium hydroxide.

Titration of a Mixture of Strong Base and Weak Base

The stepwise acidimetric titration of a mixture of strong, soluble base, such as sodium hydroxide, and a weak soluble base, such as ammonia or hydrazine (N_2H_4), involves exactly the same principles as those given for titration of a mixture of strong and weak acid.

The hydroxides of most of the polyvalent cations, except those of the alkaline earths (calcium, strontium, barium) are weakly ionized. Although their step-wise ionization might be considered analogous to the stepwise ionization of polyprotic acids, the situation is complicated by the fact that such hydroxides are so slightly soluble in water that an ionization constant would be of doubtful significance. The direct titration of such hydroxides, and, indeed, of insoluble compounds in general, is rarely attempted, because of the slow attainment of a new solubility equilibrium when additional titrant is added. Substances of this kind are determined, when necessary, by addition of a known amount of standard acid in excess of that required for complete reaction, and back titration of the excess acid. The same method is generally used also for determination of the weak organic nitrogen bases, such as aniline ($C_6H_5NH_2$) and phenyl-hydrazine ($C_6H_5NHNH_2$), which are sparingly soluble in water. Titration of these substances in nonaqueous solvents is sometimes feasible.

Titration of the Anion of a Weak Acid with a Strong Acid

The anion of a very weak acid is a strong base, that is, it has a high proton affinity; its reaction with hydrogen ion is therefore extensive and its titration by strong acid is feasible. The essential features of this type of titration are illustrated by a generalized treatment, followed by reference to specific examples.

Consider the titration of the alkali salt of the anion, A^-, of a very weak acid HA, for which $K_a = 1.0 \times 10^{-11}$. Assume that 50.0 ml of 0.100 M solution of A^- are titrated with 0.100 M HCl.

a. The original solution is quite alkaline,

$$A^- + H_2O \rightleftharpoons HA + OH^-$$

and the pH is calculated as illustrated previously for the stoichiometric point in a weak acid–strong base titration:

$$pH = \tfrac{1}{2}(pK_w + pK_a + \log[A^-])$$

$$= \tfrac{1}{2}(14.00 + 11.00 - 1.00) = 12.00$$

b. The titration reaction is $A^- + H^+ \rightleftharpoons HA$, and the pH during titration is calculated from $K_a = [H^+][A^-]/[HA]$. For example, when 30.0 ml of the HCl have been added, $[H^+] = 1.0 \times 10^{-11} \times 30.0/20.0 = 1.5 \times 10^{-11}$, and $pH = 10.82$. At 49.9 ml of HCl added, $[H^+] = 1.0 \times 10^{-11} \times 49.9/0.1 = 5.0 \times 10^{-9}$, and $pH = 8.30$.

c. At the stoichiometric point the titration mixture consists of a solution of HA of 0.050 M concentration in equilibrium with its ions.

$$[H^+] = \sqrt{K_a[HA]} = \sqrt{(1.0 \times 10^{-11})(5.0 \times 10^{-2})} = 7.1 \times 10^{-7}$$

and $pH = 6.15$.

d. Beyond the stoichiometric point the pH is calculated from the volume of excess HCl and the total volume of solution. In the case illustrated, when 0.10 ml excess HCl has been added, $pH = 4.00$.

The solution undergoes rapid change of pH very close to the stoichiometric point, and the titration is feasible. An indicator such as chlorphenol red (pH interval 6.8 to 5.4) would be suitable.

Previously it was stated that if $K_a[HA]$ is less than about 10^{-8}, the titration of HA by strong base is not feasible. The generalization may now be made that if the titration of HA by strong base is not feasible, the titration of its anion, A^-, by strong acid is feasible. The converse is also true; that is, if the titration of a weak acid by a strong base is feasible, the titration of its conjugate base by strong acid is not feasible. For example, the titration of acetic acid ($K_a = 1.8 \times 10^{-5}$) is feasible; the titration of acetate ion by a strong acid is therefore not feasible. The titration of boric acid ($K_a = 6.0 \times 10^{-10}$) is not feasible; the titration of borate ion by strong acid is feasible. The direct titration of HPO_4^{--} ($K_3 = 4.7 \times 10^{-13}$) by NaOH is not feasible; the titration of PO_4^{---} to HPO_4^{--} by HCl is feasible. The titration of $H_2PO_4^-$ ($K_2 = 6.2 \times 10^{-8}$) with NaOH is about at the limit of feasibility, and the end point is not very sharp; the same is true of the titration of HPO_4^{--} to $H_2PO_4^-$ by hydrochloric acid.

In the same way that polyprotic acids can be titrated stepwise by alkali if the different ionization constants have appropriate values, so the tri- and divalent anions of very weak polyprotic acids can be titrated stepwise by strong acids.

Titration of Alkali Carbonate. The two ionization constants of H_2CO_3 are $K_1 = 4.6 \times 10^{-7}$ ($pK_1 = 6.34$), and $K_2 = 5.6 \times 10^{-11}$ ($pK_2 = 10.25$). Assume 50.0 ml of 0.100 M Na_2CO_3 solution are titrated with 0.100 M (N) HCl. For the reaction $CO_3^{--} + H^+ \rightarrow HCO_3^-$, the molecular weight of Na_2CO_3 is also its equivalent weight, so the solution is 0.100 N for this reaction. Sodium carbonate solution is alkaline, and for 0.100 M solution, $pH = \frac{1}{2}(14.00 + 10.25 - 1.00) = 11.62$. During the first step of the titration with HCl, $[H^+] = K_2[HCO_3^-]/[CO_3^{--}]$. At 25.0 ml of added HCl (half-titration point), $[HCO_3^-] = [CO_3^{--}]$ and $pH = pK_2 = 10.25$. As the first stoichiometric point is approached, $[HCO_3^-]$ is increasing and $[CO_3^{--}]$ is decreasing. This results in an increase in $[H^+]$ and a lower pH. At the first stoichiometric point, $[H^+] = \sqrt{K_1K_2}$, and $pH = \frac{1}{2}(pK_1 + pK_2) = \frac{1}{2}(6.34 + 10.25) = 8.30$. Phenolphthalein or thymol blue is a suitable indicator. The end point of this first titration stage, however, is not very sharp. This situation is in general true of the titration of the di- or trivalent anion of a very weak di- or triprotic acid.

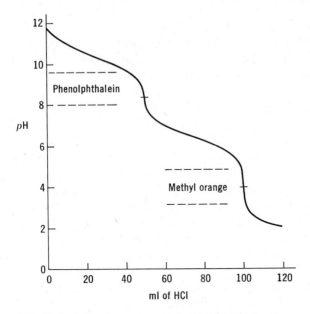

Fig. 23-6   Titration curve. 50.0 ml of 0.100 M sodium
carbonate solution titrated with 0.100 M (N)
hydrochloric acid.

At the first stoichiometric point the solution contains 5.00 gme of HCO_3^-
in 100 ml, and $[HCO_3^-] = 0.050$. During the second titration step the pH is
calculated from the first ionization constant; $[H^+] = K_1[H_2CO_3]/[HCO_3^-]$.
For example, after the addition of 40.0 ml more of the 0.100 N HCl, $[H^+] =$
$4.6 \times 10^{-7} \times 40.0/10.0 = 1.84 \times 10^{-6}$ and $pH = 5.74$. At the second stoichiometric point the solution contains H_2CO_3 at a concentration of 0.033 M,
provided none of the acid decomposes and volatilizes as CO_2. $[H^+] =$
$\sqrt{K_1[H_2CO_3]} = \sqrt{(4.6 \times 10^{-7})(3.3 \times 10^{-2})} = 1.23 \times 10^{-4}$, and $pH = 3.91$,
which is about in the middle of the methyl orange color change interval. The
end point in this titration can be sharpened considerably by boiling the solution to decompose the H_2CO_3 and expel CO_2; the solution is then practically
neutral, and addition of one or two drops of dilute acid causes a large change
in pH and a sharp transition to the acid color of the indicator.

A titration curve for sodium carbonate is shown in Fig. 23-6.

Titration of Phosphates.   The third ionization of phosphoric acid is very weak
($K_3 = 4.2 \times 10^{-13}$); the phosphate ion, PO_4^{---}, is therefore a strong base, and
can be titrated to HPO_4^{--} with strong acid. The second ionization is also quite
weak, and HPO_4^{--} is slightly stronger as a base ($K_b = K_w/K_2 = 1.6 \times 10^{-7}$)
than is $H_2PO_4^-$ as an acid ($K_2 = 6.2 \times 10^{-8}$); HPO_4^{--} can therefore be
titrated to $H_2PO_4^-$ with strong acid. Thus, stepwise titration of PO_4^{---} with

acid is feasible. The calculations of pH during the two-stage titration of phosphate ion are completely analogous to those previously illustrated for carbonate. The stepwise titration of PO_4^{---} by acid, and the stepwise titration of H_3PO_4 by alkali, make possible the titrimetric determination of compatible mixtures of phosphate species, as described in Chap. 24.

Titration of the Cation of a Weak Base with a Strong Base

The same principles formulated for titration of the anion of a weak acid apply here. Titration of NH_4OH ($K_b = 1.8 \times 10^{-5}$) by strong acid is feasible; therefore, the titration of NH_4^+ by a strong base is not feasible. The titration of the very weak base hydroxylamine, NH_2OH ($K_b = 6.6 \times 10^{-9}$) is not feasible; the titration of its conjugate acid, the cation NH_3OH^+, by alkali is feasible. The pH at various stages of the titration can be calculated by exactly the same principles as illustrated for titration of the anion of a weak acid. Cations of the heavy metals can also be titrated by strong base, because the hydroxides of the heavy metals are very weakly ionized. The titration is complicated by the fact that the heavy metal hydroxides are insoluble, highly hydrophilic substances, and the gelatinous precipitates may adsorb a considerable amount of cations from the solution during titration. The end point is likely to be somewhat transient, and exact stoichiometric reaction is often difficult to attain.

RELATIVE PRECISION OF END POINTS

At the stoichiometric point in an acid-base titration the pH vs. titrant curve has its maximum slope—the solution has its minimum buffer capacity—and the steepness of the curve around the stoichiometric point indicates the relative precision of the end point. Quantitatively, the relative precision can be defined as the fraction of the stoichiometric amount of titrant required to change the pH by 0.2 unit around (i.e., 0.1 pH unit on either side of) the stoichiometric point. The relative precision is also related to the buffer capacity at the equivalence point. Without giving here the mathematical development, it can be shown[3] that for $\Delta pH = 0.2$, the relative precision is given by

$$\text{r.p.} = \frac{0.2}{C} \beta_{\text{equiv}}$$

where β_{equiv} is the buffer capacity, and C is the solute concentration, at the equivalence point. Using the appropriate expressions for buffer capacity[4] (see p. 77), the relative precision of various types of titration is as follows:

[3] H. A. Laitinen, *Chemical Analysis*, New York, McGraw-Hill, 1960, pp. 41–43.
[4] J. E. Ricci, *Hydrogen Ion Concentration*, Princeton, N. J., Princeton Univ. Press, 1952.

1. Strong acid–strong base titration:

$$\text{r.p.} = \frac{0.2}{C} \times 2.3 \times 2\sqrt{K_w} \cong \sqrt{K_w/C}$$

2. Weak acid–strong base titration:

$$\text{r.p.} = \frac{0.2}{C} \times 2.3 \times 2\sqrt{\frac{K_w C}{K_a}} \cong \sqrt{\frac{K_w}{K_a C}}$$

3. Weak base–strong acid titration:

$$\text{r.p.} = \frac{0.2}{C} \times 2.3 \times 2\sqrt{\frac{K_w C}{K_b}} \cong \sqrt{\frac{K_w}{K_b C}}$$

4. Intermediate end points in titration of polyprotic acids:

$$\text{r.p.} = \frac{0.2}{C} \times 2.3 \times 2C\sqrt{K_2/K_1} \cong \sqrt{K_2/K_1}$$

Similarly, for a second intermediate end point in the titration of a triprotic acid, r.p. $\cong \sqrt{K_3/K_2}$. The relative precision of the final end point is calculated as for a weak monoprotic acid, using the last ionization constant of the polyprotic acid; that is, r.p. $\cong \sqrt{K_w/(K_n C)}$, where n represents the last ionization step. In the titration of alkali salts of polyprotic acids the same formulations for intermediate end points are used, but in reverse order if more than one intermediate end point is involved.

In applying the above formulations, C is often used as the initial concentration of the substance titrated, and dilution by the titrant is ignored.

EXAMPLE 9

Estimate the relative precision of the end points in each of the following titrations (neglect dilution).

(*a*) Titration of 0.0010 *M* NaOH by HCl.

$$\text{r.p.} = \sqrt{K_w/C} = \sqrt{10^{-14}/10^{-3}} = 10^{-4} \quad \text{or} \quad 0.01\%.$$

(*b*) Titration of 0.0010 *M* benzoic acid by NaOH.

$$\text{r.p.} = \sqrt{\frac{K_w}{K_a C}} = \sqrt{\frac{1.0 \times 10^{-14}}{(6.6 \times 10^{-5})(10^{-3})}} = 4 \times 10^{-4} \quad \text{or} \quad 0.04\%.$$

(*c*) Titration of 0.010 *M* H_2SO_3 with NaOH.
First end point:

$$\text{r.p.} = \sqrt{K_2/K_1} = \sqrt{(6.3 \times 10^{-8})/(1.3 \times 10^{-2})}$$
$$= 2.2 \times 10^{-3} \quad \text{or} \quad 0.2\%.$$

Second end point:

$$r.p. = \sqrt{\frac{K_w}{K_2 C}} = \sqrt{\frac{1.0 \times 10^{-14}}{(6.3 \times 10^{-8})(10^{-2})}}$$

$$= 4 \times 10^{-3} \quad \text{or} \quad 0.4\%.$$

EXAMPLE 10

Show that the third step in the titration of 0.1 M phosphate ion by strong acid is not feasible.

$$K_{b_3} \text{ for phosphate ion} = K_w/K_{a_1} = (1.0 \times 10^{-14})/(7.5 \times 10^{-3})$$

$$= 1.3 \times 10^{-12}$$

$$r.p. = \sqrt{\frac{K_w}{K_b C}} = \sqrt{\frac{1.0 \times 10^{-14}}{(1.3 \times 10^{-12})(10^{-1})}} = 0.28 \quad \text{or} \quad 28\%.$$

An *ad hoc* method of calculating end point errors is given by Walton.[5]

ACID-BASE INDICATORS

The substances used as indicators in neutralization titrations are weak acids or weak bases, the ions of which are of different color from the undissociated forms. Their ionization equilibria in solution may be treated mathematically the same as other weak ionogens.

For an indicator acid, represented for simplicity by HIn,

$$\underset{\text{"Acid" form}}{\text{HIn}} \rightleftarrows \text{H}^+ + \underset{\text{"Alkaline" form}}{\text{In}^-} \tag{23-7}$$

$$K_a = \frac{[\text{H}^+][\text{In}^-]}{[\text{HIn}]} \quad \text{and} \quad \frac{[\text{In}^-]}{[\text{HIn}]} = \frac{K_a}{[\text{H}^+]} \tag{23-8}$$

The observed color, that is, the ratio $[\text{In}^-]/[\text{HIn}]$, depends on $[\text{H}^+]$; at high $[\text{H}^+]$ this ratio is small, and the indicator shows its acid color; at low $[\text{H}^+]$ the ratio is large, and the indicator shows its alkaline color.

For an indicator base, represented by InOH,

$$\underset{\text{"Alkaline" form}}{\text{InOH}} \rightleftarrows \underset{\text{"Acid" form}}{\text{In}^+} + \text{OH}^- \tag{23-9}$$

$$K_b = \frac{[\text{In}^+][\text{OH}^-]}{[\text{InOH}]} \quad \text{and} \quad \frac{[\text{In}^+]}{[\text{InOH}]} = \frac{K_b}{[\text{OH}^-]} \tag{23-10}$$

At low $[\text{OH}^-]$, the ratio $[\text{In}^+]/[\text{InOH}]$ is large, and the acid color is shown; at high $[\text{OH}^-]$, where this ratio is small, the alkaline color appears.

[5] H. F. Walton, *Principles and Methods of Chemical Analysis*, 2nd ed., Englewood Cliffs, N. J., Prentice-Hall, 1964, pp. 266–268.

With individuals of normal color vision, experiments have shown that in a two-color system, one color can be detected in the presence of a second color when the ratio of the intensities of the first to the second is about 1/10. Thus, in going from the acid form to the alkaline form of an indicator, the color change can be detected when [alkaline form]/[acid form] is about 1/10; in changing in the reverse direction, the color change is first observed when the ratio is 10/1. Putting equation (23-8) in logarithmic form gives

$$pH = pK_a + \log([In^-]/[HIn]) \tag{23-11}$$

The color change interval, in terms of pH, is then

$$pH = pK_a \pm \log(1/10) = pK_a \pm 1$$

Experimentally, the color change interval for most indicators is about 1.6 pH units. When half of the indicator is in either form, $[In^-] = [HIn]$, and $pH = pK_a$. Because the colors are based upon subjective judgment by the observer, and the eye has different sensitivity for different colors, the limiting values are only approximate and may not symmetrically bracket the pK_a of the indicator (see Table 23-3).

For an indicator base, $[OH^-] = K_b[InOH]/[In^+]$; substituting this value of $[OH^-]$ into the water constant expression gives

$$[H^+] = \frac{K_w}{K_b \dfrac{[InOH]}{[In^+]}} = \frac{K_w}{K_b} \cdot \frac{[In^+]}{[InOH]}$$

K_w/K_b is a constant that may be designated K_{ind}. Hence,

$$pH = pK_{ind} + \log([InOH]/[In^+]) \tag{23-12}$$

Equations (23-11) and (23-12) are of the same general form, and in each the logarithmic term involves the ratio [alkaline form]/[acid form]. The generalization may be written

$$pH = pK_{ind} + \log[\text{alkaline form}]/[\text{acid form}] \tag{23-13}$$

If the indicator is an acid, $K_{ind} = K_a$; if the indicator is a base, $K_{ind} = K_w/K_b$. Tables of indicators generally give numerical values for K_{ind} or pK_{ind}, so that it is not necessary to know whether the indicator is an acid or a base in order to apply the constant in using equation (23-13).

Table 23-3 lists the common acid-base indicators.

Several points in the use of acid-base indicators are important.

1. The indicator used should have a color change interval which coincides with or "brackets" the pH at the stoichiometric point of the titration. If there is much departure from this condition, the observed end point will not coincide with the stoichiometric point and will result in considerable error.

Table 23-3 Acid-Base Indicators

Common Name	Chemical Name	$pK_{ind}{}^a$	pH Interval	Color Acid	Color Alkaline
Cresol red ^{b}	o-Cresolsulfonphthalein		0.2– 1.8	Red	Yellow
Thymol blue ^{b}	Thymolsulfonphthalein	1.6	1.2– 2.8	Red	Yellow
Tropeoline 00	Diphenylamino p-benzene sodium sulfonate		1.3– 3.0	Red	Yellow
Methyl yellow	Dimethylaminoazobenzene		2.8– 4.0	Red	Yellow
Bromphenol blue	Tetrabromophenolsulfonphthalein	3.8	3.0– 4.6	Yellow	Purple
Methyl orange	Dimethylaminoazobenzene sodium sulfonate	3.5	3.1– 4.4	Red	Yellow
Bromcresol green	Tetrabromophenol m-cresolsulfonphthalein	4.7	3.8– 5.4	Yellow	Blue
Methyl red	Dimethylaminoazobenzene sodium carbonate	5.0	4.2– 6.2	Red	Yellow
Chlorphenol red	Dichlorosulfonphthalein	6.0	4.8– 6.4	Yellow	Red
Bromcresol purple	Dibromo o-cresolsulfonphthalein	6.1	5.2– 6.8	Yellow	Purple
Bromthymol blue	Dibromothymolsulfonphthalein	7.1	6.0– 7.6	Yellow	Blue
Phenol red	Phenolsulfonphthalein	7.8	6.4– 8.0	Yellow	Red
Neutral red	Dimethyldiaminophenazine chloride	6.8	6.8– 8.0	Red	Yellow-brown
Cresol red ^{c}	o-Cresolsulfonphthalein	8.1	7.2– 8.8	Yellow	Red
Cresol purple ^{c}	m-Cresolsulfonphthalein	8.3	7.4– 9.0	Yellow	Purple
Thymol blue ^{c}	Thymolsulfonphthalein	8.9	8.0– 9.6	Yellow	Blue
Phenolphthalein	Phenolphthalein	9.3	8.0– 9.8	Colorless	Red-violet
Thymolphthalein	Thymolphthalein		9.3–10.5	Colorless	Blue
Alizarin yellow	p-Nitroaniline azo sodium salicylate		10.1–12.0	Yellow	Violet

^{a} pK_{ind} is given only to the first decimal place, or one significant figure in K_{ind}.
^{b} Acid range; the indicator has two color change intervals.
^{c} Alkaline range; the indicator has two color change intervals.

2. Only a very small amount of indicator should be used. The indicator colors are so intense that only about two drops of very dilute solution (e.g., 0.1%) of indicator are used per 100 ml of solution. The amount of titrant required to react with the indicator should be negligible compared to the total volume of titrant used to reach the end point.

3. The *first detectable color change* of the indicator should be taken as the end point. Once the minute amount of indicator has been about 90% converted to its second colored form, the observed color does not change appreciably by addition of more titrant. A common student practice is to show a flask of titration mixture to the laboratory assistant and ask "Is this the end point?" Instantaneous color judgment and color memory are very unreliable, but slight color *changes* are quite readily discerned. The best judgment of the end point of a titration is therefore made by the operator performing the titration who observes the color *change*.

Color Blindness. Individuals vary widely in their ability to detect and judge color, all the way from slightly deficient color-vision acuity to virtually complete color blindness. Some persons have gone through many years of their lives not knowing that their color vision was deficient. The incidence of color blindness is much higher than most people suppose; it is estimated that one female in a hundred and eight to ten males in a hundred are red-green color blind.[6] A student who knows he has poor color vision, or who discovers this fact when starting laboratory work on neutralimetry, should make it known to the laboratory assistant. A student having low acuity for red-green will find it difficult or impossible to get satisfactory end points in titrations using methyl orange (yellow-red), modified methyl orange (green-red), and phenolphthalein (colorless-pink). Color blindness for yellow-blue is much less common than for red-green; a student who is red-green color blind would very likely be able to use bromphenol blue (*p*H 3.0–4.6, yellow-purple), bromthymol blue (*p*H 6.0–7.6, yellow-blue), and thymolphthalein (*p*H 9.3–10.5, colorless-blue) for the various end point regions.

Structural Changes in Acid-Base Indicator Action. Most of the acid-base indicators are organic aromatic compounds containing two or more benzene rings joined through one or more atoms of carbon or nitrogen. In the process of reacting with acid or base, a **benzenoid** type of structure changes to a **quinoid** type of structure:

Benzenoid   Quinoid

[6] R. L. Clark and R. W. Cumley, *The Book of Health*, Houston, Texas, Elsevier, 1953, p. 510.

The quinoid structure is commonly associated with color (there are other chromophoric groups or structures, also). The structural changes for methyl orange are

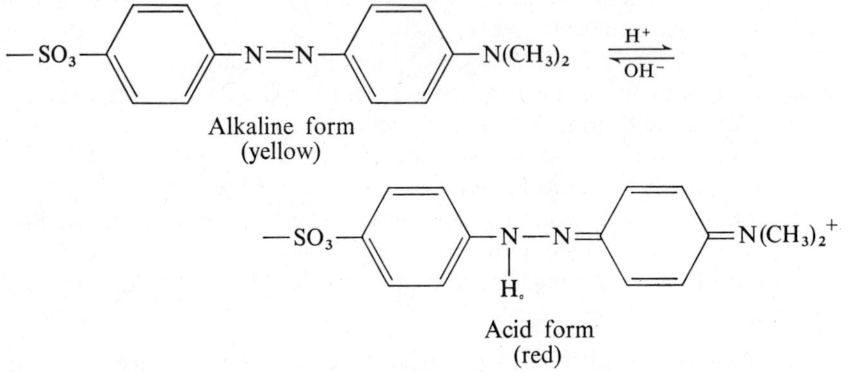

Alkaline form
(yellow)

Acid form
(red)

PROBLEMS

See Appendixes II and III for ionization constants needed.

23-1 50.0 ml of 0.250 M acetic acid is titrated with 0.250 M sodium hydroxide. Calculate the pH of the solution when the volume of sodium hydroxide added is (a) 0.0 ml, (b) 5.0 ml, (c) 25.0 ml, (d) 49.0 ml, (e) 50.0 ml, (f) 50.1 ml, (g) 51.0 ml.

Ans. (a) 2.68,   (b) 3.79,   (c) 4.74,   (d) 6.43,   (e) 8.92,   (f) 10.40,   (g) 11.39.

23-2 40.0 ml of 0.1500 N ammonium hydroxide (NH_3) is titrated with 0.1200 N hydrochloric acid. Calculate the pH of the solution when the volume of hydrochloric acid added is (a) 0.0 ml, (b) 10.0 ml, (c) 24.0 ml, (d) 49.0 ml, (e) 50.0 ml, (f) 52.0 ml.

Ans. (a) 11.21,   (b) 9.86,   (c) 9.29,   (d) 7.57,   (e) 5.22,   (f) 2.58.

23-3 Calculate the pH of a solution containing bromthymol blue indicator ($pK_{ind} = 7.0$) when the following percentages of indicator are in the alkaline form: 1, 25, 60, 90, 99.

Ans. 5.0, 6.5, 7.2, 8.0, 9.0.

23-4 For the titration designated, calculate the pH at the following percentages of the stoichiometric amount of titrant: 0 (initial point), 10, 50, 90, 95, 99, 100 (stoichiometric point), 101, 105, 110. Construct the titration curve by plotting pH against percent titration. State whether or not the titration is feasible; if feasible, select an appropriate indicator.

Solution to be titrated	Titrant
(a) 50.0 ml of 0.0100 N HCl	0.0100 N NaOH
(b) 50.0 ml of 0.00100 N HCl	0.00100 N NaOH
(c) 40.0 ml 0.0500 N NaOH	0.0500 N H_2SO_4
(d) 100.0 ml 0.0100 N NaOH	0.100 N HCl
(e) 50.0 ml 0.200 N $HC_2H_3O_2$	0.200 N NaOH
(f) 50.0 ml 0.0200 N $HC_2H_3O_2$	0.0200 N NaOH
(g) 200.0 ml of 0.0250 N NH_4OH (NH_3)	0.250 N HCl
(h) 50.0 ml 0.500 N NH_2OH	0.500 N HCl
(i) 100 ml 0.100 N HBO_2	0.200 N NaOH

(*j*) 40.0 ml 0.100 N KCN   0.100 N HCl
(*k*) 40.0 ml 0.0200 N C$_6$H$_5$NH$_3$Cl   0.0200 N NaOH
(*l*) 50.0 ml 0.200 N NaBO$_2$ 0.400 N HCl

23-5   For each titration in Problem 23-4, calculate the buffer capacity at each of the points specified; calculate also the relative precision of the end point.

23-6   The solution specified is titrated with 0.1000 N NaOH. Calculate the pH of the solution (1) at the start, (2) at half titration, (3) at the stoichiometric point. Select an appropriate indicator.

(*a*) 0.4370 g sulfamic acid dissolved in 75.0 ml water.
(*b*) 0.6105 g benzoic acid dissolved in 100.0 ml water.
(*c*) 0.2741 g hydrazine hydrochloride (N$_2$H$_5$Cl) dissolved in 40.0 ml water.
(*d*) 2.300 g formic acid solution containing 40.0 wt-% HCOOH, diluted to 100 ml.
(*e*) 0.4000 g of hydrogen fluoride dissolved in 100 ml water.

23-7   In each part of Problem 23-6 calculate the buffer capacity of the solution at the three points specified; calculate also the relative precision of the end point.

23-8   In each of the titrations of Problem 23-6, what percent of the original acid remains unneutralized at pH 4.00, 6.00, 7.00?

23-9   For the specified titration, made with 0.200 N NaOH, calculate (1) the stoichiometric-point pH, (2) the relative precision of the end point, (3) the percent of the original acid remaining unneutralized at 50% conversion of chlorphenol red indicator.

(*a*) 40.0 ml of 0.250 N acetic acid.
(*b*) 100.0 ml of 0.0800 N acetic acid.
(*c*) 50.0 ml of 0.0800 N formic acid.
(*d*) 40.0 ml of 0.150 N hydrofluoric acid.
(*e*) 80.0 ml of 0.0400 N benzoic acid.

23-10   The solution specified is titrated with 0.1000 N sulfuric acid. Calculate the pH of the solution (1) at the initial point, (2) at half titration, (3) at the stoichiometric point. Select an appropriate indicator.

(*a*) 20.0 ml of 0.250 N NH$_4$OH (NH$_3$).
(*b*) 25.0 ml of 0.1000 N ethylamine, C$_2$H$_5$NH$_2$.
(*c*) 100.0 ml of 0.0500 N methylamine, CH$_3$NH$_2$.
(*d*) 50.0 ml of 0.0600 N hydrazine, N$_2$H$_4$.
(*e*) 40.0 ml of 0.125 N triethylamine, (C$_2$H$_5$)$_3$N.

23-11   For each titration in Problem 23-10, calculate the buffer capacity at each of the points specified; calculate also the relative precision of the end point.

23-12   In each of the titrations of Problem 23-10, what percent of the original base remains unneutralized at pH 9.40, 8.30, 7.00?

23-13   The solution given is titrated with NaOH or with HCl, as appropriate, of the same molar concentration as the solute given. Calculate the pH at the following points: (1) initial, (2) midpoint of the first step, (3) first stoichiometric point, (4) midpoint of the second step, (5) second stoichiometric point. Select an indicator for each point. Is *stepwise* titration feasible? (Consider each step for feasibility.) Give basis for your answer.

(*a*) 0.300 M oxalic acid.
(*b*) 0.200 M tartaric acid.
(*c*) 0.0600 M sulfurous acid.

(d) 0.333 M phthalic acid.

(e) 0.0500 M hydrosulfuric acid (H_2S).

(f) 1.50 M phosphoric acid. Calculate also the pH at the midpoint and stoichiometric point of the third step.

(g) 0.210 M sodium carbonate.

(h) 0.180 M sodium sulfide.

(i) 0.240 M sodium sulfite.

(j) 1.00 M sodium phosphate, Na_3PO_4. Calculate also the pH at the midpoint and stoichiometric point of the third step.

23-14   Calculate the relative precision of the end points in each titration of Problem 23-13.

23-15   How many grams of each solute (assume salts to be potassium compounds, e.g., K_3PO_4, K_2CO_3, etc.) are present, per liter, in the solution specified?

(a) Solution of pH 1.65, in which total phosphate is 0.40 M.

(b) Solution of pH 2.60, in which total phosphate is 0.40 M.

(c) Solution of pH 6.51, in which total phosphate is 0.30 M.

(d) Solution of pH 7.89, in which total phosphate is 0.24 M.

(e) Solution of pH 11.30, in which total phosphate is 0.36 M.

(f) Solution of pH 10.92, in which total carbonate is 0.50 M.

(g) Solution of pH 10.02, in which total carbonate is 0.60 M.

23-16   Calculate the buffer capacity of each solution of Problem 23-15.

23-17   What weight of solid NaOH must be added to the solution specified to give the stated pH?

(a) One liter of 0.100 M H_3PO_4 to give a solution of pH 2.60.

(b) 500 ml of 0.100 M H_3PO_4 to give a solution of pH 7.51.

(c) 200 ml of 0.100 M H_3PO_4 to give a solution of pH 11.00.

(d) One liter of 0.0800 M $H_2C_2O_4$ to give a solution of pH 2.02.

(e) 250 ml of 0.0800 M $H_2C_2O_4$ to give a solution of pH 4.30.

23-18   Calculate the buffer capacity of each solution of Problem 23-17.

23-19   Calculate the pH of a solution containing phenol red indicator ($pK_{ind} = 7.8$) when the following percentages of the indicator are in the alkaline form: 1, 10, 25, 50, 75, 90, 99.

23-20 pK_{ind} of methyl red $= 5.0$.

(a) Calculate the ratio of concentration of alkaline form to that of the acid form of the indicator at the following pH values: 3.0, 4.0, 5.5, 6.0, 6.5, 7.0.

(b) Plot the values of the ratio from (a) against the corresponding pH values.

(c) Plot the logarithm of the ratios against the pH values.

23-21   Calculate K_a of the weak acid, or K_b of the weak base, as the case may be, from the data given.

(a) A solution of the weak acid requires 40.0 ml of alkali to reach the stoichiometric point; after the addition of 30.0 ml of alkali the pH of the solution is 4.70.

(b) The pH of the solution is 5.15 when the acid is 30% titrated.

(c) A 0.100 N solution of the acid, titrated with 0.100 N NaOH, has an equivalence-point pH of 9.55.

(d) A solution of the weak base has a pH of 8.20 when 22.0 ml of acid have been added; to reach the stoichiometric point, 33.0 ml of acid must be added.

(e) The pH of the solution is 11.30 when the base is 20.0% titrated.

(*f*) The weak base, MOH, is titrated with HCl; at the stoichiometric point $[M^+] =$ 0.500 and the *p*H of the solution is 4.00.

23-22   Titration of 50.0 ml of solution of a weak acid, HA ($K_a = 1.0 \times 10^{-6}$), to the phenolphthalein end point at *p*H 9.00 requires 50.0 ml of NaOH. What was the molar concentration of the original acid solution?

23-23   A 0.500-g sample containing only Na_2CO_3 and $NaHCO_3$ is dissolved in 50.00 ml of water; the *p*H of the solution is 9.70. Calculate % Na_2CO_3 in the sample.

23-24   50.0 ml of sodium carbonate solution is titrated with 0.100 *N* HCl, requiring 52.5 ml of the acid to reach the methyl red end point, at which the pH is 5.50. What was the molar concentration of sodium carbonate in the original solution?

23-25   One-tenth mole of H_3PO_4 is dissolved in water, and NaOH is added until the *p*H is 8.16, and the final volume is one liter. List, in order of decreasing molar concentration (substance present in largest concentration first), the formulas of all ions and molecules (except water) present in the solution.

23-26   25.00 ml of a solution containing an unknown amount of hydrochloric acid and acetic acid, titrated with 0.100 *N* NaOH, gave the following data:

ml NaOH added:	11.35	20.00	32.00	40.00
*p*H of solution:	2.00	4.27	5.50	11.88

Calculate the molar concentration of HCl and of $HC_2H_3O_2$ in the original solution.

24

NEUTRALIZATION METHODS

Titrant Solutions

Ideally, the solutes used as titrants in neutralimetry should be highly ionized, nonvolatile, nonoxidizing, stable on exposure to light and air, and should not form insoluble salts in the titration reaction. (The student should consider the reason for each of these requirements.)

Acids. The relative merits of the acids most commonly used as titrants are given below.

Hydrochloric acid is a strong, nonoxidizing acid. The solute is not volatile at the concentrations (about 0.1 to 0.2 N) used in acidimetry; most of its salts are soluble. Usually, an approximate solution is made and then standardized. If either a concentrated or a dilute solution is distilled, eventually a constant boiling mixture is reached, containing 20.24% HCl by weight (about 6 N) when distillation is made at 760 mm pressure. Compositions at various distillation pressures are published in handbooks. The constant boiling solution can be measured from a weight buret and diluted to known volume to make a dilute, direct standard solution.

Sulfuric acid is a strong, nonvolatile acid. At the concentrations used in acidimetry it is not an oxidizing agent. Usually an approximate solution is prepared from the concentrated acid, and then standardized.

Perchloric acid is a strong, nonvolatile acid, with no oxidizing properties when cold and/or dilute. It is especially useful for titrations in nonaqueous solvents.

Oxalic acid is suitable only for the titration of strong bases. Its principal advantage is that a standard solution can be prepared directly from pure, solid $H_2C_2O_4 \cdot 2H_2O$.

314

Nitric acid is seldom used as a reagent titrant. It will destroy the color of some indicators by oxidation, and the solution is not very stable toward heat and light.

Bases.   The following bases may be used in alkalimetry.

Sodium hydroxide is a strong base, the salts of which are soluble. The solid reagent chemical contains more or less carbonate, which is a disadvantage for use in titration of weak acids. When a carbonate-free alkali is required, it may be obtained by making a 50% solution of sodium hydroxide, in which sodium carbonate is quite insoluble; the carbonate is filtered off (Gooch crucible), or the clear liquid is decanted, and the solution is diluted to the required concentration with water that has been recently boiled to remove dissolved carbon dioxide. The solution is stored in a siphon bottle the air inlet of which is protected with a soda-lime tube to prevent contamination by carbon dioxide of the air. Solutions of sodium hydroxide, even when dilute, slowly attack glass and become contaminated with silicate.

Potassium hydroxide, a strong base, is seldom used because of its higher cost compared with sodium hydroxide.

Barium hydroxide, a strong base, has the disadvantage that most barium salts are insoluble in water and alkaline solutions. Its principal advantage is for use when a carbonate-free base is required. When the solid is dissolved in water, any carbon dioxide present is precipitated as barium carbonate, which can be filtered off and the clear solution standardized. If, during storage, carbon dioxide is absorbed, it causes turbidity due to insoluble barium carbonate, which warns the analyst that the solution should either be filtered and restandardized, or a new solution prepared.

Sodium carbonate can be used only for the titration of strong acids. The advantage in its use as a titrant is the fact that a standard solution can be prepared by the direct method.

Ammonium hydroxide is *not* used as a titrant because of the volatility of ammonia even from dilute solution.

Primary Standards

The first compound listed in each class below is generally accepted as the best primary standard. Others given may have advantages in some respects but also disadvantages. The student should deduce the equivalent weight of the standard from the formula weight given in parentheses.

Alkaline Primary Standards

Sodium carbonate, Na_2CO_3 (105.99). Titration of sodium carbonate to bicarbonate cannot be done with the accuracy demanded in standardizations; it is always titrated to the second hydrogen equivalent, using an indicator in the appropriate range, such as methyl orange. Sodium carbonate is only slightly hygroscopic.

Potassium bicarbonate, $KHCO_3$ (100.12), and *thallous carbonate*, Tl_2CO_3 (468.75), are not hygroscopic; the latter compound has an especially high equivalent weight.

Sodium tetraborate decahydrate (borax), $Na_2B_4O_7 \cdot 10H_2O$ (381.37), is titrated according to the following equation:

$$B_4O_7^{--} + 2H^+ + 5H_2O \rightarrow 4H_3BO_3$$

or

$$B_4O_7^{--} + 2H^+ + H_2O \rightarrow 4HBO_2$$

using methyl orange indicator. Compared to sodium carbonate, borax gives a sharper end point and has a much higher equivalent weight.

Sodium oxalate, $Na_2C_2O_4$ (134.00), upon heating to incipient fusion, decomposes to the carbonate:

$$Na_2C_2O_4 \rightarrow CO + Na_2CO_3$$

which is then titrated with the acid being standardized.

Potassium iodate, KIO_3 (214.00), and *potassium acid iodate*, $KH(IO_3)_2$ (389.91), are excellent primary standards for sodium thiosulfate solution, which titrates the iodine formed by the reaction

$$IO_3^- + 5I^- + 6H^+ \rightarrow 3H_2O + 3I_2$$

This reaction is quantitative for any one of the three reactants when the other two are present in excess. A solution containing a weighed amount of potassium iodate (or the acid iodate) and an excess of potassium iodide, upon titration with strong acid will not become acidic until all the iodate has reacted. The color of the liberated iodine would, of course, obscure the color change of acid-base indicators. In practice, therefore, sodium thiosulfate, in an amount in excess of equivalency to the iodate, is added to reduce the iodine back to iodide ion (colorless). The first slight excess of acid then changes the color of the acid-base indicator. The principal disadvantage in the use of these compounds is the low equivalent weight.

Gravimetric Standardization.   The gravimetric precipitation standardization of acids is indirect for the hydrogen ion concentration of the solution. The anion from a measured volume of the acid is precipitated, and the product is weighed. Hydrochloric acid is standardized as silver chloride; sulfuric acid is standardized as barium sulfate.

A "residue method" for standardizing an acid (or a base) consists in exact neutralization of a known volume of solution with a base (or an acid) and evaporation to dryness and ignition of the salt to constant weight.

Acidic Primary Standards

Potassium acid phthalate, $KHC_8H_4O_4$ or $C_6H_4(COOK)COOH$ (204.23), in primary standard quality, usually has an assay value of 99.95 to 100.05%. The compound should be dried at temperatures below 125°, above which some phthalic anhydride may be volatilized. Phenolphthalein indicator is used. The neutralization reaction is

$$HC_8H_4O_4^- + OH^- \rightarrow C_8H_4O_4^{--} + H_2O$$

Oxalic acid dihydrate, $H_2C_2O_4 \cdot 2H_2O$ (126.07), may be used not only for standardization of alkalies, but also for standardizing permanganate solutions. The product crystallized from water is heated to expel occluded water, and the resulting powder is exposed to an atmosphere of about 60% relative humidity (e.g., in a desiccator over saturated sodium bromide solution) to attain the exact dihydrate composition. It titrates as a diprotic acid; phenolphthalein or thymol blue indicator is used. *Potassium tetroxalate dihydrate*, $KHC_2O_4 \cdot H_2C_2O_4 \cdot 2H_2O$ (245.20), is somewhat less stable than oxalic acid with respect to hydrate composition. *Potassium acid oxalate*, KHC_2O_4 (128.13), although anhydrous, is somewhat difficult to prepare.

Benzoic acid, $HC_7H_5O_2$ or C_6H_5COOH (122.12), when purified by sublimation is very fluffy and difficult to handle in weighing; it is therefore melted down in a platinum dish and the cooled cake is ground in an agate mortar. The acid is sparingly soluble in water; the weighed sample is first dissolved in a small amount of alcohol, then diluted with carbonate-free water and titrated with alkali to the phenolphthalein end point. A blank test on the alcohol-water solution should always be made.

Sulfamic acid, NH_2SO_3H (97.09), a crystalline solid readily soluble in water, is a strong, monoprotic acid. Although the compound in solution slowly hydrolyzes,

$$NH_2SO_3H + H_2O \rightarrow NH_4^+ + H^+ + SO_4^{--}$$

this does not change its equivalent weight.

Potassium acid iodate, $KH(IO_3)_2$ (389.91), is stable and nonhygroscopic; it is a strong acid of very high equivalent weight.

Hydrazine sulfate, $N_2H_4 \cdot H_2SO_4$ (130.12), is recrystallized from water, then dried at 140–150°C. With methyl red indicator, it titrates as a monoprotic acid:

$$2N_2H_4 \cdot H_2SO_4 + 2OH^- \rightarrow (N_2H_4)_2 \cdot H_2SO_4 + SO_4^{--} + 2H_2O$$

2,4,6-Trinitrobenzoic acid, $C_6H_2(NO_2)_3COOH$ (257.12), a solid, strong acid, serves as its own indicator, turning from colorless to red at the equivalence point when titrated with sodium hydroxide.

Potassium acid 3,5-dinitrobenzoate, $C_6H_3(NO_2)_2COOK \cdot C_6H_3(NO_2)_2COOH$ (462.23), is a strong monoprotic acid; thymol blue indicator is used in its titration by alkali. Note the very high equivalent weight.

Calcium acid malate hexahydrate, $CaC_4H_4O_5 \cdot H_2C_4H_4O_5 \cdot 6H_2O$ (414.33), has been proposed[1] as a primary standard of great versatility. It is prepared from a waste product of the maple sugar industry. The saturated solution at 25°C has a pH of 3.66, and has been proposed for calibration of pH meters. Ignition in platinum converts the compound into calcium oxide, which then serves as a standard for acid solutions. It can be used as a calcium reference material for standardization of EDTA solutions. Based upon its content of water of hydration, it has also been suggested as a primary standard source of water for standardization of the Karl Fischer reagent used in the determination of water in organic substances.

APPLICATIONS

The analytical applications of neutralimetry are so numerous and varied that specific discussion of many individual determinations will not be given. Applications are found in many branches of chemical production and utilization, as well as in research programs in chemistry, biology, medicine, and other sciences.

Commercial sodium hydroxide always contains varying amounts of sodium carbonate and moisture, from absorption of carbon dioxide and water vapor from the air; inert matter may also be present. Sodium carbonate, or "soda ash," is prepared commercially by thermal decomposition of sodium bicarbonate; the latter is often present in the product. Because sodium carbonate and sodium bicarbonate have different equivalencies for complete neutralization, the composition of soda ash is of much importance to the user. The composition of water with respect to carbonate and bicarbonate hardness is of concern to many industrial users, hence water analysis for these components is important. The various alkali phosphates are widely used in commercial products. The analysis of samples containing different alkaline substances, alone or in certain mixtures, offers an interesting application of the use of different indicators; the details are given below.

Determination of Mixed Alkali Carbonates

In compatible mixtures of NaOH, Na_2CO_3, and $NaHCO_3$ the separate amounts of the constituents can be determined by titrations involving the use of two indicators (and by other special methods). Double-indicator titrations of mixed alkalies are possible on the basis of the following considerations.

a. Phenolphthalein shows its alkaline color (pink) at a pH of 9 or above, and its acid color (colorless) below pH 9.

b. Methyl orange shows its alkaline color (yellow) at a pH above about 4, and its acid color (red) below pH 4.

[1] A. C. Shead, *Anal. Chem.*, **24**, 1415 (1952).

c. When NaOH solution is titrated with standard HCl (solutions not too dilute), practically the same volume of HCl is required, whether phenolphthalein or methyl orange indicator is used, because a very small amount of titrant at the equivalence point changes the pH through several units (e.g., pH 9 to pH 4).

d. Sodium carbonate, in dilute solution, is alkaline to phenolphthalein. Upon titration with HCl, the indicator is decolorized at a pH corresponding to the conversion of CO_3^{--} to HCO_3^- (sometimes referred to as "half titration of carbonate"). If now methyl orange is added, it shows its alkaline color (yellow). Continued titration with HCl gives the color change of methyl orange to its acid form (red) at the pH corresponding to conversion of HCO_3^- to H_2CO_3, representing the "second half" of the titration of CO_3^{--} to H_2CO_3.

e. Sodium bicarbonate is not alkaline to phenolphthalein, that is, the pH of the solution is slightly less than 9, hence no HCl is required to "reach the phenolphthalein end point." If now methyl orange is added, titration with HCl causes color change to red when HCO_3^- has been titrated to H_2CO_3, just as in the second half of the carbonate in part *d.*

By titrating a sample containing the above-mentioned alkalies with HCl with successive use of the two indicators, the amount of HCl used for each indicator end point not only establishes the *identity* of the alkaline constituent(s), but it also is the basis of computation for the *amount* of each alkaline constituent. The following cases arise.

1. *NaOH as the only alkaline constituent.* On titration with HCl, the same volume is required whether the indicator is phenolphthalein or methyl orange.

2. *Na$_2$CO$_3$ as the only alkaline constituent.* On titration with HCl, the amount of *additional* acid to reach the second (methyl orange) end point is exactly equal to the amount of acid required to reach the first (phenolphthalein) end point.

3. *NaHCO$_3$ as the only alkaline constituent.* No HCl is required with phenolphthalein—the solution is already colorless. With methyl orange, titration with HCl converts HCO_3^- to H_2CO_3.

4. *Mixture of NaOH and Na$_2$CO$_3$.* It follows from the above considerations that, if

$$T \text{ ml} = \text{acid required for PhP end point}$$

and $\qquad t \text{ ml} = additional \text{ acid required for M.O. end point}$

then $\quad (T - t) \text{ ml} = \text{acid equivalent to the NaOH}$

$$2t \text{ ml} = \text{acid equivalent to conversion of } Na_2CO_3 \text{ to } H_2CO_3$$

5. *Mixture of Na$_2$CO$_3$ and NaHCO$_3$.* From the previous considerations, if

$$V \text{ ml} = \text{acid required for PhP end point}$$

and $\qquad v \text{ ml} = \text{additional acid required for M.O. end point}$

then $\qquad 2V \text{ ml} = \text{acid equivalent to conversion of } Na_2CO_3 \text{ to } H_2CO_3$

$$(v - V) \text{ ml} = \text{acid equivalent to the } original \text{ NaHCO}_3 \text{ to } H_2CO_3$$

6. *Mixture of NaOH and NaHCO₃*. Although mixtures of these two alkalies can occur in the dry state, they are not compatible in solution:

$$HCO_3^- + OH^- \rightarrow CO_3^{--} + H_2O$$

The solution then behaves as a mixture of either NaOH and Na_2CO_3, or $NaHCO_3$ and Na_2CO_3, depending on whether NaOH or $NaHCO_3$ is present in larger equivalent amount.

The volume relations exhibited by the various alkalies and mixtures, on titration with different indicators, are shown in Fig. 24-1. The horizontal distance, from left to right, shows the relative volume of acid equivalent to the various constituents.

Instead of titrating a sample successively to the two end points, the titrations can be made on separate samples (preferably identical amounts, to simplify calculations), one using phenolphthalein and the other using methyl orange indicator. The latter titration indicates total alkalinity, and the former titration shows only NaOH or/and Na_2CO_3.

The titration of carbonate to bicarbonate is not highly reliable; near the stoichiometric point the rate of change of pH with small increments of added acid is not very great, hence the color change of the indicator is not sharp. In

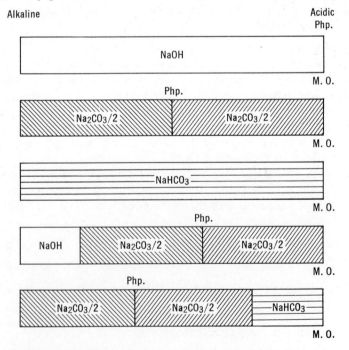

Fig. 24-1 Volume relations of alkalies and alkali mixtures in double-indicator titration with hydrochloric acid.

the determination of mixed alkalies this difficulty can be avoided by the methods outlined below. For these methods, the computations are simplified if a relatively large sample is made to known volume, and identical aliquots are taken for the two parts of the analysis.

4b. *Mixture of NaOH and* Na_2CO_3.

(1) Determine total alkalinity by titration with standard acid, using methyl orange indicator.

(2) To another identical sample (aliquot) add excess barium chloride, which precipitates carbonate ion as $BaCO_3$, but leaves the hydroxide unchanged. Titrate the hydroxide with standard HCl, using phenolphthalein (*not* methyl orange). The acid must be added slowly and with good stirring, so that the barium carbonate is not attacked.

If X ml = acid required for total alkalinity (1)

and x ml = acid required for NaOH (2)

then $(X - x)$ ml = acid required for complete neutralization of Na_2CO_3

5b. *Mixture of* Na_2CO_3 *and* $NaHCO_3$.

(1) Determine total alkalinity by titration with standard acid, using methyl orange indicator.

(2) To another identical sample (aliquot) add a measured volume of standard NaOH solution, in excess of the amount required to complete the reaction

$$HCO_3^- + OH^- \rightarrow H_2O + CO_3^{--}$$

The original carbonate does not react with the NaOH. Then add an excess of barium chloride to precipitate, as $BaCO_3$, *all the carbonate now present*, and back titrate the excess OH^- with standard HCl [as in part 4b (2) above], using phenolphthalein indicator, in order to determine the net amount of OH^- used in converting HCO_3^- to CO_3^{--}.

If Y ml = acid required for total alkalinity

and y ml = acid equivalent to the NaOH used to convert HCO_3^- to CO_3^{--} (= amount of NaOH added − amount NaOH found by back titration)

then $(Y - y)$ ml = acid required for complete neutralization of Na_2CO_3

Determination of Phosphoric Acid and Phosphates

In Chap. 23 it was shown that phosphoric acid can be titrated stepwise with alkali to a second equivalence point, and phosphate ion can be titrated stepwise with acid to a second equivalence point. The end points, which are essentially independent of concentration, occur at pH 4.7 and pH 9.8, corresponding to the color change of bromcresol green (BCG) and thymolphthalein

(ThP), respectively. The spread of the pK values of phosphoric acid precludes the existence in solution of other than adjacent phosphate species. For example, PO_4^{---} (strong base) and $H_2PO_4^-$ (weak acid) cannot coexist in solution:

$$PO_4^{---} + H_2PO_4^- \rightarrow 2HPO_4^{--}$$

and on titration the solution will react as a mixture of HPO_4^{--} and either PO_4^{---} or $H_2PO_4^-$, depending upon which one of the latter is present in the solid sample in larger equivalent amount.

The above facts serve as the basis for the titrimetric determination of *compatible* mixtures of phosphate species, even in the presence of strong acid or strong alkali with which certain phosphate species are compatible. Alkaline solutions that are to be titrated with HCl can be titrated stepwise in the same solution, since the acid form of thymolphthalein is colorless and does not interfere with the color change of bromcresol green; alternatively, separate samples may be titrated, one with each indicator. Titration with NaOH of acidic solutions must be done on separate samples, one with each indicator. Figure 24-2 shows the relations of the various components in titrations using HCl or NaOH as the titrant. Assuming an acid and base of the same normality, the volume relations given below are for titration of *separate samples*, and show the qualitative composition of the solution; the student can deduce the amount of titrant equivalent to each component of mixtures, as well as the volume relations that would prevail in stepwise double-indicator titration of the alkaline solutions with acids.

1. *H_3PO_4 only:* ml NaOH for ThP = 2(ml NaOH for BCG).
2. *H_3PO_4 and strong acid:* ml NaOH for ThP < 2(ml NaOH for BCG).
3. *H_3PO_4 and $H_2PO_4^-$:* ml NaOH for ThP > 2(ml NaOH for BCG).
4. *$H_2PO_4^-$ only:* already "alkaline" to BCG; titrate with NaOH to ThP end point.
5. *HPO_4^{--} only:* already "acidic" to ThP; titrate with HCl to BCG end point.

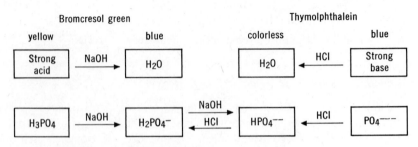

Fig. 24-2 Diagrammatic representation of double-indicator titration of phosphate species in solution.

6. $H_2PO_4^-$ *and* HPO_4^{--}: titrate one sample with NaOH as in 4, and titrate a second sample with HCl as in 5. Alternatively, titrate a sample with NaOH, using ThP, to the blue color of the indicator: then add BCG indicator to the solution and titrate with HCl to the yellow color of the indicator.

7. PO_4^{---} *only:* ml HCl for BCG $\approx$ 2(ml HCl for ThP).

8. PO_4^{---} *and* HPO_4^{--}: ml HCl for BCG > 2(ml HCl for ThP).

9. PO_4^{---} *and strong alkali:* ml HCl for BCG < 2(ml HCl for ThP).

EXAMPLE 1

An acidic solution containing phosphate requires 12.25 ml of 0.1000 N NaOH for titration to the bromcresol green end point; another identical sample requires 33.75 ml of the same NaOH to reach the thymolphthalein end point. Calculate the grams of each phosphate present (assume that salts are sodium compounds). Because the ml of NaOH for ThP end point is more than twice the ml for BCG end point, the components are H_3PO_4 and NaH_2PO_4.

$$g\ H_3PO_4 = 12.25 \times 0.1000 \times 0.09800 = 0.1200$$

$$g\ NaH_2PO_4 = (33.75 - 24.50) \times 0.100 \times 0.1200 = 0.1110$$

Orthophosphate can also be determined by precipitating it from nitric acid solution with ammonium molybdate, then dissolving the yellow precipitate in a known excess of standard sodium hydroxide solution, the excess of which is back titrated with standard acid to the phenolphthalein end point. Ideally,

$$(NH_4)_3P(Mo_3O_{10})_4 + 23OH^- \rightarrow 12MoO_4^{--} + HPO_4^{--} + 3NH_4^+ + 11H_2O$$

In practice, somewhat higher ratios of base to phosphate than 23 : 1 are found, because the yellow precipitate usually contains some nitric acid (compare p. 239), and some of the phosphate may go to PO_4^{---} rather than only to HPO_4^{--}. Also, some ammonia may be lost from the alkaline solution, or may not be completely titrated in the back titration step; this error can be largely avoided by addition of formaldehyde to fix the ammonia.

Determination of Boric Acid

Boric acid is so weak ($K_a = 6.0 \times 10^{-10}$) that it cannot be titrated directly with alkali. However, in the presence of polyhydroxy compounds such as mannitol, glucose, or glycerol, complexes with the borate ion are formed and the acid can then be titrated with alkali to the phenolphthalein end point; it titrates as a monoprotic acid.

Determination of Nitrogen by the Kjeldahl Method

Many nitrogen compounds, when treated with concentrated sulfuric acid at high temperatures and in the presence of a catalyst, are decomposed with the formation of ammonia, which is fixed by the acid as ammonium ion. The mixture is then made strongly alkaline with sodium hydroxide and heated to boiling; the ammonia that distills over is absorbed in an excess of standard acid. Back titration with standard alkali gives the amount of ammonia, and therefore the nitrogen content of the sample, by difference. The Kjeldahl determination consists of three steps.

1. Digestion. The compound is heated with concentrated sulfuric acid, often with the addition of potassium sulfate to raise the boiling point of the acid and effect a more rapid decomposition of the sample. A catalyst is required; substances that have been used include copper oxide, copper sulfate, mercury, mercuric oxide, selenium, and copper selenite. The reaction is carried out in a long-necked (Kjeldahl) flask. Copious evolution of sulfur dioxide and sulfur trioxide requires the use of a good fume hood. Digestion is continued until the reaction mixture is completely colorless, and then for several minutes longer.

Although the entire mechanism of the Kjeldahl digestion is not completely understood, certain changes that occur are quite apparent. Organic compounds are charred by the concentrated sulfuric acid. At the high temperature, the carbon is slowly oxidized to carbon dioxide by the sulfuric acid, which is reduced to sulfur dioxide. The latter is a strong reducing agent, converting nitrogen of higher oxidation states to its lowest state (-3), NH_3, which is retained as NH_4^+ in the acidic medium. The organic nitrogen bases, such as the primary, secondary, and tertiary amines, RNH_2, R_2NH, and R_3N, can be considered as ammonia in which one or more of the hydrogen atoms has been replaced by the organic radical, R. The nitrogen is apparently already in its lowest oxidation state, and in general these classes of compounds are most easily converted to NH_4^+ in the digestion process. Certain types of compounds require pretreatment in order to respond to the Kjeldahl digestion. Azo compounds and hydrazine derivatives are first reduced, using reducing agents such as tin(II) chloride, formaldehyde, or zinc dust and hydrochloric acid. For some nitrates and nitro compounds, salicylic acid and sodium thiosulfate are added to the digestion mixture. Inorganic nitrates are often reduced directly to ammonia by use of sodium hydroxide solution and Devarda's alloy (Al, Zn, Cu); the ammonia is then distilled out and analysis continued. Obviously, ammonium salts need not be digested with sulfuric acid; they may be started directly at the distillation step in the procedure.

2. Distillation. After the digestion mixture has cooled, an excess of concentrated sodium hydroxide (or sodium hydroxide pellets) is added (caution!) and the flask is promptly connected to a condenser the delivery tip of which dips just under the surface of a measured volume of standard acid in an amount more than equivalent to the ammonia expected. The mixture in the flask is distilled until about one-third or more of the liquid has passed over, to ensure complete volatilization of the ammonia. Boiling chips or other devices are used to prevent bumping of the liquid, and a spray trap between flask and condenser is used to prevent alkaline spray from carrying over into the condenser and receiver.

3. Titration. The excess acid in the receiver is titrated with standard sodium hydroxide. Although this is a strong acid–strong base titration, the solution at the stoichiometric point is not neutral because of the presence of the ammonium ion, which hydrolyzes to give a slightly acidic solution. Methyl red indicator is used.

A blank is always carried through all steps of the procedure, using sucrose as the organic compound in the digestion step.

Use of semimicro equipment is especially convenient for the Kjeldahl determination; digestion flasks are of 100-ml size; Hengar tubes[2] are used to absorb the sulfur trioxide, and the distillation step uses simply a large diameter inverted U-tube as an air condenser. The acid and base used in the semimicro method are about 0.02 N.

The *boric acid modification* of the Kjeldahl method has the advantage over the classical method that only a standard solution of acid is required. The ammonia is absorbed in a solution of boric acid, usually about 4%, the concentration of which is of no concern so long as the amount of acid is more than equivalent to the ammonia to be absorbed. The reaction is

$$NH_3 + HBO_2 \rightarrow NH_4{}^+ + BO_2{}^-$$

The $BO_2{}^-$ formed is titrated with standard acid:

$$BO_2{}^- + H^+ \rightarrow HBO_2$$

The acid required in the titration is directly equivalent to the ammonia obtained and to the nitrogen content of the sample.

Acid–Base Titrations in Nonaqueous Solvents

The titration of organic acids and bases in water solution is of quite limited application because of the slight solubility of most of these compounds in water, and because the acidic or basic strength is often so small that sharp end points are impossible. Since about 1927, many methods for acid-base titrations in nonaqueous solvents have appeared,[3] and very many organic compounds not formerly determinable titrimetrically can now be analyzed by this technique.

[2] The Hengar tube is a porous clay finger or thimble that fits into the neck of the digestion flask. Sulfur trioxide is retained in the pores of the tube, which is prepared for reuse by heating to redness to expel SO_3. Tubes, selenized granules for catalyst and use as boiling chips, and other equipment for the Kjeldahl determination are obtainable from the Hengar Company, 1833 Chestnut Street, Philadelphia, Pa.

[3] J. S. Fritz, *Acid-Base Titrations in Nonaqueous Solvents*, Columbus, Ohio, G. Frederick Smith Chemical Co., 1952.

Many substances of very feeble acidic or basic strength in water are strong acids or bases in solvents such as glacial acetic acid, dioxane, acetonitrile, ethylene glycol and isopropanol mixture (1:1), benzene, chloroform, ethyl acetate, and many others.

For the titration of bases, glacial acetic acid, dioxane, acetonitrile, and 1:1 ethylene glycol–isopropanol are widely used as solvents. Hydrogen chloride gas dissolved in the organic solvent is sometimes used as the titrant, but perchloric acid, dissolved in the solvent, is far superior. In some cases no water may be tolerated; in this case the 28 to 30% water in perchloric acid is removed by the addition of acetic anhydride, which reacts with the water to form glacial acetic acid. The method is widely used in the titration of amines, amino acids, and alkali salts of weak carboxylic acids. A very large number of *inorganic salts* dissolved in glacial acetic acid can be titrated as bases. The indicators commonly used include methyl red, modified methyl orange, methyl violet, and crystal violet.

Carboxylic acids, sulfonamides, alcohols, phenols, and salts of weak bases are determined by titration as acids in solvents such as benzene, ethylenediamine, butylamine, and dimethylformamide, using sodium methoxide, CH_3ONa, as the base titrant. Indicators used for titration of acids by sodium methoxide include phenolphthalein, thymolphthalein, thymol blue, and azoviolet. Sodium triphenylmethane is also a strong base in the above solvents; its deep red color can serve as a self-indicator, but the compound is very unstable toward oxygen and water.

In many instances the color changes of the indicators in nonaqueous solvents are sharper than in aqueous solutions. Many of the titrations can also be followed and the end point determined by potentiometric methods, often by the use of conventional electrode systems.

PROBLEMS

24-1 Calculate the normality of the solution given, for use in neutralimetry; assume complete neutralization.

(*a*) 2.882 g of acetic acid in 400.0 ml.   *Ans.* 0.11997.
(*b*) 4.500 g of potassium hydroxide in 500.0 ml.   *Ans.* 0.16040.
(*c*) 0.5000 g of benzoic acid in 250.0 ml.   *Ans.* 0.16377.
(*d*) 0.3236 g of sulfur trioxide in one liter.
(*e*) 0.4320 g of calcium oxide in 250.0 ml.
(*f*) 1.000 g of oxalic acid dihydrate in 300.0 ml.
(*g*) 6.500 g of sodium carbonate in 400.0 ml.
(*h*) 5.000 g of borax in two liters.
(*i*) 2.500 g of sodium hydroxide in 400.0 ml.
(*j*) 8.000 g of sulfur dioxide in one liter.

24-2   How many grams of solute are present in the solution given? Assume complete neutralization.

(*a*) 150.0 ml of 0.07750 *N* Ba(OH)$_2$.   *Ans.* 0.9962.
(*b*) 45.58 ml of 0.1188 *N* H$_2$SO$_4$.   *Ans.* 0.2657.
(*c*) 400.0 ml of 0.1550 *N* NH$_2$SO$_3$H (sulfamic acid).   *Ans.* 6.020.
(*d*) 500.0 ml of 0.1330 *N* Na$_2$CO$_3$.
(*e*) 200.0 ml of 0.0625 *N* Ba(OH)$_2$·8H$_2$O.
(*f*) 42.25 ml of 0.1220 *N* H$_2$SO$_4$.
(*g*) 150.0 ml of 0.2345 *N* KOH.
(*h*) 50.0 ml of 0.0775 *N* NH$_3$.
(*i*) 400.0 ml of 0.2121 *N* NH$_2$SO$_3$H.
(*j*) 500.0 ml of 0.5460 *N* KHC$_8$H$_4$O$_4$ (potassium acid phthalate).

24-3   Calculate the normality and the molarity of the solution given; assume complete neutralization. [Parts (*a*) through (*f*) are the common laboratory reagents.]

Solute	Sp. Gr.	Wt.-percent	
(*a*) HCl	1.179	36.0	*Ans.* 11.64 *N*, 11.64 *M*.
(*b*) H$_2$SO$_4$	1.835	96.0	*Ans.* 35.92 *N*, 17.96 *M*.
(*c*) HNO$_3$	1.405	68.0	
(*d*) HClO$_4$	1.670	70.0	
(*e*) HC$_2$H$_3$O$_2$	1.051	99.5	
(*f*) NH$_3$	0.898	28.0	
(*g*) NaOH	1.043	4.00	
(*h*) Na$_2$CO$_3$	1.040	4.00	
(*i*) H$_3$PO$_4$	1.042	8.00	
(*j*) H$_2$C$_2$O$_4$·2H$_2$O	1.035	10.00	

24-4   From the weight of the primary standard and the volume of titrant used for complete neutralization, calculate the normality of the titrant.

(*a*) 0.2588 g Na$_2$CO$_3$, 41.52 ml HCl.   *Ans.* 0.11761 *N*.
(*b*) 1.0655 g Na$_2$B$_4$O$_7$·10H$_2$O, 39.46 ml H$_2$SO$_4$.   *Ans.* 0.14160 *N*.
(*c*) 0.2586 g H$_2$C$_2$O$_4$·2H$_2$O, 38.85 ml NaOH.
(*d*) 0.9757 g KHC$_8$H$_4$O$_4$, 46.26 ml KOH.
(*e*) 1.3360 g AgCl obtained from 50.00 ml HCl.
(*f*) 0.5045 g BaSO$_4$ obtained from 40.00 ml H$_2$SO$_4$.
(*g*) 0.3987 g KHCO$_3$, 40.00 ml HClO$_4$.
(*h*) 0.4224 g KHC$_2$O$_4$·H$_2$C$_2$O$_4$·2H$_2$O, 39.46 ml NaOH.
(*i*) 1.3300 g KH(IO$_3$)$_2$, 37.50 ml NaOH.
(*j*) 0.6147 g C$_6$H$_5$COOH, 41.42 ml NaOH.
(*k*) 0.4850 g NH$_2$SO$_3$H, 43.05 ml NaOH.

24-5   How many milliliters of 0.1065 *N* NaOH solution must be added to exactly one liter of 0.1090 *N* HCl solution so that, after thorough mixing, the acid solution has the same normality as the alkali solution?   *Ans.* 11.7.

24-6   A sample of a pure organic diprotic acid weighing 0.4526 g requires 39.80 ml of 0.1515 *N* alkali for complete neutralization. Calculate the molecular weight of the acid.   *Ans.* 150.1.

24-7   What must be the normality of a hydrochloric acid solution so that when a 0.5000-g sample of impure mercuric oxide is taken, each milliliter of acid used will represent 2.000% HgO in the sample?   *Ans.* 0.09234.

24-8 A sample of impure calcium carbonate weighing 0.3448 g is treated with 50.00 ml of 0.1363 N hydrochloric acid. After boiling out the carbon dioxide, the excess acid requires 4.45 ml of alkali for back titration. The volume ratio of acid/alkali is 1.060. Calculate the analysis to percentage of (a) $CaCO_3$; (b) CaO; (c) Ca.

Ans. (a) 89.58; (b) 50.19; (c) 35.86.

24-9 A 1.000-g sample that may contain NaOH, $NaHCO_3$, and/or Na_2CO_3, alone or in certain admixtures, requires 15.00 ml of 0.1100 N HCl for titration to the phenolphthalein end point, and an additional 50.00 ml of the same acid to reach the methyl orange end point. Calculate the percentage of each alkaline component present.

Ans. 17.49% Na_2CO_3, 32.35% $NaHCO_3$.

24-10 A 0.5000-g sample consisting only of CaO and MgO is dissolved in 50.00 ml of 0.5000 N acid, which is an excess requiring 16.20 ml of 0.4000 N alkali for back titration. Calculate the percentages of Ca and Mg in the sample.

Ans. 64.40% Ca, 5.97% Mg.

24-11 A sample of constant boiling hydrochloric acid, prepared by distillation at 760 mm pressure, has a sp. gr. of 1.1016 and contains 20.24% HCl by weight. By means of a weight buret 18.750 g of the acid is taken and diluted to exactly one liter. Calculate the normality of the diluted acid.

24-12 Calculate the normality, as acid or base, of the mixture given. Assume complete neutralization of polyprotic acids or their conjugate bases.

(a) 35.50 ml of 0.0800 N acid + 46.50 ml of 0.1200 N acid.

(b) 2.00 g of NaOH + 2.00 g of KOH in 1 liter of solution.

(c) 3.500 g of $H_2C_2O_4 \cdot 2H_2O$ + 4.200 g of $KHC_2O_4 \cdot H_2C_2O_4 \cdot 2H_2O$ in 500.0 ml of solution.

(d) 35.00 ml of 0.0906 N HCl + 25.00 ml of 0.1414 N H_2SO_4 + 60.00 ml of 0.1010 N KOH.

(e) 40.00 ml of 0.1256 N acid + 30.00 ml of 0.1333 N alkali.

(f) 1.166 g of NaOH + 2.025 g of Na_2CO_3 in 400.0 ml of solution.

24-13 How many milliliters of water must be added to the solution given in order to make it exactly tenth-normal?

(a) 185.0 ml of 0.1065 N acid.

(b) 50.0 ml of 0.2250 N acid.

(c) 75.0 ml of 0.1667 N HCl + 35.0 ml of 0.0800 N H_2SO_4.

(d) 3.600 g of NaOH in 400.0 ml of solution.

(e) 8.000 g of $Ba(OH)_2 \cdot 8H_2O$ in 300.0 ml of solution.

24-14 What volume of water would have to be evaporated from 200.0 ml of 0.1500 N sulfuric acid so that the remaining solution is 0.1750 N?

24-15 What volume of 0.4500 N NaOH must be added to 500.0 ml of 0.2000 N NaOH to make a 0.2500 N alkali solution?

24-16 What volume of 0.2025 N acid must be added to 150.0 ml of 0.1225 N acid to make a 0.1500 N acid solution?

24-17 What volume of 0.1065 N NaOH must be added to 500.0 ml of 0.1120 N HCl so that, after thorough mixing, the acid solution has the same normality as the alkaline solution?

24-18 What volume of 0.0903 N acid must be added to 200.0 ml of 0.1033 N alkali so that the two solutions will have the same normality?

24-19 What volume of 0.500 M HCl must be added to 500 ml of 0.100 M Na_2CO_3 to give a solution of pH 10.92?

24-20 What volume of 1.00 M NaOH must be added to 200 ml of 0.200 M $NaHCO_3$ to give a solution of pH 10.14?

24-21 What volume of 5.00 M NaOH must be added to 350 ml of 1.00 M H_3PO_4 to give a solution of pH 2.52? 4.67? 7.51?

24-22 What volume of 1.50 M HCl must be added to 300 ml of 0.300 M Na_3PO_4 to give a solution of pH 11.70? 9.60? 6.51?

24-23 What weight of soda ash sample should be taken for analysis so that when a one-tenth aliquot of the sample solution is titrated to the methyl orange end point, each milliliter of 0.1120 N HCl used will represent 2.000% of Na_2CO_3 in the sample?

24-24 Calculate the percentage of the substance sought from the titration data given. Assume complete neutralization.

Sought	Sample, g	Titration requires
(a) C_6H_5COOH	0.6140	40.04 ml of 0.1224 N NaOH
(b) CH_3COOH	5.030	46.58 ml of 0.922 N NaOH
(c) $Na_2B_4O_7 \cdot 10H_2O$	0.8234	39.90 ml of 0.1006 N H_2SO_4
(d) Na_2CO_3	0.3802	42.36 ml of 0.1104 N HCl
(e) BaO	0.6000	47.75 ml of 0.1220 N HCl
(f) $H_2C_2O_4 \cdot 2H_2O$	0.7575	44.42 ml of 0.1115 N NaOH

24-25 A 0.4500-g sample of a pure acid of molecular weight approximately 75, requires 42.20 ml of 0.1422 N NaOH for neutralization. How many protons per molecule does the acid furnish?

24-26 A sample of pure diprotic acid weighing 0.5246 g requires 44.00 ml of 0.1360 N NaOH for complete neutralization. Calculate the molecular weight of the acid.

24-27 A sample of impure calcium carbonate weighing 0.4348 g is treated with 50.00 ml of 0.1326 N hydrochloric acid. After boiling out the carbon dioxide, the excess acid requires 5.45 ml of alkali for back titration. The volume ratio of acid/alkali is 1.050. Calculate the analysis to percentage of (a) $CaCO_3$, (b) CaO, (c) Ca, (d) CO_2.

24-28 A 0.7500-g sample of cream of tartar (potassium acid tartrate) is dissolved in 40.00 ml of 0.1010 N alkali, which is an excess requiring 8.75 ml of 0.1140 N acid for back titration. Calculate the percentage of $KHC_4H_4O_6$ in the sample.

24-29 A 0.4800-g sample of soda ash requires 30.00 ml of hydrochloric acid for complete neutralization. 35.00 ml of the HCl solution is equivalent to 42.00 ml of a sodium hydroxide solution, 45.00 ml of which is required to titrate 0.2553 g of primary standard $H_2C_2O_4 \cdot 2H_2O$. Calculate the percentage of Na_2CO_3 in the sample.

24-30 A 1.0000-g sample that may contain NaOH, $NaHCO_3$, and/or Na_2CO_3, alone or in a compatible mixture, requires 28.46 ml of 0.1205 N HCl for titration to the phenolphthalein end point, and an additional 43.78 ml of the same acid to reach the methyl orange end point. Calculate the percentage of each alkaline component present.

24-31 A 0.5445-g sample containing mixed alkalies requires 36.75 ml of 0.1357 N acid to reach the phenolphthalein end point and an additional 10.45 ml to reach the methyl orange end point. Calculate the percentages of the alkaline components of the sample (assume sodium compounds).

24-32 A 0.7500-g sample containing mixed alkalies requires 35.52 ml of 0.2000 N HCl for complete neutralization. Another identical sample is treated with 25.00 ml of 0.0810 N sodium hydroxide solution. After adding barium chloride to precipitate barium carbonate, the mixture requires 5.40 ml of the same hydrochloric acid for titration to the phenolphthalein end point. Calculate the percentage of each alkaline component of the sample (assume sodium compounds).

24-33 A sample of dried whole milk weighing exactly one gram is analyzed by the Kjeldahl method. The ammonia is distilled into 50.00 ml of 0.1220 N HCl. The excess acid requires 20.70 ml of 0.1450 N NaOH for titration. The factor for converting nitrogen to protein is 6.38. Calculate the percentage of protein in the sample.

24-34 A 1.000-g sample of commercial fertilizer is analyzed by the Kjeldahl method. The ammonia is distilled into 100.0 ml of 4% boric acid solution, which then requires 45.32 ml of 0.0980 N hydrochloric acid for titration. Calculate the percentage of nitrogen in the fertilizer.

24-35 A certain high-protein cereal contains 26.0% protein. Calculate the maximum weight of cereal sample that may be taken so that when analyzed by the boric acid modification of the Kjeldahl method, no more than 50.0 ml of 0.0250 N hydrochloric acid will be used in the titration. The factor for converting nitrogen to cereal protein is 5.70.

24-36 Calculate the percent sulfur in steel from the following data: the SO_3 formed by oxidation of a 2.500-g sample of steel is absorbed in 50.00 ml of 0.03000 N NaOH. The excess alkali requires 35.70 ml of 0.02500 N acid for back titration.

24-37 Fuming sulfuric acid (oleum) consists of a solution of SO_3 in H_2SO_4; when water is added, the SO_3 reacts to form H_2SO_4. Upon titration with alkali, fuming sulfuric acid reacts as if it were sulfuric acid of more than 100% concentration or as a mixture of two pure diprotic acids. A 0.5000-g sample of fuming sulfuric acid requires 26.75 ml of 0.4000 N NaOH for titration.

(*a*) Calculate the acidity in terms of percent H_2SO_4.

(*b*) Calculate the percentages of SO_3 and H_2SO_4 in the sample.

24-38 Calculate the volume of 0.6000 N alkali required for titration of a 1.0000-g sample of fuming sulfuric acid that contains 10.00 wt.-percent SO_3.

24-39 A 1-gram sample consisting only of $CaCO_3$ and $BaCO_3$ requires 47.54 ml of 0.4000 N hydrochloric acid for neutralization. Calculate the percentages of CaO and BaO in the sample.

24-40 A 0.5000-g sample consisting only of CaO and MgO is dissolved in 70.00 ml of 0.4000 N acid, which is an excess requiring 25.83 ml of 0.3500 N alkali for back titration. Calculate the percentages of Ca and Mg in the sample.

24-41 A 0.5000-g sample containing only $H_2C_2O_4 \cdot 2H_2O$ and C_6H_5COOH requires 42.12 ml of 0.1200 N alkali for complete neutralization. Calculate the percentage of each acid present.

24-42 A 0.6000-g sample containing only $KHC_2O_4 \cdot H_2C_2O_4 \cdot 2H_2O$ and $H_2C_2O_4 \cdot 2H_2O$ requires 41.58 ml of 0.1800 N NaOH for complete neutralization. Calculate the percentage of each acid present.

24-43 A 2.000-g sample known to contain Na_3PO_4, Na_2HPO_4, NaH_2PO_4, or compatible mixtures of these salts (along with inert matter) requires 35.00 ml of 0.1000 N NaOH for titration, using thymolphthalein indicator. Another identical sample requires 40.00 ml of 0.1500 N HCl for titration, using bromcresol green indicator. Calculate the percentage of each phosphate component present.

24-44 In each lettered part below, the solution contains H_3PO_4, NaH_2PO_4, Na_2HPO_4, alone or in a compatible mixture. The sample is first titrated with 0.8000 N NaOH to the thymolphthalein end point, and the resulting solution is then titrated with 0.4000 N HCl to the bromcresol green end point. Calculate the grams of each component present in the sample solution.

	ml NaOH used	ml HCl used
(a)	15.80	37.50
(b)	28.00	40.40
(c)	24.50	49.00
(d)	23.24	23.24

25

TITRIMETRIC PRECIPITATION, COMPLEXATION, AND WEAK IONOGEN FORMATION

Many precipitation, complexation, and weak ionogen formation reactions fulfill the requirements for titrimetric application, except that no visual indicator is as yet known to mark the end point of the titration. Potentiometric, conducto-metric, or amperometric methods can be used for indicating the end point of most of these titrations, but visual indicators are available for only relatively few. The methods discussed below are limited to the latter cases.[1]

In this type of titrimetry, the equivalent weight is the weight of substance that will furnish, react with, or be chemically equivalent to one gram-atom of univalent cation in the precipitate, complex, or weak ionogen formed.

Titrants and Standards

The titrants and standards used are summarized in Table 25-1, along with the principal uses. The applications are discussed below in some detail.

PRECIPITATION

Determination of Silver

1. **Volhard Method.**   The reaction of this determination is

$$Ag^+ + CNS^- \rightarrow AgCNS \quad \text{(white precipitate)}$$

When this reaction is complete, the next small amount of thiocyanate added

---

[1] A review of Chaps. 6 and 7 is strongly recommended.

332

Table 25-1   Titrants, Standards, and Uses

Titrant	Standardization Method	Use
$AgNO_3$	1. Direct from $AgNO_3$ 2. Direct from $Ag + HNO_3$ 3. Against KCl or NaCl	Titration of Cl^-, Br^-, CN^- and certain mixtures of these ions
KCNS	1. Against $AgNO_3$ 2. Against Hg or HgO dissolved in HNO_3	Titration of Ag^+, Hg^{++}
KCN[a]	Against Cu dissolved in HNO_3; add NH_3	Titration of Cu^{++}, Ni^{++}
$Hg(NO_3)_2$, $Hg(ClO_4)_2$	Against KCl, NaCl or KCNS	Titration of Cl^-, Br^-, CNS^-
KCl, NaCl	1. Direct preparation 2. Against $AgNO_3$	Titration of Ag^+
$K_4Fe(CN)_6$	Against Zn or ZnO dissolved in H_2SO_4	Titration of Zn^{++}
$(NH_4)_2MoO_4$	Against $PbSO_4$ dissolved in NH_4Ac	Titration of Pb^{++}
EDTA	1. Direct preparation 2. Against $CaCO_3$ dissolved in HCl, then buffered at pH 10	Direct and indirect titration of many cations

[a] Metal cyanides, and HCN gas liberated from them by reaction with acids, are violent poisons; use only in alkaline solution, in a well-ventilated hood, and exercise great caution.

causes formation of a red color with ferric alum (ferric ammonium sulfate) solution used as the indicator:

$$Fe^{+++} + CNS^- \rightarrow Fe(CNS)^{++} \quad \text{(red solution}^2\text{)}$$

The ferric alum indicator is used in high concentration (about 5 ml of saturated solution per 100 ml of titration mixture), to ensure prompt formation of a detectable amount of the red complex upon addition of the first slight excess of thiocyanate beyond the stoichiometric point of the precipitation reaction. At the stoichiometric point,

$$[Ag^+] = [CNS^-] = \sqrt{K_{sp}} = \sqrt{1.0 \times 10^{-12}} = 1.0 \times 10^{-6}$$

[2] The red color in this reaction has often been attributed to weakly ionized $Fe(CNS)_3$, or to the complex ion $Fe(CNS)_6^{---}$. Spectrophotometric studies of this reaction have shown that the red color is the result of reaction of Fe^{+++} and CNS^- in a 1 : 1 mole ratio, corresponding to the formation of $Fe(CNS)^{++}$.

The amount of silver ion remaining unprecipitated is therefore negligible. Upon addition of even a minute excess of thiocyanate titrant, the solubility of AgCNS is still further diminished by common ion effect.

The Volhard method is especially useful because the end point is very sharp, and because the titration is carried out in nitric acid solution, whereas some other methods for titration of silver ion must be made in nearly neutral solution. Nitric acid prevents the hydrolysis of Fe^{+++} to insoluble basic salts; it also suppresses the color of ferric ion in the indicator solution, making the end point much sharper. The nitric acid used in the preparation of the indicator solution and for the dissolution of samples for titration must be free from chloride ion. Most of the common cations do not interfere; a notable exception is mercury(II), which prevents the formation of the red ferric complex, because $Hg(CNS)_2$ is less ionized than $FeCNS^{++}$. Anions such as phosphate and carbonate, the silver salts of which are insoluble in water but soluble in nitric acid, do not interfere if sufficient nitric acid is present.

2. Chloride Method. Although silver ion can be determined by titration with standard chloride solution, some of the indicators (e.g., chromate in the Mohr method) are not satisfactory when titration is made in this direction. The titration of chloride ion by standard silver nitrate, however, is a widely applied titrimetric precipitation method.

Determination of Chloride

The variations in the titrimetric determination of chloride ion by silver ion are concerned with the methods of detecting the end point. Because this determination is so widely used, a brief discussion of the equilibrium features of the reaction is appropriate. The reaction is

$$Ag^+ + Cl^- \rightarrow AgCl \quad \text{(white precipitate)}$$

For silver chloride, $K_{sp} = 1.8 \times 10^{-10}$. From this relation the chloride ion concentration of the solution at any stage of the titration can be calculated, and the change of $[Cl^-]$ can be represented graphically by a titration curve in all respects analogous to the titration curve of a strong acid by a strong base. Suppose, for example, that 50.0 ml of 0.100 N (also 0.100 M) chloride solution are titrated with 0.100 N AgNO$_3$ solution. At the start of the titration, $[Cl^-] = 0.100$. By the time the stoichiometric point is reached, the chloride ion concentration will have decreased through several orders of magnitude; it is convenient, therefore, to express the chloride ion concentration of the solution on a logarithmic basis similar to the pH scale, by the definition $pCl = -\log [Cl^-]$. Thus, at the start of the titration, $[Cl^-] = 0.100$, and $pCl = 1.00$.

Upon addition of some silver nitrate solution, say 5.0 ml, an equivalent amount of chloride ion is precipitated as silver chloride; the solution then contains $(50.0 \times 0.100) - (5.0 \times 0.100) = 4.50$ gme of chloride ion in a volume of 55.0 ml. $[Cl^-] = 4.50/55.0 = 0.082$, and $pCl = 1.09$. At 25.0 ml of added silver nitrate, 2.50 gme of chloride remain unprecipitated in a total volume of 75.0 ml; $[Cl^-] = 2.50/75.0 = 0.033$, and $pCl = 1.48$. Similar calculations are made up to the stoichiometric point. In these calculations, complete reaction of the added silver ion with chloride ion is assumed. This assumption is justified not only by the small solubility of silver chloride in water, but also by the fact that its solubility in solution containing chloride ion is diminished to even smaller values by the common ion effect.

At the stoichiometric point, $[Cl^-] = [Ag^+] = \sqrt{K_{sp}} = \sqrt{1.8 \times 10^{-10}} = 1.34 \times 10^{-5}$, and $pCl = 4.87$. After the stoichiometric point, the chloride ion concentration diminishes still further because of the common ion effect of excess silver ion. The chloride ion concentration is calculated from $[Cl^-] = K_{sp}/[Ag^+]$. For 1.00 ml of silver nitrate in excess, $[Ag^+] = (1.00 \times 0.100)/101.0 = 9.9 \times 10^{-4}$. $[Cl^-] = (1.8 \times 10^{-10})/(9.9 \times 10^{-4}) = 1.8 \times 10^{-7}$, and $pCl = 6.74$. Table 25-2 shows additional values of pCl during the titration; the student should

Table 25-2 Titration of 50.0 ml of 0.100 N
Cl^- with 0.100 N Ag^+

AgNO$_3$ Added, ml	$[Cl^-]$ in Solution	pCl
0.0	1.0×10^{-1}	1.00
5.0	8.2×10^{-2}	1.09
10.0	6.7×10^{-2}	1.17
25.0	3.3×10^{-2}	1.48
45.0	5.3×10^{-3}	2.28
49.0	1.1×10^{-3}	2.96
49.5	5.2×10^{-4}	3.28
49.9	1.0×10^{-4}	4.00
50.0	1.3×10^{-5}	4.87
50.5	5.0×10^{-7}	6.44
51.0	1.8×10^{-7}	6.47
55.0	3.8×10^{-8}	7.42

confirm the calculations. The titration curve of pCl against volume of silver nitrate solution is shown in Fig. 25-1.

At the stoichiometric point in the titration, the precipitate of silver chloride has its maximum solubility, the molar concentration of silver chloride being the square root of its K_{sp}. On either side of the stoichiometric point, that is, in the presence of either excess Cl^- or excess Ag^+, the solubility of silver chloride

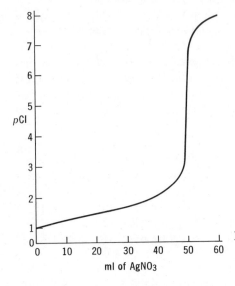

Fig. 25-1 Titration curve. 50.0 ml of 0.100 N sodium chloride titrated with 0.100 N silver nitrate.

is decreased by common ion effect of the ion present in excess; the molar solubility can be calculated from the K_{sp} and the concentration of the ion that is present in excess. Figure 25-2 shows the way in which the solubility of silver chloride changes in solution containing a slight excess of either ion.[3]

In the determination of chloride ion by titration with silver ion (or the reverse), the indicator must show the end point when the concentration of the ion being titrated has been decreased to 1.34×10^{-5}, or when the concentration of the ion of the titrant is only slightly greater than 1.34×10^{-5}.

1. Mohr Method: Chromate Indicator. The end point in this method is marked by the first formation of an orange-red precipitate of silver chromate after precipitation of silver chloride is complete; the indicator is potassium chromate solution.

$$Cl^- + Ag^+ \rightarrow AgCl \quad \text{(white precipitate)}$$

$$CrO_4^{--} + 2Ag^+ \rightarrow Ag_2CrO_4 \quad \text{(orange-red precipitate)}$$

Silver chloride is less soluble than silver chromate; the latter cannot form permanently in the mixture until precipitation of chloride ion as silver chloride has lowered the chloride ion concentration to a very small value. Any silver chromate

[3] The calculated values, on which Fig. 25-2 is based, are not rigorously correct, on account of the presence of other ions, such as K^+ and NO_3^-, which contribute to the ionic strength of the solution and change the activities of the silver and chloride ions. The difference between the approximate and the rigorous calculations is not significant except at relatively high concentration of diverse ions. In solutions of high chloride ion concentration the solubility of silver chloride is increased also by the formation of chloro complexes, such as $AgCl_2^-$ and $AgCl_3^{--}$.

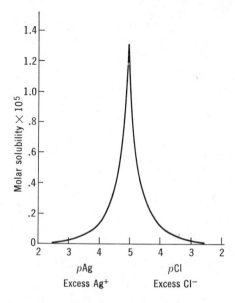

Fig. 25-2 Solubility of silver chloride in excess silver ion and in excess chloride ion solutions.

formed temporarily from a localized excess of silver ion where the titrant is added to the mixture is transposed by untitrated chloride ion in the solution:

$$Ag_2CrO_4 + 2Cl^- \rightarrow CrO_4^{--} + 2AgCl$$

From the solubility product constants of AgCl and Ag_2CrO_4 it is possible to calculate the concentration of chromate ion that will show the end point at the stoichiometric point of the titration reaction. It has already been shown that at the stoichiometric point $[Ag^+] = [Cl^-] = 1.34 \times 10^{-5}$. For silver chromate, $K_{sp} = [Ag^+]^2[CrO_4^{--}] = 1.3 \times 10^{-12}$. The $[CrO_4^{--}]$ in equilibrium with 1.34×10^{-5} M Ag^+ is given by

$$[CrO_4^{--}] = \frac{K_{sp}}{[Ag^+]^2} = \frac{1.3 \times 10^{-12}}{(1.34 \times 10^{-5})^2} = 7.2 \times 10^{-3}$$

On this basis, the chromate ion concentration should be just slightly larger than 0.007 M to form a precipitate of Ag_2CrO_4 at the stoichiometric point of the titration of chloride ion by silver ion. In practice, the chromate ion concentration is made about 0.005 M. The $[Ag^+]$ in equilibrium with this concentration of chromate ion is 1.6×10^{-5}, an amount that will just saturate the solution with silver chromate, and a slightly higher concentration of silver ion is required to precipitate a visible amount of the orange-red silver chromate. The end point therefore occurs slightly beyond the stoichiometric point of the chloride precipitation. A blank test on the indicator, in the absence of chloride, gives the correction to be applied to the titration data. The blank is negligible when 0.1 N solution is used in the titration, but it becomes significant when the titrant is 0.01 N or less.

The Mohr method is used not only for the determination of relatively large amounts of chloride in solution, but also for small amounts, such as found in water, and it is widely used in water analysis. The end point in the determination is very much sharper if the titration is conducted under a yellow light; the chromate solution then appears to be almost colorless, and the first formation of the orange-red precipitate is easily observed.

The Mohr method is applicable only in solution in which the pH is in the range about 7 to 10. The first ionization of chromic acid, H_2CrO_4, is strong, but the second ionization is weak, $K_2 = 3.2 \times 10^{-7}$. In acid solution, the chromate ion concentration is decreased by reaction with hydrogen ion:

$$CrO_4^{--} + H^+ \to HCrO_4^- \qquad (2HCrO_4^- \to H_2O + Cr_2O_7^{--})$$

and silver chromate will not precipitate until the silver ion has been added considerably in excess of the stoichiometric amount for the chloride precipitation. In fact, precipitation of silver chromate can be entirely prevented by sufficient acid. If the solution for titration were alkaline, silver hydroxide ($K_{sp} = 2.6 \times 10^{-8}$) may be precipitated before silver chromate.

Titration of bromide by the Mohr method is satisfactory, but the method is not applicable for the titration of iodide or thiocyanate because of extensive adsorption of these anions on the silver precipitate. The titration of silver ion by chloride ion, with chromate indicator to the disappearance of silver chromate, is not satisfactory.

2. Fajans Method: Adsorption Indicator.

Fajans and his co-workers found that certain organic ions are strongly adsorbed on some precipitates, with a resulting change in color that serves to mark the end point in the precipitation titration. Fluorescein and its derivatives are among the indicators that function in this manner. The mechanism of the indicator action in the silver chloride precipitation is as follows. When a small amount of silver nitrate is added to a chloride solution, chloride ion is strongly adsorbed on the colloidal silver chloride particles formed, and cations form the counter ion layer. The particles can be represented thus: $AgCl \cdot Cl^- : K^+$. In an excess of silver ions, either by adding an excess of Ag^+ beyond the stoichiometric point in a chloride titration, or at the start of titration of Ag^+ by Cl^-, silver ion is the primary adsorbed ion, and anions form the counter ion layer; thus: $AgCl \cdot Ag^+ : NO_3^-$. When the titration of chloride ion by silver ion is made in the presence of fluorescein (a weak acid), the chloride ions adsorbed on the precipitate attract only cations, as indicated before. But after the stoichiometric point has been reached, the first excess of Ag^+ is adsorbed on the precipitate, and these attract the fluorescein anions, thus: $AgCl \cdot Ag^+ : Fluor^-$. In this process the fluoresceinate ion undergoes a deformation or change of structure resulting in a change of color from yellow-green to pink-red. When silver ion is titrated by chloride ion, the precipitate is colored pink-red from the start. Addition of chloride ion just beyond the stoichiometric point causes a reversal of the ionic adsorption; the adsorbed fluoresceinate ion is displaced into the solution, and the pink color disappears from the precipitate.

Because the indicator action is an adsorption phenomenon, it is imperative that the precipitate be prevented from coagulating, so that a large specific surface of precipitate is presented in contact with the solution. Stabilization of the colloidal particles is effected by adding a protective colloid, such as dextrin. Titration must be done in diffuse light on account of the photosensitivity of the silver halide. The photochemical action is especially pronounced on the very small particles required for good adsorption indicator action. If the precipitate begins to turn gray during titration, a satisfactory end point cannot be obtained.

Fluorescein and its derivatives are weak acids of different strengths. Their action is therefore influenced by the hydrogen ion concentration of the solution. In the titration of chloride with fluorescein indicator, the pH should be in the range 7 to 10. Dichlorofluorescein is a stronger acid than fluorescein and can therefore be used in solutions that are slightly acidic. Tetrabromofluorescein (eosin), a still stronger acid, can be used in solutions of acidity down to pH 2, but it is adsorbed on silver chloride so strongly that it shows an end point too soon when chloride is being titrated, or too late when silver ion is being titrated. However, eosin is satisfactory for the titration of bromide, iodide, and thiocyanate by silver ion.

Adsorption indicators for many other precipitation titrations have been discovered.

3. Gay-Lussac Method: Cessation of Precipitation, or Clear-Point Method. Although silver chloride precipitate is well stabilized by chloride ion during most of the titration by silver ion (and conversely), as the stoichiometric point is approached and the stabilizing ion is removed by precipitation, the precipitate readily coagulates and settles out. The titration is completed by dropwise addition of the titrant until no further precipitate or turbidity is formed. Although the method is somewhat tedious, it is capable of good accuracy.

4. Mulder Method: Equal Turbidities. At the stoichiometric point in the titration of chloride ion by silver ion (or the reverse), Ag^+ and Cl^- are present in exactly equal molar concentrations, which are the equilibrium amounts for the saturated solution. When two separate test portions of solution, upon addition of the same amount of chloride ion to one as the amount of silver ion to the other, give equal turbidities due to precipitation of equal amounts of silver chloride by common ion effect, the solution tested is at the stoichiometric point. In carrying out this method, account must be taken of the amount of unreacted material in the portions of solution taken for test before the stoichiometric point is reached. Although the method is tedious, it is in fact the most exact method of establishing the silver-to-chloride ratio in the formation of silver chloride. This method has been much used in determining the atomic weight of an element, by bringing the pure chloride of the element into reaction with silver ion. An instrument called a nephelometer was originally designed for the purpose of making the turbidity comparisons. The reverse titration (silver ion by chloride ion) is used for silver analysis in government mint laboratories.

5. Volhard Method. This is an indirect method for chloride, in which a measured volume of standard silver nitrate solution is added in excess of the amount of chloride in the solution. The excess silver ion is back titrated with standard potassium thiocyanate solution, using ferric alum indicator. The method derives its name, therefore, from the back titration, and its particular utility from the very sharp end point of the thiocyanate titration. If the excess silver ion is titrated with thiocyanate in the presence of the silver chloride precipitate, some of the latter may be transposed to the less soluble silver thiocyanate:

$$AgCl + CNS^- \rightarrow AgCNS + Cl^-$$

The slow transposition gives a transient end point; the amount of thiocyanate used in the back titration is too large, and the calculated amount of chloride is too low. The error can be avoided by filtering off the silver chloride and titrating the filtrate and washings with thiocyanate.

In the *Caldwell modification* of the Volhard method, filtration of the silver chloride is avoided by adding a small amount of nitrobenzene to the suspension. The silver chloride particles become coated with a film of the liquid nitrobenzene and are thereby protected from contact with the thiocyanate solution in the back titration.

The Volhard determination of chloride has been re-examined by Schulek,[4] who showed that the slow end point is not due to the difference in solubility of AgCl and AgCNS and the slow transposition of the former to the latter, but is due to silver ion adsorbed on the silver chloride precipitate. By heating the silver chloride suspension with potassium nitrate solution, the adsorbed silver ion is displaced by potassium ion. Titration of the excess silver ion with thiocyanate then gives a sharp end point and reliable results for the chloride analysis.

The Volhard method can be used for the determination of bromide, iodide, and thiocyanate. In these cases, filtration or protection of the main precipitate is unnecessary because of the very small solubility of the first precipitate. In the determination of iodide, ferric alum is not added until after precipitation of the silver iodide; otherwise, iodide would be oxidized to iodine by the ferric ion.

Determination of Oxidized Forms of the Halogens

Oxidized forms of the halogens, such as the free elements and the oxy anions ClO_4^-, ClO_3^-, ClO^-, and BrO_3^-, can be reduced to the corresponding halide

---

[4] E. Schulek, E. Pungor, and J. Kéthelyi, *Anal. Chim. Acta*, **8**, 229 (1953).

ion by treatment with sulfite or nitrite, as described on p. 215. The halide ion can then be titrated with silver ion in the usual way. The titration of iodide with silver ion is seldom used because of extensive coprecipitation on silver iodide; there are other, more reliable methods for titrimetric determination of iodide. Also, the method is seldom applied for analysis of free halogens, because there are more convenient and reliable methods for them.

Other Applications of Precipitation by Silver Ion

Anions of weak acids that form silver salts insoluble in neutral solution but soluble in nitric acid can be determined by the Volhard method. The anion in question is precipitated by addition of excess silver nitrate. The precipitate is filtered off and washed free from excess silver ion, and it is then dissolved in dilute nitric acid. The silver ion in solution is titrated with standard potassium thiocyanate solution. Alternatively, the anion is precipitated by addition of a known volume of standard silver nitrate solution. The precipitate is filtered off and washed, and the excess silver ion is determined in the filtrate and washings. The method is applicable to the determination of a number of anions: PO_4^{---}, AsO_4^{---}, AsO_3^{---}, CrO_4^{--}, IO_3^-, CO_3^{--}, S^{--}, SO_3^{--}, MoO_4^{--}, $Fe(CN)_6^{---}$, and $Fe(CN)_6^{4-}$.

Miscellaneous Precipitation Methods

Determination of Zinc with Ferrocyanide (Hexacyanoferrate(II)). The reaction of this titration is represented by

$$3Zn^{++} + 2K^+ + 2Fe(CN)_6^{4-} \rightarrow K_2Zn_3[Fe(CN)_6]_2$$

The zinc ion solution should be 0.5 to 1.4 N in sulfuric acid, and titration should be done in solution at about 60°C. Although the titrant can be prepared directly from $K_4Fe(CN)_6 \cdot 3H_2O$, it is preferable to standardize the solution against pure zinc or zinc oxide that has been dissolved in sulfuric acid, using an amount of zinc approximating that expected in the unknown sample.

The end point in the titration was formerly determined by use of uranyl acetate indicator externally (spot plate); when the precipitation of zinc is complete, the first excess of ferrocyanide produces a brown color in the uranyl solution, due to insoluble $K_2(UO_2)Fe(CN)_6$. Internal redox indicators, now used for this titration, depend upon the reaction of the ferricyanide-ferrocyanide couple. A small amount of diphenylamine or diphenylbenzidine and potassium ferricyanide are added to the zinc solution; the ferricyanide oxidizes the indicator to an intense blue-purple product. When all the zinc has been precipitated, the first excess of ferrocyanide titrant reduces the oxidized indicator to its colorless form. More recently, naphthidine and its derivatives have been used as indicators for this titration, with superior results; their oxidized forms are red to red-purple.

Determination of Lead with Molybdate. Lead ion in solution can be determined titrimetrically with ammonium molybdate solution, forming a precipitate of lead molybdate, $PbMoO_4$. The end point can be detected by tannin (tannic acid) solution used on a spot plate; the end point is the first yellow color when molybdate is present in slight excess. Various dyes, such as eosin, erythrosine, and Solochrome Red B, can be used internally as adsorption indicators.

WEAK IONOGEN FORMATION

Many of the soluble compounds of mercury(II) are very weakly ionized, and many anions also form complexes with mercury(II). The highly ionized nitrate, $Hg(NO_3)_2$, or perchlorate, $Hg(ClO_4)_2$, can therefore be used for titrimetric determination of anions that form weakly ionized salts or complex ions with mercury(II). The mercury(II) titrant solutions are standardized against pure sodium chloride or potassium chloride, as in the determination outlined below.

Determination of Chloride

The mercury(II) titrant is added to the chloride solution,

$$2Cl^- + Hg^{++} \rightarrow HgCl_2 \quad \text{(weakly ionized)}$$

in the presence of sodium nitroprusside, $Na_2Fe(CN)_5NO$, to the appearance of the first white turbidity:

$$Fe(CN)_5NO^{--} + Hg^{++} \rightarrow HgFe(CN)_5NO \quad \text{(insoluble, white)}$$

There is a slight end-point error due to the reaction

$$HgCl_2 + Hg^{++} \rightarrow 2HgCl^+$$

A blank correction should be determined on a solution containing about the same amount of $HgCl_2$ as in the sample solution at the end point.

This method is especially suited to the determination of chloride in acid solution, and to determination of very small amounts of chloride. The end point is much sharper than in the Mohr method for chloride. The cations Cd^{++}, Cu^{++}, Co^{++}, and Ni^{++} interfere by forming slightly soluble nitroprussides.

Diphenylcarbazide and diphenylcarbazone can also be used as indicators; with Hg^{++} these compounds form products having an intense violet color. Control of the pH between 1.5 and 2.0 is required to ensure that the end point coincides with the stoichiometric point.

Determination of Bromide

Titration with standard mercury(II) solution can be used for the determination of bromide in exactly the same way as for determination of chloride.

Determination of Iodide

Addition of a mercury(II) solution to an iodide[5] first produces a soluble, colorless complex:

$$4I^- + Hg^{++} \rightarrow HgI_4^{--}$$

Near the equivalence point of this reaction, mercury(II) iodide begins to precipitate:

$$HgI_4^{--} + Hg^{++} \rightarrow 2HgI_2 \quad \text{(red precipitate)}$$

The mercury(II) iodide comes down first in the yellow variety, but it quickly changes to the red form. The end point in the titration is the first permanent turbidity. Calculations from the formation constant of the HgI_4^{--} complex and from the solubility product constant of HgI_2 show that the visual end point occurs slightly prior to the stoichiometric point of the first reaction. Correction for the end-point error can be calculated, or it can be determined experimentally. For very dilute iodide solutions, diphenylcarbazide or diphenylcarbazone indicator is often used.

Determination of Thiocyanate

The thiocyanate solution containing ferric alum indicator (to form some red $Fe(CNS)^{++}$ in solution) is treated with mercury(II)

$$2CNS^- + Hg^{++} \rightarrow Hg(CNS)_2 \quad \text{(weakly ionized)}$$

to the disappearance of the red color:

$$2Fe(CNS)^{++} + Hg^{++} \rightarrow 2Fe^{+++} + Hg(CNS)_2$$

The reaction between mercury(II) and thiocyanate ion is also useful in the reverse direction, for the titration of mercury(II) in nitric acid solution with a standard thiocyanate solution in the presence of ferric alum. Used in this direction, the method is analogous to the Volhard method for silver. The end point is not very sharp, however, because $Hg(CNS)_2$ can form complexes with either of its constituent ions:

$$Hg(CNS)_2 + Hg^{++} \rightarrow 2Hg(CNS)^+$$

$$Hg(CNS)_2 + 2CNS^- \rightarrow Hg(CNS)_4^{--}$$

Consequently, the thiocyanate ion concentration does not increase very rapidly just after the stoichiometric point. $Hg(CNS)_2$ is not very soluble, and it may precipitate as the end point is approached.

[5] This method is really an example of complexation, analogous to the Liebig method for cyanide, p. 344; it is treated here for convenience in discussing the use of mercury(II) as a titrant.

Determination of Cyanide

The determination of cyanide is an indirect method, analogous to the Volhard method for determining chloride. An excess of standard mercury(II) solution is added:

$$2CN^- + Hg^{++} \to Hg(CN)_2 \quad \text{(weakly ionized)}$$

and the excess Hg^{++} is back titrated with standard thiocyanate solution, using ferric alum indicator. The presence of the $Hg(CN)_2$ in solution does not interfere, because it is much less ionized than is $Hg(CNS)_2$.

COMPLEXATION

Determination of Cyanide

1. Liebig Method. When a cyanide solution is titrated with silver nitrate, dicyanoargentate(I) ion is formed:

$$2CN^- + Ag^+ \to Ag(CN)_2^-$$

The very large value of the formation constant of $Ag(CN)_2^-$ ($K_f = 7.1 \times 10^{19}$) shows that the reaction is very complete. After the stoichiometric amount of silver ion for this reaction has been added, the next small amount of silver ion produces a permanent turbidity due to formation of the slightly soluble silver dicyanoargentate(I):

$$Ag(CN)_2^- + Ag^+ \to Ag[Ag(CN)_2] \quad \text{(white precipitate)}$$

(The precipitate is sometimes considered merely as silver cyanide, AgCN, two moles of which are formed in the reaction.) From the formation constant of the complex and the K_{sp} of silver cyanide (1.6×10^{-14}), it can be shown that in the titration of 0.1 M cyanide solution, the stoichiometric point of the complex formation practically coincides with the start of the precipitation reaction. Precipitate formed by localized excess of silver ion redissolves quite slowly near the stoichiometric point, and care must be exercised lest a false end point be taken.

The Liebig method may be done in solutions alkaline with *sodium* hydroxide up to about 0.1 M. *Ammonium* hydroxide (NH_3) interferes on account of its reaction with silver cyanide to form $Ag(NH_3)_2^+$ ($K_f = 1.1 \times 10^7$):

$$AgCN + 2NH_3 \to CN^- + Ag(NH_3)_2^+$$

Depending upon the concentration of NH_3, the silver cyanide precipitate would form either too late or not at all.

2. Liebig-Denigès Method. In this method titration is made in ammoniacal solution, with potassium iodide as the indicator. Ammonia prevents precipitation of silver cyanide, as explained above, by forming the ammonia complex, $Ag(NH_3)_2^+$. The solubility of silver iodide ($K_{sp} = 8.3 \times 10^{-17}$) is very much smaller than that of silver cyanide ($K_{sp} = 1.6 \times 10^{-14}$). In the presence of ammonia and iodide ion, the addition of the first excess of silver ion beyond the stoichiometric point of the main reaction produces a turbidity due to precipitated silver iodide. The end point is much sharper than in the original Liebig method. The concentration of ammonia to be used is quite important. If too little ammonia is used the end point comes too soon, and if too much ammonia is used the end point comes too late. The concentration of potassium iodide is also important in obtaining an end point that coincides with the stoichiometric point. A solution that is 0.3 M in ammonia and contains 0.2 g of potassium iodide per 100 ml gives reliable results.

Determination of Cyanide and Chloride in Same Sample

By a combination of the Liebig and the Volhard methods, both cyanide and chloride can be determined in the same solution. The solution is titrated with standard silver nitrate solution,

$$2CN^- + Ag^+ \rightarrow Ag(CN)_2^-$$

to the first turbidity, which marks the completion of the above reaction and the start of the precipitation of silver cyanide (Liebig method). An additional amount of the standard silver nitrate solution is then added, in excess of the amount required to *complete* the precipitation of silver cyanide and also precipitate silver chloride:

$$Ag(CN)_2^- + Ag^+ \rightarrow Ag[Ag(CN)_2] \quad \text{or} \quad 2AgCN$$
$$Cl^- + Ag^+ \rightarrow AgCl$$

The precipitates are filtered off, washed well, and the excess silver ion in the filtrate and washings is back titrated with standard potassium thiocyanate solution, using ferric alum indicator (Volhard method). The cyanide content of the sample is calculated from the number of gme of Ag^+ required to produce the first turbidity. It must be remembered that in this reaction $2CN^-$ are one equivalent. If X gme of Ag^+ are required to produce the first turbidity, then X gme are also required to precipitate the silver cyanide from the complex. If the additional Ag^+ added beyond the first turbidity is W gme, then $(W - X)$ gme represents the amount of Ag^+ required to precipitate the silver chloride and provide the excess Ag^+. If Y gme of thiocyanate are used in the back titration, Y gme of Ag^+ were present in excess in the solution. Therefore Z gme of chloride $= (W - X - Y)$.

The method can also be applied to mixtures of cyanide and bromide, cyanide and iodide, and cyanide and thiocyanate.

Determination of Copper by Cyanide

Copper(II) in ammoniacal solution is titrated with standard potassium cyanide solution,

$$2Cu(NH_3)_4{}^{++} + 7CN^- + H_2O \rightarrow 2Cu(CN)_3{}^{--} + CNO^- + 2NH_4{}^+ + 6NH_3$$

to the disappearance of the blue color of the ammonia complex (all the products are colorless). The amount of potassium cyanide consumed is somewhat dependent upon the temperature, the ammonia concentration, and the amount of ammonium salts present. The cyanide solution should be standardized, usually against pure copper which has been dissolved to Cu^{++}, under the same conditions that prevail in the analysis. Calculations are usually made by the titer method (see pp. 278–279).

Determination of Nickel by Cyanide

The titration reaction,

$$Ni(NH_3)_4{}^{++} + 4CN^- \rightarrow Ni(CN)_4{}^{--} + 4NH_3$$

is similar to that for copper, except that no redox reaction occurs, and a different end-point method is required. (The purple-blue color of $Ni(NH_3)_4{}^{++}$ is not very intense, and $Ni(CN)_4{}^{--}$ is yellow.) End-point detection is the same as in the Liebig-Denigès method for cyanide. A small amount of potassium iodide is added to the $Ni(NH_3)_4{}^{++}$ solution, plus a small measured amount (e.g., 0.5 ml) of standard silver nitrate to give a suspension of silver iodide. The mixture is titrated with potassium cyanide to the disappearance of the silver iodide: $AgI + 2CN^- \rightarrow Ag(CN)_2{}^- + I^-$. More standard silver nitrate is then added, to the first turbidity due to silver iodide. The total volume of cyanide solution is corrected for the amount equivalent to the silver ion added, to give the net amount required for the nickel reaction.

The method can be applied to the analysis of nickel in steel without removing other cations from the solution. The steel is dissolved in acid, any chromium and manganese are oxidized with peroxydisulfate (persulfate) to their oxy anions, and citric acid is added to complex the iron(III) to prevent its precipitation in ammoniacal solution. The titration is then made as described above.

Titrations with EDTA

A brief discussion of ethylenediaminetetraacetic acid (EDTA) was given in Chap. 7. The compound, $(HOOC—CH_2)_2N—CH_2—CH_2—N(CH_2COOH)_2$, is a tetraprotic acid, conveniently represented by H_4Y.[6-8] The acid is only

---

[6] F. J. Welcher, *The Analytical Uses of Ethylenediaminetetraacetic Acid*, Princeton, N. J., Van Nostrand, 1958.

[7] R. Pribil, *Chelometry*, Prague, Czechoslovakia, Chemapol, 1961.

[8] G. Schwarzenback and H. Flaschka, *Die komplexometrische Titration*, Stuttgart, Ferdinand Enke, 1965.

sparingly soluble in water, but its disodium salt is moderately soluble; unless stated to the contrary, the abbreviation EDTA used in this discussion will mean the disodium salt, Na_2H_2Y.

EDTA is unique among ligands in that it forms $1:1$ complexes with all cations, regardless of the ionic charge and the chemical coordination number of the cation; thus,

$$M^+ + H_2Y^{--} \rightarrow MY^{---} + 2H^+$$

$$M^{++} + H_2Y^{--} \rightarrow MY^{--} + 2H^+$$

$$M^{+++} + H_2Y^{--} \rightarrow MY^- + 2H^+$$

$$M^{4+} + H_2Y^{--} \rightarrow MY + 2H^+$$

The metal-EDTA complexes vary widely in stability (see table of formation constants in Appendix IV); in general, cations of high ionic charge form the more stable complexes and can be formed in the more acidic (lower pH) solutions.

The three-dimensional structure of metal-EDTA complexes, Fig. 25-3, shows EDTA to be a hexadentate coordinator. The multiplicity of five-membered chelate rings is an important factor in the greater stability of EDTA complexes as compared to complexes formed by unidentate ligands such as CN^- and NH_3.

Indicators. The visual indicators used are various organic compounds that form highly colored complexes with metal ions. The metal ion indicator complex must be quite stable, yet less stable than the corresponding metal-EDTA complex, in order to obtain a sharp color change by displacement of the metal ion from the indicator complex:

$$\text{M-Ind} + \text{EDTA} \rightarrow \text{M-EDTA} + \text{Ind}$$

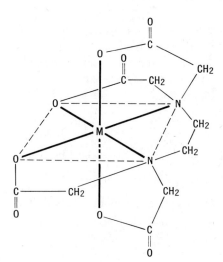

Fig. 25-3   Three-dimensional structure of metal-EDTA complexes.

For a satisfactory end point, the ratio $K_{\text{M-EDTA}}/K_{\text{M-Ind}}$ must be at least 10^4. The compounds used as metallochrome indicators are mostly azo dyes and triphenylmethane dyes; certain redox indicators and acid-base indicators also find limited use. One of the earliest, and still the most widely used, indicators is 1-(1-hydroxy-2-naphthylazo)-6-nitro-2-naphthol-4-sulfonate, known as erio-chrome black T (EBT).

The end point in EDTA titrations can also be determined by potentiometric titration, using a mercury–mercury-EDTA indicator electrode or an inert (platinum) electrode to show change in reduction potential due to preferential stabilization by EDTA of one of the oxidation states of a metal; by conducto-metric titration; by amperometric titration; and by chronopotentiometric titration. The amount of metal ion can also be determined by titration of the liberated hydrogen ion with alkali, using ordinary acid-base indicators. The colors of many metal-EDTA complexes are more intense than the colors of their aquo complexes; in these cases a spectrophotometric detection of the end point is feasible.

Methods. Owing to the wide range of stabilities of the various metal-indicator and metal-EDTA complexes, the influence of pH on the ionization of EDTA, and the control of metal ion concentrations by various masking agents (e.g., fluoride, cyanide, phosphate, etc.), several methods of operation are possible.

1. *Direct titration.* To the metal ion in solution, buffered at an appropriate pH (often about pH 10 with ammonia–ammonium chloride) a metal ion indica-tor is added, and the solution is titrated with EDTA to the color change. For example,

$$\underset{\text{(wine red)}}{\text{Mg-EBT}} + H_2Y^{--} + 2NH_3 \rightarrow MgY^{--} + 2NH_4^+ + \underset{\substack{\text{(sky blue in} \\ \text{alkaline solution)}}}{\text{EBT}}$$

2. *Back titration.* Metals that form EDTA complexes very slowly (true of several), or precipitate at the pH required for titration, or do not react with the indicators are determined by adding a measured excess amount of standard EDTA, then back titrating the excess EDTA with standard Mg^{++} or Zn^{++} solution to the first appearance of the colored metal-indicator complex. For example,

Main reaction: $Co^{++} + H_2Y^{--} \rightarrow CoY^{--} + 2H^+$ (in acid solution)

Back titration: $H_2Y^{--} + Mg^{++} \rightarrow MgY^{--} + 2H^+$ (removed by NH_3)

Indicator reaction: $EBT \text{ (blue)} + Mg^{++} \rightarrow Mg\text{-}EBT$ (red)

Insoluble salts can also be determined by this general method. For example,

$$PbSO_4 + H_2Y^{--} \rightarrow PbY^{--} + SO_4^{--} + 2H^+$$

The excess EDTA is back titrated as above.

3. *Displacement of metal ion.* If a solution of metal ion that forms a much more stable EDTA complex than that of magnesium or zinc is treated with a solution of the latter, replacement occurs and the magnesium or zinc ion liberated is then titrated with standard EDTA. For example,

$$Fe^{+++} + ZnY^{--} \rightarrow FeY^- + Zn^{++}$$

The liberated Zn^{++}, which is indirectly a measure of the amount of Fe^{+++}, is titrated with EDTA, using EBT (or other) indicator. A variation involves the use of other than EDTA complexes for liberation of a cation for EDTA titration. For example, silver ion is not titrated directly with EDTA, but it will displace nickel ion from tetracyanonickelate(II):

$$2Ag^+ + Ni(CN)_4^{--} \rightarrow 2Ag(CN)_2^- + Ni^{++}$$

The Ni^{++} is titrated with EDTA, as a measure of the amount of Ag^+ present.

4. *Titration of hydrogen ion liberated.* Reaction of EDTA with metal ions liberates two hydrogen ions for each metal ion reacting (see p. 347). The hydrogen ion can be titrated with sodium hydroxide, giving indirectly the amount of cation. Indeed, pure $Na_2H_2Y \cdot 2H_2O$ can serve as an acidic primary standard for standardization of alkali.

5. *Determination of anions.* Certain anions that form insoluble salts or stable complexes with cations, can be determined by adding a known excess of standard solution of the cation, then titrating the unused cation with EDTA. For example,

$$SO_4^{--} + Ba^{++} \text{ (excess)} \rightarrow BaSO_4$$

$$Ba^{++} + H_2Y^{--} \rightarrow BaY^{--} + 2H^+$$

Another approach, when the cation cannot be titrated directly with EDTA, involves displacement of a cation that can be titrated:

$$I^- + Ag^+ \rightarrow AgI$$

$$2AgI + Ni(CN)_4^{--} \rightarrow 2Ag(CN)_2^- + 2I^- + Ni^{++}$$

The Ni^{++} is then titrated with EDTA.

Applications. The titrimetric applications of EDTA are many and varied, as can be inferred from the variety of operational methods listed above. EDTA is widely used for the titrimetric determination of magnesium and calcium, for which no other simple, direct titrimetric methods have been devised.

1. *Determination of magnesium.* The solution containing magnesium ion is treated with ammonia-ammonium chloride buffer solution (pH 10) and a few drops of EBT indicator (0.4% in alcohol). The sample solution is titrated with standard EDTA solution until the wine-red color (of the Mg-EBT complex) changes to the blue color of the free indicator in alkaline solution.

2. *Determination of calcium.*

a. The sample solution containing Ca^{++} (and no Mg^{++}) is made alkaline with buffer, EBT indicator is added, and the mixture is titrated with EDTA solution to which a small, known amount of magnesium ion has been added to give the indicator action. The CaY^{--} complex is more stable than MgY^{--} hence Ca^{++} reacts not only with the EDTA but also with the small amount of, MgY^{--} in the titrant:

$$Ca^{++} + MgY^{--} \rightarrow CaY^{--} + Mg^{++}$$

The Mg^{++} forms the red indicator complex, Mg-EBT, which reacts with the first excess of EDTA to liberate the free dye (blue). The EDTA used is corrected for the slight amount of Mg^{++} added to it, to give the net amount required for calcium.

b. The sample solution is made alkaline (*p*H 12) with sodium hydroxide; murexide indicator (the ammonium salt of purpurin) is added, and the solution is titrated with EDTA to a color change from orange to violet. (Murexide solutions are not stable; the indicator used is a 1:100 solid mixture of murexide and sodium chloride.) Moderate amounts of magnesium and aluminum do not interfere. Alternatively, calcein indicator (fluoresceiniminodiacetic acid) may be used;[9] the color change is from yellow-green to brown.

3. *Determination of calcium and magnesium in the same sample.* This determination, which has many applications, is standard procedure for determining hardness in water. Direct titration with EDTA at *p*H 10, using EBT indicator, gives both calcium and magnesium (total hardness). A second sample, made acidic with hydrochloric acid, is treated with excess ammonium oxalate, then slowly neutralized with ammonia to the methyl-red end point. After one-half hour the calcium oxalate precipitate is filtered off and washed; the filtrate and washings are buffered to *p*H 10, and the solution is titrated with EDTA, using EBT indicator. (If the titration for magnesium is done rapidly, filtration from calcium oxalate is not required.) The magnesium hardness is subtracted from the total hardness to give the calcium hardness.

Other complexones or chelons, similar to EDTA, that have been studied quite extensively include iminodiacetic acid, $HN(CH_2COOH)_2$, and its methyl and phenyl derivatives, and nitrilotriacetic acid, $N(CH_2COOH)_3$.

PROBLEMS

25-1 Calculate the normality of silver nitrate solution from the data given.

(*a*) 3.3977 g of pure $AgNO_3$ in 250.0 ml of solution.

(*b*) 2.5000 g of pure silver, dissolved in nitric acid and made up to 500.0 ml.

(*c*) 40.00 ml of solution yield 0.4468 g of AgCl.

[9] H. Diehl and J. L. Ellingboe, *Anal. Chem.*, **28**, 882 (1956).

(*d*) 0.3000 g of pure KCNS is equivalent to 30.00 ml of $AgNO_3$.

(*e*) 0.2265 g of pure NaCl is dissolved in water; after adding 50.00 ml of $AgNO_3$ solution and filtering off the AgCl, the filtrate requires 4.60 ml of KCNS. The volume ratio of KCNS/$AgNO_3$ is 1.150. Calculate also the normality of the KCNS solution.

(*f*) 5.948 g of pure $AgNO_3$ in 500.0 ml of solution.

(*g*) 39.38 ml of $AgNO_3$ solution titrates 41.46 ml of 0.1425 *N* KCl solution.

(*h*) 1.000 ml of $AgNO_3$ solution is equivalent to 7.850 mg of $BaCl_2 \cdot 2H_2O$.

(*i*) 46.21 ml of $AgNO_3$ requires 42.74 ml of KCNS solution that contains 1.4578 g of pure KCNS in 250.0 ml.

(*j*) 0.3507 g of pure NaCl is treated with 100.0 ml of $AgNO_3$ solution, which is an excess requiring 32.00 ml of 0.0800 *N* KCNS for back titration.

                                  Ans. (*a*) 0.08000.   (*b*) 0.04635.   (*c*) 0.07794.

25-2   A 0.6000-g sample consisting only of $BaCl_2$ and KBr requires 46.20 ml of 0.1200 *N* $AgNO_3$ for precipitation of the halides as AgCl and AgBr. Calculate the percentage of $BaCl_2$ in the mixture.   *Ans.* 69.6.

25-3   A 0.2500-g sample containing As_2O_3 is dissolved in alkali; the solution is neutralized and treated with 50.00 ml of 0.2000 *N* $AgNO_3$. The precipitate of Ag_3AsO_3 is filtered off and washed; the filtrate and washings require 21.15 ml of 0.1500 *N* KCNS for titration (Volhard method). The precipitate of Ag_3AsO_3 is dissolved in nitric acid, and titrated with 45.55 ml of the same KCNS solution. Calculate the percentage of As_2O_3 in the sample (*a*) from the titration of the excess silver ion in the filtrate, and (*b*) from the titration of the solution of Ag_3AsO_3 in nitric acid.

                                      Ans. (*a*) 90.06.   (*b*) 90.12.

25-4   If, in Problem 25-3, the sample also contained 2.50% NaCl, what volume of the KCNS would have been used (*a*) to titrate the excess silver ion in the filtrate, and (*b*) to titrate the nitric acid solution of the precipitate?

25-5   A 0.3533-g sample containing only NaCl, NaBr, and NaI requires 45.00 ml of 0.1000 *N* $AgNO_3$ to precipitate all the halides as their silver salts. Another identical sample of the mixture is treated with dichromate in acid solution, to oxidize bromide and iodide to bromine and iodine, respectively, which are expelled by boiling. The remaining solution requires 30.00 ml of the same $AgNO_3$ solution for precipitation of the chloride. Calculate the percentages of NaCl, NaBr, and NaI in the sample.

                        Ans. 49.61% NaCl, 29.04% NaBr, 21.34% NaI.

25-6   A 0.2500-g sample of washing powder containing Na_3PO_4 and NaCl (and inert matter) is dissolved in water, and 40.00 ml of 0.1250 *N* $AgNO_3$ is added. The precipitated silver salts are filtered off and washed. The filtrate and washings are treated with 45.00 ml of 0.1000 *N* KCN solution, the excess of which requires 20.00 ml of 0.1250 *N* $AgNO_3$ for titration to the first turbidity. The precipitated Ag_3PO_4 and AgCl mixture is treated with dilute nitric acid (which dissolves only the Ag_3PO_4); the solution requires 50.00 ml of 0.05000 *N* KCNS for titration. Calculate the percentages of Na_3PO_4 and NaCl in the sample.   *Ans.* 54.65% Na_3PO_4, 11.69% NaCl.

25-7   A 0.7500-g sample containing $KClO_3$ and inert matter is reduced to chloride. Determination by the Volhard method uses 50.00 ml of 0.1225 *N* $AgNO_3$ and 9.60 ml of 0.1080 *N* KCNS for back titration. Calculate the percentage of $KClO_3$ in the sample.   *Ans.* 83.14.

25-8 The solution of a 0.6000-g sample containing cyanide, chloride, and inert matter requires 27.50 ml of $AgNO_3$ solution for titration to the first turbidity (Liebig method). 70.00 ml more of the same $AgNO_3$ solution is added, the silver precipitate is filtered off, and the filtrate requires 17.00 ml of 0.1200 N KCNS for titration (Volhard method). The silver nitrate solution contains 3.398 g of pure $AgNO_3$ in 250.0 ml. Calculate the percentages of KCN and KCl in the sample.

Ans. 47.76% KCN, 16.91% KCl.

25-9 A ten-cent coin weighing 2.505 g is dissolved in nitric acid and the solution is made up to 250.0 ml. A 25.00-ml aliquot of the solution requires 41.00 ml of 0.05100 N KCNS for titration. Calculate the percentage of Ag in the coin. *Ans.* 90.07.

25-10 A 1.000-g sample of nickel ore is dissolved in nitric acid. The solution is made ammoniacal, and 0.50 ml of 0.1000 N $AgNO_3$ and 0.2 g of KI are added. The solution containing $Ni(NH_3)_4^{++}$ and suspended AgI is titrated with 45.00 ml of 0.1000 M KCN, which is slightly in excess of the amount required to react with the nickel and dissolve the AgI. Back titration of the excess cyanide ion requires 1.50 ml of the 0.1000 N $AgNO_3$ to produce the first turbidity. Calculate the percentage of Ni in the ore. *Ans.* 6.020.

25-11 50.00 ml of 0.1000 M chloride solution is titrated with 0.1000 M silver nitrate solution by the Mohr method (chromate indicator). Calculate the percent titration error if the final concentration of CrO_4^{--} is 0.0020 M. *Ans.* +0.037.

25-12 A 1.0000-g sample containing the stated component and inert matter is titrated with $AgNO_3$ solution, as indicated. Calculate the percent of the component specified.

(*a*) KCl: 46.24 ml of 0.1172 N $AgNO_3$.

(*b*) $BaCl_2 \cdot 2H_2O$: 38.67 ml of 0.08852 N $AgNO_3$.

(*c*) NaBr: 41.58 ml of 0.1008 N $AgNO_3$.

(*d*) $Ba(CNS)_2$: 43.22 ml of 0.06990 N $AgNO_3$.

(*e*) NH_4Cl: 45.75 ml of 0.2000 N $AgNO_3$.

25-13 A 0.6000-g sample containing $KClO_4$, KCl, and inert matter requires 16.10 ml of 0.01000 N $AgNO_3$ for titration of the chloride. A 0.2000-g sample of the same material is reduced with nitrite, and the total chloride is titrated, requiring 36.00 ml of 0.04000 N $AgNO_3$. Calculate the percentages of KCl and $KClO_4$ in the sample.

25-14 A 0.5000-g sample containing trisodium phosphate (and inert impurities) is dissolved and neutralized. After adding 50.00 ml of 0.2000 N silver nitrate, the silver phosphate is filtered off and washed. The filtrate and washings require 22.75 ml of 0.1500 N KCNS for titration (Volhard method). The silver phosphate precipitate is dissolved in nitric acid; titration of this solution requires 43.85 ml of the same KCNS solution. Calculate percent P_2O_5 in the sample (*a*) from titration of excess Ag^+ in the filtrate, and (*b*) from titration of the solution of the precipitate in nitric acid.

25-15 If, in Problem 25-14, the sample had contained also 2.00% NaCl, what volume of the KCNS solution would have been used to titrate (*a*) the excess Ag^+ in the filtrate, and (*b*) the nitric acid solution of the precipitate?

25-16 In each lettered part, the substance sought is converted to an anion, which is precipitated from neutral solution as its silver salt. The washed silver precipitate is dissolved in nitric acid and the silver ion in the solution is titrated with 0.1000 N KCNS. Calculate percent of the component sought.

	Sample, g	Silver salt precipitated	KCNS used, ml	Sought, %
(a)	0.2500	Ag_3AsO_4	43.62	As
(b)	0.6135	Ag_2CrO_4	38.86	Cr_2O_3
(c)	0.8000	$AgIO_3$	42.10	KI
(d)	0.9950	Ag_2MoO_4	36.72	Mo_2O_3
(e)	0.3222	$Ag_4Fe(CN)_6$	28.54	Fe_2O_3
(f)	0.2000	Ag_2SO_3	45.00	FeS_2

25-17 The sample in each lettered part consists of a mixture of the pure components given (no inert matter). Each sample is titrated with 0.1000 N $AgNO_3$ to precipitate the silver salts. Calculate the percent composition of the sample.

	Sample, g	Composition	ml $AgNO_3$
(a)	0.2600	LiCl + KCl	43.45
(b)	0.4356	KCl + KBr	45.00
(c)	0.4000	NaCl + KCNS	48.66
(d)	0.2450	$BaBr_2$ + LiCl	40.80
(e)	0.5942	$Ba(CNS)_2$ + KCNS	50.00

25-18 A 0.4000-g sample containing only NaCl, NaBr, and NaI requires 44.32 ml of 0.1250 N $AgNO_3$ to precipitate all the halides as their silver salts. Another identical sample is treated with dichromate and acid to oxidize bromide and iodide to bromine and iodine, respectively, which are expelled by boiling. The remaining solution requires 32.85 ml of the same $AgNO_3$ solution for precipitation of the chloride. Calculate the percentages of NaCl, NaBr, and NaI.

25-19 Exactly one gram of a pure chloride of a trivalent metal, that is, MCl_3, requires 35.84 ml of 0.4000 N $AgNO_3$ for titration of the chloride. Calculate the atomic weight of the element M, and identify the element by reference to a table of atomic weights.

25-20 A silver nitrate solution contains 2.1576 g of silver in 200.0 ml. 50.00 ml of a certain cyanide solution requires 36.00 ml of the silver nitrate solution for titration to the first turbidity (Liebig method). How many grams of KCN are contained in a liter of the cyanide solution?

25-21 50.00 ml of a certain KCN solution requires 44.46 ml of $AgNO_3$ solution for titration to the first turbidity. The $AgNO_3$ solution contains 1.2500 g of silver per 250.0 ml. Calculate the normality and the molarity of the KCN solution.

25-22 The solution of a 0.5000-g sample containing cyanide, chloride, and inert matter requires 32.50 ml of $AgNO_3$ solution for titration to the first turbidity. 75.00 ml more of the same $AgNO_3$ solution is added, the silver precipitate is filtered off, and the filtrate requires 20.33 ml of 0.1200 N KCNS for titration. The silver nitrate solution contains 3.398 g of pure $AgNO_3$ in 250.0 ml. Calculate the percentages of KCN and KCl in the sample.

25-23 A 0.6000-g sample which contains 80.00% KCN, 10.00% KCl, and inert matter is analyzed by the Liebig-Volhard method.

(a) What volume of 0.1080 N $AgNO_3$ is required for the Liebig titration?

(b) What additional volume of the same $AgNO_3$ solution must be added so that the excess silver ion will require 19.90 ml of 0.1000 N KCNS for the Volhard titration?

25-24 A 0.7500-g sample that contains KCN, KCl, KCNS, and inert matter is dissolved in water and analyzed as follows. 20.00 ml of 0.1100 N AgNO$_3$ is required for titration to the first turbidity. 80.00 ml more of the same AgNO$_3$ solution is then added, and the silver salts are filtered off and washed. The silver ion in the filtrate and washings requires 40.00 ml of 0.09000 N KCNS for titration (Volhard method). The silver salts that were filtered off are boiled with nitric acid, which decomposes the AgCNS and AgCN to Ag$^+$, leaving the AgCl unchanged. The AgCl is filtered off, and the filtrate is titrated with the 0.09000 N KCNS, requiring 50.00 ml. Calculate the percentages of KCN, KCl, and KCNS in the sample.

25-25 50.0 ml of 0.100 M KCN is titrated with 0.0500 N AgNO$_3$ by the Liebig method. Use values of the solubility product constant of AgCN and the formation constant of Ag(CN)$_2$$^-$, and make calculations to show whether or not a turbidity of AgCN will have appeared when 99.5% of the stoichiometric amount of AgNO$_3$ has been added.

25-26 Potassium iodide, 0.100 M, is titrated with 0.0250 M Hg(NO$_3$)$_2$ according to the equation: $4I^- + Hg^{++} \rightarrow HgI_4^{--}$. Make appropriate calculations and explanations to show whether or not any precipitate of HgI$_2$ can form ($HgI_4^{--} + Hg^{++} \rightarrow 2HgI_2$) at the stoichiometric point of the complexation reaction. (Neglect any dilution of the solution by addition of the titrant.)

25-27 In the titration of 50.0 ml of 0.100 M chloride solution with 0.100 M silver nitrate solution by the Mohr method, calculate the percent titration error, in terms of the volume of silver ion solution required, for the condition stated.

(*a*) 1.00 millimole of K$_2$CrO$_4$ in solution.

(*b*) Final concentration of CrO$_4$$^{--}$ = 0.100 M.

(*c*) 1.00 millimole of K$_2$CrO$_4$, solution of pH 4.00.

25-28 Calculate the molar concentration of chromate ion that would be required in solution so that in the Mohr titration of Br$^-$ by Ag$^+$ the end point would coincide with the stoichiometric point. Comment on the practical aspects of this titration.

25-29 The red color of FeCNS^{++} that marks the end point in the Volhard titration is detectable when its concentration reaches 6.4×10^{-6} M. Calculate the concentration of Fe^{+++} indicator that would have to be present in solution so that the end point of the Volhard titration will coincide with the stoichiometric point of the silver chloride precipitation without filtering off the AgCl before titrating the excess silver ion with thiocyanate. (*Hint:* in order to be free of error, the following condition must be fulfilled: [Ag$^+$] = [Cl$^-$] + [CNS$^-$] + [FeCNS^{++}].)

25-30 During World War II, when nickel was in critically short supply, U.S. five-cent coins were minted from an alloy of silver, copper, and manganese. Such a coin weighing 4.865 g was dissolved in nitric acid and the solution made to 250.0 ml.

(*a*) A 50.00-ml aliquot of the coin solution required 21.05 ml of 0.1500 N KCNS for titration (Volhard method). Calculate percent Ag.

(*b*) The silver ion in a 25.00-ml aliquot of the coin solution was precipitated by adding chloride ion, and the AgCl was filtered off and washed. The filtrate, containing the copper, was made ammoniacal and titrated with 34.10 ml of KCN solution having a copper titer of 8.00 mg/ml. Calculate the percentage of Cu.

25-31 A 4.000-g sample of silver solder is dissolved in nitric acid and made up to 250.0 ml.

(*a*) A 25.00-ml aliquot of the solution requires 38.95 ml of 0.06000 *N* KCNS for titration. Calculate percent Ag.

(*b*) After removing the silver ion by precipitation as AgCl from a 50.00-ml aliquot of the sample solution, the filtrate is made ammoniacal, and titrated with 36.95 ml of KCN solution. In standardizing the KCN solution, 43.07 ml was required to titrate a solution made from 0.2800 g of pure copper. Calculate the percentage of Cu in the solder.

25-32   1.2500 g of pure HgO is dissolved in nitric acid and made up to 500.0 ml.

(*a*) Calculate the normality of the mercury(II) solution.

(*b*) A 1.5000-g sample of sodium nitrate, contaminated with alkali halide, is dissolved and titrated with the above mercury(II) solution, in the presence of sodium nitroprusside indicator, requiring 20.20 ml to produce the first turbidity. Calculate impurity as percentage of NaCl.

(*c*) By a separate analysis it is found that the sample contained 0.600% NaBr, which also is titrated with mercury(II). What is the true percent NaCl in the sample?

25-33   A standard solution of $Hg(ClO_4)_2$ is prepared by dissolving 1.1033 g of pure mercury in perchloric acid, and diluting the solution to one liter. A 100.0-ml sample of water is titrated with this solution (sodium nitroprusside indicator), requiring 32.00 ml. Calculate the chloride content of the water in parts per million.

25-34   A sample of nickel ore weighing 1.1000 g is dissolved in nitric acid. The solution is made ammoniacal, and 0.50 ml of 0.1000 *N* $AgNO_3$ and 0.2 g of KI are added. The solution containing $Ni(NH_3)_4^{++}$ and suspended AgI is titrated with 48.00 ml of 0.0900 *M* KCN, which is slightly in excess of the amount to react with the nickel and dissolve the AgI. Back titration of the excess cyanide requires 2.50 ml of the 0.1000 *N* $AgNO_3$ to produce the first turbidity. Calculate the percentage of Ni in the ore.

25-35   Exactly ten grams of pure $K_4Fe(CN)_6 \cdot 3H_2O$ is dissolved in water and made to one liter.

(*a*) If the reaction with Zn^{++} is stoichiometric for precipitation of $K_2Zn_3[Fe(CN)_6]_2$, what is the zinc titer of the ferrocyanide solution?

(*b*) A zinc carbonate ore weighing 1.000 g is dissolved in sulfuric acid and titrated with 44.20 ml of the above ferrocyanide solution. Calculate the zinc content of the ore as (1) percentage of Zn, (2) percentage of ZnO.

25-36   Calculate the normality of a molybdate solution for precipitation of $PbMoO_4$, in each part below.

(*a*) Solution contains 7.550 g of MoO_3 per liter.

(*b*) 41.50 ml of molybdate solution titrate lead ion from 0.3525 g of pure lead.

(*c*) 0.5840 g of pure $PbSO_4$, dissolved in ammonium acetate, requires 32.10 ml of molybdate solution.

25-37   A 1.2000-g sample of lead ore is dissolved in nitric acid; the solution is evaporated with sulfuric acid, the $PbSO_4$ is filtered off and washed, then dissolved in ammonium acetate solution. Titration requires 38.80 ml of a molybdate solution which contains 1.8000 g of MoO_3 in 500.0 ml. Calculate the percentage of Pb in the ore.

25-38   A standard solution of EDTA, prepared by dissolving 10.000 g of pure $Na_2H_2C_{10}H_{12}O_8N_2 \cdot 2H_2O$ and making up to 500.0 ml, is used in each of the following titrations. The unknown sample is dissolved in water or acid, if and as necessary the solution is buffered to pH 10, and is then titrated with the EDTA, using an appropriate indicator.

(a) Calculate the molar concentration of the EDTA solution.

(b) A 0.2500-g sample of impure calcium carbonate requires 40.00 ml of the standard EDTA. Calculate percent $CaCO_3$.

(c) A sample of Epsom salt ($MgSO_4 \cdot 7H_2O$) weighing 0.4500 g requires 32.40 ml of the EDTA solution. Calculate percent purity of the Epsom salt.

(d) 100.0 ml of tap water, buffered to pH 10, requires 35.00 ml of EDTA solution, prepared by a 1 : 10 volumetric dilution of the above standard, for titration of both the Ca^{++} and the Mg^{++} in the water. Another 100.0 ml sample of the tap water is treated with ammonium oxalate to precipitate the calcium as oxalate. The filtrate from the calcium oxalate requires 10.00 ml of the diluted (1 : 10) standard EDTA for titration of the Mg^{++}. Calculate (1) total hardness, expressed as ppm calcium; (2) calcium hardness, in ppm; (3) magnesium hardness, in ppm.

26

REDOX THEORY

Definitions. Reactions in which electrons are transferred from one atom, ion, or molecule to another are called **oxidation-reduction** or **redox** reactions. **Oxidation** is the process in which an atom, ion, or molecule **loses** one or more electrons; **reduction** involves the **gain** of one or more electrons by an atom, ion, or molecule. **A reducing agent** is a substance that **loses** one or more electrons, and in this process it is **oxidized**; an **oxidizing agent gains** one or more electrons and is thereby **reduced**. Stated in another way, **a reducing agent is an electron donor**, and **an oxidizing agent is an electron acceptor**.

Oxidation and reduction cannot occur independently, but only simultaneously by transfer of electrons from the donor to the acceptor. However, it is convenient to consider the oxidation and the reduction processes separately in terms of the half reaction that occurs, as represented by the ion-electron half-reaction equation. The following examples are illustrative.

1. Oxidation half reactions:

$$Zn \rightarrow Zn^{++} + 2e$$

$$Fe^{++} \rightarrow Fe^{+++} + e$$

$$SO_3^{--} + H_2O \rightarrow SO_4^{--} + 2H^+ + 2e$$

2. Reduction half reactions:

$$I_2 + 2e \rightarrow 2I^-$$

$$Ce^{4+} + e \rightarrow Ce^{+++}$$

$$Cr_2O_7^{--} + 14H^+ + 6e \rightarrow 2Cr^{+++} + 7H_2O$$

These half reactions are reversible; each of the half reactions in 1 is a reduction when written in the opposite direction, and each half reaction in 2 is an oxidation when written in the opposite direction. The change can be represented by the general relation

$$Ox + ne \rightleftarrows Red$$

where Ox designates the oxidized form and Red designates the reduced form of the substance undergoing change, and n is the number of electrons involved in the half reaction.

By combining the separate ion-electron half-reaction equations, the equation for the over-all reaction is obtained. The student should review the writing and balancing of redox equations in Chap. 3.

The transfer of electrons from one site to another constitutes a flow of electric current. An appropriate combination of chemical reactions (a galvanic cell) can be used to generate an electric current. Conversely, an electric current can be used to produce chemical changes (electrolysis) at the electrodes in an electrolytic cell. Two features of redox changes are of major interest in quantitative analysis: (1) the quantity of electricity associated with the chemical changes that occur; (2) the force or potential with which electrons are transferred.

Equivalency in Redox Reactions

Faraday's law shows that a definite amount of electricity (96,492 coulombs, or one faraday) is associated with the change of one gram-equivalent weight of a substance. One faraday of electricity is therefore associated with the transfer of one gram-atom or mole of electrons, and the equivalent weight of a substance in redoximetry is defined on this basis. **The equivalent weight is that weight of substance which will furnish, react with, or be chemically equivalent to one gram-atom or mole of electrons transferred in the reaction that occurs.** Several illustrations were given in Chap. 22; other examples are given in the discussion of specific redox methods.

The Potential in Redox Reactions

Half Cells (Single Electrodes, Redox Couples).   If a piece of metal, for example zinc, is placed in water or a dilute solution of zinc ions, the zinc has a tendency to lose electrons and become zinc ion. This change will continue until the concentration of zinc ion in solution increases to some value such that an equilibrium is reached between the metal and its ions:

$$Zn \rightleftarrows Zn^{++} + 2e$$

A similar situation exists in the cases of other metals in contact with solutions of their ions, for example,

$$Cu \rightleftarrows Cu^{++} + 2e$$

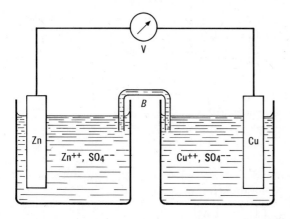

Fig. 26-1   Galvanic cell.

Each half reaction is characterized by a certain half cell or single electrode potential, which represents the tendency of the metal to be oxidized to its ions, or the tendency of the ions to be reduced to the metal.

The potential of a single electrode or half cell cannot be measured directly. However, if two half cells are connected, the electromotive force (emf) of the cell is measurable. Such a galvanic cell is illustrated in Fig. 26-1. The cell consists of a zinc electrode dipping into zinc sulfate solution, and a copper electrode dipping into a solution of copper sulfate. The electrodes are connected externally by a conductor (wire), and the circuit is completed by a salt bridge, *B*, containing a conducting solution such as potassium chloride, from one solution to the other. The voltmeter, *V*, measures the over-all cell emf. If one of the half cells is arbitrarily assigned a value of zero potential, the measured emf of the cell represents the potential of the other half cell.

Conventions.   Several conventions of sign of the half-cell potential, direction of writing the half-cell reaction, and form of the Nernst equation (p. 364) have been used in the literature on electrochemistry. By one convention the half-cell reaction is written in the direction of reduction, and the sign of the standard electrode potential, $E°$ (p. 365), is invariant and corresponds to the electrostatic charge of the metal. For example,

$$Zn^{++} + 2e \rightleftarrows Zn \qquad E° = -0.763 \text{ v}$$

By another convention the sign of the potential is bivariant, and depends upon the direction in which the half-cell equation is written. For example,

$$Zn^{++} + 2e \rightleftarrows Zn \qquad E° = -0.763 \text{ v} \qquad (26\text{-}1)$$

$$Zn \rightleftarrows Zn^{++} + 2e \qquad E° = +0.763 \text{ v} \qquad (26\text{-}2)$$

By the convention of equation (26-1), $E°$ has been called the "standard reduction potential." By the convention of equation (26-2), $E°$ has been called the "standard oxidation potential"; this convention has been used extensively, especially in the United States, by many physical chemists and analytical chemists, and is used in an important reference work.[1] Depending on the convention used, the sign of the second term of the Nernst equation is either positive or negative.

In an endeavor to have a consistent convention of half-cell potentials, the International Union of Pure and Applied Chemistry (IUPAC) adopted a report of the Commission on Electrochemistry and the Commission on Physico-chemical Symbols and Terminology, entitled "Convention Concerning the Signs of Electromotive Forces and Electrode Potentials."[2] The main features of the IUPAC report are summarized below.

A galvanic (voltaic) cell should be represented by a diagram; for example, the cell shown in Fig. 26-1 is diagrammed thus:

$$Zn \,|\, Zn^{++} \,\|\, Cu^{++} \,|\, Cu$$

where $|$ indicates a phase boundary, and $\|$ indicates a salt bridge. The emf of the cell is equal in magnitude and sign to the electrical potential of the metallic conductor on the right when that of a similar metallic conductor on the left is taken as zero, the cell being open. Corresponding to the above cell formulation, the cell reaction

$$Zn + Cu^{++} \rightleftarrows Zn^{++} + Cu$$

is spontaneous from left to right when the cell is short-circuited, and the cell emf is positive. If the cell formulation is written in the reverse direction, that is,

$$Cu \,|\, Cu^{++} \,\|\, Zn^{++} \,|\, Zn$$

the corresponding equation is

$$Cu + Zn^{++} \rightleftarrows Cu^{++} + Zn$$

The cell reaction is spontaneous from right to left, and the cell emf is negative. In either case, the cell reaction is the reduction of Cu^{++} by Zn.

The emf of a half cell, for example, Zn^{++}, Zn, is the emf of a cell consisting of the standard hydrogen electrode on the left and the half cell under consideration on the right; thus,

$$Pt \,|\, H_2 \,(1\ atm) \,|\, H^+(a = 1) \,\|\, Zn^{++} \,|\, Zn$$

for which the cell reaction is

$$H_2 + Zn^{++} \rightleftarrows 2H^+ + Zn$$

By the criteria given above, this reaction proceeds from right to left, the emf of the cell is negative, and if Zn^{++} and Zn are at unit activity, the emf is -0.763 v; this value, with its sign, is the **standard potential** of the Zn^{++}, Zn half cell.

[1] W. M. Latimer, *The Oxidation States of the Elements and Their Potentials in Aqueous Solutions*, 2nd ed., Englewood Cliffs, N. J., Prentice-Hall, 1952.

[2] For the text of the IUPAC report, see T. S. Licht and A. J. de Béthune, *J. Chem. Educ.*, **34**, 433 (1957).

The half cell written as Zn, Zn^{++} implies a cell in which the right-hand electrode is the standard hydrogen electrode, and the cell emf is $+0.763$ v, but this emf *should not be called the electrode potential*, rather the *half-cell emf*. The IUPAC report therefore recognized the dual character of sign and direction of half reaction, but reserved the use of the term *potential* for the emf of the half-cell reaction written in the direction of reduction, implying that the half cell in question is the right-hand electrode in a cell formulation having the standard hydrogen electrode as the left-hand half cell. The "Stockholm convention" (IUPAC) will be used in the discussions in this text.

When the Stockholm conventions are used, the following "rules" will apply.

1. All half-cell potentials will be referred to the standard hydrogen electrode arbitrarily assigned a value of zero potential at all temperatures; this is one point on which all systems of conventions agree.

2. Half-cell reaction equations will be written in the general form

$$Ox + ne \rightleftarrows Red$$

where Ox and Red represent, respectively, the oxidized and the reduced species of the system concerned.

3. The half-cell potential is *positive* if the oxidized form of the reactant is a stronger oxidizing agent than hydrogen ion, and *negative* if the reduced form of the reactant is a stronger reducing agent than hydrogen. For example, for the half cell Zn^{++}, Zn, $E° = -0.763$ v; zinc metal is a stronger reducing agent than hydrogen, and the potential is negative. For the half cell Cu^{++}, Cu, $E° = +0.337$ v; Cu^{++} is a stronger oxidizing agent than H^+, and the potential is positive. In metal ion–metal half cells, the sign of the potential corresponds to the electrostatic charge on the metal and to the polarity of the half cell against the standard hydrogen electrode. A table of standard electrode potentials is given in Appendix V.

4. The emf of a cell can be derived from the cell formulation and the corresponding half-cell potentials, and certain conclusions can be reached regarding the direction of spontaneous cell reaction and the polarity of the electrodes. These deductions also require the adoption of specified rules:

a. The cell will be represented by a diagram. For example, assuming the ions to be at standard state, the cell illustrated in Fig. 26-1 would have the diagram

$$Zn \,|\, Zn^{++} \,(1\ M) \,\|\, Cu^{++} \,(1\ M) \,|\, Cu$$

b. The ion-electron equation for the right half cell will be written first, in the conventional form, along with its potential, E. (If all reactants are at standard state or unit activity the potential is the standard potential, $E°$.)

c. The ion-electron equation for the left half cell will be written second, also in the conventional form, along with its potential, E.

d. The second (left) half-reaction equation will be subtracted from the first (right) half-reaction equation, transposing reactants to opposite sides of the reaction arrows to avoid negative signs in the final equation for the cell reaction. The cell reaction must balance for electrons transferred.

e. The second E will be subtracted from the first E to give the cell voltage, E_{cell}. *Note:* if one or both ion-electron equations must be multiplied by an integer to account for equality in the number of electrons (i.e., to balance the over-all equation), the E values are *not* multiplied by these integers, but are used as such; the E value of a given half cell is independent of any other half cell with which it may be combined.

f. The sign ($+$ or $-$) of E_{cell} is the polarity of the right-hand electrode as the cell is formulated.

g. If E_{cell} is positive, the cell reaction is spontaneous in the left-to-right direction as the equation is written in *d*; if E_{cell} is negative, the reaction is spontaneous in the right-to-left direction.

EXAMPLE 1

Given the cell formulation:

$$Zn \mid Zn^{++}(1\ M) \parallel Cu^{++}(1\ M) \mid Cu$$

$$E° = -0.763\ v \qquad E° = +0.337\ v$$

(If the solutes are at standard state or unit activity, that is, pure metals and solute ions at 1 M concentration, the electrode potentials are standard potentials, $E°$.)

(1)	$Cu^{++} + 2e \rightleftarrows Cu$	$E°_1 = +0.337\ v$
(2)	$Zn^{++} + 2e \rightleftarrows Zn$	$E°_2 = -0.763\ v$
(1) − (2):	$Cu^{++} + Zn \rightleftarrows Zn^{++} + Cu$	$E°_{cell} = +1.100\ v$

Because $E°_{cell}$ is positive, it is known that the right-hand electrode is the positive electrode and that the cell reaction is spontaneous in the left-to-right direction as the equation is written. If the cell formulation had been written in the reverse order and the same rules followed, the final expression would have been

$$Zn^{++} + Cu \rightleftarrows Cu^{++} + Zn \qquad E°_{cell} = -1.100\ v$$

In either case, the conclusion is that the copper metal dipping into the Cu^{++} solution is the positive electrode, and the spontaneous cell reaction is the reduction of Cu^{++} by Zn and the oxidation of Zn by Cu^{++}. One of the advantages of the IUPAC convention is that the polarity of an electrode in a galvanic cell is the same as the sign of the half-cell potential of that electrode, under the conditions (e.g., concentration, etc.) specified in the cell formulation.

If the relative values of the half-cell potentials are known in advance (e.g., from $E°$ values from a table and/or the conditions of concentration of reactants), writing the cell formulation with the more positive half cell on the right will always result in a positive value for E_{cell} and a cell reaction that proceeds from left to right as the equation is deduced.

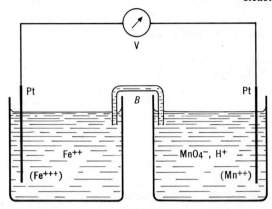

Fig. 26-2   Oxidation of iron(II) by permanganate in a galvanic cell.

Half cells are not limited to a metal in contact with its ions; *any* ion-electron half-reaction system can be made a half cell. If the half-cell reaction involves two different oxidation states of an element in solution, an inert electrode such as platinum or carbon is used to collect the electrons from the reductant and/or supply them to the oxidant in the cell. Figure 26-2 represents such a cell, consisting of the half cell Fe^{+++}, Fe^{++} and the half cell MnO_4^-, Mn^{++}, H^+. When electrical connection of the electrodes and of the solution is made, the voltmeter registers an emf, and current flows through the circuit. This cell affords a simple means of demonstrating the fact that redox reactions are associated with transfer of electrons. An acidic solution of a ferrous salt, for example, $FeSO_4$, is placed in the left-hand compartment, and an acidic solution of $KMnO_4$ is placed in the right-hand compartment. If a little potassium thiocyanate solution is added to the left compartment, the solution around the platinum electrode turns red as soon as the circuit is completed, showing the formation of Fe^{+++} resulting from oxidation of Fe^{++}. In the right-hand compartment, the solution around the electrode becomes decolorized, because of the reduction of the purple MnO_4^- to colorless Mn^{++}. Although the solutions are not in physical contact, the same reaction takes place as when ferrous and permanganate solutions are mixed together in acid solution.

The cell shown in Fig. 26-2 is represented diagrammatically thus:

$$Pt\,|\,Fe^{+++},\,Fe^{++}\,\|\,MnO_4^-,\,Mn^{++},\,H^+\,|\,Pt$$

Following the rules previously given, and assuming that all of the solutes are at unit activity (1 M), the cell reaction and emf are derived:

(1) $MnO_4^- + 8H^+ + 5e \rightleftarrows Mn^{++} + 4H_2O$ $E^\circ_1 = +1.51$ v   *red*

(2) $Fe^{+++} + e \rightleftarrows Fe^{++}$ $E^\circ_2 = +0.77$ v   *ox*

(1)−(2): $5Fe^{++} + MnO_4^- + 8H^+ \rightleftarrows$

                $5Fe^{+++} + Mn^{++} + 4H_2O$ $E^\circ_{cell} = +0.74$ v

Relation of Potential to Concentration: The Nernst Equation

In 1889 Nernst formulated an expression relating the potential of a half cell to the concentration of the reactants. For the general case,

$$Ox + ne \rightleftarrows Red \tag{26-3}$$

the Nernst equation is written

$$E = \text{Constant} - \frac{RT}{nF} \ln \frac{[\text{Red}]}{[\text{Ox}]} \tag{26-4}$$

E is the half-cell potential, R is a constant having a value of 8.314 joules per degree, T is absolute temperature, n is the number of electrons in the half-cell reaction, F is the faraday number (96,493 coulombs), and [Red] and [Ox] are the molar concentrations (more exactly, the activities) of the reduced and oxidized forms of the substance involved in the half reaction. For a temperature of 25°C (298° abs.), and using 2.303 to convert natural to common logarithms, the Nernst equation becomes

$$E = \text{Constant} - \frac{2.303 \times 8.314 \times 298}{n \times 96,493} \log \frac{[\text{Red}]}{[\text{Ox}]}$$

$$= \text{Constant} - \frac{0.0591}{n} \log \frac{[\text{Red}]}{[\text{Ox}]} \tag{26-5}$$

Standard Potentials. Because the potential of an electrode varies with concentration (activity) of the reactants, it is necessary, in order to have a basis for comparison of different half-cell potentials, to define a "standard state" or unit activity of the substances entering into the electrode reaction.

1. A pure liquid or pure solid is in its standard state or is at unit activity. For example, in the Zn^{++}, Zn half cell, metallic zinc is at unit activity.

2. A gas is at standard state when at a pressure of 760 mm of mercury (one atmosphere) at 0°C.

3. A soluble solute, for example, an ion, is at standard state when its activity is unity. The activity, a, is given by the relation $a = C \cdot f$, where C is the molar concentration and f is the activity coefficient, which depends upon the ionic strength of the solution (see Chap. 4). Because of reactions such as hydrolysis and complex formation, many simple metal ions cannot exist in aqueous solution at an activity of 1. For a few cases, "formal potentials" have been measured; in these cases the solute is at a concentration of 1 F ("one formal"), that is, one formula weight of solute per liter. Such a concentration designation makes no commitment about the nature or distribution of the various species that may be present at equilibrium. For all but the most rigorous calculations, it may be assumed that molar concentrations are proportional to activities, whereupon the standard state is the solute at 1 M concentration. This approximation will be followed in the calculations based upon the Nernst equation.

4. A slightly soluble solute, e.g., AgCl, is at standard state when its concentration in the solution is its solubility, that is, when the solution is saturated with the solute.

5. A dissolved gas is at standard state when its concentration in the solution is its solubility at one atmosphere pressure and 0°C.

Referring to the Nernst equation (26-5), when the reactants are at standard state or unit activity the ratio $[Red]/[Ox] = 1/1$, the logarithm of which is zero. Hence E is equal to the constant in the Nernst equation. This constant, designated by the symbol $E°$, is the standard potential of the half cell. The Nernst equation can now be written in the form

$$E = E° - \frac{0.0591}{n} \log \frac{[Red]}{[Ox]} \tag{26-6}$$

For half cells consisting of a metal in contact with a solution of its ions,

$$M^{n+} + ne \rightleftarrows M \qquad E = E° - \frac{0.0591}{n} \log \frac{1}{[M^{n+}]}$$

$$= E° + \frac{0.0591}{n} \log [M^{n+}]$$

because the metal is at unit activity; the potential therefore depends upon the concentration of the metal ion in solution. Because the potential depends upon conditions, it is important, in formulating cells, to stipulate the conditions. For example,

$$Zn \,|\, Zn^{++} \,(0.10\ M) \,\|\, H^+ \,(1\ M) \,|\, H_2 \,(1\ atm) \,|\, Pt$$

$$Pt \,|\, Fe^{++}(1\ M),\ Fe^{+++} \,(0.1\ M) \,\|\, Mn^{++} \,(1\ M),\ MnO_4^- \,(0.1\ M),\ H^+ \,(1\ M) \,|\, Pt$$

Calculation of Potential and EMF at Nonstandard Conditions

When the reactants are not at standard state or unit activity, the potential of a half cell is calculated by the use of the Nernst equation, using the standard potential and the known concentrations of the reactants; the E_{cell} is then the difference between the half-cell potentials.

EXAMPLE 2

Given the cell:

$$Pt \,|\, Cr^{++}(0.001\ M),\ Cr^{+++}(1\ M) \,\|\, V^{+++}(0.01\ M),\ V^{++}(1\ M) \,|\, Pt$$

$$E° = -0.41\ v \qquad\qquad E° = -0.26\ v$$

For the right-hand half cell,

$$E_1 = E°_1 - \frac{0.0591}{n} \log \frac{[V^{++}]}{[V^{+++}]} = -0.26 - 0.0591 \log 1/0.01$$

$$= -0.26 - (0.0591 \times 2) = -0.26 - 0.12 = -0.38\ v$$

For the left-hand half cell,

$$E_2 = E°_2 - \frac{0.0591}{n} \log \frac{[Cr^{++}]}{[Cr^{+++}]} = -0.41 - 0.0591 \log 0.001/1$$

$$= -0.41 - (0.0591 \times -3) = -0.41 + 0.18 = -0.23 \text{ v}$$

Hence,

(1)	$V^{+++} + e \rightleftarrows V^{++}$	$E_1 = -0.38$ v
(2)	$Cr^{+++} + e \rightleftarrows Cr^{++}$	$E_2 = -0.23$ v
(1) − (2):	$V^{+++} + Cr^{++} \rightleftarrows V^{++} + Cr^{+++}$	$E_{cell} = -0.15$ v

The cell emf can be calculated in a slightly different manner, although it is fundamentally identical with the above.

$$E_1 = E°_1 - \frac{0.0591}{n} \log \frac{[V^{++}]}{[V^{+++}]} \qquad E_2 = E°_2 - \frac{0.0591}{n} \log \frac{[Cr^{++}]}{[Cr^{+++}]}$$

$$E_{cell} = E_1 - E_2 = \left\{ E°_1 - \frac{0.0591}{n} \log \frac{[V^{++}]}{[V^{+++}]} \right\} - \left\{ E°_2 - \frac{0.0591}{n} \log \frac{[Cr^{++}]}{[Cr^{+++}]} \right\}$$

$$= E°_1 - E°_2 - \frac{0.0591}{n} \log \frac{[V^{++}][Cr^{+++}]}{[V^{+++}][Cr^{++}]}$$

$$= -0.26 - (-0.41) - 0.0591 \log \left(\frac{1 \times 1}{0.01 \times 0.001} \right)$$

$$= -0.26 + 0.41 - 0.0591 \log 10^5$$

$$= +0.15 - (0.0591 \times 5) = -0.15 \text{ v}$$

Because E_{cell} is negative, the cell reaction is spontaneous in the right-to-left direction as written; that is, Cr^{+++} is reduced by V^{++} under the conditions of concentration given. The platinum electrode dipping into the vanadium solution is negative. By contrast, note that when all substances are at standard state, $E°_{cell} = -0.26 - (-0.41)$ $= +0.15$ v; V^{+++} is reduced by Cr^{++}, and the electrode dipping into the vanadium solution is positive.

In practice, half-cell potentials are often changed from their standard state values by use of a large excess of one of the components of the half-cell reaction; by decreasing the concentration of one of the ions to a very small value by precipitation or by complex formation; or by change of pH if H^+ or OH^- is involved in the half-cell reaction. These methods may be used to make reactions more complete or less complete, or in some cases actually to influence the direction of the reaction.

Change of EMF During Redox Titration

In a redox titration the emf up to the stoichiometric point is calculated from $E°$ of the half reaction of the substance titrated. Beyond the stoichiometric point the emf is calculated from $E°$ of the half reaction of the titrant. At the stoichiometric point the $E°$ values of both half reactions are involved. In the following examples it is assumed that the titration is carried out in a cell in which the reference electrode is a standard hydrogen electrode, for which $E° = 0.00$ v, and the indicator electrode is a platinum wire (inert) dipping into the solution. The measured emf of the cell therefore corresponds to the potential of the half-reaction systems involved in the titration reaction. (Other reference electrodes and indicator electrodes, and potentiometric determination of end points are discussed more fully in Chap. 32.)

EXAMPLE 3

50.0 ml of 0.100 N Fe^{++} solution are titrated with 0.100 N Ce^{4+} solution. $E°$ for Fe^{+++}, $Fe^{++} = +0.77$ v. $E°$ for Ce^{4+}, $Ce^{+++} = +1.61$ v. Calculate emf values for construction of a titration curve. (For the reactants given, one equivalent is one mole; each half reaction involves one electron.) For simplicity, the constant in the Nernst equation will be used as 0.059.

a. At the start of the titration, that is, before any Ce^{4+} is added, the solution contains, for all practical purposes, only Fe^{++}. If $[Fe^{+++}]$ were indeed zero, E would have an infinite negative value; this would represent an infinitely strong reducing agent, and result in reduction of some solution component and formation of some Fe^{+++}. Also, Fe^{++} is easily air oxidized. Hence, a finite but variable amount of Fe^{+++} is present, and an exact value for E cannot be defined.

b. During the titration, E_1 is determined by the ratio $[Fe^{++}]/[Fe^{+++}]$ in the solution. Because the reacting solutions given are of the same normality (and molarity), equivalent volumes can be used in lieu of actual molar concentrations.

(1) When 1.0 ml of Ce^{4+} has been added, $[Fe^{++}[/[Fe^{+++}] = 49.0/1.0$ and

$$E_1 = 0.77 - 0.059 \log (49.0/1.0) = 0.77 - (0.059 \times 1.69)$$

$$= 0.77 - 0.10 = 0.67 \text{ v}$$

(2) When 5.0 ml of Ce^{4+} have been added, $[Fe^{++}]/[Fe^{+++}] = 45.0/5.0$ and

$$E_1 = 0.77 - 0.059 \log (45.0/5.0) = 0.77 - 0.059(0.96)$$

$$= 0.77 - 0.06 = 0.71 \text{ v}$$

(3) When 25.0 ml of Ce^{4+} have been added (half-titration point), $[Fe^{++}]/[Fe^{+++}] = 25.0/25.0 = 1$, the log of which is zero. Hence, $E_1 = 0.77$ v. In all cases, at half titration $E_1 = E°_1$.

(4) At 49.0 ml of added Ce^{4+}, $[Fe^{++}]/[Fe^{+++}] = 1.0/49.0$, and

$$E_1 = 0.77 - 0.059 \log (1.0/49.0) = 0.87 \text{ v}$$

(5) When 49.9 ml of Ce^{4+} have been added, $[Fe^{++}]/[Fe^{+++}] = 0.1/49.9$, and

$$E_1 = 0.77 - 0.059 \log (0.1/49.9) = 0.93 \text{ v}$$

c. At the stoichiometric point in the reaction,

$$Fe^{++} + Ce^{4+} \rightleftarrows Fe^{+++} + Ce^{+++}$$

if it is assumed for the time being that the reaction is sufficiently complete for titrimetric analysis, virtually all the original Fe^{++} has been oxidized to Fe^{+++}, and an equivalent amount of Ce^{+++} is in the solution, from reduction of Ce^{4+}. $[Fe^{++}]$ and $[Ce^{4+}]$ have very small, although finite, values. During the titration the emf has become more and more positive, as $[Fe^{+++}]$ increased at the expense of $[Fe^{++}]$. Eventually a point is reached at which the emf due to the low ratio of $[Fe^{++}]/[Fe^{+++}]$ is equal to the emf due to a high ratio of $[Ce^{+++}]/[Ce^{4+}]$. This equality of half-reaction potentials occurs at the equivalence point in the titration, and the system of reactants is at stoichiometric equilibrium. Again, writing the Nernst expressions for the half reactions,

$$E_1 = E°_1 - 0.059 \log ([Fe^{++}]/[Fe^{+++}])$$

$$E_2 = E°_2 - 0.059 \log ([Ce^{+++}]/[Ce^{4+}])$$

Adding the two equations gives

$$E_1 + E_2 = E°_1 + E°_2 - 0.059 \log \frac{[Fe^{++}][Ce^{+++}]}{[Fe^{+++}][Ce^{4+}]}$$

But at the stoichiometric point, $[Fe^{+++}] = [Ce^{+++}]$, and $[Fe^{++}] = [Ce^{4+}]$, hence the combined concentration terms are equal to one, the log of which is zero. At this point, also, $E_1 = E_2 = E_{eq}$, the equivalence point emf; hence, $2E_{eq} = E°_1 + E°_2$, and $E_{eq} = (E°_1 + E°_2)/2$. For the titration illustrated, $E_{eq} = (0.77 + 1.61)/2 = 1.19$ v.

 d. After the stoichiometric point, the emf is calculated from the Nernst equation for the titrant, Ce^{4+}. At the stoichiometric point in the case being illustrated, 50.0 ml of 0.100 N Fe^{++} require 50.0 ml of 0.100 N Ce^{4+}, and the volume of the solution is then 100.0 ml, containing the Ce^{+++} formed by reduction.

Table 26-1 Titration of
50.0 ml of 0.100 N Fe^{++}
with 0.100 N Ce^{4+}

Ce^{4+} Added, ml	E, v
0.0	—
1.0	0.67
5.0	0.71
10.0	0.73
25.0	0.77
45.0	0.83
49.0	0.87
49.9	0.93
50.0	1.19
50.1	1.45
51.0	1.51
60.0	1.57
100.0	1.61

(1) At 1.0 ml excess Ce^{4+}, $[Ce^{4+}] = 0.100 \times 1.0/101.0 = 0.0010$, and $[Ce^{+++}] = 0.100 \times 50.0/101.0 = 0.050$. Hence,

$$E_2 = E^\circ{}_2 - 0.059 \log ([Ce^{+++}]/[Ce^{4+}])$$
$$= 1.61 - 0.059 \log (0.050/0.0010) = 1.61 - 0.10 = 1.51 \text{ v}$$

Or, with equivalent volumes, $[Ce^{+++}]/[Ce^{4+}] = 50/1.0$, and $E_2 = 1.51$ v.

(2) At 10.0 ml excess Ce^{4+}, $[Ce^{4+}] = 0.100 \times 10.0/110 = 0.009$, and $[Ce^{+++}] = 0.100 \times 50.0/110 = 0.045$; then

$$E_2 = E^\circ{}_2 - 0.059 \log (0.045/0.009) = 1.61 - 0.04 = 1.57 \text{ v}$$

The same value is obtained by using equivalent volumes, $[Ce^{+++}]/[Ce^{4+}] = 50.0/10.0$.

Additional points during titration or after the stoichiometric point can be computed as illustrated above. Table 26-1 gives several values in addition to those for the points calculated in the illustrations. The change in emf with the amount of titrant added can be represented by plotting a titration curve, as in Fig. 26-3 for the case illustrated.

When the two half reactions involve a different number of electrons, slight modification of certain calculations is required.

EXAMPLE 4

50.0 ml of 0.100 N Sn^{++} are titrated with 0.100 N Ce^{4+} solution. E° for Sn^{4+}, $Sn^{++} = +0.15$ v. E° for Ce^{4+}, $Ce^{+++} = +1.61$ v. Calculate values of emf for construction of the titration curve.

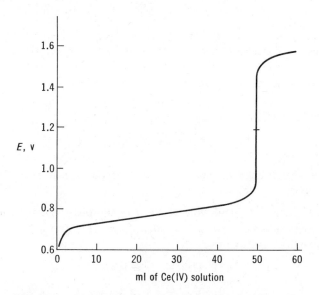

Fig. 26-3   Titration curve. 50.0 ml of 0.100 N iron(II)
solution titrated with 0.100 N cerium(IV).

a. At the start, E is indeterminate, as explained in the previous example.

b. During titration, the method of calculation is the same as illustrated in the previous example, except that two electrons are involved in the half reaction, requiring the use of the factor $0.059/2 = 0.0295$ in the Nernst equation. Although a 0.100 N solution of Sn^{++} is 0.050 M in this reaction, the logarithmic term in the Nernst equation involves the ratio of the molar concentrations of Sn^{++} and Sn^{4+}; the ratio of the molarities is the same as the ratio of their normalities. For the calculation, therefore, the "equivalent volumes" of the two oxidation states can be used as before. For example, when 10.0 ml of Ce^{4+} have been added, the ratio $[Sn^{++}]/[Sn^{4+}] = 40.0/10.0$, and

$$E_1 = E°_1 - 0.0295 \log ([Sn^{++}]/[Sn^{4+}]) = 0.15 - 0.0295 \log 4.00$$

$$= 0.15 - 0.02 = 0.13 \text{ v}$$

Similar calculations are made for other points during titration.

c. At the stoichiometric point in the reaction,

$$Sn^{++} + 2Ce^{4+} \rightarrow Sn^{4+} + 2Ce^{+++}$$

$$E_1 = E°_1 - \frac{0.059}{2} \log \frac{[Sn^{++}]}{[Sn^{4+}]}$$

$$E_2 = E°_2 - \frac{0.059}{1} \log \frac{[Ce^{+++}]}{[Ce^{4+}]}$$

The first equation is multiplied by 2 and then added to the second equation:

$$2E_1 + E_2 = 2E°_1 + E°_2 - 0.059 \log \frac{[Sn^{++}][Ce^{+++}]}{[Sn^{4+}][Ce^{4+}]}$$

But $[Ce^{+++}] = 2[Sn^{4+}]$, and $[Ce^{4+}] = 2[Sn^{++}]$; also, $E_1 = E_2 = E_{eq}$. Substituting concentrations, the concentration term becomes unity, so that $3E_{eq} = 2E°_1 + E°_2$, or

$$E_{eq} = \frac{2E°_1 + E°_2}{3}$$

For the example illustrated,

$$E_{eq} = \frac{2(0.15) + 1.61}{3} = 0.64 \text{ v}$$

d. After the stoichiometric or equivalence point the potential is calculated as illustrated in the previous example.

The general case for calculation of the emf at the stoichiometric point is given below. The subscripts are used to identify the reactants and half reactions 1 and 2. The half-cell reactions are:

$$(1) \quad Ox_1 + n_1e \rightleftarrows Red_1$$

$$(2) \quad Ox_2 + n_2e \rightleftarrows Red_2$$

Obtain the balanced equation for the reaction by multiplying the first equation by n_2 and the second equation by n_1, then subtracting the second equation from the first, to give:

$$n_2 \, Ox_1 + n_1 Red_2 \rightleftarrows n_2 \, Red_1 + n_1 Ox_2 \qquad (26\text{-}7)$$

The corresponding Nernst equations are

$$E_1 = E°_1 - \frac{0.059}{n_1} \log \frac{[Red_1]}{[Ox_1]} \qquad (26\text{-}8)$$

$$E_2 = E°_2 - \frac{0.059}{n_2} \log \frac{[Red_2]}{[Ox_2]} \qquad (26\text{-}9)$$

The first Nernst equation is multiplied by n_1 and the second Nerst equation is multiplied by n_2, and the two equations are then added:

$$n_1 E_1 + n_2 E_2 = n_1 E°_1 + n_2 E°_2 - 0.059 \log \frac{[Red_1][Red_2]}{[Ox_1][Ox_2]} \qquad (26\text{-}10)$$

At the stoichiometric point, $n_1[Red_1] = n_2[Ox_2]$, and $n_1[Ox_1] = n_2[Red_2]$. By substituting concentrations, the concentration fraction becomes unity, hence the last term drops out because $\log 1 = 0$. Also, $E_1 = E_2 = E_{eq}$. Therefore $(n_1 + n_2)E_{eq} = n_1 E°_1 + n_2 E°_2$, and

$$E_{eq} = \frac{n_1 E°_1 + n_2 E°_2}{n_1 + n_2} \qquad (26\text{-}11)$$

Note that each standard potential is multiplied by the number of electrons *in the half reaction it represents*. The sum of these products is then divided by the sum of the number of electrons in the two half reactions, to give the equivalence point emf. In other words, the emf at the equivalence point is a *weighted average* of the standard potentials of the two half reactions, the weighting factors being the number of electrons in the respective half reactions.[3]

INDICATORS FOR REDOX TITRATIONS

Colored Reactant as Own Indicator

If the titrant used is highly colored and the reaction products are colorless or only very faintly colored, the first slight excess of titrant may serve as a self-indicator; this is the case with permanganate when used in acid solution. The end point is the first faint pink color of a very slight excess of permanganate.

---

[3] For a reaction in which the coefficient of the reduced and the oxidized form of a reagent is not the same, as in

$$6Fe^{++} + Cr_2O_7^{--} + 14H^+ \rightarrow 6Fe^{+++} + 2Cr^{+++} + 7H_2O$$

the mathematical treatment is somewhat more complex. For a complete generalized treatment, see A. J. Bard and S. H. Simonsen, *J. Chem. Ed.*, 37, 364 (1960).

Cerium(IV), either as the cation or in anionic complexes such as $Ce(NO_3)_6^{--}$, is yellow-orange, and its reduction product, Ce^{+++}, is colorless. The first faint yellow color of excess cerium(IV) in solution marks the end point. Sharper end points can be obtained, however, by the use of certain redox indicators.

The color of free iodine as a self-indicator, either in aqueous medium or when extracted into certain organic solvents, is discussed in Chap. 29.

Disappearance of Substance Titrated

In the reduction of iron(III) by titanium(III),

$$Fe^{+++} + Ti^{+++} \rightarrow Fe^{++} + Ti^{4+}$$

in the presence of thiocyanate, the red color of $Fe(CNS)^{++}$ persists until all of the iron(III) is reduced; the end point is the disappearance of the red color of the solution.

Redox Indicators

Several organic compounds have the ability to undergo oxidation or reduction, accompanied by a change in color. These indicators are typical redox systems that can be represented by the general half-reaction equation

$$In_{ox} + ne \rightleftarrows In_{red}$$

The indicator half reaction is characterized by a definite standard potential. For a given titration, a redox indicator should be selected that has a potential that coincides with or is very close to the equivalence point emf of the titration system. A moderate latitude of choice is permissible, because the emf of the system changes very rapidly around the stoichiometric point.

The colors and standard potentials of several redox indicators are shown in Table 26-2. Some of the indicator half reactions involve hydrogen ion, and the potentials are therefore influenced by pH; the tabular $E°$ values for these substances are for $1 M H^+$ solution. A few of these indicators are discussed below.

Diphenylamine and Related Compounds. In 1923, Knop found that diphenylamine could be used as a reversible indicator in the titrimetric determination of Fe^{++} by $Cr_2O_7^{--}$. The changes involved in the use of diphenylamine are, first, an irreversible oxidation to colorless diphenylbenzidine, followed by a reversible oxidation to diphenylbenzidine violet:

$$2C_6H_5 \cdot NH \cdot C_6H_5 \rightarrow C_6H_5 \cdot NH \cdot C_6H_4 \cdot C_6H_4 \cdot NH \cdot C_6H_5 + 2H^+ + 2e$$
Diphenylamine   Diphenylbenzidine

$$\rightleftarrows C_6H_5 \cdot N : C_6H_4 : C_6H_4 : N \cdot C_6H_5 + 2H^+ + 2e$$
Diphenylbenzidine violet

Table 26-2 Redox Indicators

| Indicator | Color | | $E°$, v |
	Reduced	Oxidized	
Ruthenium tridipyridine dichloride[a]	Colorless	Yellow	+1.33
Ferrous 5-nitro-1,10-phenanthroline (nitroferroin)	Red	Blue	1.25
p-Nitrodiphenylamine	Colorless	Violet	1.06
Ferrous 1,10-phenanthroline (ferroin)	Red	Blue	1.06
Ferrous 5-methyl-1,10-phenanthroline sulfonate	Red	Blue	1.02
Erioglaucine A	Red	Green	1.00
Ferrous 2,2'-bipyridine sulfate	Red	Blue	0.97
N,N'-Tetramethylbenzidine-3-sulfonic acid[b]	Colorless	Yellow	0.88
Diphenylamine sulfonic acid	Colorless	Violet	0.84
3,3'-Dimethylnaphthadine sulfonate[c]	Colorless	Red-purple	0.80
Diphenylamine	Colorless	Violet	0.76
3,3'-Dimethylnaphthadine[d]	Colorless	Red-purple	0.71
1-Naphthol-2-sulfonic acid indophenol	Colorless	Red	0.54
Methylene blue	Colorless	Green-blue	0.36
Phenosafranine	Colorless	Blue	0.28
Indigo monosulfonate	Colorless	Blue	0.26

[a] J. Steigmann, N. Birnbaum, and S. M. Edwards, *Ind. Eng. Chem., Anal. Ed.*, **14**, 30 (1942).
[b] R. N. Adams and E. M. Hammaker, *Anal. Chem.*, **23**, 744 (1951).
[c] R. Belcher, A. J. Nutten, and W. I. Stephen, *J. Chem. Soc.*, **1951**, 1520, 3444.
[d] R. Belcher, A. J. Nutten, and W. I. Stephen, *Analyst*, **76**, 378 (1951).

In practice, the more soluble sodium or barium diphenylamine sulfonate is used, rather than the free base. Various derivatives of diphenylamine, such as p-nitro- and p-aminodiphenylamine, also act as redox indicators of somewhat different $E°$ values.

Ferrous Phenanthroline and Its Derivatives. The compound 1,10-phenanthroline, $C_{12}H_8N_2$, reacts with Fe^{++} to form an intense red-colored polydentate coordination complex, $Fe(C_{12}H_8N_2)_3^{++}$, called by the trivial name "ferroin." It is oxidized to the corresponding ferric complex, called "ferriin," which is pale blue in color:

$$\underset{\text{red}}{Fe(C_{12}H_8N_2)_3^{++}} \rightleftarrows \underset{\text{pale blue}}{Fe(C_{12}H_8N_2)_3^{+++}} + e$$

Several derivatives, such as the 5-nitro compound and the 5,6-dimethyl compound, react in a similar manner and with similar color changes, but have different $E°$ values.

Ferrous Dipyridine. The compound 2,2'-dipyridine, $C_{10}H_8N_2$,

forms a ferrous coordination complex $Fe(C_{10}H_8N_2)_3^{++}$, which is similar to ferrous phenanthroline in its indicator action; the color change is from intense red to pale blue.

Irreversible Redox Indicators. Some highly colored organic compounds that undergo irreversible oxidation or reduction can nevertheless be used as internal redox indicators if the color change is very sensitive to a small excess of titrant. Methyl red and methyl orange, which are also acid-base indicators, are red in acid solution and are decolorized irreversibly by strong oxidants. Naphthol blue black, used in the titration of arsenite by bromate, changes from green to pink to colorless with the first excess of bromate. Considerable care must be exercised in the use of irreversible indicators, lest a localized excess of titrant causes the color change of the indicator before the true end point is reached.

Potentiometric Method

The determination of the end point of redox titrations by measuring the emf of the titration system is discussed in Chap. 32.

EXTENT OF REACTION: EQUILIBRIUM CONSTANTS

The equilibrium constant of a redox reaction can be calculated from the $E°$ values of the two half reactions, and the concentration of the unreacted substance at equilibrium can be calculated from the equilibrium constant.

EXAMPLE 5

Calculate the equilibrium constant for the reaction between Fe^{++} and Ce^{4+}; calculate also the concentration of unoxidized Fe^{++} at the stoichiometric point.

$$Ce^{4+} + e \rightleftarrows Ce^{+++} \qquad E^\circ{}_1 = 1.61 \text{ v} \qquad E_1 = E^\circ{}_1 - 0.059 \log \frac{[Ce^{+++}]}{[Ce^{4+}]}$$

$$Fe^{+++} + e \rightleftarrows Fe^{++} \qquad E^\circ{}_2 = 0.77 \text{ v} \qquad E_2 = E^\circ{}_2 - 0.059 \log \frac{[Fe^{++}]}{[Fe^{+++}]}$$

The reaction is

$$Fe^{++} + Ce^{4+} \rightleftarrows Fe^{+++} + Ce^{+++}$$

and $E^\circ{}_1 - E^\circ{}_2 = +0.84$ v, indicating that the reaction left-to-right, as the equation is written, is the spontaneous reaction. It is to be remembered, however, that the reaction is *reversible*, and that the equilibrium condition may be approached from either direction, that is, by mixing solutions of Fe^{++} and Ce^{4+}, or by mixing solutions of Fe^{+++} and Ce^{+++}. When solutions of Fe^{++} and Ce^{4+} are mixed, the potential of the Fe^{+++}, Fe^{++} system becomes more positive as the Fe^{++} is oxidized to Fe^{+++}, decreasing the value of the ratio $[Fe^{++}]/[Fe^{+++}]$; the potential of the Ce^{4+}. Ce^{+++} system becomes less positive as Ce^{4+} is reduced to Ce^{+++}, increasing the value of the ratio $[Ce^{+++}]/[Ce^{4+}]$. Eventually the two half reactions reach the same potential; no further change in the concentrations of the reactants can occur, because the driving force or potential for electron transfer is the same for each half reaction. The system is then in a condition of equilibrium, because $E_1 - E_2 = 0$. This equilibrium emf is the same as the equivalence point emf, E_{eq}, calculated in connection with the titration curve for this system (p. 368). It should be emphasized that the emf of the reaction system, referred to the standard hydrogen half cell, is *not* zero; it is only the *difference* in the two half-cell *potentials* that is zero. Therefore,

$$E_1 = 1.61 - 0.059 \log \frac{[Ce^{+++}]}{[Ce^{4+}]} = E_2 = 0.77 - 0.059 \log \frac{[Fe^{++}]}{[Fe^{+++}]}$$

Collecting similar terms to the same side of the equality sign,

$$1.61 - 0.77 = 0.059 \log \frac{[Ce^{+++}]}{[Ce^{4+}]} - 0.059 \log \frac{[Fe^{++}]}{[Fe^{+++}]}$$

$$0.84 = 0.059 \log \left\{ \frac{[Ce^{+++}][Fe^{+++}]}{[Ce^{4+}][Fe^{++}]} \right\}$$

But

$$\frac{[Ce^{+++}][Fe^{+++}]}{[Ce^{4+}][Fe^{++}]} = K_{eq}$$

the equilibrium constant for the reaction; hence

$$0.84 = 0.059 \log K_{eq} \qquad \log K_{eq} = 0.84/0.059 = 14.2$$

$$K_{eq} = 10^{14.2} = 1.6 \times 10^{14}$$

This large value for K_{eq} indicates that the oxidation of Fe^{++} by Ce^{4+} is very extensive.

Referring again to the equation for the reaction, it is noted that at the equivalence point $[Fe^{+++}] = [Ce^{+++}]$, and $[Fe^{++}] = [Ce^{4+}]$; hence,

$$\frac{[Fe^{+++}]}{[Fe^{++}]} = \frac{[Ce^{+++}]}{[Ce^{4+}]}$$

But

$$\frac{[Fe^{+++}]}{[Fe^{++}]} \cdot \frac{[Ce^{+++}]}{[Ce^{4+}]} = K_{eq}$$

Therefore,

$$\frac{[Fe^{+++}]}{[Fe^{++}]} = \frac{[Ce^{+++}]}{[Ce^{4+}]} = \sqrt{K_{eq}} = \sqrt{10^{14.2}} = 10^{7.1} = 1.3 \times 10^7$$

If 0.100 N (M) Fe^{++} is titrated with 0.100 N (M) Ce^{4+}, then at the equivalence point $[Fe^{+++}]$ is, for all practical purposes, 0.050 M. The large value for the $[Fe^{+++}]/[Fe^{++}]$ ratio shows that virtually all the iron is present as Fe^{+++}. The concentration of Fe^{++} is then easily calculated:

$$[Fe^{+++}]/[Fe^{++}] = 1.3 \times 10^7$$

and

$$[Fe^{++}] = 0.050/(1.3 \times 10^7) = 3.8 \times 10^{-9}$$

The amount of Fe^{++} remaining unoxidized is so small as to be negligible in the titrimetric calculations.

EXAMPLE 6 (Refer to Example 4.)

Calculate the equilibrium constant and the concentration of Sn^{++} unoxidized in the titration of 0.100 N (0.050 M) Sn^{++} by 0.100 N Ce^{4+}.

$$Ce^{4+} + e \rightleftarrows Ce^{+++} \qquad E^\circ{}_1 = 1.61 \text{ v} \qquad E_1 = E^\circ{}_1 - 0.059 \log \frac{[Ce^{+++}]}{[Ce^{4+}]}$$

$$Sn^{4+} + 2e \rightleftarrows Sn^{++} \qquad E^\circ{}_2 = 0.15 \text{ v} \qquad E_2 = E^\circ{}_2 - \frac{0.059}{2} \log \frac{[Sn^{++}]}{[Sn^{4+}]}$$

At the stoichiometric point of the reaction

$$Sn^{++} + 2Ce^{4+} \rightleftarrows Sn^{4+} + 2Ce^{+++}$$

$E_1 = E_2$, and

$$E_1 = 1.61 - 0.059 \log \frac{[Ce^{+++}]}{[Ce^{4+}]} = E_2 = 0.15 - \frac{0.059}{2} \log \frac{[Sn^{++}]}{[Sn^{4+}]}$$

In order to take out $(0.059/n)$ log as a common factor, the first log term is multiplied by 2/2, to give

$$\frac{0.059}{2} 2 \log \frac{[Ce^{+++}]}{[Ce^{4+}]} = \frac{0.059}{2} \log \frac{[Ce^{+++}]^2}{[Ce^{4+}]^2}$$

Then

$$1.61 - 0.15 = \frac{0.059}{2} \log \frac{[Ce^{+++}]^2}{[Ce^{4+}]^2} - \frac{0.059}{2} \log \frac{[Sn^{++}]}{[Sn^{4+}]}$$

$$1.46 = \frac{0.059}{2} \log \left\{ \frac{[Ce^{+++}]^2[Sn^{4+}]}{[Ce^{4+}]^2[Sn^{++}]} \right\} = \frac{0.059}{2} \log K_{eq}$$

$$\log K_{eq} = (2 \times 1.46)/0.059 = 49.5 \quad \text{and} \quad K_{eq} = 3.2 \times 10^{49}$$

The equilibrium constant expression can be written

$$\frac{[Ce^{+++}]}{[Ce^{4+}]} \cdot \frac{[Ce^{+++}]}{[Ce^{4+}]} \cdot \frac{[Sn^{4+}]}{[Sn^{++}]} = K_{eq}$$

At the stoichiometric point in the titration,

$$[Ce^{+++}] = 2[Sn^{4+}] \quad \text{and} \quad [Ce^{4+}] = 2[Sn^{++}]$$

Hence,

$$\frac{2[Sn^{4+}]}{2[Sn^{++}]} \cdot \frac{2[Sn^{4+}]}{2[Sn^{++}]} \cdot \frac{[Sn^{4+}]}{[Sn^{++}]} = \frac{[Sn^{4+}]^3}{[Sn^{++}]^3} = K_{eq}$$

Therefore,

$$\frac{[Ce^{+++}]}{[Ce^{4+}]} = \frac{[Sn^{4+}]}{[Sn^{++}]} = \sqrt[3]{K_{eq}} = \sqrt[3]{10^{49.5}} = 3.2 \times 10^{16}$$

If 0.100 N (0.050 M) Sn^{++} is titrated with 0.100 N Ce^{4+}, then at the stoichiometric point $[Sn^{++}] = 0.025/(3.2 \times 10^{16}) = 7.8 \times 10^{-19}$.

The calculation methods illustrated by the above examples can be generalized for the reaction of the reduced form of one substance with the oxidized form of another substance.

$$Ox_1 + n_1 e \rightleftarrows Red_1 \qquad E_1 = E^{\circ}_1 - \frac{0.059}{n_1} \log \frac{[Red_1]}{[Ox_1]} \qquad (26\text{-}12)$$

$$Ox_2 + n_2 e \rightleftarrows Red_2 \qquad E_2 = E^{\circ}_2 - \frac{0.059}{n_2} \log \frac{[Red_2]}{[Ox_2]} \qquad (26\text{-}13)$$

Let a and b be coefficients by which the equations must be multiplied so that $an_1 = bn_2$ = number of electrons transferred. The balanced equation for the reaction is then

$$a \, Ox_1 + b \, Red_2 \rightleftarrows a \, Red_1 + b \, Ox_2$$

The last term of the Nernst equation (26-12) is multiplied by $an_1/bn_2 (= 1)$:

$$E_1 = E^{\circ}_1 - \frac{0.059}{bn_2} a \log \frac{[Red_1]}{[Ox_1]} = E^{\circ}_1 - \frac{0.059}{bn_2} \log \frac{[Red_1]^a}{[Ox_1]^a} \qquad (26\text{-}14)$$

The last term of the Nernst equation (26-13) is multiplied by b/b:

$$E_2 = E^\circ{}_2 - \frac{0.059}{bn_2} b \log \frac{[\text{Red}_2]}{[\text{Ox}_2]} = E^\circ{}_2 - \frac{0.059}{bn_2} \log \frac{[\text{Red}_2]^b}{[\text{Ox}_2]^b} \quad (26\text{-}15)$$

At stoichiometric equilibrium, $E_1 = E_2$, hence

$$E^\circ{}_1 - \frac{0.059}{bn_2} \log \frac{[\text{Red}_1]^a}{[\text{Ox}_1]^a} = E^\circ{}_2 - \frac{0.059}{bn_2} \log \frac{[\text{Red}_2]^b}{[\text{Ox}_2]^b} \quad (26\text{-}16)$$

$$E^\circ{}_1 - E^\circ{}_2 = \frac{0.059}{bn_2} \log \left\{ \frac{[\text{Red}_1]^a[\text{Ox}_2]^b}{[\text{Ox}_1]^a[\text{Red}_2]^b} \right\} \quad (26\text{-}17)$$

The expression within the brackets is the equilibrium constant for the reaction; hence,

$$E^\circ{}_1 - E^\circ{}_2 = \frac{0.059}{bn_2} \log K_{eq} \quad \text{and} \quad \log K_{eq} = \frac{bn_2(E^\circ{}_1 - E^\circ{}_2)}{0.059}$$

$$(26\text{-}18)$$

where $bn_2 = an_1 = $ number of electrons *transferred* in the reaction. Since

$$K_{eq} = \frac{[\text{Red}_1]^a[\text{Ox}_2]^b}{[\text{Ox}_1]^a[\text{Red}_2]^b}$$

$$\frac{[\text{Red}_1]}{[\text{Ox}_1]} = \frac{[\text{Ox}_2]}{[\text{Red}_2]} = \sqrt[a+b]{K_{eq}} \quad (26\text{-}19)$$

where a and b are the coefficients of Ox_1, Red_1, and Ox_2, Red_2, respectively, in the balanced equation for the reaction.[4]

Rate of Reaction. The equilibrium constant for a reaction represents the *extent* to which the reaction has proceeded *when equilibrium has been established*; it gives no information whatever about the *rate* of the reaction, i.e., the time required for the system to reach equilibrium. A reaction is useful for titrimetry only if it is so rapid as to be practically instantaneous. It is sometimes possible for a slow reaction to be catalyzed and made suitable for titrimetry.

The oxidation of oxalate ion by permanganate ion in acid solution is very slow at first. After a trace of Mn^{++} has been formed by reduction of MnO_4^-, the Mn^{++} catalyzes the reaction of $C_2O_4^{--}$ with MnO_4^-, and the remainder of the oxalate is oxidized instantaneously by the permanganate. A reaction that is catalyzed by a product of the reaction is called **autocatalytic**.

The reaction of cerium(IV) solutions with arsenite is catalyzed by iodine monochloride or by osmium tetroxide. The oxidation of arsenite by dichromate is catalyzed by a small amount of potassium iodide or of osmium tetroxide.

[4] *Ibid.*

The oxidation of arsenite by permanganate is catalyzed by a trace of iodide or of iodate. These reactions, which would otherwise be too slow for titrimetric use, are entirely satisfactory when catalyzed.

Potential Requirements for Complete Reaction

The extent of a redox reaction is dependent upon the difference in the potentials of the half-reaction systems involved, and also upon the number of electrons transferred; log K_{eq} is proportional to the difference between the half-reaction potentials and to the number of electrons transferred; see equation (26-18).

The potential difference to give a quantitative reaction can be calculated for the reaction

$$a\ Ox_1 + b\ Red_2 \rightleftarrows a\ Red_1 + b\ Ox_2$$

by use of the corresponding Nernst equation (26-18), and the relations shown in equation (26-19), rearranged to the form

$$K_{eq} = \frac{[Red_1]^a[Ox_2]^b}{[Ox_1]^a[Red_2]^b} = \left\{\frac{[Red_1]}{[Ox_1]}\right\}^{a+b} = \left\{\frac{[Ox_2]}{[Red_2]}\right\}^{a+b} \qquad (27\text{-}20)$$

Assume, for example, that the reaction is quantitative when the ratio $[Ox_2]/[Red_2] = 10^5$, that is, when only one molecule in a hundred thousand of the reducing agent remains unoxidized. The following situations will illustrate the calculations.

1. When $an_1 = bn_2 = 1$, that is, when each half reaction involves one electron, $a + b = 2$, $K_{eq} = (10^5)^2 = 10^{10}$, and log $K_{eq} = 10$. $E°_1 - E°_2 = \Delta E° = (0.059 \times 10)/1 = 0.59$ v.

2. When one half reaction involves one electron and the other involves two electrons, $an_1 = bn_2 = 2$, and $a + b = 3$. $K_{eq} = (10^5)^3 = 10^{15}$, and log $K_{eq} = 15$. $\Delta E° = (0.059 \times 15)/2 = 0.44$ v.

3. When the two half reactions involve one and three electrons, respectively, $an_1 = bn_2 = 3$, and $a + b = 4$. $K_{eq} = (10^5)^4 = 10^{20}$, and log $K_{eq} = 20$. $\Delta E° = (0.059 \times 20)/3 = 0.39$ v.

4. When five electrons are transferred, $a + b = 6$, and $\Delta E° = (0.059 \times 30)/5 = 0.35$ v.

For cases in which the difference in the standard potentials is insufficient to give quantitative reaction, the actual or "working" potential of a half-reaction system may be changed by decreasing the concentration of a product or by use of an excess of reactant. For the half reactions

$$Fe^{+++} + e \rightleftarrows Fe^{++} \qquad E°_1 = +0.77\ v$$

$$\tfrac{1}{2}I_2 + e \rightleftarrows I^- \qquad E°_2 = +0.53\ v$$

the reaction and the difference in standard potentials are

$$Fe^{+++} + I^- \rightleftarrows Fe^{++} + \tfrac{1}{2}I_2 \qquad E°_1 - E°_2 = 0.24\ v$$

Log $K_{eq} = 0.24/0.059 \cong 4$, $K_{eq} = 10^4$, and $[Fe^{++}]/[Fe^{+++}] = 10^2$. The reaction is far from complete when equivalent amounts of Fe^{+++} and I^- are brought together. By the use of a large excess of iodide ion, or by the removal of iodine by extraction into an immiscible solvent such as carbon tetrachloride, the ratio of the concentrations iodine/iodide can be made very small, E for the iodine-iodide system is then less positive than $E°_2$, and the oxidation of I^- by Fe^{+++} is more complete. On the other hand, if fluoride ion is added to the mixture, it reacts with Fe^{+++} to form a very stable complex ion, FeF_6^{---}; at this very low concentration of Fe^{+++}, E for the ferric-ferrous system is less positive than $E°_1$; further, by the use of an excess of iodine, E for the iodine-iodide system is made more positive than $E°_2$. The effects of these changes are to reverse the relative positions of the two half-reaction "working" potentials, and make the oxidation of Fe^{++} by I_2 quantitative. The changes described above are exactly as would be predicted by application of the LeChatelier principle. The influence of various conditions on the potentials of redox couples is discussed in more detail in the following sections.

Influence of pH on Potentials

Half reactions may be considered in two general categories, with respect to the influence of *pH*.

1. Reactions in which there is no change in oxy-content of the reactant. Examples are the half reaction of a metal and its ions, such as $Cu^{++} + 2e \rightleftarrows Cu$, and the half reaction involving two different oxidation states of a simple ion, such as $Fe^{+++} + e \rightleftarrows Fe^{++}$, or $S + 2e \rightleftarrows S^{--}$. Reactions of these substances are very little influenced by the *pH* of the solution, unless a secondary reaction occurs between one of the components and H^+ or OH^-, as in the case of $S^{--} + H^+ \rightarrow HS^-$, or $Fe^{+++} + 3OH^- \rightarrow Fe(OH)_3$. If H^+ or OH^- is not involved in the half reaction, the potential is not *directly* influenced by *pH*, although changes in the hydrogen or hydroxyl ion concentration may influence the activities of the ions and change the potential somewhat on that account.

2. Reactions in which the oxy-content of a reactant changes, as in the following examples:

$$SO_4^{--} + 2H^+ + 2e \rightleftarrows SO_3^{--} + H_2O$$

$$Cr_2O_7^{--} + 14H^+ + 6e \rightleftarrows 2Cr^{+++} + 7H_2O$$

$$H_3AsO_4 + 2H^+ + 2e \rightleftarrows HAsO_2 + 2H_2O$$

Reactions of this type are markedly influenced by the *pH* of the solution. The Nernst equation for the dichromate-chromium(III) couple

$$E = E° - \frac{0.059}{6} \log \frac{[Cr^{+++}]^2}{[Cr_2O_7^{--}][H^+]^{14}}$$

shows that E is influenced as the fourteenth power of the hydrogen ion concentration. When $[H^+]$ is high (greater than $1\ M$), and the other ions are at standard state, E is more positive than $E°$, which has the effect of making dichromate ion a stronger oxidizing agent. Conversely, when $[H^+]$ is small (less than $1\ M$), E is less positive than $E°$, and dichromate ion is a weaker oxidizing agent than when $[H^+] = 1$.

The extent of reaction, and indeed in certain cases the direction of reaction, can be changed by merely changing the pH of the solution. $E°$ for the iodine-iodide half cell is $+0.534$ v; $E°$ for the arsenate-arsenite half cell is $+0.559$ v. When the reactants, including H^+, are at standard state, the reaction

$$2I^- + H_3AsO_4 + 2H^+ \rightleftarrows I_2 + HAsO_2 + 2H_2O$$

is very incomplete, because the difference in the $E°$ values is only 0.025 v. In strong acid solution, the potential of the arsenate-arsenite system is much more positive than its $E°$, and arsenate quantitatively oxidizes iodide ion to iodine. In a solution buffered with sodium bicarbonate, $[H^+]$ is very small, the potential of the arsenate-arsenite system is much less positive than its $E°$, and arsenite is quantitatively oxidized by iodine.

In some cases the pH influences the product that is formed. In acid solution, MnO_4^- is reduced to Mn^{++}, whereas in neutral or alkaline solution the reduction product is MnO_2; each of the half reactions concerned has its characteristic standard potential.

Influence of Precipitation

The precipitation of a metal ion by formation of a slightly soluble compound lowers the metal ion concentration to a very small value, and therefore changes the potential of the metal ion–metal electrode in the negative direction.

EXAMPLE 7

$E°$ of the Ag^+, Ag couple $= +0.799$ v. K_{sp} of AgCl $= 1.8 \times 10^{-10}$. Calculate $E°$ for the half cell represented by

$$AgCl + e \rightleftarrows Ag + Cl^-$$

In this half cell the standard state for chloride ion is $[Cl^-] = 1$; hence, $[Ag^+] = K_{sp}/[Cl^-] = 1.8 \times 10^{-10}$.

$$E = E° - 0.059 \log (1/[Ag^+]) = E° + 0.059 \log [Ag^+]$$

$$= 0.799 + 0.059(-9.74) = 0.799 - 0.576 = 0.224 \text{ v}$$

Because all components, AgCl, Ag, and Cl^-, are at standard state, this value is $E°$ for the reaction in question. This calculated value compares favorably with the value 0.2222 v given in $E°$ tables.

Electrodes of this type are often used for emf measurements from which the solubility products of slightly soluble ionogens are determined. The silver chloride electrode can be used as a reference electrode ($E° = 0.2222$ v when $[Cl^-] = 1$). It can also function as an indicator electrode for chloride ion, the potential changing from the standard value with change in $[Cl^-]$:

$$E = 0.2222 - 0.059 \log [Cl^-]$$

Other insoluble metal salt–metal electrodes can be used in a manner similar to the silver chloride–silver electrode.

Influence of Complex Formation

A decrease in metal ion concentration due to formation of complexes changes the potential of a metal ion–metal electrode in the negative direction from its $E°$ value.

EXAMPLE 8

Calculate $E°$ for the half cell

$$Cu(NH_3)_4^{++} + 2e \rightleftarrows Cu + 4NH_3$$

$E°$ of the Cu^{++}, Cu couple $= +0.337$ v. K_f of $Cu(NH_3)_4^{++} = 1.07 \times 10^{12}$. When both $Cu(NH_3)_4^{++}$ and NH_3 are at standard state (1 M), $[Cu^{++}] = 9.3 \times 10^{-13}$ (calculated from K_f). Hence,

$$E = E° - \frac{0.059}{2} \log \frac{1}{[Cu^{++}]} = E° + 0.0295 \log [Cu^{++}]$$

$$= 0.337 + 0.0295(-12.03) = 0.337 - 0.355 = -0.018 \text{ v}$$

($E°$ tables give a value of -0.05 v for this reaction).

Calculations of the above type are likely to give values somewhat different from the tabular values owing to the existence of intermediate complexes; the highest order complex is formed extensively only in the presence of a large excess of ligand. The calculations often are further complicated by the fact that slightly soluble intermediates may be formed (e.g., $Cu(OH)_2$ in the reaction of Cu^{++} with NH_3, or $Ni(CN)_2$ in the reaction of Ni^{++} with CN^-, etc.), and the K_{sp} of the slightly soluble ionogen is involved. A more common problem than that illustrated is the measurement of the emf of a suitably planned cell (electrodes and electrolyte components) in order to determine the concentration of the simple metal ion, from which the formation constant of a complex can be calculated; see Chap. 32.

Electron (Potential) Buffers

Solutions containing both the reduced and the oxidized forms of an ion are electron or potential buffers in that they contain both an electron donor and an electron acceptor. Addition of a small amount of either an oxidizing agent or a reducing agent to such a solution results in only a very small change in potential. In the titration of a reducing (or an oxidizing) agent, the titration curve is very flat around the half-titration point, where the reduced and the oxidized forms of the substance titrated are present in about equal concentrations. This fact is shown in the titration curve of Fig. 26-3. Near the half-titration point the solution contains about equal concentrations of Fe^{++} and Fe^{+++}, and moderate changes in the concentration ratio of these ions cause only small changes in the potential of the system. A redox buffered solution is said to be well "poised." The "redox poising capacity" (analogous to the buffer capacity of an acid-base system) is a measure of the rate of change of emf with change in the [Red]/[Ox] ratio.

Irreversible Electrode Reactions

Thermodynamically, a half-cell reaction is reversible if it can be made to proceed in either direction by an infinitesimal change of potential from its equilibrium value.[5] A change of potential will produce a flow of current; if the current drawn is very small in comparison to the current passing in both directions at equilibrium (the "exchange current"), the change of potential can be made so small as to be neglibible, although the attainment of a new equilibrium condition may be very slow.

In case the reduction (cathodic) half reaction is not the reverse of the oxidation (anodic) half reaction, a net chemical change is occurring at the electrode, and the potential of the electrode is not characteristic of either half reaction. For example, consider a cell consisting of metallic zinc and metallic platinum (inert) dipping into a solution of sulfuric acid. When it operates as a galvanic cell the reactions are:

at the Zn electrode, oxidation: $Zn \rightleftarrows Zn^{++} + 2e$　　　$E° = +0.76$ v

at the Pt electrode, reduction: $2H^+ + 2e \rightleftarrows H_2$　　　$E° = 0.00$ v

net reaction: $Zn + 2H^+ \rightarrow Zn^{++} + H_2$

When operating in the opposite direction, as an electrolytic cell, the reactions are:

at the Zn electrode, reduction: $2H^+ + 2e \rightleftarrows H_2$　　　$E° = 0.00$ v

at the Pt electrode, oxidation: $2H_2O \rightleftarrows 4H^+ + O_2 + 4e$　　　$E° = +1.23$ v

net reaction: $2H_2O \rightarrow 2H_2 + O_2$

The potential of the zinc electrode is not characteristic of the Zn^{++}, Zn system, but lies somewhere between that of the zinc system and that of the H^+, H_2 system; similar considerations apply to the potential of the platinum electrode.

---

[5] For a more complete discussion, see H. A. Laitinen, *Chemical Analysis*, New York, McGraw-Hill, 1960, pp. 293–296.

The definition of reversibility given at the beginning of this section is not conveniently subject to experimental test, and is not necessarily a valid basis for experimental test. The practical test of reversibility is conformity of the system to the relations expressed by the Nernst equation. A half-reaction system will never follow the Nernst equation when the oxidized and the reduced forms of the reactant in the half-reaction equation can form an intermediate species. For example, iodate and iodide can interact to form elemental iodine, an intermediate oxidation state of iodine. The potential of the half reaction

$$IO_3^- + 6H^+ + 6e \rightleftarrows I^- + 3H_2O \qquad E° = +1.08 \text{ v}$$

is a mixed potential, lying somewhere between the potential of the IO_3^-, I_2 system ($E° = +1.20$ v) and that of the I_2, I^- system ($E° = +0.53$ v), and the iodate-iodide system does not follow the Nernst equation with changes in the concentration of these reactants. Although the potential of the iodate-iodide half cell cannot be determined directly from cell emf data, it can be calculated from thermodynamic data, as illustrated in the next section.

In many of the irreversible half-cell reactions, the total reaction may proceed through the intermediate oxidation states, the formation and/or subsequent reaction of which may take place at different rates; sometimes the intermediate reaction or reactions may be autocatalytic or subject to promoter action of other ions present. Nevertheless, if the original and final states of the reactants are known (and the reaction proceeds fast enough for titrimetric application), the stoichiometry of the over-all reaction can be used for titrimetric calculations. For example, titration of oxalate in acid solution with permanganate is used to standardize a solution of the latter:

$$5H_2C_2O_4 + 2MnO_4^- + 6H^+ \rightarrow 10 CO_2 + 2Mn^{++} + 8H_2O$$

The half reaction

$$2CO_2 \text{ (gas)} + 2H^+ + 2e \leftarrow H_2C_2O_4 \qquad E° = -0.49 \text{ v}$$

is irreversible, that is, carbon dioxide in acid solution is not reducible to oxalic acid. A thorough study of the oxalate-permanganate reaction has shown that in the presence of oxygen, hydrogen peroxide is an intermediate in the oxidation of oxalate, and manganese oxidation states of 6, 4, and 3, some in the form of oxalato complexes, are formed as intermediates in the reduction of MnO_4^- to Mn^{++}. Titration under suitable conditions, however, proceeds according to the over-all $5H_2C_2O_4 : 2MnO_4^-$ stoichiometry.

Potentials of irreversible half-cell reactions are useful in the calculation of equilibrium constants. It should be recalled that an equilibrium constant depends on the initial and final species of reactants, and not upon the route or mechanism whereby the initial substances are converted to final products. However, use of mixed potentials of irreversible half reactions for predicting the behavior of electrodes should be applied cautiously.

DERIVATION OF HALF-CELL POTENTIALS
FROM OTHER HALF REACTIONS

By application of certain thermodynamic concepts it can be shown that for a redox couple,

$$RT \ln K = nFE^\circ_{cell} = -\Delta G^\circ$$

where ΔG° is the standard free energy change, and the other symbols represent the usual terms in the Nernst equation. By the IUPAC conventions, E° assumes that the given half cell is the right-hand electrode in a cell having the standard hydrogen electrode on the left; therefore, E°_{cell} is numerically equal to E° associated with the half reaction in question. Half reactions may be combined, by addition or subtraction, and the E° of the resulting half reaction can be calculated by adding or subtracting the free energy changes (nFE°) associated with the half reactions. Because F, the faraday number, is common to all the free energy changes, the calculations are simplified by the use of nE°, the dimensions of which are electron volts.

EXAMPLE 9

From the E° values of the Sn^{++}, Sn and the Sn^{4+}, Sn^{++} half cells, calculate E° of Sn^{4+}, Sn.

$$Sn^{4+} + 2e \rightleftarrows Sn^{++} \qquad E^\circ = +0.15 \text{ v} \qquad nE^\circ = +0.30 \text{ ev}$$
$$Sn^{++} + 2e \rightleftarrows Sn \qquad E^\circ = -0.14 \text{ v} \qquad nE^\circ = -0.28 \text{ ev}$$

Adding: $Sn^{4+} + 4e \rightarrow Sn,$ $nE^\circ = +0.02 \text{ ev}$

In the final half reaction, $n = 4$, therefore $E^\circ = +0.02 \text{ ev}/4e = +0.005$ v.

EXAMPLE 10

Calculate E° for the reduction of IO_3^- to I^- in acid solution.

$$IO_3^- + 6H^+ + 5e \rightleftarrows \tfrac{1}{2}I_2 + 3H_2O \qquad E^\circ = 1.195 \text{ v} \qquad nE^\circ = 5.975 \text{ ev}$$
$$\tfrac{1}{2}I_2 + e \quad \rightleftarrows I^- \qquad E^\circ = 0.536 \text{ v} \qquad nE^\circ = 0.536 \text{ ev}$$

Adding: $IO_3^- + 6H^+ + 6e \rightarrow I^- + 3H_2O$ $nE^\circ = 6.511 \text{ ev}$

But $n = 6$, therefore $E^\circ = 6.511 \text{ ev}/6e = 1.085$ v.

In both of the above examples the calculated E° is a mixed potential; the half cell represented by the final equation is irreversible, for reasons given in the previous section.

PROBLEMS

See Appendix V for standard potentials required.

26-1 For the cell formulated, calculate the cell emf (magnitude and sign), determine the polarity of the electrodes, and the direction of spontaneous cell reaction. Assume all substances are at standard state unless information to the contrary is given in the formulation. Use 0.059 for the Nernst constant. Parenthetical numbers are molar concentrations of the ions preceding the numbers.

(a) $Cu \mid Cu^{++} \parallel Ag^+ \mid Ag$.

(b) $Pt \mid Sn^{4+}, Sn^{++} \parallel Cr^{+++}, Cr^{++} \mid Pt$.

(c) $Sn \mid Sn^{++}(0.0010) \parallel Cu^{++}(0.010) \mid Cu$.

(d) $Pt \mid ClO_4^-(0.10), ClO_3^-(0.010), H^+(0.050) \parallel Fe^{+++}(0.10), Fe^{++}(0.0010) \mid Pt$.

(e) $Ni \mid Ni^{++} \parallel Zn^{++} \mid Zn$.

(f) $Cd \mid Cd^{++} \parallel H^+ \mid H_2 \mid Pt$.

(g) $Pt \mid Cr_2O_7^{--}, Cr^{+++}, H^+ \parallel Mn^{+++}, Mn^{++} \mid Pt$.

(h) $Co \mid Co^{++}(0.0050) \parallel Ni^{++} \mid Ni$.

(i) $Pt \mid VO^{++}(0.010), V^{+++}, H^+ \parallel Fe(CN)_6^{---}(0.010), Fe(CN)_6^{4-}(0.10) \mid Pt$.

(j) $Tl \mid Tl^+ \parallel Tl^{+++}, Tl^+ \mid Pt$.

(k) $Pt \mid I_3^-, I^-(0.010) \parallel Fe^{+++}(0.0010), Fe^{++} \mid Pt$.

          Ans. (a) $+0.462$ v. Cu (negative electrode) reduces Ag^+.

              (b) -0.56 v. Cr^{++} (at negative electrode) reduces Sn^{4+}.

              (c) $+0.502$ v. Sn (negative electrode) reduces Cu^{++}.

26-2 A solution of the cation given is treated with an excess of the metal indicated. Calculate (1) the equilibrium constant of the reaction; (2) the final concentration of the original cation.

(a) $0.020\ M\ Ag^+$ and metallic copper.   *Ans.* (a) (1) 5×10^{15}.   (2) $1.4 \times 10^{-9}\ M$.

(b) $0.010\ M\ Hg^{++}$ and metallic copper.

(c) $0.020\ M\ Cu^{++}$ and metallic lead.

(d) $0.050\ M\ Pb^{++}$ and metallic tin $(\rightarrow Sn^{++})$.

(e) $0.010\ M\ Ni^{++}$ and metallic cobalt $(\rightarrow Co^{++})$.

(f) $0.010\ M\ Cd^{++}$ and metallic zinc.

26-3 From the measured emf of the cell formulated, calculate the item indicated.

(a) $Zn \mid Zn^{++}(x\ M) \parallel Cu^{++}(0.10\ M) \mid Cu$.   emf $= 1.150$ v. Calculate x.

(b) $Cd \mid Cd^{++}(x\ M) \parallel Cu^{++}(y\ M) \mid Cu$.   emf $= 0.799$ v. Calculate x/y.

(c) $Cu \mid Cu^{++}(x\ M) \parallel Ag^+(0.10\ M) \mid Ag$.   emf $= 0.441$ v. Calculate x.

(d) $Cu \mid Cu^{++}(0.10\ M) \parallel Ag^+(x\ M) \mid Ag$.   emf $= 0.356$ v. Calculate x.

(e) $Zn \mid Zn^{++}(1\ M) \parallel Cu^{++}(x\ M) \mid Cu$.   emf $= 1.020$ v. Calculate x.

(f) $Pt \mid Fe^{+++}(x\ M), Fe^{++}(y\ M) \parallel Tl^{+++}(0.10\ M), Tl^+(0.010\ M) \mid Pt$.   emf $= 0.64$ v. Calculate the ratio x/y.   *Ans.* (a) 0.0020.   (b) 1/100.

26-4 In the following cases, assume that a 0.100 *molar* solution of the first substance is titrated with an *equivalent* (equi-*normal*) solution of the titrant; if H^+ is involved in the reaction, assume that the solution is buffered at $[H^+] = 1$. Calculate values for 10, 20, 50, 90, 95, 99, 100, 101, 105, and 110% of the stoichiometric amount of titrant, and plot E against percent titration. (All E-values are to be referred to the H^+–H_2 half cell $= 0.00$ v.)

(a) V^{++} titrated with Sn^{4+}, to give V^{+++} and Sn^{++}.

(b) Fe^{+++} titrated with Ti^{+++} to give Fe^{++} and TiO^{++}.

(c) Sn^{++} titrated with MnO_4^- (acid solution) to give Sn^{4+} and Mn^{++}.

(d) Sn^{++} titrated with Fe^{+++} to give Sn^{+4} and Fe^{++}.

(e) H_2SO_3 titrated with BrO_3^- (acid solution) to give SO_4^{--} and Br^-.

(f) $HAsO_2$ titrated with Ce^{4+} (H_2SO_4 solution) to give H_3AsO_4 and Ce^{+++}.

(g) H_2S titrated with Ce^{4+} (HCl solution) to give S and Ce^{+++}.

(*h*) Ti^{+++} titrated with $Fe(CN)_6^{---}$ (acid solution) to give TiO^{++} and $Fe(CN)_6^{4+}$·

Ans. (*a*) $-0.32, -0.30, -0.26, -0.20, -0.18, -0.14,$
$+0.01, +0.09, +0.11, +0.12$ v.

26-5 One milli*mole* of the first substance is mixed with an *equivalent* amount of the second substance in a final volume of 100 ml. If H^+ or OH^- is involved in the reaction, assume $[H^+] = 1$ or $[OH^-] = 1$. Calculate (1) the potential of the system (vs. standard hydrogen electrode); (2) the equilibrium constant of the reaction; (3) the molar concentration of the first-named substance remaining unreacted at equilibrium. If the reaction were carried out as a titration, what redox indicator (see Table 26-2) would be suitable?

(*a*) Fe^{++} and MnO_4^- ($\rightarrow Fe^{+++}$ and Mn^{++}).
(*b*) Cr^{++} and Fe^{+++} ($\rightarrow Cr^{+++}$ and Fe^{++}).
(*c*) Ag^{++} and Mn^{++} ($\rightarrow Ag^+$ and Mn^{+++}).
(*d*) Sn^{++} and Fe^{+++} ($\rightarrow Sn^{4+}$ and Fe^{++}).
(*e*) H_2SO_3 and BrO_3^- ($\rightarrow SO_4^{--}$ and Br^-).
(*f*) $HAsO_2$ and $Ce(SO_4)_2$ ($\rightarrow H_3AsO_4$ and Ce^{+++}).
(*g*) Ti^{+++} and $Fe(CN)_6^{---}$ ($\rightarrow TiO^{++}$ and $Fe(CN)_6^{4-}$).
(*h*) V^{++} and VO^{++} ($\rightarrow V^{+++}$).
(*i*) Mn^{++} and IO_4^- ($\rightarrow MnO_4^-$ and IO_3^-).

Ans. (*a*) 1.39 v. 5×10^{62}. 3.6×10^{-13}.

26-6 For each of the titrations of Problem 26-4, calculate the limits of values of $E°$ of a redox indicator so that the titration (indicator) error does not exceed $\pm 2\%_0$. Assume that the redox indicator changes color at 50% conversion from one form to the other.

26-7 What should be the $E°$ value of a redox indicator that undergoes a two-electron change and shows its oxidized color when 40% of the indicator is in the oxidized form, suitable for the titration of $Fe(CN)_6^{4-}$ by Ce^{4+} (sulfate solution)?

Ans. 0.905 v.

26-8 Calculate the titration (indicator) error (sign and magnitude) in the titration of Fe^{++} by Ce^{4+} (sulfate solution), assuming that the color change occurs when 50% of the indicator is in the oxidized form, if the indicator used is (*a*) 2,2'-bipyridine; (*b*) diphenylamine sulfonic acid.

26-9 For a certain half reaction

$$Ox_1 + ne \rightleftarrows Red_1 \qquad E°_1 = +0.23 \text{ v.}$$

For another half reaction

$$Ox_2 + 2e \rightleftarrows Red_2 \qquad E°_2 = -0.28 \text{ v.}$$

The equilibrium constant of the reaction of Ox_1 with Red_2 is 10^{52}. What is the value of *n*, the number of electrons in the first half reaction?   *Ans.* 3.

26-10 Given:

$$Ox_1 + e \rightleftarrows Red_1 \qquad E°_1 = 1.28 \text{ v.}$$

$$Ox_2 + ne \rightleftarrows Red_2 \qquad E°_2 = 0.49 \text{ v.}$$

The equilibrium constant of the reaction of Ox_1 with Red_2 is 10^{40}. Calculate *n*, the number of electrons in the second half reaction.

26-11   Given:

$$Ox_1 + e \rightleftarrows Red_1 \qquad E°_1 = 1.25 \text{ v.}$$

$$Ox_2 + 2e \rightleftarrows Red_2 \qquad E°_2 = \quad ?$$

The equilibrium constant of the reaction of Ox_1 with Red_2 is 5×10^{31}. Calculate the value of $E°_2$.

26-12   Use the half-reaction equations and the standard potentials of the half cells given, to derive the standard potential of the half cell indicated.

Half cells given	Derive $E°$ for
(a) ClO_3^-, Cl^-, H^+ and Cl_2, Cl^-	ClO_3^-, Cl_2, H^+
(b) Ag^{++}, Ag^+ and Ag^+, Ag	Ag^{++}, Ag
(c) UO_2^{++}, UO_2^+ and UO_2^+, U^{4+}	UO_2^{++}, U^{4+}
(d) MnO_4^-, MnO_2, H^+ and MnO_2, Mn^{++}, H^+	MnO_4^-, Mn^{++}, H^+
(e) PbO_2, Pb^{++}, H^+ and Pb^{++}, Pb	PbO_2, Pb, H^+
(f) NO_3^-, HNO_2, H^+ and HNO_2, NO, H^+	NO_3^-, NO, H^+
(g) H_2O_2, H_2O and O_2, H_2O_2, H^+	O_2, H_2O, H^+
(h) Fe^{+++}, Fe^{++} and Fe^{++}, Fe	Fe^{+++}, Fe

Ans. (a) $+1.47$ v.   (b) $+1.39$ v.

26-13   From the pH dependence of the potential of half reaction (1), calculate $E°$ for half reaction (2).

(a) (1) $MnO_4^- + 4H^+ + 3e \rightleftarrows MnO_2 + 2H_2O$

   (2) $MnO_4^- + 2H_2O + 3e \rightleftarrows MnO_2 + 4OH^-$ *Ans.* $+0.58$ v.

(b) (1) $BrO_3^- + 6H^+ + 6e \rightleftarrows Br^- + 3H_2O$

   (2) $BrO_3^- + 3H_2O + 6e \rightleftarrows Br^- + 6OH^-$

26-14   Equivalent amounts of H_3AsO_4 and $Fe(CN)_6^{4-}$ are mixed in solution.

(a) Calculate the equilibrium constant of the reaction.

(b) Calculate the ratio $[HAsO_2]/[H_3AsO_4]$ in a solution of pH 1.00, 5.00, 9.00.

(c) Under what circumstances and in which direction might this redox system be used titrimetrically? Explain.

26-15   In the reaction

$$H_3AsO_4 + 2H^+ + 3I^- \rightleftarrows HAsO_2 + I_3^- + 2H_2O$$

assume that the final concentration of I^- is 0.100 M and that the starch end point has been reached when I_3^- is 1.0×10^{-6} M.

(a) Calculate the ratio $[HAsO_2]/[H_3AsO_4]$ at pH 0.00, 2.00, 4.00, 9.00.

(b) What conditions of pH are required for quantitative oxidation of I^- by H_3AsO_4? oxidation of $HAsO_2$ by I_3^-?

27

PRELIMINARY REDOX
METHODS

Many elements can exist in more than one oxidation state; there are therefore many substances that can be determined by titrimetric redox reactions. Relatively few titrants are needed, because a strong oxidizing agent, for example potassium permanganate or cerium(IV) solution, can be used to titrate a large number of reducing agents; similarly, a strong reducing agent can be used for the determination of a large number of oxidizing agents. The former method is more widely used in practice, mainly because of the difficulty of storing standard solutions of strong reducing agents in such a way as to prevent their oxidation by atmospheric oxygen.

The oxidizing agents commonly used as titrants are potassium permanganate, potassium dichromate, cerium(IV) solutions, potassium bromate, and iodine. The reducing titrants most commonly used are ferrous solutions, sodium arsenite, sodium oxalate or oxalic acid, and sodium thiosulfate. Some well-known reagents, such as nitric acid, hydrochloric acid, chlorine, and hydrogen peroxide, are not used as titrants, because the solutions are not sufficiently stable and/or because they may not react according to a single stoichiometric reaction. However, these reagents (and others) may be used for preliminary oxidation or reduction of substances in preparation for titration by other reagents.

Some determinations are made indirectly by a sequence of redox reactions, rather than directly, usually in order to attain a satisfactory titrimetric end point. For example, the direct reaction of Cu^{++} with $Na_2S_2O_3$ is not suitable for titration; copper is determined by reaction of Cu^{++} with an excess of iodide to liberate iodine, which is then titrated with standard $Na_2S_2O_3$ solution.

389

A titrimetric redox determination requires that all of the desired constituent be in the appropriate oxidation state. Also, the solution to be titrated must not contain another substance, besides the desired constituent, that will react with the titrant, if the amount of titrant is to represent a single substance. (Occasionally one substance may be determined by difference, by carrying out two titrations, one in which two components are titrated and another in which only one of the components is in the proper oxidation state to react with the titrant.) The relative strengths of reagents in redox reactions are indicated by their standard potentials. However, the potential that can be attained is markedly influenced by concentration and by temperature, and often by the pH of the solution. Reaction *rate* may also be important; some reactions that have favorable equilibrium concentrations take place so slowly that they are not practical. Sometimes advantage can be taken of different rates of reaction in order to accomplish differential reductions or oxidations.

Reducing Agents

1. *Metals.* Because of the ease with which active metals lose electrons, they are good reducing agents. Selectivity in the reductions that can be accomplished is attained by judicious choice of the metal used. Metals may be in several forms, such as wire, sheet, granules, powder, and liquid amalgams; after reduction is complete, the excess metal is easily removed mechanically. Granular metals are often used in a reductor column, Fig. 27-1; the solution to be reduced

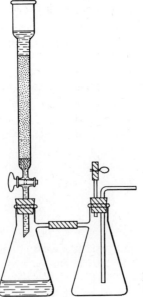

Fig. 27-1 Jones reductor.

is run slowly through the column and collected in the suction flask; the reduced solution is then titrated.

The **Jones reductor** uses zinc granules that have been amalgamated (alloyed with mercury) to decrease the reduction of hydrogen ion from the sulfuric acid solution of the sample. The **Walden reductor** uses metallic silver and 1 M hydrochloric acid. The reductions accomplished by zinc and by silver are shown in Table 27-1. Other metals used as reducing agents include aluminum, cadmium,

Table 27-1   Reductions by Zinc and by Silver

Oxidized Form	Reduced Form Produced by Zinc	Silver
Fe^{+++}	Fe^{++}	Fe^{++}
Ti^{4+}	Ti^{+++}	Not reduced
Ce^{4+}	Ce^{+++}	Ce^{+++}
MnO_4^-	Mn^{++}	Mn^{++}
$Cr_2O_7^{--}$	Cr^{++}	Cr^{+++}
MoO_4^{--}	Mo^{+++}	MoO^{+++}
VO_3^-	V^{++}	VO^{++}
UO_2^{++}	U^{4+} and U^{+++}	U^{4+} only
Cu^{++}	Cu	Cu^+ (as $CuCl_3^{--}$)

lead, bismuth, and sodium; the last three are used in the form of their liquid amalgams. Liquid amalgams are used by shaking the solution to be reduced and the amalgam in a separatory funnel, then drawing off the excess amalgam. Sodium amalgam gives rapid reduction at room temperature without introducing any heavy metal ion into the solution.

2. *Stannous chloride* is comparable in reducing strength to silver. A common use is for reducing Fe^{+++} to Fe^{++} in the determination of iron (see p. 398).

3. *Ferrous salts*, which are mild reducing agents, are usually added either as a measured volume of standard solution or as a weighed amount of pure $FeSO_4 \cdot (NH_4)_2SO_4 \cdot 6H_2O$. The amount of the excess is then determined by titration with an oxidizing agent.

4. *Sulfur dioxide*, or a *sulfite in acid solution*, is a mild reducing agent, effecting reductions similar to those with silver. It is advantageous because no heavy metal ion is introduced into the sample, and the excess sulfur dioxide can be removed either by boiling the acid solution or by displacement by bubbling carbon dioxide through the solution.

5. *Hydrogen sulfide* is comparable to sulfur dioxide in reducing strength and in method of removing excess. It is not recommended if the solution to be reduced contains cations the sulfides of which are insoluble in acid.

6. *Sodium hyposulfite*, $Na_2S_2O_4$, is a strong reducing agent, especially in alkaline solution. Excess reagent is removed by boiling the acidified solution:

$$2HS_2O_4^- + 2H^+ + H_2O \rightarrow H_2S_2O_3 + 2H_2SO_3$$
$$H_2S_2O_3 \rightarrow S + H_2SO_3$$
$$H_2SO_3 \rightarrow H_2O + SO_2$$

7. *Hydrochloric acid* (concentrated) is used as a reducing agent principally for the dissolution of higher oxides of lead and manganese:

$$MO_2 + 2Cl^- + 4H^+ \rightarrow M^{++} + Cl_2 + 2H_2O \qquad (M = Pb \text{ or } Mn)$$

Most of the excess hydrochloric acid can be removed by evaporation nearly to dryness; complete removal is effected by fuming down with sulfuric acid.

Miscellaneous reducing agents include chromium(II) chloride, hydrazine, and hypophosphorous acid and hypophosphites. A mixture of hypophosphorous and hydriodic acids is a very potent reducing agent, and will reduce sulfate ion quantitatively to hydrogen sulfide.

Oxidizing Agents

1. *Perchloric acid*, $HClO_4$, when both hot and concentrated, is one of the most powerful oxidizing agents. It is often used for dissolution of alloy steels; chromium and vanadium are oxidized to their highest oxidation numbers. A particular advantage in using perchloric acid is that its oxidizing action can be quenched merely by diluting and/or cooling; the diluted solution must be boiled to remove dissolved chlorine which was formed as the reduction product.

2. *Peroxydisulfate* [$K_2S_2O_8$ or $(NH_4)_2S_2O_8$] is one of the very powerful oxidizing agents, but its action is generally slow unless catalyzed by a small amount of silver ion. The mechanism of the catalytic action has been explained as due to the oxidation of Ag^+ to a higher oxidation state, which is then rapidly reduced to Ag^+ by the substance being oxidized.[1] Peroxydisulfate is useful for the oxidation of manganese(II) to permanganate, for subsequent titrimetric or colorimetric determination, and for the oxidation of carbon in the dissolution of steel samples. Excess peroxydisulfate is destroyed by boiling the solution:

$$S_2O_8^{--} + 2H_2O \rightarrow 2H^+ + 2SO_4^{--} + H_2O_2$$
$$2H_2O_2 \rightarrow 2H_2O + O_2$$

3. *Potassium periodate*, KIO_4, finds its principal use in the oxidation of manganese(II) to permanganate for colorimetric determination.[2] When necessary, removal of periodate is accomplished by adding mercury(II) to precipitate the paraperiodate, $Hg_5(IO_6)_2$.

---

[1] D. M. Yost, *J. Am. Chem. Soc.*, **48**, 152 (1926).
[2] H. H. Willard and L. H. Greathouse, *J. Am. Chem. Soc.*, **39**, 2366 (1917).

4. *Sodium bismuthate*, $NaBiO_3$, is also used for oxidation of manganese(II) to permanganate; the insoluble $NaBiO_3$ is removed by filtration through an inert filter, such as sintered glass.

5. *Potassium chlorate*, $KClO_3$, in acid solution or in alkaline fusions, is a strong oxidizing agent. Following its use, the excess is destroyed by boiling with excess hydrochloric acid:

$$ClO_3^- + 5Cl^- + 6H^+ \rightarrow 3Cl_2 + 3H_2O$$

6. *Potassium permanganate*, $KMnO_4$, in addition to use as an oxidation titrant, can be used for effecting preliminary oxidations. It is a strong oxidizing agent in either acidic or neutral solution. The excess is removed by reducing it with $NaNO_2$ or NaN_3.

7. *Hydrogen peroxide*, H_2O_2, is not only a powerful oxidizing agent but also a mild reducing agent. It is an attractive oxidizing agent because its use introduces no foreign ions into the solution, and the excess is easily destroyed by boiling the solution:

$$2H_2O_2 \rightarrow 2H_2O + O_2$$

8. *Silver(II) oxide*, Ag_2O_2, in acid solution is useful for oxidizing manganese(II) to permanganate, chromium(III) to dichromate, and cerium(III) to cerium(IV), at room temperature. Excess reagent is removed by heating the solution:

$$4Ag^{++} + 2H_2O \rightarrow O_2 + 4H^+ + 4Ag^+$$

9. *Ozone*, O_3, can be prepared in low yield by passing oxygen gas through a glass tube across the walls of which a silent electric discharge is maintained. No foreign ions are introduced, and the excess is removed by boiling the solution to decompose ozone to oxygen. Ozone is also a valuable reagent in organic chemistry.

10. *Nitric acid* can give a variety of reduction products (NO_2, NO, N_2O, etc.); the product formed depends upon the strength of the reducing agent, the nitric acid concentration, and the temperature. Its principal use is for the dissolution of samples such as inactive metals and very insoluble sulfides, that are not attacked by hydrochloric acid. The oxidation products will be found in their higher oxidation states, such as SO_4^{--}, Fe(III), Cu(II), Sn(IV), and Sb(V). Excess nitric acid is removed by repeated evaporation of the solution with hydrochloric acid:

$$2NO_3^- + 2Cl^- + 4H^+ \rightarrow 2NO_2 + Cl_2 + 2H_2O$$

11. *Halogens.* Chlorine and bromine find some use for effecting preliminary oxidations; the excess of the element is removed by boiling the acidic solution. Iodine is a rather weak oxidizing agent; however, it is used extensively as a titrant for strong reducing agents; see Chap. 29.

Summary

Table 27-2 summarizes the reagents that have been discussed in this chapter; the reagents are listed in order from strongest oxidizing agent to strongest reducing agent as represented by the standard electrode potential.

Table 27-2   Summary of Reagents Used for Oxidation or Reduction Prior to Titration

Oxidizing Agent	Reduction Product	$E°$, v	Method of Removal of Excess Reagent
Ozone, O_3	O_2	+2.07	Boil acid solution
$K_2S_2O_8$	SO_4^{--}	2.01	Boil to decompose H_2O_2
$HClO_4$ (hot conc.)	Cl_2	2.	Dilute with water, boil out Cl_2
Ag_2O_2	Ag^+	2.	Boil the solution
H_2O_2	H_2O	1.77	Boil acid solution
KIO_4	IO_3^-	1.7	Precipitate as $Hg_5(IO_6)_2$
$KMnO_4$ (low H^+)	MnO_2	1.695	Add $NaNO_2$ or NaN_3; filter off MnO_2
$NaBiO_3$	Bi^{+++}	1.59	Filter off excess
$KBrO_3$	Br_2	1.52	Add HCl, boil out halogens
$KMnO_4$ (high H^+)	Mn^{++}	1.51	Add $NaNO_2$ or NaN_3
$KClO_3$	Cl_2	1.47	Add HCl, boil out Cl_2
HNO_3	NO	0.96	Evaporate with excess HCl
HNO_3	NO_2	0.80	Evaporate with excess HCl
Reducing Agent	Oxidation Product		
HCl (conc.)	Cl_2	1.36	Evaporate; or displace with H_2SO_4
Fe^{++} salts	Fe^{+++}	0.77	Back titration
Silver (HCl)	AgCl	0.222	Mechanical removal of metal
SO_2, H_2SO_3	SO_4^{--}	0.20	Boil, or displace with CO_2
$SnCl_2$	Sn^{4+}	0.15	Add $HgCl_2$ to oxidize Sn^{++}
H_2S	S	0.14	Boil, or displace with CO_2
$Na_2S_2O_4$ (H^+)	H_2SO_3	−0.08	Boil acid solution
Zinc (H_2SO_4)	Zn^{++}	−0.76	Mechanical removal of metal
$Na_2S_2O_4$ (OH^-)	SO_3^{--}	−1.12	Acidify and boil solution

QUESTIONS

See Appendix V for standard potentials.

27-1   An alloy containing iron, titanium, and vanadium is dissolved in hot concentrated perchloric acid.

(*a*) In what form is each component now present?

(*b*) In what ionic form is each component present after use of a zinc reductor? a lead reductor? a silver (HCl) reductor?

(*c*) Outline a method whereby each component in the mixture can be determined by differential reduction followed by titration with an oxidant. Include information regarding calculation of results.

27-2 What reagent can be used to carry out the following change? Write appropriate ionic equations.

(*a*) Reduce vanadium(IV) to vanadium(III) without further reduction of the latter.

(*b*) Reduce vanadium(V) to vanadium(IV) without further reduction of the latter.

(*c*) Reduce iron(III) but not chromium(III) or titanium(IV).

(*d*) Reduce titanium(IV) and vanadium(IV) but not chromium(III).

(*e*) Oxidize iron(II) without oxidizing chromium(III).

(*f*) Oxidize chromium(III) but not cobalt(II).

28

PERMANGANATE METHODS

The wide application of permanganate is due to the fact that it is a very strong oxidizing agent, and it serves as its own indicator. For most applications, permanganate is used in acid solution, giving Mn^{++} as the reduction product. For some applications, however, it is used in nearly neutral solution or in alkaline solution, giving MnO_2 as the reduction product. In the presence of F^- or $P_2O_7^{4-}$, complexes of manganese(III) are formed. When used for the oxidation of organic compounds in alkaline solution in the presence of barium ion, reduction occurs only to manganate ion, MnO_4^{--}, which is precipitated as $BaMnO_4$. The reduction of MnO_4^- to Mn^{++} is a very complex process involving the formation of intermediate oxidation states of manganese; however, if the conditions are adjusted to give Mn^{++} as the final reduction product, the proper stoichiometry between permanganate and the reducing agent will be obtained, regardless of the mechanism of the reaction.

In neutral solution potassium permanganate slowly decomposes:

$$4MnO_4^- + 2H_2O \rightarrow 4MnO_2 + 4OH^- + 3O_2$$

and acidic solutions are even less stable. The reaction is autocatalyzed by manganese dioxide. Traces of reducing substances in the distilled water used to make the solution reduce permanganate to manganese dioxide, which catalyzes further decomposition. Decomposition of permanganate solution is also accelerated by light. The solution is therefore prepared by boiling the solution for about one-half hour to complete the oxidation of reducing substances in the water. After standing overnight or longer to allow the manganese dioxide to settle, the solution is filtered through a sintered glass filter, and then stored in a dark bottle. A 0.1 N solution prepared and stored in this way is quite stable if protected from dust and reducing vapors.

Standardization

Sodium oxalate and arsenic(III) oxide are the most reliable primary standards for general use; some other standards mentioned below have special applications.

1. *Sodium oxalate*, $Na_2C_2O_4$, (called "Sørensen" sodium oxalate) in acid solution is oxidized to carbon dioxide:

$$HC_2O_4^- \rightarrow 2CO_2 + H^+ + 2e$$

The reaction with permanganate, which has an induction period of several seconds, is autocatalyzed by manganese(II). It is important to observe certain rules and precautions in the standardization procedure.

a. The oxalate should be titrated promptly after the solid is dissolved.

b. The solution should be about 1 to 1.5 N in sulfuric acid.

c. The oxalate solution should be heated to 80–90°C for titration, which must be completed in solution which is above 60°C.

d. The permanganate should be added with good mixing (see *e*); accumulation of a large localized excess may result in the formation of a dark precipitate (MnO_2), due to local depletion of hydrogen ion. This is a general precaution for *all* permanganate titrations.

e. In the presence of air, some oxalate may be converted to percarbonic acid, $H_2C_2O_6$, which decomposes into carbon dioxide and hydrogen peroxide. Although hydrogen peroxide and oxalate ion have the same equivalency toward permanganate, vigorous shaking or stirring should be avoided lest some hydrogen peroxide be decomposed by disproportionation.

f. The permanganate solution should be added directly into the solution being titrated—not down the sides of the titration vessel. This is a general precaution for all permanganate titrations.

g. A blank test must always be made in permanganate titrations.

The compounds $H_2C_2O_4 \cdot 2H_2O$, $KHC_2O_4 \cdot H_2C_2O_4 \cdot 2H_2O$, and KHC_2O_4 can serve as sources of oxalate ion as a reducing agent. The relative merits of these compounds as primary standards have been discussed previously (see p. 317).

2. *Arsenic(III) oxide*, As_2O_3, dissolves only slowly in water, but readily in 2 N sodium hydroxide:

$$As_2O_3 + 2OH^- \rightarrow 2AsO_2^- + H_2O$$

The arsenite solution is acidified and then titrated.

3. *Iron.* Metallic iron for standardizing is available in the form of soft iron wire of 99.99% purity. Iron prepared by electrodeposition, or by decomposition of iron carbonyl, $Fe(CO)_5$, is of even higher purity. Before weighing, iron wire or electrolytic iron must be cleaned from surface corrosion (iron oxide). The metal is dissolved in dilute sulfuric acid; evolution of hydrogen gas and blanketing with carbon dioxide or nitrogen ensure that the iron is in the ferrous condition. After dilution and adjustment of acidity, the solution is titrated with

permanganate. If the permanganate is to be used solely for analysis of iron ores, standardization against National Bureau of Standards iron ore is recommended.

4. *Ferrous ammonium sulfate hexahydrate* (*Mohr's salt*), $FeSO_4 \cdot (NH_4)_2SO_4 \cdot 6H_2O$, formerly used as a primary standard, has the advantages of very high equivalent weight and water solubility. Although at present it does not have official status as a primary standard, the analytical reagent grade chemical in the form of fine crystals uniformly light green in color usually assays for the theoretical iron(II) content, within the accuracy of student work. *Ferrous ethylenediammonium sulfate tetrahydrate* (Oesper's salt), $Fe[C_2H_4(NH_3)_2](SO_4)_2 \cdot 4H_2O$, has also been proposed as a primary standard.

5. *Potassium hexacyanoferrate(II) trihydrate*, $K_4Fe(CN)_6 \cdot 3H_2O$, has as its chief merit a high equivalent weight. The amber color of the hexacyanoferrate-(III) formed makes impossible the observation of the first excess of permanganate; redox indicators, such as diphenylamine or iron(II) phenanthroline, or a potentiometric method may be used.

6. *Silver*, in the form of fine powder prepared in nonoxidizing conditions, can be used indirectly by treating a weighed amount of the silver with a saturated solution of ferric alum:

$$Ag + Fe^{+++} \rightarrow Ag^+ + Fe^{++}$$

and titrating the iron(II) in acid solution with the permanganate.

DETERMINATION OF IRON

Metallic iron and any iron compound can easily be brought to the ferrous condition for titration; many other strong reducing agents can be determined indirectly by reaction with excess ferric salt, followed by titration of the ferrous ion formed. Analysis of iron ore by the Zimmermann-Reinhardt method is discussed below in some detail, especially with reference to the functions of the components of the Zimmermann-Reinhardt "titrating solution" and their relation to the various half-reaction systems involved.

1. Dissolution. Iron ores are best dissolved in concentrated hydrochloric acid; dissolution of the oxide ores is facilitated by the addition of tin(II) chloride.

2. Reduction. Although many different methods can be used to reduce iron(III) to iron(II), the Zimmermann-Reinhardt method uses tin(II) chloride. The solution for reduction should be of small volume, rather concentrated in hydrochloric acid, and hot. Tin(II) chloride is added dropwise, to the disappearance of the yellow color of Fe^{+++}:

$$2Fe^{+++} + Sn^{++} \rightarrow 2Fe^{++} + Sn^{4+}$$

No more than two or three drops of excess tin(II) chloride should be used (see step 3 below). The mixture is then cooled and diluted.

3. Removal of Excess Reductant.   The slight excess of tin(II) chloride used in step 2 is removed by rapid addition of excess mercury(II) chloride:

$$Sn^{++} + 2HgCl_2 \rightarrow Sn^{4+} + 2Cl^- + Hg_2Cl_2$$

The insoluble mercurous chloride is not readily oxidized by permanganate and need not be removed. The Hg_2Cl_2 usually appears as a "silky" precipitate. If no precipitate or turbidity appears, insufficient tin(II) chloride was used in the reduction step, and the analysis must be started over. If too much tin(II) chloride was used, it will further reduce the Hg_2Cl_2 to free mercury, which will act as a reducing agent during titration and require more permanganate than is equivalent to the iron. If addition of mercury(II) chloride gives a gray or black precipitate (free mercury) the sample must be discarded.

4. Titration.   To the solution from step 3, "titrating solution" (H_2SO_4, H_3PO_4, and $MnSO_4$) is added, and the mixture is titrated with permanganate to the first permanent pink tinge. Sulfuric acid provides the necessary hydrogen ion, to ensure the reduction of permanganate to manganese(II); if the acidity is too low, some reduction of MnO_2 may occur; if the acidity is too high, the danger of oxidation of chloride ion is increased and the end point is somewhat indistinct. Phosphoric acid complexes the iron(III), forming colorless $Fe(PO_4)_2^{---}$, so that the pink tinge marking the end point is easily observed. Removal of Fe^{+++} by complex formation also makes ferrous ion in effect a stronger reducing agent, thus ensuring its complete oxidation by permanganate. The iron in the solution induces the oxidation of chloride ion, but this reaction is effectively blocked by the presence of a high concentration of manganous sulfate in the solution. The mechanism of the effect of Mn^{++} is quite complex;[1] in oxidations with permanganate, intermediate oxidation states of manganese (VI, IV, III) are involved. The potential of the Mn^{+++}, Mn^{++} couple is markedly influenced by the presence of other ions (e.g., phosphate, sulfate) that form complexes with one or both of these oxidation states. In addition to its direct effect on the potential of this couple, a high concentration of manganese(II) may be needed to ensure conversion of the higher oxidation states of manganese to manganese(III), which oxidizes iron(II) rather than chloride ion.

The solution to be titrated should be cold, to minimize the danger of atmospheric oxidation of iron(II), and also to minimize the possibility of oxidation of chloride ion by permanganate. The permanganate should be added slowly and with good stirring. A blank determination, carried through all steps with the same amounts of reagents, should always be made.

Some analysts prefer to avoid the possibility of oxidation of chloride ion by working in chloride-free solutions. After dissolution of the ore in hydrochloric

---

[1] For a detailed discussion, see H. A. Laitinen, *Chemical Analysis*, New York, McGraw-Hill, 1960, pp. 369–372.

acid, the solution is fumed down with sulfuric acid to expel the excess hydro-chloric acid. Reduction of the iron(III) is then effected with zinc or cadmium, and the iron(II) is titrated with permanganate. Phosphoric acid must be added before titration, to suppress the color of iron(III) formed.

SUMMARY OF ADDITIONAL DETERMINATIONS

There are many and varied substances that can be determined directly or indirectly with permanganate; several of these determinations are outlined below. In cases where the equation is not given, it is recommended that the student write the ion-electron half-reaction equation and combine it with the half-reaction equation for the reduction of permanganate to obtain the over-all equation.

Direct Determinations

1. In Acidic Solution. Most of the titrations with permanganate are made in acid solution, with the formation of manganese(II) as the reduction product. (The few exceptions will be treated later.) Determination of the following substances requires no special treatment or precautions other than have been discussed previously.

Substance Titrated	Oxidation Product
$C_2O_4^{--}$	CO_2
$Fe(CN)_6^{4-}$	$Fe(CN)_6^{---}$
As(III)	As(V)
Sb(III)	Sb(V)
H_2O_2, peroxides and percarbonates	O_2
SO_2, SO_3^{--}	SO_4^{--}
H_2S and soluble sulfides	S
HCNS	SO_4^{--} ($+HCN$)
NO_2^-	NO_3^-

The following determinations are discussed in more detail because of special applications and/or special conditions required.

a. Titanium is often associated with iron in iron ores, and is present in many ferrous metallurgical products. The dioxide, TiO_2, is a widely-used paint base and white pigment. Titanium determination is therefore required frequently. If, in the determination of iron, reduction is effected by zinc or cadium, both iron(III) and titanium(IV) are reduced, and both iron(II) and titanium(III) are titrated by permanganate. By use of a weaker reducing agent, for example silver, titanium(IV) is not reduced, and titration gives only the iron. The differential reduction makes possible the determination of titanium by difference. Titanium(III) can also be titrated directly with a standard iron(III) solution, using thiocyanate indicator, or with standard methylene blue solution, which is reduced to its colorless leuco form.

b. Vanadium. For the determination of vanadium in steel, the sample is dissolved under oxidizing conditions, giving HVO_3, metavanadic acid. Passage of the solution through a Jones reductor reduces the vanadic acid to vanadium-(II). Although vanadium(II) can be titrated directly with permanganate:

$$V^{++} + 3H_2O \rightarrow HVO_3 + 5H^+ + 3e$$

it is so easily oxidized that special precautions must be used. By the use of sulfur dioxide or bismuth amalgam, vanadium(V) is reduced only to vanadium(IV), which is then titrated:

$$VO^{++} + 2H_2O \rightarrow HVO_3 + 3H^+ + e$$

Vanadium is also determined by titrimetric reduction of HVO_3 to VO^{++} (vanadyl ion) with standard ferrous solution. An indirect method of determination of vanadium will be given later.

c. Uranium. By passage through a Jones reductor, uranium(VI) (i.e., uranyl ion, UO_2^{++}) solutions are reduced to a mixture of uranium(III) and uranium(IV) (i.e., UO^{++}). A rapid stream of air bubbled through the solution for several minutes oxidizes all the uranium(III) to uranium(IV), which is then titrated with permanganate:

$$UO^{++} + H_2O \rightarrow UO_2^{++} + 2H^+ + 2e$$

d. Metallic iron in the presence of iron oxide. A reagent must be used that reacts with metallic iron but not with iron oxide, to give Fe^{++} for titration. Most often, the sample is treated with excess ferric alum solution:

$$Fe + 2Fe^{+++} \rightarrow 3Fe^{++}$$

and the Fe^{++} is titrated. (What is the equivalent of iron in this determination?)

e. Manganese. In the presence of fluoride ion or pyrophosphate ion to form stable complexes of manganese(III), manganese(II) is oxidized to manganese-(III), which is also the reduction product of the permanganate titrant. Manganese ores, such as pyrolusite, MnO_2, are dissolved in concentrated hydrochloric acid:

$$MnO_2 + 4H^+ + 2Cl^- \rightarrow Mn^{++} + 2H_2O + Cl_2$$

in preparation for titration. In the fluoride method, ammonium fluoride is added; the titration reaction is

$$4Mn^{++} + MnO_4^- + 8H^+ + 25F^- \rightarrow 5MnF_5^{--} + 4H_2O$$

In the pyrophosphate method, the solution is saturated with sodium pyrophosphate, and the pH is adjusted to between 4 and 7; the titration reaction is

$$4Mn^{++} + MnO_4^- + 15H_2P_2O_7^{--} + 8H^+ \rightarrow 5Mn(H_2P_2O_7)_3^{---} + 4H_2O$$

Potentiometric detection of the end point is generally used.

2. In Approximately Neutral Solution. Under these conditions MnO_2 is the reduction product of permanganate.

Manganese by Volhard Method. This is the only common titrimetric method in which permanganate is reduced to manganese(IV), which is also the oxidation product of the manganese(II) titrated. The stoichiometry of the titration reaction may be represented by

$$3Mn^{++} + 2MnO_4^- + 2H_2O \rightarrow 5MnO_2 + 4H^+$$

However, reliable results are not obtained unless special precautions and additives are used. Excess acid from dissolution of the manganese ore is nearly neutralized with alkali. Zinc sulfate and a suspension of zinc oxide in water are added; the pH is then sufficient to precipitate the hydrous oxides of iron(III), titanium-(IV), etc., that may be present. Titration of the solution with permanganate gives a dark brown to black precipitate of $Zn(HMnO_3)_2$ which, near the end point of the titration, coagulates well and settles rapidly, allowing observation of the first excess of permanganate that marks the end point. Usually, a large sample is taken, and after buffering with zinc oxide, the solution is made to known volume and aliquots are taken for titration.

3. In Alkaline Solution. Many oxidations with alkaline permanganate, although stoichiometric, are too slow to permit direct titration; an excess of standard permanganate is used, and after allowing 15–20 minutes for completion of the reaction, the excess permanganate is determined. By this method the lower oxidation states of sulfur are oxidized to sulfate.

In solutions 1 to 2 N in sodium hydroxide and in the presence of barium ion, the reduction product is manganate ion, which is precipitated as $BaMnO_4$.[2] An excess of standard permanganate is used, and the excess is then titrated with standard sodium formate solution. By this method iodide and iodate are oxidized to periodate, cyanide to cyanate, thiocyanate to cyanate and sulfate, and phosphite to phosphate. Many organic substances, especially aldehydes and polyhydroxy compounds, are completely oxidized to carbon dioxide and water.

Indirect Determinations

1. *Cations that form insoluble oxalates.* The metal oxalate is precipitated quantitatively, is filtered off and washed free from soluble oxalate used as the

[2] H. Stamm, *Angew. Chem.*, **47**, 191 (1934); **48**, 710 (1935).

precipitant, and is dissolved in sulfuric acid:

$$MC_2O_4 + H^+ \rightarrow M^{++} + HC_2O_4^-$$

The $HC_2O_4^-$ is then titrated in the usual way. The method is commonly applied to the determination of calcium in limestone analysis; it is also applicable to the determination of Sr^{++}, Mg^{++}, Pb^{++}, Cd^{++}, Zn^{++}, Ni^{++}, Co^{++}, Bi^{+++}, and to the rare earths La^{+++}, Ce^{4+}, etc.

2. *Substances that reduce iron(III) to iron(II).* The reducing agent is treated with an excess of ferric salt solution, the concentration of which need not be known; the iron(II) formed is titrated with permanganate. The following examples will illustrate.

a. *Titanium.* Titanium(IV) solution is reduced by passage through a Jones reductor. The titanium(III) solution is received in an excess of ferric chloride or ferric alum solution:

$$Ti^{+++} + Fe^{+++} \rightarrow Ti^{4+} + Fe^{++}$$

The Fe^{++}, which is equivalent to the titanium in the original solution, is titrated with permanganate.

b. *Vanadium.* Upon passage through a Jones reductor, a solution of vanadic acid, HVO_3, is reduced to V^{++}: the solution is received in ferric alum solution:

$$V^{++} + 2Fe^{+++} + H_2O \rightarrow VO^{++} + 2Fe^{++} + 2H^+$$

The vanadyl ion, VO^{++}, *and also the* Fe^{++}, are titrated with permanganate to HVO_3 and Fe^{+++}, respectively. In terms of the equivalency of vanadium, the over-all effect is the same as if V^{++} were titrated directly to HVO_3.

3. *Substances that oxidize iron(II), arsenic(III), and oxalate.* In these determinations a measured excess of the reducing agent (iron(II), etc.) is allowed to react with the oxidizing agent, and the amount of the excess reductant is determined by permanganate titration. The method is applicable to the higher oxides such as PbO_2, Pb_3O_4, and MnO_2, peroxydisulfate, nitrate (reduced to nitric oxide), oxyhalogen compounds (reduced to halide), etc. The following reactions are illustrative:

$$MnO_2 + 2H^+ + HAsO_2 \rightarrow Mn^{++} + H_3AsO_4$$
$$S_2O_8^{--} + 2Fe^{++} \rightarrow 2SO_4^{--} + 2Fe^{+++}$$
$$2NO_3^- + 8H^+ + 3C_2O_4^{--} \rightarrow 2NO + 6CO_2 + 4H_2O$$

4. *Sodium.* The sodium ion is precipitated as $NaZn(UO_2)_3(C_2H_3O_2)_9 \cdot 6H_2O$, which is filtered off and washed, then dissolved in sulfuric acid and the solution passed through a Jones reductor. The uranium is then determined as in item 1c under Direct Determinations. (What is the equivalent of sodium in this determination?)

5. *Potassium.* Potassium ion is precipitated as $K_2NaCo(NO_2)_6$, which is filtered and washed, then dissolved in a measured excess of acidified permanganate:

$$K_2NaCo(NO_2)_6 + 6H_2O \rightarrow 2K^+ + Na^+ + Co^{++} + 6NO_3^- + 12H^+ + 11e$$

The excess permanganate is back titrated. (What is the equivalent of potassium in this determination?)

PROBLEMS

28-1 Calculate the normality of $KMnO_4$ solution from the data given; assume that blank corrections have been made.

Primary standard	ml $KMnO_4$
(a) 0.3378 g $Na_2C_2O_4$	43.45
(b) 0.2471 g As_2O_3	40.80
(c) 0.2290 g Fe	41.50
(d) 1.0570 g KIO_3	36.60
(e) 0.2750 g $H_2C_2O_4 \cdot 2H_2O$	40.67
(f) 0.8844 g $K_4Fe(CN)_6 \cdot 3H_2O$	42.64
(g) 0.8000 g $Fe(NH_4)_2(SO_4)_2 \cdot 6H_2O$	41.75
(h) 0.2500 g Fe	47.48
(i) 0.6800 g KIO_3	38.33
(j) 0.4260 g Ag	43.16

Ans. (a) 0.11604. (b) 0.12245.

28-2 What weight of $KHC_2O_4 \cdot H_2C_2O_4 \cdot 2H_2O$ must be mixed with 1.0000 g of $Na_2C_2O_4$ so that the normality of the solution as a reducing agent is twice its normality as an acid?   *Ans.* 1.8970 g.

28-3 A solution of $KHC_2O_4 \cdot H_2C_2O_4 \cdot 2H_2O$ is 0.1200 N as an acid; 36.00 ml of the tetroxalate solution require 40.00 ml of $KMnO_4$ for titration. Calculate the normality of the $KMnO_4$.   *Ans.* 0.1440.

28-4 What is the ratio of the normalities of solutions of $Ba(OH)_2$ and $KMnO_4$ if the same volume of the solution is required to titrate the same weight of potassium tetroxalate dihydrate?   *Ans.* $N\ Ba(OH)_2/N\ KMnO_4 = 3/4$.

28-5 A 0.7500-g sample of iron ore is dissolved, reduced, and titrated with 35.70 ml of $KMnO_4$. In standardizing the $KMnO_4$, 47.84 ml are used in titrating a 1.5000-g sample of Mohr's salt which contains 14.25% iron. Calculate the percentage of Fe_2O_3 in the iron ore.   *Ans.* 30.39.

28-6 A 0.2500-g sample containing iron pyrites, FeS_2, is roasted to Fe_2O_3 and SO_2.

(a) The SO_2 gas is absorbed in 50.00 ml of 0.1100 N $KMnO_4$ (an excess). 0.1675 g of pure $Na_2C_2O_4$ is added, and the titration is completed by 22.50 ml of the same $KMnO_4$ solution. Calculate the percentage of FeS_2.   *Ans.* 65.68.

(b) If the Fe_2O_3 residue from the sample is determined by the Zimmermann-Reinhardt method, what volume of 0.1100 N $KMnO_4$ is required for the titration?   *Ans.* 12.44 ml.

28-7 A 0.9500-g sample of vanadium ore is dissolved in acid and passed through a Jones reductor. The reduced vanadium is received in excess ferric alum ($V^{++} + 2Fe^{+++} + H_2O \rightarrow VO^{++} + 2Fe^{++} + 2H^+$), and the VO^{++} and Fe^{++} are titrated with 27.10 ml of 0.09250 N $KMnO_4$. Calculate the percentage of V_2O_5 in the ore.   *Ans.* 7.995.

28-8 0.2148 g of a pure element, E, is dissolved in acid to give the ion E^{+++}; titration to EO_4^{--} requires 42.50 ml of 0.1500 N KMnO$_4$. Calculate the atomic weight of the element E.   *Ans.* 101.07.

28-9 A 0.2000-g sample consisting of metallic iron, ferric oxide, and inert matter is treated with excess ferric alum solution: $Fe + 2Fe^{+++} \rightarrow 3Fe^{++}$; titration requires 40.60 ml of 0.2060 N KMnO$_4$. Another 0.2000-g sample is dissolved in acid, and the solution is passed through a Jones reductor; titration of the solution uses 15.30 ml of the same KMnO$_4$ solution. Calculate the percentages of metallic iron and Fe$_2$O$_3$ in the sample.

28-10 What weight of sample of impure potassium nitrite should be taken for analysis so that each milliliter of 0.0750 N KMnO$_4$ used in the titration will represent 0.500% of nitrogen in the sample?

28-11 A solution of KHC$_2$O$_4 \cdot$ H$_2$C$_2$O$_4 \cdot$ 2H$_2$O is 0.1080 N as an acid. 50.00 ml of the tetroxalate solution requires 40.00 ml of KMnO$_4$ for titration. Calculate the normality of the KMnO$_4$.

28-12 Exactly five grams each of Na$_2$C$_2$O$_4$, H$_2$C$_2$O$_4 \cdot$ 2H$_2$O and KHC$_2$O$_4 \cdot$ H$_2$C$_2$O$_4 \cdot$ 2H$_2$O are mixed, dissolved in water, and diluted to 1 liter. Calculate the normality of the solution (*a*) as a reducing agent; (*b*) as an acid.

28-13 How many grams of KHC$_2$O$_4 \cdot$ H$_2$C$_2$O$_4 \cdot$ 2H$_2$O must be mixed with 1.0000 g of Na$_2$C$_2$O$_4$ so that the solution of the compounds as a reducing agent is three times its normality as an acid?

28-14 What weight of H$_2$C$_2$O$_4 \cdot$ 2H$_2$O must be added to 1.0000 g of KHC$_2$O$_4$ so that a solution of the mixture will have the same normality as a reducing agent as the same weight of KHC$_2$O$_4 \cdot$ H$_2$C$_2$O$_4 \cdot$ 2H$_2$O in the same volume of solution?

28-15 What is the ratio of the normalities of solutions of Ba(OH)$_2$ and KMnO$_4$ if the volume of Ba(OH)$_2$ required to titrate a given weight of KHC$_2$O$_4 \cdot$ H$_2$C$_2$O$_4 \cdot$2H$_2$O is twice the volume of KMnO$_4$ required to titrate the same weight of the tetroxalate?

28-16 0.2500 g of pure iron, dissolved in acid under reducing conditions, requires 44.24 ml of KMnO$_4$ for titration.

(*a*) Calculate the normality of the KMnO$_4$ solution.

(*b*) If the iron contained 2.00% of its own weight of Fe$_2$O$_3$, what is the true normality of the KMnO$_4$? (*Note:* Fe$_2$O$_3$ dissolves in acid to form Fe^{+++}, which reacts with metallic iron: $Fe + 2Fe^{+++} \rightarrow 3Fe^{++}$.)

28-17 A 0.5000-g sample of a meteorite is dissolved in acid: $Fe_3O_4 + 8H^+ \rightarrow 4H_2O + 2Fe^{+++} + Fe^{++}$. Titration of the solution requires 15.00 ml of 0.1200 N KMnO$_4$.

(*a*) Calculate the percentage of Fe$_3$O$_4$ in the sample.

(*b*) What volume of the same KMnO$_4$ would be required if the iron is determined by the Zimmermann-Reinhardt method?

28-18 20.00 ml of commercial hydrogen peroxide is diluted to 250.0 ml. A 25.00-ml aliquot of the diluted solution requires 41.00 ml of 0.0850 N KMnO$_4$ for titration.

(*a*) Calculate the strength of the original solution, expressing the results as a weight-volume percent of H$_2$O$_2$.

(*b*) What volume of oxygen gas (STP) can be obtained by the decomposition ($2H_2O_2 \rightarrow 2H_2O + O_2$) of 10.0 ml of the original peroxide solution?

28-19 A sample of barium peroxide weighing 0.4200 g is dissolved in 50.00 ml of 0.1180 N KMnO$_4$ solution acidified with sulfuric acid; after gassing out the oxygen, the excess $KMnO_4$ is back titrated with 26.60 ml of 0.07500 N ferrous solution. Calculate the percentage of BaO_2 in the sample.

28-20 What must be the normaiity of a permanganate solution so that when a 1-gram sample is titrated, the milliliters of $KMnO_4$ used is the same as the percentage of Fe_2O_3 in the sample? ·

28-21 What volume of 0.1067 N $KMnO_4$ solution is required for the titration of the $HSbO_2$ obtained from a 1.2500-g sample of stibnite ore that contains 30.30% Sb_2S_3?

28-22 A 2.000-g sample of pyrolusite (impure MnO_2) is dissolved in concentrated hydrochloric acid and prepared for analysis by the Volhard method, finally making the solution up to 500.0 ml. Titration of a 50.00-ml aliquot of the sample solution requires 38.30 ml of $KMnO_4$ solution which is 0.1200 N against oxalate in acid solution. Calculate the percentage of MnO_2 in the sample.

28-23 A 1-gram sample of ferrotitanium alloy is dissolved in acid, giving Fe^{+++} and TiO^{++}, and is diluted to 250.0 ml. A 50.00-ml aliquot of the solution, after passage through a Jones reductor, requires 41.45 ml of 0.0800 N $KMnO_4$ for titration. Another 50.00-ml aliquot of the solution, analyzed for iron by the Zimmermann-Reinhardt method, requires 33.62 ml of the same $KMnO_4$. Calculate the percentages of Fe and Ti in the alloy.

28-24 A sample of vanadium ore weighing 0.7500 g is dissolved in acid and passed through a Jones reductor, giving V^{++}. The reduced vanadium solution is received in excess ferric alum solution, and the VO^{++} and Fe^{++} formed in this reaction are titrated with 41.40 ml of 0.06000 N $KMnO_4$. Calculate the percentage of V_2O_5 in the ore.

28-25 A 0.3000-g sample of pyrolusite ore containing 23.50% MnO_2 requires 38.60 ml of $KMnO_4$ for titration by the Volhard method. Calculate the normality of the $KMnO_4$ when it is used in acid solution against oxalate.

28-26 A 2.000-g sample of manganese steel is dissolved in sulfuric acid, and the Mn^{++} in solution is oxidized to MnO_4^- by addition of excess $K_2S_2O_8$. After boiling to decompose the excess of peroxydisulfate, titration of the MnO_4^- in solution requires 43.80 ml of 0.0800 N arsenite solution. Calculate the percentage of Mn in the steel.

28-27 In each part below, calculate the percent of the substance sought (column 1) from the data given. Titration with permanganate accomplishes the change indicated in column 3.

Sought	Sample, g	Titration	$KMnO_4$ used
(a) Sb_2S_3	0.4000	$H_2S \rightarrow S$	44.50 ml 0.09000 N
(b) Sb_2S_3	0.4000	$HSbO_2 \rightarrow H_3SbO_4$	44.50 ml 0.09000 N
(c) FeS_2	0.2500	$SO_2 \rightarrow SO_4^{--}$	35.20 ml 0.1700 N
(d) KCNS	0.2000	$HCN \rightarrow HCN + SO_4^{--}$	32.00 ml 0.2500 N
(e) $Na_2S_2O_3$	1.2000	$S_2O_3^{--} \rightarrow S_4O_6^{--}$	41.50 ml 0.09500 N
(f) KNO_2	0.6400	$NO_2^- \rightarrow NO_3^-$	48.00 ml 0.07500 N
(g) U_3O_8	1.5000	$UO^{++} \rightarrow UO_2^{++}$	46.60 ml 0.02500 N
(h) BaO_2	2.0000	$H_2O_2 \rightarrow O_2$	33.50 ml 0.06000 N
(i) As_2O_3	1.0000	$HAsO_2 \rightarrow H_3AsO_4$	40.08 ml 0.5000 N

28-28 A sample of the given weight (column 1) is analyzed for the stated component (column 2) by treating, in acid solution, with the reducing agent given (column 3), which is an excess requiring back titration with the given volume (column 5) of 0.05000 N $KMnO_4$. Calculate percent of the the sought component.

Sample, g	Sought	Reducing agent added	Reduction product	Back titration, ml
(a) 0.4000	MnO_2	50.00 ml 0.1350 N Fe^{++}	Mn^{++}	21.40
(b) 0.2500	MnO_2	45.00 ml 0.1120 N $HAsO_2$	Mn^{++}	32.50
(c) 0.8000	PbO_2	0.2500 g pure As_2O_3	Pb^{++}	41.00
(d) 1.2000	Pb_3O_4	0.3300 g pure $H_2C_2O_4 \cdot 2H_2O$	Pb^{++}	41.72
(e) 0.5000	$KClO_3$	40.00 ml 0.1500 N $H_2C_2O_4$	Cl^-	48.00
(f) 0.3000	$K_2S_2O_8$	1.0000 g pure Mohr's salt	SO_4^{--}	13.20
(g) 1.0000	HNO_3	0.2010 g pure $Na_2C_2O_4$	NO	35.00

28-29 An orange paint pigment weighing 1.0000 g and containing Pb_3O_4 (red lead), PbO (litharge), and inert matter is treated with 50.00 ml of 0.05000 *molar* oxalic acid, which reduces Pb_3O_4 to Pb^{++} and dissolves the PbO, giving Pb^{++}. The solution is neutralized with ammonia, causing all of the lead ion to precipitate as PbC_2O_4. The precipitate is filtered off, and the acidified filtrate requires 14.58 ml of 0.1000 N $KMnO_4$ for titration of the excess oxalate ion. The precipitated lead oxalate is dissolved in acid and titrated with 31.05 ml of the same $KMnO_4$ solution. Calculate the percentages of PbO and Pb_3O_4 in the sample.

28-30 A 1.2000-g sample that contains PbO, PbO_2, and inert matter is treated with 30.00 ml of 0.2500 *molar* oxalic acid solution, which reduces PbO_2 to Pb^{++} and also dissolves PbO to Pb^{++}. The resulting solution is neutralized with ammonia, causing precipitation of lead ion as PbC_2O_4. The precipitate is filtered off, and the filtrate is acidified and titrated with permanganate, requiring 20.00 ml of 0.04000 *molar* $KMnO_4$. The PbC_2O_4 precipitate is dissolved in acid; titration of this solution requires 40.00 ml of the same $KMnO_4$ solution. Calculate the percentages of PbO and PbO_2 in the sample.

28-31 A 2.0000-g sample containing iron, titanium, manganese, and vanadium (plus inert matter) is brought into acidic solution as iron(III), titanium(IV), manganese(II), and vanadium(V), and made up to 250.0 ml. A 50.00-ml aliquot of the solution is passed through a Jones reductor, giving iron(II), titanium(III), and vanadium(II), and is immediately titrated with permanganate, requiring 43.12 ml of $KMnO_4$, which is 0.08000 N against oxalate in acid solution; the oxidation products are iron(III), titanium(IV), and vanadium(V). A second 50.00-ml aliquot of the solution is passed through a Walden reductor; the solution, now containing iron(II) and vanadium(IV) [titanium(IV) and manganese(II) do not react in the reductor], requires 23.75 ml of the same $KMnO_4$ solution for titration. After addition of pyrophosphate to this titrated solution, the manganese(II) now present [original manganese(II) plus that formed in the permanganate titration] requires 15.47 ml of the same $KMnO_4$ solution for titration of manganese(II) to manganese(III), which is also the reduction product of permanganate in this titration. A third 50.00-ml aliquot of the solution is passed through a Walden reductor, as before; the solution requires 28.75 ml of 0.04000 N V^{++} solution for titrimetric reduction of titanium(IV → III) and vanadium(IV → III). [Vanadium(III) is also the oxidation product of the V^{++} titrant.] Calculate the percentages of Fe, Ti, Mn, and V in the sample.

28-32 0.1000 g of a pure element, E, is dissolved in acid to give the ion E^{++}; titration to EO_3^- requires 39.22 ml of 0.1500 N $KMnO_4$. Calculate the atomic weight of the element E. By reference to a table of atomic weights, identify the element.

28-33 0.1955 g of a pure element, X, of atomic weight approximately 186, is dissolved under oxidizing conditions to give XO_4^-, which requires 47.75 ml of 0.1100 N Fe^{++} solution for titration. What is the oxidation (valence) number of the element X resulting from the reduction by Fe^{++}?

28-34 A solution of $KMnO_4$, thought to have been standardized against $H_2C_2O_4 \cdot 2H_2O$ and having a normality of 0.1145 on this basis, was used to determine iron in an iron ore, and gave a value of 34.50% Fe_2O_3. Later it was found that the primary standard used was $Na_2C_2O_4$, and not $H_2C_2O_4 \cdot 2H_2O$. What was the correct percentage of Fe_2O_3 in the sample?

28-35 A 0.5000-g sample containing vanadium and molybdenum is dissolved in hot concentrated perchloric acid, to give VO_2^+ and MoO_4^{--}. The cold, diluted solution is treated with SO_2, which reduces only the vanadium (to VO^{++}); after boiling out the excess SO_2, the solution requires 8.00 ml of $KMnO_4$ solution, which is 0.1100 N against oxalate in acid solution. The solution just titrated (the Mn^{++} does not interfere) is passed through a Jones reductor, which reduces VO_2^+ to V^{++} and MoO_4^{--} to Mo^{+++}; the effluent from the reductor is received in excess Fe^{+++} solution, which oxidizes only the V^{++}, giving VO^{++}. The solution (containing what ions?) requires 42.00 ml of the same $KMnO_4$ solution for titration. Calculate the percentages of V_2O_5 and MoO_3 in the sample.

29

IODINE METHODS

Iodine is soluble in water only to the extent of about 0.001 mole per liter at room temperature. However, in the presence of soluble iodides, such as potassium iodide, iodine readily dissolves by conversion to the triiodide complex:

$$I_2 + I^- \rightarrow I_3^-$$

The triiodide ion, rather than molecular iodine, is the principal species present in "iodine" solutions, either as the titrant in direct methods, or formed by oxidation of iodide ion in indirect methods. (For convenience in writing equations, I_2 will usually be written, rather than the complex, I_3^-.)

The standard potential of the system

$$I_3^- + 2e \rightleftarrows 3I^- \qquad E^\circ = +0.536 \text{ v}$$

makes this a very versatile half reaction in titrimetry. Strong oxidizing agents will oxidize I^- to I_3^-, and strong reducing agents will reduce I_3^- to I^-. The methods are therefore conveniently divided into two classes:

1. *Direct methods (iodimetry)*, in which a standard solution of iodine is used to titrate strong reductants, usually in neutral or slightly acidic solution.

2. *Indirect methods (iodometry)*, in which oxidizing agents are determined by bringing them into reaction with an excess of iodide; the iodine liberated is titrated, usually in slightly acidic solution, with a standard reductant such as sodium thiosulfate or sodium arsenite; the former is more often used:

$$I_2 + 2S_2O_3^{--} \rightarrow 2I^- + S_4O_6^{--}$$

Iodine methods cannot be applied in strongly alkaline solution, due to the following disproportionation (internal redox) reactions:

$$I_2 + 2OH^- \rightarrow H_2O + I^- + IO^-$$

$$3IO^- \rightarrow 2I^- + IO_3^-$$

Furthermore, in alkaline solution the titration of iodine by thiosulfate does not proceed by a single reaction; some of the thiosulfate is oxidized to sulfate:

$$S_2O_3^{--} + 4I_2 + 10OH^- \rightarrow 2SO_4^{--} + 8I^- + 5H_2O$$

The amount of thiosulfate that oxidizes to sulfate increases with the alkalinity of the solution.

Thiosulfate cannot be used in solution of high acidity unless very good stirring is provided so that it is oxidized at once. Thiosulfuric acid undergoes disproportionation:

$$H_2S_2O_3 \rightarrow H_2SO_3 + S$$

but this reaction is quite slow relative to the rate of oxidiaton by iodine. H_2SO_3 is also a reducing agent for iodine, but its equivalency is different from that of thiosulfate.

There are two common sources of error in iodine methods.

1. Iodine is somewhat volatile from solution. This source of error is minimized by the presence of excess potassium iodide in the solution, to form the triiodide complex, I_3^-. Iodine titrations, whether direct or indirect, are not made in hot solution, because this would increase the volatility loss of iodine.

2. Iodide ion is oxidized by oxygen of the air:

$$4I^- + O_2 + 4H^+ \rightarrow 2H_2O + 2I_2$$

This oxidation is not appreciable in neutral solution, but it becomes increasingly significant with increase of hydrogen ion concentration. Atmospheric oxidation of iodide ion is accelerated by strong light, and by certain catalysts such as copper(I), nitrite, and oxides of nitrogen. Water used for dilution and/or for dissolving potassium iodide in indirect iodine methods should be recently boiled to remove dissolved oxygen, and the iodine liberated should be titrated promptly. If prompt titration is not practical, the air of the titration flask should be displaced with carbon dioxide, either by addition of a small amount of sodium bicarbonate to the acid solution, or by use of a small piece of "dry ice" (solid carbon dioxide).

Effect of Conditions on Equilibria in Iodine Methods

The triiodide-iodide half reaction is very little influenced by *p*H. On the other hand, the potentials of half reactions involving a change of oxy-content of molecules or ions are markedly influenced by hydrogen ion concentration; the reaction between iodide ion and oxygen-containing oxidizing agents, or the reverse of such a reaction, is therefore greatly modified by changes in *p*H. For example, dichromate ion in acid solution quantitatively oxidizes iodide to iodine, but in neutral solution, chromate does not react with iodide ion.

If the standard potentials of two half reactions are not too different, it may be possible to make the reaction quantitative in either direction by change in *p*H. For example,

$$H_3AsO_4 + 2H^+ + 2e \rightleftarrows HAsO_2 + 2H_2O \quad E° = +0.559 \text{ v}$$

$$I_3^- + 2e \rightleftarrows 3I^- \qquad\qquad\qquad E° = +0.536 \text{ v}$$

In strong acid solution H_3AsO_4 quantitatively oxidizes iodide to iodine; a high concentration of iodide ion also favors this reaction. However, at low hydrogen ion concentration (*p*H about 8 or 9) arsenite is quantitatively oxidized by iodine. (The student should explain these effects in terms of the half-reaction potentials.)

Lowering the concentration of an ion by precipitation or by complex formation may change the potential of a half reaction system in such a way as to make the reaction more complete. Comparison of the half-reaction potential

$$Cu^{++} + e \rightleftarrows Cu^+ \qquad E° = +0.153 \text{ v}$$

with that of the iodine-iodide couple shows that iodine should oxidize Cu^+ to Cu^{++}. However, in solution containing iodide ion, Cu^+ is precipitated as CuI; at the very low concentration of Cu^+ in the saturated solution of CuI the potential of the cupric-cuprous system is much more positive than 0.153 v, and Cu^{++} quantitatively oxidizes iodide ion to iodine:

$$2Cu^{++} + 4I^- \rightarrow 2CuI + I_2$$

But in the presence of ions such as citrate or tartrate that form stable complexes with Cu^{++}, copper(I) is quantitatively oxidized by iodine.

The potential of the ferric-ferrous couple ($E° = +0.771$ v) indicates that Fe^{+++} will oxidize iodide ion to iodine, although the reaction is not sufficiently complete for quantitative use unless the iodine is removed from solution by boiling or by extracting it into an immiscible solvent. Lowering the Fe^{+++} concentration by formation of stable complex ions, such as FeF_6^{---} or $Fe(PO_4)_2^{---}$, lowers the potential of the ferric-ferrous system to such an extent that under these conditions Fe^{++} is oxidized by iodine.

Indicator

One of the advantages of iodine methods is the ease and sensitivity of end point detection: in direct iodine methods by the first appearance of excess iodine titrant; in indirect methods by the disappearance of the iodine being titrated.

1. *Iodine as self-indicator.* A small drop of 0.1 *N* iodine solution will impart a distinct yellow color to 100–200 ml of water. When other components of the reaction mixture are colorless, iodine can serve as its own indicator. However,

this method of detecting the end point is not quite as sensitive as the other methods listed below.

2. *Starch.* When starch granules are heated in water, they burst and yield various decomposition products, including β-amylose, which gives a deep blue color with iodine in the presence of iodide. The colored material is probably an adsorption complex of iodine, β-amylose, and iodide. Upon standing for a considerable time, the starch solution undergoes decomposition and becomes insensitive for detection of iodine. The solution should be prepared fresh daily, unless an additive is used to prevent decomposition; a trace of mercuric iodide preserves its sensitivity for weeks or even months.

Starch indicator cannot be used in strong acid solution because its hydrolytic decomposition is accelerated by acid. The sensitivity to iodine is also decreased by alcohol, and the blue color fails to appear at alcohol concentrations in excess of about 50%. The blue color is completely discharged at temperatures only moderately above room temperature, but the color returns when the mixture is cooled. A properly prepared starch indicator will detect about 10^{-5} N iodine solution at room temperature. In the indirect iodine methods, starch indicator should not be added until most of the iodine has been titrated; a high concentration of iodine gives with starch a complex that has poor indicator properties.

3. *Color in organic solvents.* Iodine dissolves in carbon tetrachloride, chloroform, and some other organic solvents to form a red-violet solution that is a somewhat more delicate test for iodine than is starch; a concentration of about 10^{-6} N can be detected. An amount of iodine that is below the visibility limit in an aqueous medium may be concentrated by extraction into a small volume of the immiscible solvent and rendered visible. This method of detecting iodine is especially useful when very dilute solutions are used in titrations, or when the required conditions preclude the use of starch, such as a strong acid medium.

Standard Solutions

Iodine. Resublimed iodine is sufficiently pure to be used as a primary standard; however, it is moderately volatile even at room temperature, and the process of weighing it accurately is inconvenient. It is customary to make an approximate solution of iodine, which is then standardized. The required amount of iodine is mixed with three or four times its own weight of potassium iodide, and triturated (ground in a mortar) repeatedly with small portions of water, pouring off each solution into the storage bottle, until all the iodine is dissolved. After diluting the solution to the desired volume, it must be shaken well and frequently to make certain that all the iodine has dissolved. It is good practice to prepare the solution one or two days before use, and shake it at frequent intervals.

Sodium thiosulfate. A solution of the approximate concentration desired is made in recently boiled distilled water, and the solution is then standardized.

Dissolved carbon dioxide (carbonic acid) in the water may be sufficient to cause slow decomposition to H_2SO_3 and S; also, certain bacteria act on thiosulfate and render the solution turbid. Small amounts of alkali, such as sodium carbonate or borax, retard both of these actions.

The reaction between sodium thiosulfate and iodine is quantitative over a considerable pH range. Iodine may be titrated in fairly strong acid solution (pH 1) if efficient stirring is provided. The upper limit of pH is about 9, above which iodine reacts with hydroxyl ion as shown earlier. The only application of sodium thiosulfate is for the titration of iodine in a more or less acidic solution:

$$I_2 + 2S_2O_3^{--} \rightarrow 2I^- + S_4O_6^{--}$$

Sodium arsenite. The titrant solution is prepared by dissolving arsenic(III) oxide in excess sodium hydroxide:

$$As_2O_3 + 2OH^- \rightarrow 2AsO_2^- + H_2O$$

The excess alkali is neutralized with hydrochloric acid and the solution is then buffered with sodium bicarbonate. The solution is generally prepared directly from primary standard As_2O_3. For use in the titration of iodine the allowable pH range is about 5 to 9.

Standardization of Iodine Solution

The only suitable primary standard for iodine is arsenic(III) oxide, As_2O_3. The weighed primary standard is dissolved and buffered with bicarbonate, as described above, and is titrated with the iodine, using starch indicator, to the first detectable blue color with starch:

$$AsO_2^- + I_2 + 2H_2O \rightarrow AsO_4^{---} + 2I^- + 4H^+$$

Standardization of Sodium Thiosulfate Solution

In these methods an oxidizing agent is treated with excess potassium iodide, and the liberated iodine is titrated with the sodium thiosulfate solution. For each of the following methods of standardization, the student should deduce and fully justify the equivalent weight of the primary standard.

1. *Potassium iodate*, KIO_3, is the most widely used primary standard for thiosulfate solution. The weighed solid is dissolved in water and treated with an excess of potassium iodide and hydrochloric acid:

$$IO_3^- + 5I^- + 6H^+ \rightarrow 3H_2O + 3I_2$$

The liberated iodine is titrated with sodium thiosulfate solution. Because potassium iodide may contain traces of iodate, and because iodide ion is rather easily oxidized by air, a blank test should always be run in parallel with the titration, and the blank correction applied.

Potassium acid iodate, $KH(IO_3)_2$, can also be used as a primary standard, but it appears to offer no advantage over KIO_3.

2. *Potassium bromate*, $KBrO_3$, reacts with excess iodide and acid in the same manner as does the iodate:

$$BrO_3^- + 6I^- + 6H^+ \rightarrow Br^- + 3H_2O + 3I_2$$

The reaction, which is somewhat slower than with iodate, can be catalyzed by ammonium molybdate.

3. *Potassium dichromate*, $K_2Cr_2O_7$, in acid solution oxidizes iodide to iodine:

$$Cr_2O_7^{--} + 14H^+ + 6I^- \rightarrow 2Cr^{+++} + 7H_2O + 3I_2$$

The reaction is somewhat slow in solution of low acidity; it is more rapid at high acidities, but this increases the oxygen error. Heating to increase the rate of reaction is not permissible owing to loss of some iodine by volatilization. It is best, therefore, to use a solution about 0.5 to 1 N in acid, displace the air from the flask with carbon dioxide, and allow the mixture to stand in the stoppered flask for about five minutes before titrating the liberated iodine with thiosulfate. The starch end point in this titration is from the deep blue color of starch–iodine to the clear green color of Cr^{+++}. The end point is so abrupt that it is quite easily overrun by an inexperienced operator, in which case the sample must be discarded. For standardization of thiosulfate for general use, potassium dichromate seems to offer no advantages over potassium iodate. The reaction is discussed here because of its application to the indirect determination of cations that form insoluble chromates, and to the indirect determination of sulfate. These methods will be outlined later.

4. *Metallic copper*. If sodium thiosulfate is to be used mainly for the determination of copper, standardization against copper is recommended. Pure electrolytic copper, readily available in the form of foil, is dissolved in nitric acid:

$$3Cu + 8H^+ + 2NO_3^- \rightarrow 3Cu^{++} + 4H_2O + 2NO$$

The solution is boiled down to incipient crystallization of the copper salt, to remove oxides of nitrogen and most of the excess acid; the remaining acid is neutralized with ammonia. The solution is then acidified with acetic acid, excess potassium iodide is added,

$$2Cu^{++} + 4I^- \rightarrow 2CuI + I_2$$

and the liberated iodine is titrated with thiosulfate.

The insoluble copper(I) iodide tends to adsorb some of the iodine from solution, and prevents or retards its reduction by thiosulfate. This source of error is largely eliminated by adding potassium thiocyanate near the end point of the titration; the copper(I) iodide is converted to the less soluble copper(I) thiocyanate:

$$CuI \, (+ \text{ adsorbed } I_2) + CNS^- \rightarrow CuCNS + I^- \, (+ I_2 \text{ in solution})$$

and the adsorbed iodine is displaced into the solution for titration.

5. *Potassium hexacyanoferrate(III)*, $K_3Fe(CN)_6$, has been proposed as a primary standard for thiosulfate. Its reaction with potassium iodide,

$$2Fe(CN)_6^{---} + 2I^- \rightarrow 2Fe(CN)_6^{4-} + I_2$$

is carried out in hydrochloric acid solution containing zinc sulfate, the latter serving to remove $Fe(CN)_6^{4-}$ by formation of insoluble $K_2Zn_3[Fe(CN)_6]_2$. The principal advantage of this standard appears to be its very high equivalent weight.

6. *Oxalic acid dihydrate*, $H_2C_2O_4 \cdot 2H_2O$. The weighed sample is dissolved in water, and an excess of magnesium chloride (to complex the oxalate ion), potassium iodate, and potassium iodide is added. Iodine is liberated in an amount equivalent to the hydrogen ions in solution (see p. 420), and the iodine is titrated as usual.

7. *Iodine* itself can be used as a primary standard for thiosulfate. Although it has a high equivalent weight, the difficulties in weighing the sample accurately preclude its general use.

8. *Tetramethylammonium tetrachloroferrate(III)*, $(CH_3)_4NFeCl_4$, has been proposed as a primary standard for thiosulfate.[1] It is readily prepared and purified, can be dried in air at 110°C, is nonhygroscopic, and is readily soluble in water. Standard solutions of the complex salt are stable if made about 0.01 M in acid. Although the compound has a high equivalent weight, it has the disadvantage that if more than a small amount of iodide is added initially, tetramethylammonium iodide is precipitated, on which the liberated iodine is adsorbed extensively and is only slowly desorbed.

APPLICATIONS OF IODINE METHODS

Direct Methods (Iodimetry)

The direct method consists in the titration of relatively strong reductants with standard iodine solution. In some cases it is advantageous to use a known excess of iodine solution, then back titrate the excess iodine with sodium thiosulfate. A few of the direct methods are discussed below.

[1] L. J. Sacks, *Anal. Chem.*, **35**, 1299 (1962).

1. *Hydrogen sulfide and metal sulfides* are treated in the following ways.

a. Hydrogen sulfide gas is absorbed in a measured volume of acidified standard iodine, more than equivalent to the hydrogen sulfide expected:

$$H_2S + I_2 \rightarrow S + 2H^+ + 2I^-$$

The excess iodine is back titrated with standard sodium thiosulfate.

b. Metal sulfides that are soluble in acid (ZnS, CdS, FeS, MnS) are treated with dilute hydrochloric acid or sulfuric acid in a closed system. The sulfide-acid mixture is heated to expel the hydrogen sulfide completely and drive it over into iodine solution for titration as described above.

c. Acid-insoluble sulfides (CuS, HgS, etc.) can be decomposed by treatment with an active metal such as zinc:

$$CuS + Zn + 2H^+ \rightarrow Cu + Zn^{++} + H_2S$$

and the hydrogen sulfide determined as in *a*.

2. *Mixture of sulfide and thiosulfate.*   These ions in solution can be analyzed by treatment with a suspension of cadmium carbonate; only the sulfide is precipitated:

$$S^{--} + CdCO_3 \rightarrow CO_3^{--} + CdS$$

The cadmium sulfide and excess cadmium carbonate are filtered off, and the solution containing the thiosulfate is titrated directly with iodine solution. The cadmium sulfide precipitate is treated with dilute acid and the hydrogen sulfide formed is determined as in 1*b* above.

3. *Antimony(III) compounds.*   In the determination of antimony in stibnite ore, Sb_2S_3, the sample is dissolved in hot concentrated hydrochloric acid:

$$Sb_2S_3 + 6H^+ \rightarrow 2Sb^{+++} + 3H_2S$$

or

$$Sb_2S_3 + 6H^+ + 4\,(5, 6)Cl^- \rightarrow 3H_2S + SbCl_4^-\,(SbCl_5^{--}, SbCl_6^{---})$$

All hydrogen sulfide must be expelled before diluting the solution, otherwise Sb_2S_3 will reprecipitate. In boiling out the hydrogen sulfide, there is danger of losing some antimony(III) chloride by volatilization. For this reason, the acid treatment is made in the presence of potassium chloride, which forms the non-volatile salt $KSbCl_4$. Antimony compounds tend to hydrolyze extensively:

$$Sb^{+++} + H_2O + Cl^- \rightarrow 2H^+ + SbOCl\,(\text{insoluble, white})$$

Dilution of the solution, which lowers the acidity, promotes the hydrolysis to the insoluble basic salt, SbOCl. Therefore, before diluting the acidic solution, tartaric acid is added to complex the antimony(III) to form the soluble antimonyl tartrate complex:

$$Sb^{+++} + H_2O + H_2C_4H_4O_6 \rightarrow 3H^+ + H[(SbO)C_4H_4O_6]$$

The excess free mineral acid is neutralized, the solution is brought to a pH of about 9 by adding excess sodium bicarbonate, and the solution is titrated with standard iodine solution:

$$H[(SbO)C_4H_4O_6] + H_2O + I_2 \rightarrow H[(SbO_2)C_4H_4O_6] + 2H^+ + 2I^-$$

Because the reverse reaction is favored by higher hydrogen ion concentration, it is essential that sufficient buffer capacity be provided to remove the hydrogen ion formed in the reaction. A slow or fading end point is indicative of insufficient buffer.

4. *Determination of water by Karl Fischer method.*[2]　　Small amounts of water in nonaqueous media are determined by titration with a reagent consisting of a solution of iodine, sulfur dioxide, and pyridine (C_5H_5N) in absolute methanol. Sulfur dioxide and pyridine are present in quite large excess relative to iodine. The reaction can be represented by the equation:

$$I_2 + SO_2 + H_2O + 3C_5H_5N \rightarrow 2C_5H_5N \cdot HI + C_5H_5N \cdot SO_3$$

The products of the reaction are colorless. Titration of a sample containing water is made with the Karl Fischer reagent until the first excess of reagent is present as shown by the color of iodine; alternatively, the end point is determined potentiometrically. The reagent is not very stable; in practice it is standardized, in parallel with the unknown, by titrating a solution containing a known small amount of water in methanol. The method has been applied to the determination of water in a wide variety of materials.[3]

Several additional direct determinations with iodine are summarized in Table 29-1.

Table 29-1　Additional Direct Iodine Methods

Substance Determined	Oxidation Product	Conditions
SO_2, SO_3^{--}	SO_4^{--}	Excess I_2 and back titration
Arsenic(III)	Arsenic(V)	$NaHCO_3$ buffer
Iron(II)	Iron(III)	In presence of F^- or PO_4^{---}
Tin(II)	Tin(IV)	Titrate in inert atmosphere
CNS^-	SO_4^{--}, ICN	$NaHCO_3$ buffer
Hydrazine, N_2H_4	N_2	$NaHCO_3$ buffer
Hydrazoic acid, HN_3	N_2	$NaHCO_3$ buffer

[2] Karl Fischer, *Z. angew. Chem.*, **48**, 394 (1935).
[3] J. Mitchell and D. M. Smith, *Aquametry*, New York, Interscience, 1948.

Indirect Methods (Iodometry)

Indirect iodine methods apply generally to the determination of substances that oxidize iodide ion to iodine, which is then titrated with standard sodium thiosulfate solution. A brief discussion of some of the methods is given in the interest of fuller understanding of the chemistry involved. The iodometric determination of copper, which is frequently required in industrial analysis, and is also a common student determination, is discussed in detail.

1. *Determination of copper.* Copper ores frequently contain more or less antimony and/or arsenic, as well as iron, and the methods of analysis are designed to prevent interference from these elements in solution.

The copper ore is dissolved in nitric acid:

$$Cu + 4H^+ + 2NO_3^- \rightarrow Cu^{++} + 2NO_2 + 2H_2O$$

$$Cu_2S + 8H^+ + 4NO_3^- \rightarrow 2Cu^{++} + S + 4NO_2 + 4H_2O$$

Iron, antimony, and arsenic in the ore will be found in the solution in their higher oxidation states, although complete oxidation of antimony and arsenic may not have been attained. Any silica is filtered off, and the filtrate is evaporated with sulfuric acid to strong fuming, to displace the excess nitric acid. Elimination of interference from iron, arsenic, and/or antimony is accomplished by a method originated by Park.[4] The sulfuric acid solution is treated with bromine water to complete the oxidation of any arsenic(III) or antimony(III):

$$HAsO_2 + 2H_2O + Br_2 \rightarrow H_3AsO_4 + 2H^+ + 2Br^-$$

The excess bromine and H^+ are destroyed with ammonium hydroxide:

$$3Br_2 + 8NH_4OH \rightarrow 6Br^- + N_2 + 6NH_4^+ + 8H_2O$$

Ammonium bifluoride is added to complex the iron(III):

$$Fe^{+++} + 3HF_2^- \rightarrow 3H^+ + FeF_6^{---}$$

otherwise iron(III) would liberate some iodine from iodide. Potassium acid phthalate is added to buffer the solution at *p*H about 3.5, so that arsenic(V) and antimony(V) will not oxidize iodide. (Ammonium bifluoride is itself a buffer for this *p*H region, and potassium acid phthalate is not necessary if sufficient ammonium bifluoride is added.) The sample solution is treated with excess potassium iodide, and the liberated iodine is titrated exactly as described earlier for the standardization of thiosulfate against metallic copper.

2. *Oxidized forms of the halogens.* "Chlorine water" is an equilibrium system that contains some dissolved chlorine and also some hypochlorous acid formed by reaction with water:

$$Cl_2 + H_2O \rightleftarrows HClO + H^+ + Cl^-$$

---

[4] B. Park, *Ind. Eng. Chem., Anal. Ed.*, **3**, 77 (1931).

Both chlorine and hypochlorous acid are oxidizing agents for iodide ion, and they have the same equivalency in oxidizing iodide. Even in acetic acid solution, both will oxidize iodide:

$$Cl_2 + 2I^- \rightarrow 2Cl^- + I_2$$

$$ClO^- + 2H^+ + 2I^- \rightarrow Cl^- + H_2O + I_2$$

Chlorite, often present in bleaching mixtures, does not oxidize iodide in acetic acid solution, but does so in strong acid:

$$ClO_2^- + 4H^+ + 4I^- \rightarrow Cl^- + 2H_2O + 2I_2$$

Hypochlorite and chlorite can therefore be determined separately in the same sample (how?). Usually, bleaching solutions are analyzed for total oxidizing components, using strong acid solution; results are then reported as "available chlorine" or as "available oxygen."

Both iodate and periodate can be determined in the same sample. In the presence of excess iodide and strong acid, both periodate and iodate react and are reduced to iodine:

$$IO_4^- + 8H^+ + 7I^- \rightarrow 4H_2O + 4I_2$$

$$IO_3^- + 6H^+ + 5I^- \rightarrow 3H_2O + 3I_2$$

In bicarbonate solution (pH about 9), iodate does not react, and periodate is reduced only to iodate:

$$IO_4^- + H_2O + 2I^- \rightarrow IO_3^- + 2OH^- + I_2$$

Note that the equivalency of the periodate is different in the two different reactions.

3. *Mixed halides.* Mixtures containing chloride, bromide, and iodide can be determined by a combination of titrimetric processes, as follows.

a. Total halide ($Cl^- + Br^- + I^-$) is determined by titration with standard silver nitrate.

b. On a separate sample, iodide and bromide are determined together by adding potassium dichromate and acid, and distilling the iodine and bromine into potassium iodide solution; the iodine dissolves and the bromine replaces iodine from the iodide; the iodine titrated represents $Br^- + I^-$ in the sample.

c. On a separate sample, iodide is oxidized to *iodate* in neutral or weak acid solution, by chlorine or bromine; for example,

$$I^- + 3H_2O + 3Br_2 \rightarrow IO_3^- + 6H^+ + 6Br^-$$

The excess bromine is removed by addition of phenol:

$$3Br_2 + C_6H_5OH \rightarrow 3H^+ + 3Br^- + C_6H_2Br_3OH$$

The solution containing the iodate is then treated with excess potassium iodide and strong acid, and the liberated iodine is titrated. The method is especially suited to the determination of small amounts of iodide (why?).

4. *Analysis of pyrolusite*, MnO_2. Manganese dioxide, in acidic medium, quantitatively oxidizes iodide to iodine:

$$MnO_2 + 4H^+ + 2I^- \rightarrow Mn^{++} + 2H_2O + I_2$$

Fe_2O_3, which is frequently found in pyrolusite ore, would interfere by liberating iodine also:

$$Fe_2O_3 + 6H^+ + 2I^- \rightarrow 2Fe^{++} + 3H_2O + I_2$$

In the **Bunsen method** for analysis of pyrolusite, interference from iron(III) is avoided by treating the sample with concentrated hydrochloric acid:

$$MnO_2 + 4H^+ + 2Cl^- \rightarrow Mn^{++} + 2H_2O + Cl_2$$

Any Fe_2O_3 present merely dissolves in the acid, giving Fe^{+++}. The chlorine, equivalent to the manganese, is distilled into excess potassium iodide solution and the liberated iodine is titrated. Analysis of pyrolusite (and other higher oxides such as PbO_2 and Pb_3O_4) is sometimes reported in terms of "available oxygen."

5. *Barium* and *lead* ions can be determined by precipitation as chromate in neutral solution. The washed precipitate is dissolved in hydrochloric acid:

$$2BaCrO_4 + 2H^+ \rightarrow 2Ba^{++} + H_2O + Cr_2O_7^{--}$$

The dichromate is then determined iodometrically, as outlined under standardization of thiosulfate.

6. *Sulfate ion*, by treatment with a mixture of hydriodic and hypophosphorous acids, is reduced quantitatively to hydrogen sulfide, which can then be determined iodimetrically. In an indirect method the sulfate, in ammoniacal solution, is treated with a paste of barium chromate:

$$SO_4^{--} + BaCrO_4 \rightarrow BaSO_4 + CrO_4^{--}$$

Filtration of the barium sulfate and excess barium chromate leaves chromate ion in the filtrate in an amount equivalent to the sulfate in the sample solution. The filtrate is acidified and the dichromate is determined iodometrically. What is the equivalent of sulfate?

7. *Peroxydisulfate* in alkaline solution oxidizes iodide to iodate:

$$3S_2O_8^{--} + I^- + 6OH^- \rightarrow 6SO_4^{--} + 3H_2O + IO_3^-$$

The mixture is then acidified, excess potassium iodide is added, and the iodate is determined as outlined under standardization of sodium thiosulfate (see p. 413).

8. *Acids.* The reaction

$$IO_3^- + 5I^- + 6H^+ \rightarrow 3H_2O + 3I_2$$

is quantitative for any one reactant when the other two are present in excess.

The method can be applied to strong acids, and also to weak acids such as carbonic and phosphoric, if a cation is present to remove the anion by precipitation or other means; see under oxalic acid as a primary standard for thiosulfate (p. 415).

9. *Peroxides and percarbonates.* Hydrogen peroxide quantitatively oxidizes iodide ion to iodine:

$$H_2O_2 + 2H^+ + 2I^- \rightarrow 2H_2O + I_2$$

Metal peroxides, such as Na_2O_2 and BaO_2, and percarbonates liberate hydrogen peroxide upon treatment with acids:

$$BaO_2 + 2H^+ + SO_4^{--} \rightarrow BaSO_4 + H_2O_2$$

$$BaC_2O_6 + 2H^+ + SO_4^{--} \rightarrow BaSO_4 + 2CO_2 + H_2O_2$$

The hydrogen peroxide is then determined as indicated above. Compare the property of hydrogen peroxide in this determination with its property when determined by permanganate titration.

10. *Nitrites* in acid solution oxidize iodide ion to iodine:

$$2NO_2^- + 4H^+ + 2I^- \rightarrow 2NO + 2H_2O + I_2$$

which is titrated with thiosulfate. Compare with the reaction of nitrite ion in a permanganate titration.

PROBLEMS

29-1 Calculate the normality of iodine (triiodide) solution from the data given.
(a) 7.330 g of I_2 in 500.0 ml solution.
(b) 0.2722 g of pure As_2O_3 requires 36.90 ml of iodine solution.
(c) 44.56 ml of iodine titrate 0.8500 g of $Na_2S_2O_3 \cdot 5H_2O$.
(d) 14.200 g of I_2 per liter of solution.
(e) 0.2642 g of As_2O_3 requires 46.82 ml of iodine solution.
(f) 38.75 ml of iodine solution titrate 43.00 ml of thiosulfate solution, 1.000 ml of which is equivalent to 5.350 mg of KIO_3.
(g) 48.65 ml of iodine titrate 1.0000 g of $Na_2S_2O_3 \cdot 5H_2O$.

Ans. (a) 0.11552 N.   (b) 0.14914 N.

29-2 Calculate the normality of the thiosulfate solution from the data given.
(a) 26.910 g of pure $Na_2S_2O_3 \cdot 5H_2O$ per liter.
(b) 0.5521 g of I_2 requires 37.75 ml of thiosulfate.
(c) 0.2834 g of copper is equivalent to 41.14 ml of thiosulfate.
(d) 0.1929 g of KIO_3 (plus excess KI and HCl) gives iodine requiring 49.90 ml of thiosulfate.
(e) 35.00 ml of $K_2Cr_2O_7$ solution (5.885 g of $K_2Cr_2O_7$ per liter) treated with excess KI in acid solution gives iodine requiring 38.70 ml of thiosulfate.
(f) 0.1990 g of $KH(IO_3)_2$ (plus excess KI and HCl) gives iodine requiring 42.36 ml of thiosulfate.

(*g*) 0.6144 g of $K_3Fe(CN)_6$ liberates iodine from KI; the iodine requires 46.49 ml of thiosulfate.

(*h*) 50.00 ml of iodine solution (1.000 ml of which is equivalent to 2.473 mg of As_2O_3) requires 40.00 ml of thiosulfate.   *Ans.* (*a*) 0.10843 *N.* (*b*) 0.11522 *N.*

29-3   Express the value of 1.000 ml of 0.0800 *N* thiosulfate in terms of milligrams of the substance given.

(*a*) Cu_2O	(*d*) Cu	(*g*) $K_2Cr_2O_7$	(*j*) Fe_2O_3
(*b*) $KBrO_3$	(*e*) NaClO	(*h*) $Ce(SO_4)_2$	(*k*) I_2
(*c*) MnO_2	(*f*) $KH(IO_3)_2$	(*i*) Pb_3O_4	(*l*) Cl_2

Ans. (*a*) 5.722.   (*b*) 2.226.

29-4   Express the value of 1.000 ml of 0.0980 *N* iodine solution in terms of milligrams of the substance given.

(*a*) As_2O_3	(*d*) SO_2	(*g*) $Na_2S_2O_3$
(*b*) Na_2HAsO_3	(*e*) KCNS	(*h*) $SnCl_2$
(*c*) H_2S	(*f*) N_2H_4	(*i*) H_2O (Karl Fischer)

Ans. (*a*) 4.847.   (*b*) 8.326.

29-5   A 1.2000-g sample of calcium arsenate insecticide powder is dissolved in hydrochloric acid; excess KI is added, and the liberated iodine is titrated with 30.30 ml of sodium thiosulfate solution, each milliliter of which is equivalent to 2.56 mg of copper. Calculate the percentage of $Ca_3(AsO_4)_2$ in the sample.   *Ans.* 10.12.

29-6   15.00 ml of commercial bleaching solution is diluted to 250.0 ml. 40.00 ml of the diluted solution, treated with excess KI and acid, liberates iodine which is titrated with 32.20 ml of 0.1040 *N* thiosulfate. Calculate the concentration of the original bleaching solution in terms of the weight-volume percent of (*a*) NaClO, (*b*) available chlorine, (*c*) available oxygen.   *Ans.* (*a*) 5.191.   (*b*) 4.946.   (*c*) 1.116.

29-7   A 25.00-ml sample of ether, sp. gr. 0.708, is analyzed for water; 36.60 ml of Karl Fischer reagent is used for the titration. In a parallel titration, 25.50 ml of the reagent is required for the titration of 10.00 ml of standard water-ethanol solution containing 15.00 g of water per liter. Calculate the percentage of H_2O in the ether.

Ans. 1.217.

29-8   A 1.5600-g sample of chalcocite ore containing 14.40% Cu_2S is analyzed by the Park method; 34.85 ml of 0.08810 *N* sodium thiosulfate is added, but through error the end point is passed. Back titration of the excess thiosulfate requires 2.47 ml of iodine solution. What is the normality of the iodine solution?   *Ans.* 0.1000 *N.*

29-9   A 0.5000-g sample containing KIO_4, KIO_3, and inert matter is dissolved in bicarbonate buffer solution containing excess KI. The liberated iodine requires 41.30 ml of 0.1000 *N* sodium thiosulfate for titration. A 0.2000-g sample of the material is treated with excess KI in strong acid solution. Titration of the liberated iodine requires 45.18 ml of 0.1500 *N* thiosulfate. Calculate the percentages of KIO_4 and KIO_3 in the sample. (Note that the equivalency of KIO_4 is different in the two reactions.)

Ans. 95.00% KIO_4, 3.00% KIO_3.

29-10   A 0.4000-g sample of a pure sulfide of arsenic is dissolved in acid. After buffering the solution to pH 9, it requires 46.50 ml of 0.1400 *N* iodine solution for titration. The hydrogen sulfide from a 0.2500-g sample of the same arsenic sulfide is absorbed in 50.00 ml of the same iodine solution. The excess iodine requires 18.12 ml of 0.05000 *N* sodium thiosulfate for back titration. Calculate the empirical formula of the arsenic sulfide.

29-11   In each part the sample is analyzed for the substance sought (column 2) by treatment with excess KI in acid solution, and titration of the liberated iodine with sodium thiosulfate. Calculate the percent of the substance sought.

Sample, g	Sought	Titration with thiosulfate
(*a*) 1.5000	$Ca_3(AsO_4)_2$	37.90 ml, 1 ml = 2.56 mg Cu
(*b*) 0.3000	Cu	41.80 ml 0.1015 N
(*c*) 1.2550	BaO_2	32.60 ml 0.05000 N
(*d*) 0.4068	MnO_2	43.26 ml 0.1540 N
(*e*) 1.4680	Pb_3O_4	38.84 ml 0.07600 N
(*f*) 0.6066	$KBrO_3$	40.64 ml 0.02000 N
(*g*) 0.8000	Cu_2O	44.48 ml 0.04840 N
(*h*) 0.2602	$K_2Cr_2O_7$	46.68 ml of 0.1115 N

29-12   In each part the sample is analyzed iodimetrically for the substance sought, by reaction of the substance indicated in column 3 with standard iodine. Calculate the percent of the substance sought. [Note the back titration with thiosulfate in parts (*e*) through (*h*).]

Sample, g	Sought	Substance titrated	Titration data
(*a*) 0.1620	As_2O_3	$HAsO_2$	38.75 ml 0.08434 N I_2
(*b*) 1.6564	Sb_2S_3	$H(SbO)C_4H_4O_6$	43.43 ml 0.08640 N I_2
(*c*) 0.3500	Sn	Sn^{++}	18.36 ml 0.02655 N I_2
(*d*) 0.4000	Fe_2O_3	Fe^{++}	35.50 ml 0.03600 N I_2
(*e*) 0.7500	ZnS	H_2S	50.00 ml 0.06000 N I_2; 11.85 ml 0.04600 N $Na_2S_2O_3$
(*f*) 0.3010	FeS_2	SO_2	100.0 ml 0.07500 N I_2; 45.00 ml 0.05000 N $Na_2S_2O_3$
(*g*) 2.5000	S	SO_2	20.00 ml 0.05000 N I_2; 27.07 ml 0.03000 N $Na_2S_2O_3$
(*h*) 0.8500	$CaSO_3$	SO_2	75.00 ml 0.08000 N I_2; 22.40 ml 0.05500 N $Na_2S_2O_3$

29-13   25.00 ml of a commercial hypochlorite bleaching solution is diluted to 500.0 ml. 50.00 ml of the diluted solution, treated with excess KI in acid solution, liberates iodine, which is titrated with 32.60 ml of 0.1050 N sodium thiosulfate. Calculate the concentration of the original bleaching solution in terms of the weight-volume percent of (*a*) NaClO, (*b*) available chlorine, (c) available oxygen.

29-14   A solution of KCNS is 0.04500 N as a precipitant for silver ion. What is its normality when titrated by iodine in a bicarbonate buffer solution?

29-15   A solution of KI is 0.04000 N when oxidized to I_2 (which is titrated with thiosulfate). What is its normality when oxidized to KIO_3, which is then treated with excess KI in acid solution, liberating iodine, which is titrated with thiosulfate?

29-16   A 0.3600-g sample containing KCNS and inert matter is dissolved in water and made to 100.0 ml. A 25.00-ml aliquot of the solution is titrated in bicarbonate buffer solution with 38.34 ml of iodine solution that is 0.1100 N against As_2O_3. Calculate the percentage of KCNS in the sample.

29-17   A bleaching solution is treated with excess KI and acidified with acetic acid. Titration of the liberated iodine requires 42.36 ml of 0.1015 N thiosulfate. The solution is then acidified with hydrochloric acid; the additional iodine liberated requires 15.95

ml of the same thiosulfate. Calculate the grams of NaClO, $NaClO_2$, and "available chlorine" in the sample titrated.

28-18 A 1.0000-g sample of potassium bromide is analyzed for iodide impurity as follows: The sample, in weak acid solution, is treated with bromine to oxidize the iodide to iodate. After removal of excess bromine with phenol, excess KI and HCl are added. The iodine liberated is titrated with 4.520 ml of arsenite solution which contains 0.2968 g of As_2O_3 per liter. Calculate the percentage of KI in the sample.

29-19 A mixture of pure KBr and pure KI weighing 0.6500 g is treated with excess $K_2Cr_2O_7$ and acid. The bromine and iodine are distilled into excess KI solution. Titration of the iodine in this solution requires 48.68 ml of 0.1000 N thiosulfate solution. Calculate the percentage of Br in the sample.

29-20 A sample containing KCl, KBr, KI, and inert matter is analyzed as follows. A 0.5000-g sample requires 37.50 ml of 0.1180 N $AgNO_3$ for precipitation of the halides as their silver salts. A 0.5000-g sample is oxidized with bromine in neutral solution to convert iodide to iodate. After removal of excess bromine, excess KI and acid are added and the liberated iodine is titrated with 47.20 ml of 0.04500 N thiosulfate. A 0.7500-g sample is treated with acid and $K_2Cr_2O_7$. The bromine and iodine are distilled into KI solution, and the iodine in this solution is titrated with 40.00 ml of the same thiosulfate solution used above. Calculate the percentages of KCl, KBr, and KI in the sample.

29-21 A 1.6000-g sample of chalcocite ore containing 14.32% Cu_2S is analyzed by the Park method; 38.45 ml of 0.08620 N thiosulfate is added, but through error the end point is passed. 4.32 ml of iodine solution are used to back titrate the excess thiosulfate. Calculate the normality of the iodine solution.

29-22 A 0.3200-g sample of sodium peroxide is dissolved in an excess of an acidified solution of KI. The liberated iodine is titrated with 43.34 ml of 0.1550 N thiosulfate.

(*a*) Calculate the percent Na_2O_2 in the sample.

(*b*) Calculate the percent available oxygen in the sample.

29-23 A 0.4000-g sample of pyrolusite is analyzed for manganese by the Bunsen method; 40.45 ml of 0.1000 N thiosulfate is required to titrate the liberated iodine.

(*a*) Calculate the percentage of MnO_2 in the pyrolusite ore.

(*b*) If the pyrolusite also contains 4.25% Fe_2O_3 and the ore is analyzed by dissolution in an acid solution of KI, what volume of the 0.1000 N thiosulfate is required for titration of the liberated iodine?

29-24 A 0.4000-g sample containing KIO_4, KIO_3, and inert matter is dissolved in bicarbonate buffer solution containing excess KI; the iodine liberated requires 34.40 ml of 0.09100 N thiosulfate for titration. A 0.2500-g sample of the unknown is treated with excess KI in strong acid solution. Titration of the liberated iodine requires 46.72 ml of 0.1750 N thiosulfate. Calculate the percentages of KIO_4 and KIO_3 in the sample.

29-25 A 0.4000-g sample containing As_2O_3, As_2O_5, and inert matter is dissolved in NaOH to give sodium arsenite and sodium arsenate. The solution, buffered with bicarbonate, is titrated with 32.04 ml of 0.1010 N iodine. The solution is then strongly acidified, excess KI is added, and the liberated iodine is titrated with 38.93 ml of 0.1000 N thiosulfate. Calculate the percentages of As_2O_3, As_2O_5, and As in the sample.

29-26 A 0.5000-g sample containing antimony(III), antimony(V), and inert matter is dissolved in alkali, the solution is buffered with bicarbonate, and is then titrated with 34.30 ml of 0.06000 N iodine. The mixture is then strongly acidified, excess KI is added, and the liberated iodine is titrated with 35.70 ml of thiosulfate solution. 40.00 ml of the iodine solution used in the first titration is equivalent to 32.00 ml of thiosulfate solution used in the second titration. Calculate the percentages of Sb_2O_3 and Sb_2O_5 in the sample.

29-27 0.2500 g of a solid containing only $K_2Cr_2O_7$ and $KBrO_3$ is treated with acid and excess KI; the liberated iodine requires 46.50 ml of $0.1600\,N$ thiosulfate for titration. Calculate the percentages of Cr and Br in the sample.

29-28 A 0.5500-g sample of mineral containing $BaCO_3$ is dissolved in acid; the solution is neutralized and the barium is precipitated as $BaCrO_4$. The precipitate is filtered off and washed and is then dissolved in hydrochloric acid. The dichromate in solution is treated with excess KI, and the liberated iodine is titrated with 36.48 ml of $0.1200\,N$ thiosulfate. Calculate the percentage of BaO in the mineral.

29-29 A 0.4000-g sample of impure sulfamic acid (NH_2SO_3H) is dissolved and treated with excess KIO_3 and KI. The liberated iodine requires 44.75 ml of $0.09000\,N$ thiosulfate for titration. Calculate the percent purity of the sulfamic acid.

29-30 A 0.2000-g sample of a pure organic compound containing oxygen is decomposed in an inert atmosphere, and the carbon monoxide formed is passed through iodine pentoxide; the iodine formed is swept from the reaction train and absorbed in 50.00 ml of $0.1000\,N$ thiosulfate. The excess thiosulfate requires 30.30 ml of $0.08000\,N$ iodine for titration. Calculate the percentage of oxygen in the organic compound.

30

DICHROMATE, CERIUM(IV), AND BROMATE METHODS

In addition to potassium permanganate and iodine, the substances most commonly used as oxidation titrants are potassium dichromate, compounds of cerium(IV), and potassium bromate.

POTASSIUM DICHROMATE

The half-cell potential of the dichromate-chromic reaction,

$$Cr_2O_7^{--} + 14H^+ + 6e \rightleftarrows 2Cr^{+++} + 7H_2O \qquad E^\circ = +1.33 \text{ v}$$

indicates that dichromate in acid solution is not as strong an oxidizing agent as potassium permanganate; however, it has a number of advantages over the latter.

1. Potassium dichromate is available in primary standard quality; standard solutions can be made by the direct method.

2. Standard solutions of potassium dichromate are stable indefinitely in storage.

3. Chloride ion in dilute solution (1 to 2 N HCl) is not oxidized by dichromate. Concentrated hydrochloric acid boiled with dichromate is partially oxidized to chlorine.

4. There is no stable oxidation state of chromium between +6 and +3, therefore only one reaction of dichromate is possible.

5. Standard solutions of dichromate can be boiled without decomposition. This fact makes it especially useful for the oxidation of organic compounds, which usually require high temperature and considerable time for complete oxidation.

426

6. Tenth-normal potassium dichromate is sufficiently transparent that the bottom of the meniscus is easily seen in a buret.

The chief use of dichromate is for the titration of iron(II), either directly for iron analysis, or for the indirect determination of oxidizing agents that have been brought into reaction with excess iron(II), the excess of which is titrated with dichromate. Prior to 1923, the chief disadvantage in the use of dichromate for titration of iron(II) was the use of an external indicator, $K_3Fe(CN)_6$, to show the disappearance of Fe^{++} from the solution. Diphenylamine was first used as an internal indicator for this titration by Knop.[1] This indicator and its derivatives are discussed in Chap. 26. The color change at the end point is from the clear green of chromium(III) to the violet color of the oxidized indicator. An indicator blank cannot be determined directly, but the volume of 0.1 N dichromate consumed in oxidizing the small amount of indicator is negligible. If more dilute dichromate solutions are required for a titration, the indicator should be partially oxidized before use. The color change of diphenylamine or diphenylamine sulfonate is reversible. Back titration of excess dichromate with ferrous solution is therefore possible provided the amount of excess oxidant is not too great and the back titration is done promptly; otherwise the indicator is oxidized beyond the diphenylbenzidine violet product. If dichromate is to be determined with ferrous solution, a measured excess of ferrous solution should be added, to reduce all the dichromate, before adding the indicator; the excess Fe^{++} is then back titrated with standard dichromate. The transition potentials of the ferroin indicators (ferrous phenanthroline and its derivatives) are too positive to be suitable for use as indicators in the tiration of iron(II) by dichromate.

Many of the substances that can be oxidized titrimetrically with permanganate can be titrated also by dichromate. Some additional applications are given below.

1. *Uranium.* The sample solution is prepared for titration as described under permanganate methods (p. 401). However, titration of the uranium(IV) with dichromate using diphenylaminesulfonate indicator does not give a satisfactory end point, due to a slow reaction. The analysis for uranium is completed by adding an excess of iron(III) and phosphoric acid before titration; a sharp end point is then obtained. The mechanism is probably a rapid oxidation of uranium-(IV) by iron(III),

$$UO^{++} + 2Fe^{+++} + H_2O \rightarrow UO_2^{++} + 2Fe^{++} + 2H^+$$

followed by the oxidation of the Fe^{++} by dichromate. Although the method is then indirect for uranium, the equivalency of the uranium is the same as if UO^{++} were titrated directly to UO_2^{++}.

2. *Sodium.* The determination is based upon the precipitation of sodium as $NaZn(UO_2)_3(C_2H_3O_2)_9 \cdot 6H_2O$, which is dissolved in acid and the solution passed through a Jones reductor. After aeration, the uranium is determined as in 1 above.

[1] J. Knop, *Z. anal. Chem.*, **63**, 79 (1923); *J. Am. Chem. Soc.*, **46**, 263 (1924).

3. *Reduced forms of certain cations.* In addition to iron(II), direct titration of tin(II) and copper(I) can be made with dichromate; an inert atmosphere should be used to prevent atmospheric oxidation.

4. *Organic compounds,* such as alcohols, aldehydes, and hydroxy acids, are determined by boiling with a measured excess of standard dichromate; after the reaction is complete, the amount of excess dichromate is determined with standard ferrous solution.

Closely related to the use of dichromate as a titrant is the determination of chromium by bringing it to the +6 oxidation state and determining it by reaction with iron(II). Because the end point is not satisfactory in the direction of titration of dichromate by iron(II), a known amount (excess) of ferrous compound is added, and the excess is back titrated with a standard dichromate solution.

Chrome ores, such as chromite, $Fe(CrO_2)_2$, are fused with sodium peroxide:

$$2Fe(CrO_2)_2 + 7Na_2O_2 \rightarrow Fe_2O_3 + 4Na_2CrO_4 + 3Na_2O$$

The melt is extracted with water and boiled to decompose excess sodium peroxide. The mixture is then acidified and again boiled, and the dichromate is determined with iron(II) as indicated above.

Chrome steels are best decomposed with hot, concentrated perchloric acid. By this treatment the chromium is brought to dichromate:

$$14Cr + 12ClO_4^- + H_2O \rightarrow 7Cr_2O_7^{--} + 6Cl_2 + 2H^+$$

The hot reaction mixture is quickly chilled and diluted by addition of cold water, and the dichromate is determined with iron(II) as above.

CERIUM(IV) METHODS

Cerium forms compounds in which the element exists in oxidation states +3 and +4. Solid compounds of cerium(IV) are yellow-orange and their solutions are similar in color to potassium dichromate; cerium(III) solutions are colorless. Although cerium(IV) solution can be self-indicating, most published directions for its use as an oxidimetric titrant specify one of the ferrous phenanthroline redox indicators, which gives a more pronounced color change, from intense red to pale blue (colorless) as the indicator is oxidized.

If the half reaction $Ce^{4+} + e \rightleftarrows Ce^{+++}$ adequately represented the cerium-(IV)–cerium(III) couple, its potential, as expressed by the Nernst equation, should be independent of acidity and of the nature of the anion present. In solutions of different acids, however, the standard potentials differ considerably from one solution to another:[2] hydrochloric, 1.28 v; sulfuric, 1.44 v; nitric, 1.61 v; perchloric, 1.70 v. Formation of complexes with cerium(IV), decreasing the concentration of this species, would decrease the potential of the couple.

[2] G. F. Smith, *Cerate Oxidimetry,* Columbus, Ohio, G. Frederick Smith Chemical Co., 1942, p. 22.

Perchlorate and nitrate ions are poor complex formers, whereas sulfate and chloride ions tend to form more stable complexes. Anionic complexes of cerium-(IV) of the form CeX_6^{--} are well known, in which X represents an equivalent of anion; for example, $CeCl_6^{--}$, $Ce(SO_4)_3^{--}$, $Ce(NO_3)_6^{--}$. The stabilities of these complexes correlate well with the observed standard potentials given above. In addition, cationic complexes such as $Ce(OH)^{+++}$ and $Ce(OH)_2^{++}$ are formed by hydrolysis, and there is also evidence for dimeric species such as Ce_2O^{6+} and others. The potential of the cerium(IV)–cerium(III) couple is almost independent of acid concentration in hydrochloric acid and sulfuric acid, but in the case of perchloric acid the potential changes from $+1.70$ to $+1.87$ v as the perchloric acid concentration is increased from 1 M to 8 M. In 8 M perchloric acid solution, cerium(IV) has the greatest oxidizing power of any titrant.

The properties of cerate solutions for oxidimetry are outlined below. The student should make comparisons with permanganate and dichromate solutions.

1. Solutions of cerium(IV) are stable indefinitely.

2. Solutions in sulfuric acid can be boiled without decomposition. Very slow decomposition results from boiling the nitrato- or the perchlorato-cerate(IV) solutions.

3. There is only one possible change in oxidation number.

4. The potential of the cerium(IV)–cerium(III) system can be varied over a considerable range by appropriate selection of the anion present.

5. Provided all other components in the reaction are colorless, it can serve as its own indicator. However, redox indicators are generally used.

6. Cerium(IV) solutions can be used only in acidic media; in alkaline media precipitation of the hydroxide or hydrous dioxide, $CeO_2 \cdot xH_2O$, occurs.

7. No oxidation of chloride ion occurs unless the solution is more than about 3 M in hydrochloric acid. Cerate solutions are therefore especially suitable for the titrimetric oxidation of iron(II) in dilute hydrochloric acid solution.

8. The compound ammonium hexanitratocerate(IV), $(NH_4)_2Ce(NO_3)_6$, is a primary standard;[3] if desired, solutions can be made by the direct method.

9. Solutions of cerium(IV) can be prepared from CeO_2, $Ce(SO_4)_2$, or $(NH_4)_2Ce(SO_4)_3 \cdot 2H_2O$ and then standardized against sodium oxalate or arsenic(III) oxide. For these reactions a catalyst (osmium tetroxide or iodine monochloride) is generally required; in 8 M perchloric acid solution, however, oxalate can be titrated in the cold without a catalyst.

In general, the substances that can be determined by permanganate can also be determined by cerium(IV) titration. Direct titration is made of iron(II), oxalate, hydrogen peroxide, arsenic(III), antimony(III), thallium(I), uranium-(IV), vanadium(IV), molybdenum(V), tin(II), plutonium(III), etc. In the determination of strong reducing agents that are easily air oxidized, such as copper-(I) and titanium(III), the reduced solution is delivered directly into a solution

---

[3] Cerium compounds are available from G. Frederick Smith Chemical Co., Columbus, Ohio.

of iron(III), and the iron(II) formed (equivalent to the strong reducing agent) is titrated. For the determination of substances that are slowly oxidized by cerium-(IV), a measured excess of the latter is added and the excess is back titrated with standard iron(II); this method is used in the determination of chromium(III), phosphite and hypophosphite, nitrite, hydroxylamine, mercury(I). Determination of organic compounds, principally hydroxy compounds such as glycerol and carbohydrates, and hydroxy-acids such as tartaric and citric acids, usually requires elevated temperature, sometimes with refluxing, and occasionally use of catalysts. The excess cerium(IV) is back titrated.

POTASSIUM BROMATE

Bromate ion, in acid solution, is a strong oxidizing agent. For reduction to bromide ion,

$$BrO_3^- + 6H^+ + 6e \rightleftarrows 3H_2O + Br^- \qquad E° = +1.44 \text{ v}$$

The potential of the bromine-bromide couple,

$$Br_2 \text{ (aq)} + 2e \rightleftarrows 2Br^- \qquad E° = +1.065 \text{ v}$$

indicates that bromide ion, formed by reduction of BrO_3^-, can be oxidized by the latter, liberating bromine:

$$BrO_3^- + 5Br^- + 6H^+ \rightarrow 3H_2O + 3Br_2$$

For the bromate-bromine half reaction,

$$BrO_3^- + 6H^+ + 5e \rightleftarrows 3H_2O + \tfrac{1}{2}Br_2 \qquad E° = +1.52 \text{ v}$$

If a substance that is a stronger reducing agent than bromide ion is treated with bromate in acid solution, no free bromine is formed in solution until all the reducing agent has been oxidized. With milder reducing agents, the reduction product of the bromate is free bromine. In the presence of mercury(II) sulfate, however, complete reduction of bromate to bromide occurs, the bromide ion being bound by the mercury(II) as the weak ionogen $HgBr_2$, or the bromo complex, $HgBr_4^{--}$.

Potassium bromate, properly recrystallized and dried at 150–180°C, can be used to make a direct standard solution. Approximate solutions of potassium bromate can be standardized against arsenic(III) oxide or against pure iron. Mercury(II) basic bromate, $Hg(OH)BrO_3$, formed by hydrolysis of $Hg(BrO_3)_2$, may be used as a primary standard for direct preparation of the titrant solution; it is only slightly soluble in water, but the solubility is increased by adding hydrochloric acid.

Certain azo indicators, such as methyl red and methyl orange, which are red in acid solution, are easily brominated to give pale yellow-colored products; these substances can serve as indicators for bromate titrations. The indigo sulfonic acids can be used similarly, changing from blue to colorless. The reactions of these indicators are irreversible. It is necessary, therefore, that the substance undergoing titration be a stronger reducing agent than bromide ion, so that free bromine is not formed until the stoichiometric point of the tiration has just been passed. Great care must be taken to titrate slowly and with good stirring to prevent a localized excess of bromate from reacting with the indicator before the true end point is reached. Also, bromination of the indicator often is not instantaneous, and thirty seconds or so may have to be allowed between drops of titrant near the end point. For these reasons, bromate titrations are frequently made by adding a measured excess of the bromate standard solution, the amount of the excess being determined by adding potassium iodide,

$$BrO_3^- + 6I^- + 6H^+ \rightarrow Br^- + 3H_2O + 3I_2$$

and titrating the iodine with standard sodium thiosulfate solution, using starch indicator.

Among the few reversible redox indicators that have been discovered for bromate titrations are *p*-ethoxychrysoidin (red to colorless), quinoline yellow (yellow-green to colorless), and α-naphthoflavone (pale yellow to orange-brown).

Standard bromate solution can be used for the titration of a number of inorganic substances, such as arsenite, antimonite, mercury(I), hexacyanoferrate-(II), and hydrazine. It is especially useful for the determination of certain organic compounds, which undergo a bromination by substitution of hydrogen atoms on aromatic rings by bromine atoms. For these bromination reactions, an acidic solution of bromate can be considered as a convenient source of free bromine, which will be used in writing the equations for the reactions. Phenol, for example, is converted to tribromophenol:

$$C_6H_5OH + 3Br_2 \rightarrow C_6H_2Br_3OH + 3H^+ + 3Br^-$$

Of special interest is the titration of 8-quinolinol as a means of determining many metal ions that form insoluble 8-quinolinolates. Using aluminum ion as an example, the metal ion is precipitated with 8-quinolinol in buffered solution (in *p*H range 4 to 9):

$$Al^{+++} + 3C_9H_7ON \rightarrow 3H^+ + Al(C_9H_6ON)_3$$

The precipitate is filtered off and washed, and is then dissolved in strong acid:

$$Al(C_9H_6ON)_3 + 3H^+ \rightarrow Al^{+++} + 3C_9H_7ON$$

The 8-quinolinol in solution is titrated with bromate:

$$C_9H_7ON + 2Br_2 \rightarrow C_9H_5Br_2ON + 2H^+ + 2Br^-$$

An alternative method is to precipitate the cation by the use of a known excess of standard 8-quinolinol solution; after filtering and washing the precipitate, the amount of the excess reagent in the filtrate and washings is determined by titration with standard bromate solution.

PROBLEMS

30-1 What weight of the given compound is required to prepare the solution specified?

(a) $K_2Cr_2O_7$ to make 500.0 ml of 0.08000 N solution.

(b) $(NH_4)_2Ce(NO_3)_6$ to make 250.0 ml of 0.1100 N solution.

(c) CeO_2 to make one liter of 0.07500 N solution.

(d) $KBrO_3$ to make two liters of 0.1155 N solution.

(e) $(NH_4)_2Ce(SO_4)_3 \cdot 2H_2O$ to make 500.0 ml of 0.05000 N solution.

Ans. (a) 1.9612 g. (b) 15.08 g.

30-2 Calculate the normality of the solution described.

(a) One ml of $K_2Cr_2O_7$ is equivalent to 5.000 mg of Fe_2O_3.

(b) One ml of $K_2Cr_2O_7$ is equivalent to 7.420 mg of As_2O_3.

(c) One ml of Ce(IV) solution is equivalent to 3.350 mg of $Na_2C_2O_4$.

(d) One ml of Ce(IV) solution is equivalent to 5.305 mg of iron.

(e) One ml of $KBrO_3$ solution contains 3.480 mg of $KBrO_3$.

Ans. (a) 0.06262 N. (b) 0.1500 N.

30-3 A certain solution of $K_2Cr_2O_7$ has the same normality (as an oxidant) as a reducing solution made by mixing 20.00 ml of 0.1200 N Fe^{++} with 30.00 ml of 0.08000 N $HAsO_2$. What weight of $K_2Cr_2O_7$ is present in a liter of its solution?

Ans. 4.708 g.

30-4 A sample of a pure oxide of iron, weighing 0.3600 g, is dissolved and reduced. 44.40 ml of 0.1050 N $K_2Cr_2O_7$ solution is required to titrate the Fe^{++}. Is the sample FeO, Fe_2O_3, or Fe_3O_4?

30-5 A 1.0000-g sample containing aluminum is dissolved, then precipitated as aluminum 8-quinolinolate, $Al(C_9H_6ON)_3$. The precipitate is washed, then dissolved in acid to give C_9H_7ON, which is titrated with 40.50 ml of $KBrO_3$. The bromate solution contains 2.2500 g of pure $KBrO_3$ (and excess KBr) per liter. Calculate the percentage of Al_2O_3 in the sample.   *Ans.* 1.391.

30-6 How many milliliters of ferrous solution, containing 14.596 g of pure $FeSO_4 \cdot 7H_2O$ per 500.0 ml, must be added to a liter of solution containing 5.394 g of $K_2Cr_2O_7$ so that the two solutions will have the same normality in redox reactions.

30-7 When a sample of iron ore weighing 0.8900 g is dissolved, reduced, and titrated with a solution of $K_2Cr_2O_7$, each milliliter of dichromate used represents 0.500% Fe_2O_3 in the ore. Calculate the normality of the dichromate solution.

30-8 Calculate the percent of the constituent sought from the data given.

Sample, g	Titrant	Sought
(a) 0.6500	42.50 ml 0.1010 N $K_2Cr_2O_7$	Fe_2O_3
(b) 0.7500	39.75 ml 0.08750 N Ce(IV)	As_2O_3
(c) 0.2900	43.40 ml 0.09800 N Ce(IV)	$Na_2C_2O_4$
(d) 0.5675	41.00 ml 0.1100 N $K_2Cr_2O_7$	$SnCl_2$
(e) 0.8642	38.00 ml 0.1200 N $K_2Cr_2O_7$	KI

30-9 A 0.5000-g sample of chromite ore is fused with sodium peroxide. After acidifying and adding 2.000 g of $Fe(NH_4)_2(SO_4)_2 \cdot 6H_2O$ the solution requires 34.60 ml of 0.06000 N $K_2Cr_2O_7$ for titration. Calculate chromium content of the ore as the percentage of (a) Cr; (b) Cr_2O_3.

30-10 In the analysis of a 0.4000-g sample of chromite ore containing 12.00% Cr_2O_3, what weight of $FeSO_4 \cdot 7H_2O$ will have to be added so that titration of the excess Fe^{++} will require 45.00 ml of 0.08800 N $K_2Cr_2O_7$?

30-11 A 0.5000-g sample of chrome steel is dissolved in hot concentrated perchloric acid. After cooling, diluting, and adding 50.00 ml of 0.1000 N ferrous solution, titration requires 33.40 ml of 0.08300 N cerium(IV) solution. Calculate the percentage of Cr in the steel.

30-12 A 1.2000-g sample of chrome-vanadium steel is dissolved and oxidized to $Cr_2O_7^{--}$ and VO_2^{+}. Reduction of both of these ions (to Cr^{+++} and VO^{++}, respectively) requires 42.20 ml of 0.1000 N Fe^{++} solution. On a separate analysis the steel is found to contain 0.750% vanadium. Calculate the percentage of Cr in the sample.

30-13 A 0.7500-g sample of a cerium(IV) compound of 98.5% purity requires 44.40 ml of 0.05000 N Fe^{++} solution for titration. Is the compound CeO_2, or $Ce(SO_4)_2$, or $(NH_4)_2Ce(NO_3)_6$?

30-14 Three different solutions, *A*, *B*, and *C*, contain the same weight in grams of CrO_3, $K_2Cr_2O_7$, and K_2CrO_4, respectively, per liter. What is the ratio of their normalities as oxidizing agents?

30-15 A 0.4000-g sample of impure potassium iodide, dissolved in hydrochloric acid, requires 42.72 ml of 0.1100 N $Ce(SO_4)_2$ solution for titration of I^- to ICl. Calculate the percent purity of the potassium iodide.

30-16 A 1.0000-g sample containing chromium and manganese is fused with Na_2O_2, forming Na_2CrO_4 and Na_2MnO_4. After dissolving the melt and decomposing the excess peroxide, the solution is acidified, causing the manganate to disproportionate to MnO_4^- and MnO_2. The MnO_2 is filtered off and washed, then treated with an acidic solution containing 0.5000 g of $FeSO_4 \cdot (NH_4)_2SO_4 \cdot 6H_2O$, which is an excess of Fe^{++} requiring 15.52 ml of 0.05000 N $Ce(SO_4)_2$ for titration. The main filtrate containing the dichromate and permanganate, is treated with 0.4500 g of pure $Na_2C_2O_4$, the excess of which requires 44.32 ml of 0.05000 N $KMnO_4$. Calculate the percentages of MnO_2 and Cr_2O_3 in the sample.

30-17 The aluminum in a 0.3000-g sample is precipitated as aluminum 8-quinolinolate, $Al(C_9H_6ON)_3$. The precipitate is washed free from excess reagent, then dissolved in acid to give C_9H_7ON, which requires 48.40 ml of 0.1260 N $KBrO_3$ solution (containing excess Br^-) for titration. Calculate the percentage of Al_2O_3 in the sample.

30-18 A 0.2500-g sample of dolomitic limestone is dissolved in acid. After adjusting the *p*H to 11, 50.00 ml of 8-quinolinol reagent is added to precipitate the magnesium as $Mg(C_9H_6ON)_2$. The precipitate is filtered off and washed (the filtrate and washings being reserved), then is dissolved in acid and titrated with 34.50 ml of $KBrO_3$ solution that contains 5.000 g of $KBrO_3$ (and excess KBr) per liter. Titration of 50.00 ml of the 8-quinolinol reagent solution requires 45.50 ml of the same bromate solution. The filtrate reserved above is titrated with 44.05 ml of bromate solution made by diluting 50.00 ml of the above $KBrO_3$ solution to 200.0 ml. Calculate the percentage of MgO in the sample from (*a*) the solution of the precipitate, and (*b*) the excess reagent in the filtrate.

Part IV □ Some Physicochemical Methods

31

ABSORPTION AND EMISSION OF RADIANT ENERGY

The absorption and emission of radiant energy constitute the most widely used physicochemical methods of analysis.[1] The wide application is the result of a number of factors: (1) the great range of wavelengths or frequencies of radiant energy and its different modes of interaction with matter; (2) the development and commercial availability of reliable instruments for making the measurements; (3) the advantages inherent in the method. In general, analysis can be made rapidly (unless considerable pretreatment is required to eliminate interferences), once the method has been standardized. The method is therefore attractive for repetitive measurements of the same constituent, as in routine control analysis. In general, also, the method is applicable to the accurate determination of much smaller amounts of constituent than are the gravimetric or titrimetric methods; it is therefore especially suited for trace analysis work. There is a common misconception that spectrophotometric methods are applicable *only* to small amounts of constituent; this is by no means the case. Often, the method is nondestructive of the sample, which may be of importance when the desired constituent is precious, as in certain biochemical or transuranium-element research programs. Spectrophotometric methods are of such importance that they are very widely used in almost every industrial, clinical, research, and academic laboratory.

Nomenclature

Unfortunately, some confusion in terminology has arisen during the development of the science of photometry, so that a given concept or property may have

---

[1] R. B. Fisher, *Anal. Chem.*, **37**, 27A (1965).

different names in the writing of different authors. Recognition of this confusion and the need to do something to eliminate it resulted in the formation of a Joint Committee on Nomenclature in Applied Spectroscopy established by the Society of Applied Spectroscopy and the American Society for Testing Materials (ASTM). The definitions, symbols, and names used in this chapter follow the recommendations of the Committee's report.[2]

Related concepts should be reflected by similarity of names. This is most readily accomplished by the use of suffixes to the root of the word expressing the basic concept. Following are some commonly used suffixes.

-or, meaning a device; reflector, comparator, resistor, etc. (Occasionally also *-er*, as in amplifier, and *-ment*, as in filament.)

-ation, meaning a process or result of a process; excitation, radiation, ionization. (Occasionally also merely *-tion*, as in absorption, or *-sion*, as in transmission.)

-ance, meaning a property of a device, or body; transmittance, absorbance resistance, capacitance.

-ity, meaning a property of a substance; density, solubility, conductivity, absorptivity, emissivity.

-meter, a measuring device; ammeter, colorimeter, densitometer, spectrophotometer.

-scope, an optical or viewing device; microscope, telescope, spectroscope.

-scopy, meaning observation; spectroscopy, microscopy.

-graph, a device for producing a record of observations; polarograph, spectrograph.

-gram, the record produced by an instrument; polarogram, spectrogram.

The Nature of Radiant Energy

Radiant energy is defined[2] as energy transmitted as electromagnetic radiation. It can be emitted by substances under high excitation conditions, such as high temperature or by an electric discharge. It can be absorbed, transmitted, reflected, and refracted by various susbstances in different states (solid, liquid, solution, and gas) if the incident radiation is of appropriate wavelength.

Electromagnetic radiation appears to have dual characteristics. In diffraction and refraction, the radiation has the properties of *waves*, although no physical medium is necessary for their propagation. In emission and absorption phenomena, electromagnetic radiation also has the properties of *particles*, called **photons** (Greek, *phot-*, pertaining to light).

The complete electromagnetic spectrum covers some 20 or more orders of magnitude of wavelengths; its representation is therefore best displayed on a logarithmic scale. Figure 31-1 shows the portion of the electromagnetic spectrum

---

[2] *Anal. Chem.*, **24**, 1349 (1952).

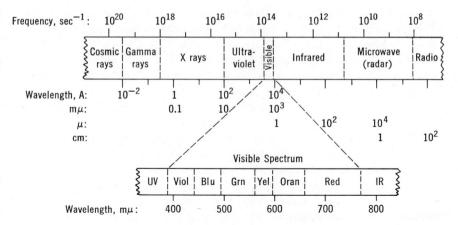

Fig. 31-1   The electromagnetic spectrum.

of principal interest, with the various regions characterized by name, wavelength, and frequency. The **wavelength**, λ, is the linear distance measured along the line of propagation, between two points that are in phase on adjacent waves. Because the wavelengths of importance in chemical spectrophotometry are very short, they are expressed in units of very small dimensions, usually the micron (μ), millimicron (mμ), or angstrom (A).

$$1 \text{ A} = 0.1 \text{ m}\mu = 10^{-4} \mu = 10^{-7} \text{ mm} = 10^{-8} \text{ cm} = 10^{-10} \text{ m}$$

or

$$10^4 \text{ A} = 10^3 \text{ m}\mu = 1 \mu = 10^{-3} \text{ mm} = 10^{-4} \text{ cm} = 10^{-6} \text{ m}$$

The **frequency**, v, is the number of waves passing a fixed point in unit time, e.g., cycles per second (cps), or megacycles per second (Mc/sec); 1 megacycle = 10^6 cycles. Frequency and wavelength are related by

$$v = c/\lambda$$

where c is the velocity of the radiation, namely, 2.9979×10^{10} cm/sec (in vacuum). Another unit, especially convenient in the middle region of the spectrum and much used in infrared spectrophotometry, is the **wave number**, $\bar{v}$, which is the number of waves in one cm: $\bar{v} = 1/\lambda$; wave number has the dimension of reciprocal centimeters, written cm^{-1}.

   Color.   The sensation of color is a combined physical, chemical, and psychological response to stimulation of certain parts of the retina of the eye by radiant energy of certain wavelengths or frequencies. The human eye is sensitive to only a very small portion of the entire electromagnetic spectrum, namely, between about 400 and 750 mμ, or 4000 and 7500 A. The various colored regions of the visible spectrum are shown in the lower part of Fig. 31-1. **Colorimetry**, in its usual sense, applies to the measurement of the fraction of " white light " from an incandescent source, that has passed through a liquid or solution medium (or has been reflected from a solid surface). A solution containing iron(III) and thiocyanate has a red color, because the $FeCNS^{++}$ in the solution absorbs the shorter (blue) waves and transmits the longer (red) waves. A solution containing $Cu(NH_3)_4^{++}$ appears blue, because it absorbs the longer (red) waves and transmits the shorter (blue) waves. A solution of permanganate appears purple, because it absorbs the radiation of intermediate wavelengths (green, yellow) and transmits both the short (blue) and the long (red) waves. If the colors are very faint, only trace amounts of iron, copper, or manganese are present. If deep or intense colors are observed, the solution is judged to contain moderate to large amounts of these substances. By interposing a light filter, such as a plate of suitably colored glass, between the light source and the sample, the radiant energy incident upon the sample consists of a more or less wide band of wavelengths, and this sharpens the sensitivity of the observation or measurement.

In **spectrophotometry**, monochromatic radiation (radiant energy of a single wavelength, or, for practical reasons, a narrow band of wavelengths) is incident upon the sample, and the measurements of the transmitted radiation are made with sensitive **transducers**, such as photocells, photomultiplier tubes, and thermo-couples.

Interaction of Radiant Energy and Matter

The energy of a photon is dependent upon its frequency or wavelength, and is given by the relation

$$E = hv = h(c/\lambda)$$

where E is the energy in ergs, v is the frequency in cycles per second, and h is Planck's constant, 6.6256×10^{-27} erg second. The relation of various energy terms to wavelength is as follows: 1 electron volt (ev) $= 1.602 \times 10^{-12}$ erg $= 23,066$ calories $\cong 8.0 \times 10^3$ cm^{-1} $\cong 1.25 \times 10^{-4}$ cm $\cong 1.25 \times 10^4$ A $\cong 1.25$ μ.

Atoms, ions, or molecules can absorb radiation if the energy of the photons corresponds to one of the natural frequencies of vibration of the electrons and/or the atoms within a molecule. The absorbing material is then said to be in an *excited state*; the change is often represented thus: $M + hv \rightarrow M^*$. The energy relation given above shows that the energy of photons increases with increasing frequency (or with decreasing wavelength). Photons of different energies (i.e., radiant energy of different wavelengths) produce different effects in the absorbing material.

1. Very short wavelengths (gamma and cosmic rays) can cause nuclear transformations. Energies are in the region of millions of electron volts (Mev).

2. X rays cause transitions of the firmly bound inner shell electrons of atoms; absorption of x rays is therefore independent of the state of combination of the atoms. Energies of several hundred to several thousand electron volts are required.

3. Absorption of radiation in the ultraviolet and visible spectral regions involves excitation of the outer (valence) electrons of atoms, hence is dependent upon the state of combination of the atoms. For example, dichromate ion is orange, chromate ion is yellow, chromium(III) is green in the aquo form and violet in certain complexes. Energies of the order of 1 to 25 ev are involved.

4. Absorption in the near infrared region alters the mode of vibration of molecules. Energies are of the order of 0.01 to 1 ev.

5. Alteration of molecular rotation, having low energy requirements (10^{-3} to 10^{-5} ev) occurs by absorption of energy in the far infrared and microwave regions.

The above processes are the basis of all absorption spectrophotometric methods. The energy absorbed by the atoms, ions, or molecules is soon dissipated within the absorbing material, usually as heat; but it may sometimes be re-emitted as radiant energy (fluorescence, phosphorescence), or it may initiate chemical reactions.

The remainder of this chapter deals principally with absorption spectrophotometry in the visible region of the spectrum by substances in solution; it should be noted, however, that the fundamental laws and many of the principles apply to other spectral regions also. Brief mention is made of emission spectrometry; detailed treatment of these and other related subjects is reserved for more advanced courses.

ABSORPTION SPECTROPHOTOMETRY

Definitions and Symbols

The following definitions and symbols are recommended by the Joint Committee on Nomenclature[2]; obsolete equivalent terms and symbols are given, for correlation with the older literature.

Absorbance, A, is the logarithm to the base 10 of the reciprocal of the transmittance, T, where pure solvent is the reference material; that is, $A = \log_{10} 1/T = -\log_{10} T$. This property was formerly called optical density ($O.D.$), or sometimes merely density (D), or extinction or extinctance (E). The symbol A for absorbance will not be confused with angstrom, which is always preceded by a number and is set in roman type (A).

Absorptivity, a, is the ratio of the absorbance to the product of length of optical path, b, and the concentration, c. That is, $a = A/bc$, or $A = abc$. It is the absorbance per unit optical path (usually in centimeters) and per unit concentration, that is, the **specific absorbance**. Concentration units should always be stated. Obsolete terms for absorptivity are specific extinction, specific absorption, extinction coefficient, absorbance index; the obsolete symbol is a Greek lowercase kappa.

[2]*Anal. Chem.*, **24**, 1349 (1952).

Molar absorptivity, ε, is the absorptivity when concentration is expressed in moles per liter and light path is in centimeters. It has the dimensions of liter per mole centimeter.

Radiant power, P, sometimes called radiant flux, is the rate at which energy is transported in a beam of radiant energy. It is the quantity that is measured by detectors such as photocells, thermocouples, and bolometers. This term was formerly designated by the letter I, for intensity.

Transmittance, T, is the ratio of radiant power transmitted by a sample (P), to the radiant power incident upon the sample (P_0), both being measured at the same spectral position and with the same slit width; $T = P/P_0$. The beam is understood to be parallel radiation and incident at right angles to plane parallel surfaces of the sample.

The Spectrophotometry Laws

When a beam of monochromatic radiant energy falls on a homogeneous layer of " transparent " substance, some energy is absorbed and the remainder is transmitted. (Actually, a small amount of energy is also reflected; generally the instrument used for making measurements is designed so that this factor cancels out.) If the incident radiant energy includes wavelengths in the visible region of the spectrum, and the medium through which it passes can selectively absorb certain wavelengths, the visual color observed will correspond to the wavelengths of energy that is transmitted. It should be within the experience of students in quantitative analysis that the intensity of color of a given solution is observed to be different when it is viewed through different thicknesses, and that when viewed through identical thicknesses, solutions of different concentrations of the same substance differ in the intensity of the observed color. These generalizations have a quantitative basis in the laws of spectrophotometry.

1. *Bouguer's law*[3] consists of two parts.

a. The monochromatic radiant power transmitted by a given homogeneous isotropic medium is proportional to the incident radiant power; or, the ratio of the transmitted radiant power, P, to the incident radiant power, P_0, is a constant:

$$P/P_0 = T$$

The constant, T, is in fact the **transmittance**, which is defined as P/P_0.

b. The transmitted radiant power decreases in geometric progression as the length of the optical path increases in arithmetic progression. Stated in another way: layers of equal thickness absorb equal fractions of the radiant power incident upon them. These relations may be made clear, to those who do not immediately recognize the mathematical significance, by a simple illustration.

---

[3] For many years this was known as Lambert's law (1760); it was then found that the same law had been enunciated by Bouguer in 1729.

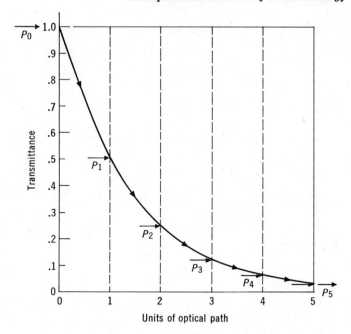

Fig. 31-2 Diagrammatic representation of Bouguer's law, assuming $T = P/P_0 = 0.50$ per unit optical path length.

Suppose that a layer of solution one unit (e.g., 1 cm) in thickness or optical path transmits 0.50 of the radiant power incident upon it, and that this radiation becomes incident upon another unit layer of the same material; the second layer will transmit 0.50 of the radiant power incident upon it, or $0.50 \times 0.50 = 0.25$ of the original radiant power; and so on for additional unit layers.

Optical path:	0	1	2	3	$\cdots$	n
Transmittance	1.00	0.50	0.50^2	0.50^3	$\cdots$	0.50^n
			0.25	0.125		

Figure 31-2 is a diagrammatic representation of these facts; the illustration shows the exponential or logarithmic relation between transmittance and optical path length. Expressed mathematically, Bouguer's law is

$$-\log T = ab$$

where T = transmittance = P/P_0
   b = optical path length (thickness)
   a = absorptivity of the medium

If a solution of unit concentration is assumed, a becomes the absorbance, A, per unit optical path. The negative sign is required in the T term, because transmittance decreases as optical path increases. The term **absorbance, A,** is the negative logarithm to the base 10 of the reciprocal of transmittance:

$$A = ab = -\log_{10}T = -\log_{10}(P/P_0) = \log_{10}(P_0/P)$$

$$= \log_{10}(1/T)$$

Because a logarithm to the base 10 is a power of 10 that gives the quantity, we may write also

$$P = P_0 \cdot 10^{-ab} \quad \text{or} \quad P_0 = P \cdot 10^{ab}$$

All these mathematical expressions are definitions of Bouguer's law.

2. *Beer's law*[4] expresses the same relation between transmittance and concentration of absorbing material as Bouguer's law expresses between transmittance and optical path, namely, that, for a given optical path, the transmittance decreases in geometric progression as the concentration increases in arithmetic progression. Hence

$$-\log T = ac$$

where c = concentration

a = absorptivity, and also the absorbance for unit concentration at unit optical path length

(Because only logarithms to the base 10 are to be used, the subscript of the base will be omitted hereafter.) For Beer's law the following relations exist:

$$A = ac = -\log T = -\log(P/P_0) = \log(P_0/P)$$

$$= \log(1/T)$$

and

$$P = P_0 \cdot 10^{-ac} \quad \text{or} \quad P_0 = P \cdot 10^{ac}$$

3. *The fundamental law of spectrophotometry* is obtained by combining Bouguer's law with Beer's law, to give the following relations[5]:

$$A = abc = -\log T = -\log(P/P_0) = \log(P_0/P)$$

$$= \log(1/T)$$

$$P = P_0 \cdot 10^{-abc} \quad \text{and} \quad P_0 = P \cdot 10^{abc}$$

---

[4] This law was formulated independently by Beer and by Bernard in 1852.

[5] Combination of the mathematical statements of the separate laws is not as simple as it might first appear. A straightforward derivation of the fundamental law can be made on the basis of the number of absorbing centers in the beam of radiant energy. The decrease in radiant power, ΔP, is proportional to the incident radiant power, P, and to the number, N, of absorbing centers in the beam. Expressing this relation in derivative form and then integrating between the limits of zero and a finite value gives the fundamental law by noting that the number of absorbing centers can be expressed as the product of concentration by optical path length. The combined laws (fundamental law) are now commonly called merely Beer's law.

The form of these equations shows that a plot of absorbance, A (of a given substance at constant optical path), against concentration c is a straight line of slope a, and a plot of $\log T$ against c is a straight line of slope $-a$, in which a is the absorptivity of the substance, with dimensions consistent with the units of concentration and optical path.

Deviations from Beer's law.   A plot of A or of $\log T$ against concentration, which serves as a calibration plot for analysis of unknowns, is commonly used also as a test for "conformity" of a system to Beer's law, or as a test for "deviations" from the law. Many "deviations" from Beer's law have been reported in the literature, especially for solutions at the high end of the applicable concentration range. Most of these "deviations" are apparent rather than real, and are due to one or both of the following causes.

1. Lack of monochromaticity of the incident radiation. Apparent deviations frequently appear in absorbance measurements made with a filter photometer, where the incident radiation encompasses a considerable band of wavelengths, especially if the center of the band does not coincide with the wavelength of maximum absorption by the system being measured.

2. Chemical changes within the system, so that the same absorbing species is not being measured at all concentrations. Changes that may be encountered are association, dissociation, interaction with the solvent (e.g., hydrolysis), pH effects, etc. For example, measurements of chromate or of dichromate ion in unbuffered solution may give rise to apparent deviations, owing to shifts in the equilibrium $2CrO_4^{--} + 2H^+ \rightleftarrows Cr_2O_7^{--} + H_2O$ with dilution. Solutions of copper(II) and ammonia contain various complexes, $Cu(NH_3)^{++}$, $Cu(NH_3)_2^{++}$, $Cu(NH_3)_3^{++}$, and $Cu(NH_3)_4^{++}$, having somewhat different absorptivities at a given wavelength; the ratio of the different species will change with change in concentration of the reactants.

The *real* deviations from Beer's law, which are insignificant at concentrations less than about 0.01 M, may arise because the constant term in the law is not absorptivity, but a function of both absorptivity and refractive index.[6] Also, at high concentrations the solute particles may be crowded so close together as to alter their charge distribution and the extent of their ability to absorb radiation of a given wavelength.

Methods of Operation

Four classes of operational methods in colorimetry or spectrophotometry are alike in that an unknown sample is compared with a known or standard sample, but they are different in the manner of making the comparison. These methods are discussed in terms of ordinary colorimetry or spectrophotometry (visible region of the spectrum), although the principles apply also to other spectral

[6] G. Kortum and M. Seiler, *Angew. Chem.*, **52**, 687 (1939).

regions where different devices may be used for making the observations or measurements. Because two of the methods, namely, dilution method and duplication method, are not much used at present, only the balancing and the standard series methods will be discussed.

Balancing Method. The unknown sample, containing any necessary color-developing reagents, is placed in a tube or cylinder having a flat, transparent bottom. A standard solution of the same substance, similarly color-developed, is placed in a second identical tube or cylinder. The depth (thickness, optical path) of the standard solution is set at some convenient fixed value, and the depth of the unknown solution is varied until, when observed from above toward a light source below the tubes, the intensities of the light transmitted are identical. The principle is illustrated in Fig. 31-3. In terms of the Bouguer-Beer law:

$$-\log(P_1/P_0) = ab_1c_1 \quad \text{and} \quad -\log(P_2/P_0) = ab_2c_2$$

Because the same substance is present in both unknown and standard, the absorptivity a is the same in both. When the two solutions have equal transmittances, $P_1/P_0 = P_2/P_0$, hence $b_1c_1 = b_2c_2$. This relation shows that concentrations are inversely proportional to optical paths at equicoloration. The observed transmittances are identical, because there are the same number of absorbers in the optical path; in one case they are merely dispersed over a longer path than in the other case. By knowing c_2 (standard) and by measuring b_1 and b_2, the concentration of the unknown, c_1, is given by $c_1 = b_2c_2/b_1$. For best results the unknown and the standard should not be widely different in concentration.

The balancing method is used in the Duboscq type of colorimeter, shown in Fig. 31-4. Light from a suitable source, such as diffuse daylight or a tungsten lamp, is reflected by the mirror into the colorimeter cups, which contain the solutions. The cups are mounted so they can be moved vertically by rack-and-pinion gears. The cups are raised until the glass plungers dip well into the solutions. One cup is set at a convenient fixed position, and the other cup is racked

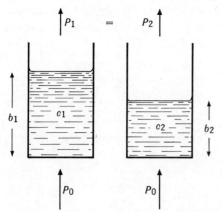

Fig. 31-3 Principle of the balancing method.

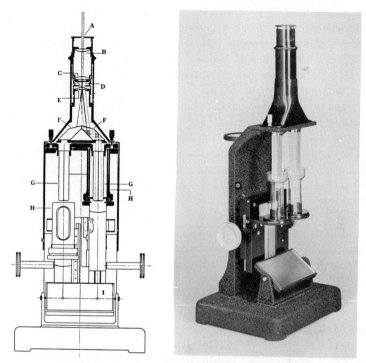

Fig. 31-4 Duboscq colorimeter. Explanation of diagram: A, eye-point; B, eye lens; C, collective; D, cover glass; E, bi-prism; F, rhomboid prism; G, plungers; H, cups; I, mirror. (Courtesy of Bausch and Lomb Optical Co.)

up or down until the colors in the two halves of the eyepiece are matched. The depth of each solution below the plunger is read on a scale attached to the cup holder. Usually the average of several settings is taken for the calculations. Accuracy of the order of 2 to 5% is expected; many factors contribute to the over-all error.

Standard Series Method.   A series of standard solutions of the desired constituent is prepared, the concentrations differing from one solution to the next by a suitable increment. The unknown sample is color-developed by the same method as the standards, and the unknown is compared with the standards. This comparision may be made by either of two methods.

a. Direct comparison or matching.   The series of standard solutions is prepared in long narrow tubes of identical bore and marked for identical depths; the unknown is placed in an identical tube. The tubes, usually held in a rack, are viewed from above toward a uniformly illuminated field below the tubes, and the standard solution that matches the unknown is determined; the unknown therefore contains the same amount of desired constituent as the matching standard. The tubes for this method are usually called Nessler tubes, because the method was applied by Nessler for the determination of ammonia in solution by color development with an alkaline solution of potassium tetraiodomercurate-(II), K_2HgI_4, Nessler's reagent. The method is capable of quite good accuracy if the standards in the series differ by only small increments. Because the method is based upon the subjective judgment of the operator, the personal error may be of considerable magnitude.

b. Indirect comparison. In this method the "color" is measured as transmittance or as absorbance in an instrument using some type of photo-converter instead of the eye. The measurement is the reading of a dial or a meter, or the position of a recorder trace on a chart. Each of the series of standards is measured in turn, and the readings, or some derived function thereof, are plotted against concentration to give a calibration curve. The unknown, prepared in the same way as the standards, is also measured, and its instrument reading is converted to a concentration by reference to the calibration curve. The method is completely free from the personal errors of visual color matching. It is capable of accuracies on the order of 0.5% relative error, or by certain modifications of technique, even 0.1% relative error. The method therefore compares favorably with good gravimetric and titrimetric methods of analysis, and is even superior to those methods for the determination of small amounts of desired constituent.

It is possible, of course, to calculate the concentration of an unknown solution from the measurement of the transmittance or absorbance of a single standard solution and of the unknown, by using the spectrophotometric laws. From the known concentration, optical path, and measured transmittance or absorbance, the absorptivity a is calculated from the relation $-\log T = A = abc$. The concentration of the unknown can then be calculated, by using this value of a and the measured value of T or A. Usually the two samples are measured in the same absorption cell, or in cells of identical optical paths, so that the term b drops out of consideration. Calculations based upon measurement of a single known concentration are less reliable than those based upon several measurements in a standard series. When calculations, rather than readings from a calibration curve, are to be used, the value of the absorptivity a should be the average obtained from measurements of the transmittance or absorbance of several different concentrations of the desired constituent. A well-constructed calibration curve averages the errors of the individual measurements.

PHOTOMETERS

Some of the basic components of various types of photometers are shown in Fig. 31-5. The diagram is schematic only, and is not intended to represent any specific instrument. In the Duboscq type colorimeter, the components are merely a source of radiant energy, cells to contain the solution, and reflecting prisms

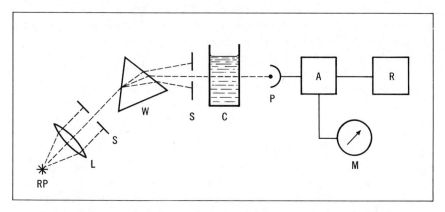

Fig. 31-5 Components of a photometer (schematic only). RP, source of radiant
power; L, lens; S, slit; W, wavelength selector (prism); C, absorption cell;
P, photocell; A, amplifier; M, meter; R, recorder.

and lenses to bring the transmitted light to the eye, which serves as the receiver.
In the simpler photoelectric instruments the photocell (receiver) is connected
directly to the meter. A somewhat more elaborate instrument may use a split
beam, one passing through the sample to one photocell, and the other through a
blank or reference solution to a second photocell. Various methods are used to
balance the photocell outputs to obtain an instrument reading that is related to
the transmittance of the sample solution. For better sensitivity, greater resolution,
greater stability, automatic recording of data, etc., the instruments are more
complex both optically and electrically.

In simple instruments, glass or gelatin (Wrattan) filters may be used to
eliminate or diminish the radiant energy of certain wavelengths and pass other
selected regions. A suitable filter for a given substance should transmit well in
the spectral region where the desired constituent absorbs strongly. In spectrophotometers, the beam from the source is dispersed into a continuous spectrum
by passage through a prism, or by a diffraction grating. In some instruments the
beam through the prism may be reflected back through it to give additional
dispersion, or both a prism and a diffraction grating may be used for this purpose.
Prisms and/or diffraction gratings, with their accessory lenses, mirrors, and slits,
are called **monochromators**. From the continuum of wavelengths emitted by the
source, a single wavelength, or usually a narrow band of wavelengths, can be
selected for use in the measurements. Different spectral regions require different
materials of construction, different sources of radiant energy, and different
photoreceivers. Table 31-1 summarizes this information for the ultraviolet,
visible, and infrared regions.

The photoreceiver should give a response that is directly proportional to the
radiant power reaching it. The less expensive photometers often use photocells

of the barrier-layer type; these cells show a fatigue effect in prolonged use, and they deteriorate with age; the output of this type of cell is not amenable to amplification. The more elaborate instruments therefore use photoemissive, photoconductive, or photomultiplier cells, thermopiles, or bolometers. These detectors are not only more reliable, but they permit amplification of their electrical output before measurement or before driving a recorder.

Meters on the less expensive instruments are often milliammeters, which indicate the current output of the photocell. The meters are usually graduated to read directly in terms of percent transmittance or in absorbance. In the more elaborate instruments the amplified output of the photoreceiver is often fed into some type of Wheatstone bridge circuit, which is brought to balance as indicated by a null position (no deflection) on the meter (galvanometer). The balancing arms of the bridge circuit are graduated to read directly the percent transmittance and/or absorbance.

The output of the photoreceiver, after amplification, can be used to make a record or chart. Usually, a synchronous drive between the recorder chart and the dispersing element (prism or grating) is used with the transmittance (or absorb-

Table 31-1   Optical Components of Spectrophotometers

Component	Ultraviolet Region	Visible Region	Infrared Region
Radiation source	Hydrogen or deuterium discharge lamp	Tungsten filament lamp	Globar (SiC), Nernst glower
Wavelength dispersion	Quartz prism, Diffraction grating	Glass prism, Diffraction grating, Filters	Prism of NaCl, KBr, LiF, CaF_2, CsBr, depending on wavelength
Lenses, cells, mirrors	Quartz lenses, cells, Aluminum mirrors	Glass lenses, cells, Silver or aluminum mirrors	Cell windows same material as prism, Aluminum mirrors
Detector	Photomultiplier, Photoconductor	Barrier-layer, Photomultiplier, Photoemissive cell	Thermopile, Bolometer, Photoconductor (PbS or PbTe)

ance) function to generate a plot of transmittance (or absorbance) against wavelength. Recording spectrophotometers are especially useful in developing spectrophotometric methods of analysis, for spectral scanning to determine the position (wavelength) of absorption peaks, and in testing the effect of various conditions (pH, solvent, excess reagent, time, etc.) on the absorption characteristics of the system. For some industrial applications, continuous sampling of a production stream through the absorption cell can be used for automatic control of the process, by using the photocell output to activate relays that open or close valves or switches if and when the sample does not conform to preset conditions.

Commercial Instruments

No attempt is made here to give a detailed description or even a complete listing of the many photoelectric photometers and spectrophotometers commercially available. Some of the instruments that have enjoyed wide use are mentioned briefly. New and improved models continue to appear on the market. Manufacturers' literature may be consulted for specific features of construction and operation.

Inexpensive filter photometers (photoelectric colorimeters) include the Lumetron (Photovolt Corp.), Evelyn (Rubicon Co.), Klett-Summerson (Klett Mfg. Co.), Photelometer (Central Scientific Co.), and Electrophotometer (Fisher Scientific Co.).

The Bausch and Lomb Spectronic 20 (Fig. 31-6) uses a replica diffraction

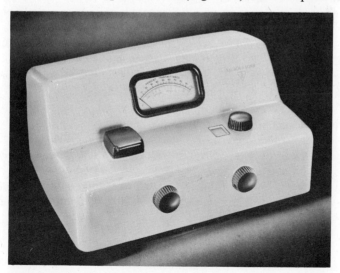

Fig. 31-6 Bausch and Lomb Spectronic 20 Colorimeter. (Courtesy of Bausch and Lomb Optical Co.)

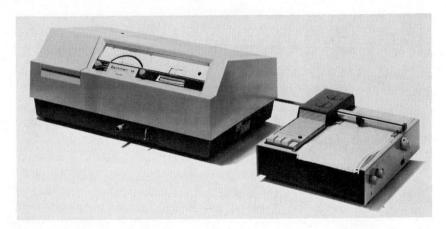

Fig. 31-7 Beckman Model DB spectrophotometer, with recorder. (Courtesy of Beckman Instruments, Inc.)

grating, a printed electric circuit, and selected test tubes for the absorption cells. It has direct read-out in both transmittance and absorbance. The low cost and narrow spectral band pass make it especially suitable for routine analytical applications.

The Beckman Model B spectrophotometer is a medium-priced instrument covering the wavelength range from 325 to 1000 mμ. It is a direct reading instrument, with several sensitivity selector positions to give scale expansion for measurement of solutions of high absorbance. It will accommodate absorption cells up to 10 cm optical path.

The Beckman Model DU spectrophotometer has quartz optics and covers the wavelength range 200 to 2000 mμ. It is a null type instrument, with the balancing potential divider graduated to read either transmittance or absorbance. The Beckman Model DB instrument (Fig. 31-7) has quartz optics. The single beam of energy leaving the monochromator is sent alternately through the sample and the reference solution by means of a vibrating mirror, thus giving a "double beam in time" effect, with direct read-out in either transmittance or absorbance. Connections are also provided for attachment of a strip-chart recorder.

The more expensive recording spectrophotometers include the Beckman Models DK–1 and DK–2 and the Cary Model 14. These instruments cover the ultraviolet, visible, and near infrared regions, and have high resolving power. They are instruments of great versatility for transmittance or absorbance recording, scale expansion, and variable scanning speed.

Recording infrared spectrophotometers (Perkin-Elmer, Baird, Beckman instruments) having rock salt optics cover the wavelength range 2 to 16 μ; optical parts made of other materials (see Table 31-1) are used for other wavelength regions or for greater resolving power. Provisions are made for analyzing gases, liquids and solutions, and finely dispersed solids. Infrared spectrophotometry finds wide application in the determination of the constitution of organic compounds (and to some extent also of inorganic compounds), and the instruments are widely used in control and research laboratories for the analysis of organic materials.

DEVELOPMENT OF A SPECTROPHOTOMETRIC METHOD

A number of inorganic ions in aqueous solution absorb sufficient radiant energy in the visible region to be suitable for direct spectrophotometric determination, even at quite low concentrations. Examples are permanganate, chromate, and dichromate. Even iron(II), which in aqueous solution has little visual color, absorbs quite strongly in the red region, and can be measured spectrophotometrically at concentrations comparable to those used in gravimetric and titrimetric analysis. Colors of many of the simple (aquo) inorganic cations are markedly enhanced by the formation of complexes; examples are the ammonia and the chloro complexes of copper(II), cobalt(II), and nickel(II), the thiocyanato complexes of iron(III) and cobalt(II), and the chelate complexes formed between many organic compounds and the aquo-cations.

After a promising colored system or color reaction is found, several factors need to be investigated in order to develop a reliable spectrophotometric determination of the desired constituent. Several of these factors are listed and briefly discussed.

1. *Selection of analytical wavelength.*   A solution of the desired constituent, color-developed by the use of an appropriate reagent, is scanned in the spectrophotometer to determine its absorption spectrum. If there is no interference from other components of the sample solution, the wavelength of maximum absorption is chosen for future measurements. It frequently happens that the color-developing reagent also shows appreciable absorption at the same wavelength; although this type of interference is diminished by the common practice of using a blank containing all the solution components except the desired constituent, this does not compensate completely for the error due to consumption of different amounts of the reagent by different amounts of desired constituent. In such a case it is advantageous to select an analytical wavelength at which the reagent absorbs little, if at all; the wavelength selected is usually the one at which the difference in absorbance between the colored component and the developing reagent is greatest. The principle is illustrated in Fig. 31-8. Although the measurements at the wavelength chosen may not be quite as *sensitive*, they will be more *reliable*.

When a filter photometer is used, a useful (although approximate) criterion for selection of a filter is that its visual color should be complementary to the visual color of the sample to be measured.

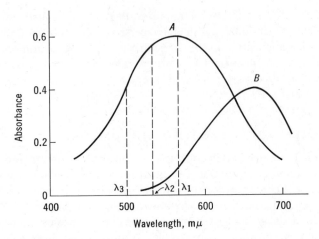

Fig. 31-8 Selection of wavelength for spectrophotometric measurement. The largest absorbance difference is at λ_2.

2. *Effect of excess reagent.* A fixed amount of desired constituent is treated with increasing amounts of color-developing reagent, and the absorbance is measured at the analytical wavelength previously selected. The procedure should be repeated for the highest concentration of desired constituent expected in the analytical scheme. If the color-forming reaction is essentially complete when stoichiometric amounts of reactants are present, addition of further amounts of reagent will cause little increase, if any, in absorbance. On the other hand, if the reaction is quite incomplete, addition of an increasing amount of excess reagent will displace the equilibrium toward formation of more of the colored species and cause a gradual increase in absorbance. In this case the amount of reagent chosen for the standardized procedure should be so large that slight differences in the amount of unused reagent cause differences in absorbance that are no greater than the precision of making the measurement.

3. *Effect of time.* Some color-forming reactions are very rapid, others are quite slow. Furthermore, some colored species undergo "fading" due to decomposition by light and/or heat, or, apparently, merely by standing. Ideally, the color reaction should be rapid, so that analytical results may be obtained promptly, and the colored species should be stable with time, so that a rigid time schedule need not be used in performing the analysis. Long time stability is also advantageous if it becomes necessary to check a previous absorbance measurement. If color development and/or fading are rather rapid, it is advantageous to plot absorbance against time in order to determine the optimum time conditions for measurement.

4. *Effect of pH.* In the ideal case, there should be a considerable range of pH over which the absorbance does not vary. When pH control is very critical,

appropriate buffers of high capacity are usually required; alternatively, the pH of the solution is adjusted to the desired value as shown by test with a pH meter.

5. *Effect of temperature.* Elevated temperature is sometimes required to hasten the formation of a colored product; but it may also increase the rate of fading. Temperature control may be necessary not only for color development, but also during the measurement of absorbance; the latter is especially important when organic solvents are used that have a high coefficient of expansion.

6. *Conformity to Beer's law.* A linear relation between concentration and absorbance simplifies the calibration procedure, as well as the calculations in multi-component analysis; it also lends confidence that satisfactory conditions of analysis have been established. However, conformity to Beer's law is not essential for satisfactory analysis (see p. 458).

7. *Effect of foreign substances.* The color-forming reagent should be specific or highly selective for the desired constituent. Foreign substances should neither prevent the desired color reaction, nor give a closely similar color (absorption spectrum). Tests should always be made for other components likely to be present in the samples to be analyzed; often, the foreign substances are very similar in chemical properties to the desired constituent, and are therefore likely to react with the chromogenic reagent. For example, in developing spectrophotometric methods for platinum, it might be expected that some of the other platinum elements (palladium, rhodium, ruthenium, osmium, iridium), as well as other transition elements such as iron, cobalt, nickel, etc., would also react. Sometimes, change in conditions such as pH, temperature, solvent, etc., may eliminate interference; if not, resort must be had to masking or removal of the unwanted reactant. If two substances react with the same reagent to give colored products whose absorption spectra are not too similar, simultaneous determination of the two components may be made; details will be given under Applications.

Other factors to be considered are the stability of the color-forming reagent, freedom of the system to be measured from precipitates or colloidal dispersions (which are very difficult to reproduce in particle size distribution), and selection of a suitable solvent.

8. *Precision of the method.* Measurement of multiplicate samples should be made in order to evaluate the precision of the method, best expressed as a standard deviation.

TREATMENT OF SPECTROPHOTOMETRIC DATA

Spectral Curves

The "color" of a solution can be represented graphically by a plot of transmittance or absorbance against wavelength. Some substances exhibit a more or less general absorption over a wide spectral region; others may show quite

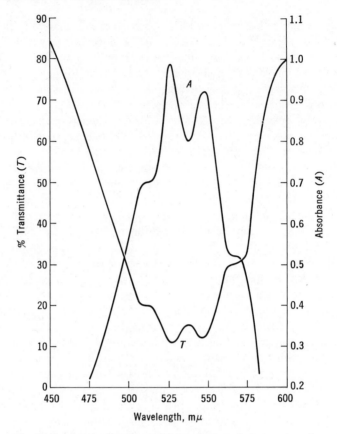

Fig. 31-9 Spectral curves of potassium permanganate solution containing 20 ppm of manganese.

specific absorption at characteristic wavelengths. The spectral curve for a solution of potassium permanganate is shown in Fig. 31-9, plotted in two different ordinate functions, percent transmittance ($\%\ T$), and absorbance ($A = -\log T$). Permanganate ion in solution has strong absorption peaks at 526 and 546 mμ, and weaker bands at about 510 and 565 mμ. Each absorbing substance has a spectral curve characteristic of that substance. In the development of a new spectrophotometric method, the spectral curve of the absorbing species should always be obtained in order to select an appropriate wavelength for making quantitative measurements (see p. 453).

Calibration Curves

After determining the wavelength at which measurements are to be made, the method (including the instrument) is calibrated by measuring a series of standards of the desired constituent. Transmittance (or absorbance) measurements, for whatever purpose, are most commonly made by setting the instrument scale or meter to read 100% transmittance (zero absorbance) when the radiant energy beam passes through a blank, identical with the sample except for the absence of the constituent to be measured. The blank should contain the reagents, additives, solvent, etc., in the same kind and amount as are to be found in the color-developed sample. The reading on the sample is then automatically corrected for any slight absorption by the reagents and the solvent. The transmittance or absorbance data for the different concentrations of the standard series are used to construct a calibration curve, from which the concentrations of unknowns are determined. Several different plotting methods, and their relative merits, are given below.

1. Percent Transmittance Against Concentration. In the early period of development of photoelectric photometry, the instrument reading was often merely a numerical value on a meter or scale. Even if the reading was a percent transmittance, some early workers in this field made calibration curves by plotting instrument readings (including percent transmittance) against concentration, both functions being on linear scales. A plot of this kind is shown in Fig. 31-10. For use as a calibration curve, this method of plotting cannot be criticized, but from the standpoint of evaluating the concentration range in which the analysis is most accurate, this method of plotting is the most misleading of all the various methods, and it has led to erroneous statements and conclusions

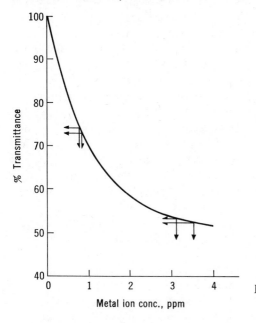

Fig. 31-10 Transmittance-concentration calibration curve.

in the literature of colorimetry. The steep slope of the curve at low concentrations has been taken to indicate high accuracy, because small differences in the con- ℯentration result in large differences in the radiant power transmitted. The higher concentrations were often said to be unsuitable because of the flatter shape of the curve and a correspondingly larger error in the determination. It must be remembered, however, that *relative error* only is of real significance in evaluating the reliability of a determination. A given difference in the photometric function may correspond to a small difference in the concentration function at low con- centration, but this may be a much larger relative difference than that produced in the concentration function at a higher concentration level. In Fig. 31-10, the horizontal parallel arrows represent a difference of 1% in transmittance; the vertical arrows mark the corresponding abscissa positions representing concentrations. Although the absolute difference in concentration is greater in the flatter portion of the curve, the *relative* difference, that is, the absolute dif- ference compared with the concentrations, is actually smaller. At *very* high concentrations, where the curve is nearly parallel with the base line, the relative error again increases. Obviously there is some intermediate point or region of transmittance and concentration where the relative error is at a minimum. (More on this subject presently.) Although these principles were formulated in the mid- 1930's, they do not seem to have been generally appreciated by many workers in colorimetry for another fifteen or so years.

2. **Log Transmittance or Absorbance Against Concentration.** The mathematical form of the Bouguer-Beer law, $-\log T = A = abc$, shows that $\log T$ and A are linear functions of the concentration. A plot of $\log T$ against concentration is a straight line of negative slope, and a plot of A against concentration is a straight line of positive slope. The slope a for unit optical path b is the **absorptivity** characteristic of the absorbing substance at the wavelength used for measure- ment. Different substances, or the same substance at different wavelengths, have different absorptivities and give straight lines of different slopes; see Fig. 31-13.

Figure 31-11 shows plots of log percent transmittance and of absorbance against concentration. Plotting of log transmittance is most conveniently done on semilog graph paper, on which the rulings on one axis are spaced logarithmi- cally, and the rulings on the other axis are spaced linearly. Graphs such as those in Fig. 31-11 are commonly referred to as " Beer's law plots," because a straight- line plot shows that the system measured conforms to Beer's law. Photometric data from standard series measurements are usually plotted in this way as a calibration curve for the method, from which unknowns are determined by finding the concentration corresponding to the measured transmittance or absorbance of the unknown sample.

Although a straight-line plot shows that the system measured conforms to Beer's law, it is not necessary that a standard series plot be linear in order to be a valid calibration curve for the determination of unknowns. The unknown is prepared by the same reagents and is measured under the same conditions as the

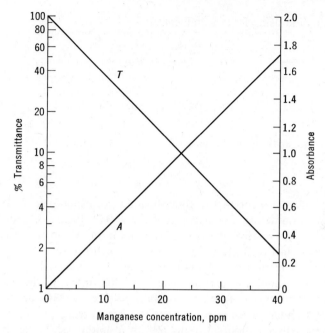

Fig. 31-11 Standard curves for permanganate solution, measured at 526 mμ in 1.00-cm cell.

standards of similar concentration. Any apparent deviation in one would appear also in the other, and the deviations would cancel when the unknown concentration is read from the calibration curve. It is, of course, easier to fit a continuous line to a series of points that are in a straight line than if they are in a curved path. This has no fundamental bearing on the validity of using a curved line as a calibration relating the photometric function to the concentration. An occasional misconception is that because a plot is a straight line, the accuracy is the same over the entire range of measurements. It has already been shown (p. 458) that the relative error is different at different concentration levels and transmittances.

The spectrophotometric law (using logarithms to the base e, written ln),

$$-\ln T = abc \qquad \text{or} \qquad \ln T = -abc$$

can be expressed as a differential:

$$\frac{dT}{T} = -ab\,dc \qquad \text{or} \qquad dc = -\frac{dT}{T} \cdot \frac{1}{ab}$$

But $abc = A$, or $ab = A/c$; hence,

$$dc = -\frac{dT}{T} \cdot \frac{c}{A}$$

Rearranging, and using finite increments,

$$\frac{\Delta c/c}{\Delta T} = -\frac{1}{TA}$$

But $A = -\ln T$; therefore,

$$\frac{\Delta c/c}{\Delta T} = \frac{1}{T \ln T}$$

Changing to logarithms to the base 10 ($e = 2.718$; $\log_{10} e = 0.4343$): gives

$$\frac{\Delta c/c}{\Delta T} = \frac{0.4343}{T \log T}$$

$\Delta c/c$ is the relative error in the concentration corresponding to ΔT, a given change in transmittance. For a value of $\Delta T = 0.01$ (i.e., a 1% difference in transmittance), the relative analysis error $\Delta c/c$ for any value of T can be calculated. The curve in Fig. 31-12 is a plot of the error function, that is, the percent relative analysis error per 1% photometric error, against the percent transmittance. Three important facts are shown by this curve: (*a*) the error is minimum at a transmittance of about 37% (absorbance = 0.434), and amounts to 2.72% relative analysis error per 1% photometric error; (*b*) the error is not much greater between about 20% and 60% transmittance; (*c*) the error is huge at very low and at very high transmittances, approaching infinity as the transmittance approaches 0 or 100%. It is obvious, therefore, that for the highest accuracy (least relative error), the measurement should be made on a sample of such concentration that its transmittance lies within the range of about 20% to 60%. (There are other methods, besides concentration adjustment, that can be used to put the transmittance in this range; these methods will be outlined later.)

3. Transmittance (or Absorptance) Against Log Concentration. In 1939

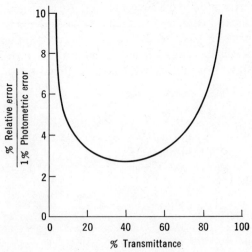

Fig. 31-12 Spectrophotometric error function curve.

Ringbom[7] introduced a new method of plotting spectrophotometric data in which percent "absorptance"[8] is plotted against the logarithm of concentration. When these functions are plotted, a sigmoid or S-shaped curve is always obtained. Ringbom showed, by derivations based on Beer's law, that the accuracy is greatest when the relation

$$\frac{\Delta T}{\Delta c/c} = \frac{\Delta T}{2.303\,\Delta \log c}$$

reaches a maximum, that is, at the point of steepest slope (the inflection point) of the curve. (2.303 = 1/0.4343, the conversion factor from natural to common logarithms.) If the system conforms to Beer's law, the inflection point occurs at 36.8 % transmittance (or $100 - 36.8 = 63.2$ on the ordinate of the Ringbom plot). This point corresponds to an absorbance of 0.4343. Furthermore, all the curves for different substances, or for the same substance at different wavelengths, have the same shape or slope. Different absorptivities, which give different slopes to the conventional Beer's law plots, merely displace the Ringbom curves along the concentration axis. The greater the absorptivity, the steeper the Beer's law plot, and the farther the Ringbom curve is displaced to the left (lower concentration) on the concentration axis. If two solutions have absorptivities a_1 and a_2, where $a_1 = x a_2$ and x is the factor by which the absorptivities differ, the Ringbom curve for the second solution is displaced from the first by a distance $x c_1$ at all ordinate (absorptance) values. These relations are shown in Figs. 31-13 and 31-14. Figure 31-13 is a Beer's law plot of log percent transmittance

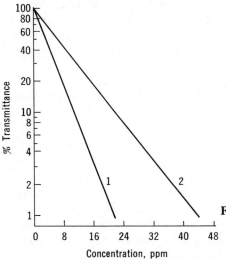

Fig. 31-13 Beer's law plots. Absorptivity of solution 1 is twice the absorptivity of solution 2.

[7] A. Ringbom, *Z. anal. Chem.*, **115**, 332 (1939).

[8] Absorptance = 1 − transmittance, or percent absorptance = 100 − percent transmittance. This term, although not recognized by the Joint Committee on Nomenclature, is useful; it must not be confused with absorbance. Actually, % T can be used equally well as the ordinate function in the Ringbom plot; the writer prefers $100 - \%\,T$, in that small concentrations are associated with small values of the ordinate function, and the curve therefore has positive slope.

against concentration, representing two solutions in which the absorptivity of solution 1 is twice the absorptivity of solution 2; that is, $a_1 = 2a_2$. The same data are shown in the Ringbom plots in Fig. 31-14. At any ordinate value (absorptance), the abscissa value (concentration) of curve 2 is twice as great as that for curve 1.

The utility of the Ringbom plot was not realized by workers in the area for about a decade or more.[9] The plot has two very useful features: (a) it shows at a glance the concentration range where the analysis error is least; this is the concentration range corresponding to the nearly linear portion of steep slope; and (b) the analysis accuracy at *any* concentration level or in any concentration range can be evaluated.

Rearrangement of the above equation gives

$$\frac{\Delta c/c}{\Delta T} = \frac{2.303}{\Delta T/\Delta \log c}$$

As before, $\Delta c/c$ is the relative analysis error for a given photometric error ΔT. If T is expressed in percent transmittance and it is desired to express the percent relative analysis error for a 1% error in transmittance, the equation is multiplied by 100 to give

$$\frac{100\,\Delta c/c}{1} = \frac{\text{percent relative analysis error}}{1\% \text{ transmittance error}} = \frac{230}{\Delta T/\Delta \log c}$$

But $\Delta T/\Delta \log c$ is merely the slope of the curve, that is, the difference between two transmittances corresponding to $\Delta \log c = 1$, or $\Delta c = 10$, i.e., a tenfold difference in concentration. In other words, at any point the relative analysis error per 1% transmittance error is 230 divided by the slope of the curve at that point.

In the middle or steep portion of the curve, the slope is easily determined by placing a straightedge along the (nearly) linear portion of the curve and extending this line in either direction to cut two abscissa values (concentrations) differing by one log cycle or by a factor of 10 (for example, 1 and 10, or 2 and 20), and reading the corresponding ordinate values. Applying this method to curve 2 of Fig. 31-14, a straight line through the steepest linear portion of the curve and extended downward cuts the abscissa 2 at about 9%, and extended upward cuts the abscissa 20 at about 92%. $\Delta T = 92 - 9 = 83$; percent relative analysis error per 1% photometric error $= 230/83 = 2.8$. Compare this value with the minimum point on the curve of Fig. 31-12. The reading error on a good spectrophotometer is of the order of 0.2% on the transmittance scale; the relative analysis error is then about $2.8 \times 0.2 = 0.6\%$ on the concentration represented.

The analysis error at *any* concentration can be evaluated by constructing a tangent to the curve at that concentration, and determining the differences in ordinate value corresponding to a tenfold change in concentration (one log

[9] G. H. Ayres, *Anal. Chem.*, **21**, 652 (1949).

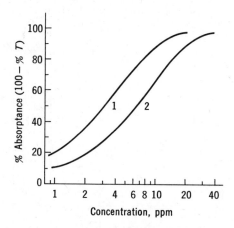

Fig. 31-14 Ringbom plots of the same data as in Fig. 31-13.

cycle). This slope, divided into 230, is the percent relative analysis error per 1% transmittance error.

Another useful application of the Ringbom plot is the determination of the concentration limits within which the relative analysis error will not exceed certain limits. Figure 31-15 is a Ringbom plot of a series of potassium permanganate standards. Suppose it is desired to estimate the concentration range within which the relative analysis error per 1% transmittance error will not exceed 5%; 230/relative error = slope, or 230/5 = 46. A straightedge is placed on the graph so that 46 units of ordinate correspond to a tenfold difference in abscissa; this slope is then translated (a navigator's parallel ruler is convenient) to points of tangency to the curve, one on the lower and one on the upper limb of the curve. These points define the concentration limits within which the relative analysis error per 1% transmittance error does not exceed 5%.

If the system under consideration does not conform to Beer's law over the entire concentration range measured, the Ringbom plot has the sigmoid shape, and the inflection point occurs at a value other than 63.2% on the ordinate (= 36.8% transmittance); the direction of these differences depends upon the direction of the "deviation" from the law. However, the curve still shows at a glance the optimum concentration range, and the relative analysis error is evaluated from the slope of the curve exactly as discussed and illustrated above.

Interpretation of the shape of the Ringbom plot in terms of the foregoing discussion leads to the same conclusions as are represented by the error function curve, Fig. 31-12. (*a*) The least error occurs at about 37% transmittance (100 − 37 = 63% absorptance) and amounts to about 2.7% relative analysis error per 1% transmittance error. (*b*) The error is not much greater over the region of about 20 to 60% transmittance (80 to 40% absorptance); this region corresponds to the nearly linear steep portion of the Ringbom curve. (*c*) At very low and at

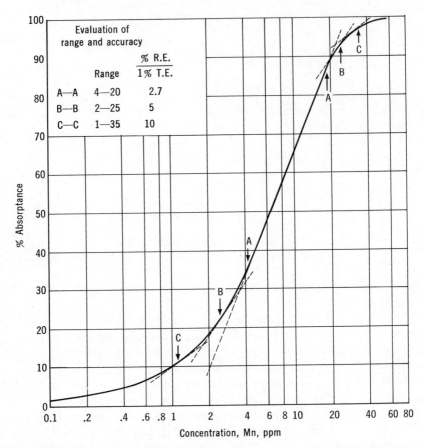

Fig. 31-15   Ringbom plot of permanganate solutions measured at 526 mμ in 1.00-cm cell.

very high transmittance the Ringbom curve has very small slope. As the transmittance approaches 0 or 100%, the Ringbom curve approaches the limiting axes asymptotically and the slope approaches zero; the relative error therefore approaches infinity.

4. Log Absorbance Against Wavelength.   In the expression of the Bouguer-Beer law, $A = abc$, the only term on the right-hand side that is dependent upon wavelength is the absorptivity, a. At a given wavelength, for two solutions of the same substance at different concentrations, and measured at the same optical path b, we may write

$$A_1 = abc_1 \quad \text{and} \quad A_2 = abc_1 f$$

where f is the factor by which the second concentration differs from the first;

that is, $c_2 = c_1 f$. Taking logarithms,

$$\log A_1 = \log a + \log b + \log c_1$$

and

$$\log A_2 = \log a + \log b + \log c_1 + \log f$$

Because a (or $\log a$) is the only term that is wavelength dependent, the curves of $\log A_1$ and $\log A_2$ against wavelength are each characteristic of the absorbing substance and are of exactly the same shape, but one is displaced in ordinate from the other, at all wavelengths, by a constant amount, namely, $\log f$.

Curves plotted in this way are shown in Fig. 31-16. Remembering that $A = \log (1/T)$, then $\log A = \log \log (1/T)$. The left-hand ordinate scale in Fig. 31-16

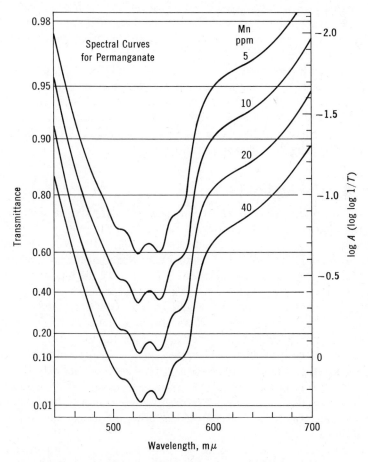

Fig. 31-16   Log absorbance vs. wavelength curves for permanganate solution of different concentrations, measured at 526 mμ in 1.00-cm cell.

is *numbered* in values of percent transmittance, but the marks or rulings are *spaced* on a log-log reciprocal basis, to facilitate plotting. The right-hand ordinate scale is linear in numbers representing log A. An alternative method is to plot absorbance A on the log scale of semilog graph paper. With any of these ordinate scales, each of the curves can be exactly superimposed at all wavelengths upon the other curves by simple translation along the ordinate axis. (This identity of curve shape may not appear to be true in regions of steep slope; confirm it by measuring the vertical distance between curves, at several wavelengths.) The test of superimposability of the spectral curves, *when plotted by this method*, is the best criterion of the identity of the absorbing substance in two or more samples measured. Although two different substances might have the same absorptivity at one or at a few wavelengths, it is outside the bounds of possibility that they would have the same absorptivity at *all* wavelengths. Considering the great utility of this method of plotting, it is unfortunate that no manufacturer has yet offered a spectrophotometer that records log absorbance against wavelength.

Curves plotted by this method can also be used for determing the concentrations of unknowns, by measuring the vertical distance, at a given wavelength, between the curve of the unknown and the curve for a known concentration. In Fig. 31-16 each curve, at all wavelengths, differs in ordinate from its nearest neighbor by an amount 0.30 on the log absorbance scale; 0.30 is the log of 2, the factor by which adjacent concentrations differ.

Adjustment to Optimum Conditions

In the foregoing discussion of various plotting methods, the fact has been emphasized that large relative errors are produced if the solution measured has a transmittance much outside the limits of about 20 to 60%. Within these limits, the concentration range for substances that conform to Beer's law includes only about a *fivefold* change in concentration. Statements in the literature of "optimum ranges" covering 100-fold or even 500-fold changes in concentration, when measurements are made at the same optical path, are grossly inaccurate.

The question naturally arises as to what may be done, in actual practice, if the solution prepared for measurement has a transmittance outside the range for best accuracy. By proper choice of sample size and of solution volume (hence, concentration), the solution is prepared so that *under the conditions of measurement* the highest accuracy is obtained. Because transmittance is a function of concentration, optical path, and absorptivity, any one or a combination of changes in these conditions may be used to bring the measurement within the optimum limits.

A very simple means of extending the range is the use of absorption cells of different optical paths. Suppose, for example, that the optimum concentration range for a certain substance measured in cells of 1.0 cm path is from 1 to 5 ppm (parts per million); solutions in the range of 5 to 25 ppm may be measured with equal reliability in cells of 0.2 mm path; solutions in the range of 0.2 to 1 ppm may be measured with equal reliability in cells of 5.0 cm path. Thus, by using cells of these three different dimensions, the range covered is from 0.2 to 25 ppm, a 125-fold change; if all the solutions were measured in the 1.0-cm cell, the relative error at the 0.2 and at the 25 ppm levels would be intolerably large.

The various means of attaining optimum conditions for measurement are as follows.

If the prepared solution is too dilute (transmittance too high or absorbance too low):

1. The solution may be measured at a longer optical path, e.g., 5 or 10 cm instead of 1 cm.

2. A larger sample, in the same volume, may be used.

3. The same size sample may be made up to smaller volume.

If the prepared solution is too concentrated (transmittance too low or absorbance too high):

1. The solution may be measured at shorter optical path, e.g., 0.1 or even 0.01 mm.

2. The solution may be diluted volumetrically to an appropriate concentration.

3. The solution may be measured at a wavelength at which the solute has lower absorptivity. In general, it is not good practice to measure at a wavelength on a steep side of an absorption band, where absorbance is changing rapidly with wavelength. Error may arise through inaccurate setting of the wavelength scale, and/or through deviations from Beer's law due to wide departure from monochromaticity of the incident radiation.

4. The solution may be measured against a standard or reference solution of the same substance at slightly lower concentration than the unknown solution.

The latter procedure is known as the "transmittance ratio" or the "high absorbance" method. By this method the relative error becomes finite at the high end (100%) of the transmittance scale, the optimum transmittance region shifts to higher transmittance values (i.e., the relative error decreases as the unknown and the reference standard approach the same concentration and therefore the same real transmittance or absorbance), and with most photometers[10] the relative error decreases with increasing concentration of the reference standard. A second method of relative absorbance (differential) spectrophotometry ("trace analysis method") involves setting the 100% transmittance point with a blank solution, as in the ordinary method, and setting the zero transmittance (dark current, as for infinitely high concentration) with a reference solution, then measuring the unknown. A third, "maximum precision" method[11]

---

[10] In order to balance the instrument (e.g., Beckman DU and several others) to 100% transmittance with the reference solution in the optical beam, it is necessary to open the slits and/or increase the gain of the instrument. These operations decrease the monochromaticity of the incident radiation and increase the electrical noise. Whether or not an improved accuracy is realized depends upon the construction of the particular instrument used. See C. F. Hiskey, J. Rabinowitz, and I. G. Young, *Anal. Chem.*, **22**, 1464 (1950).

[11] C. N. Reilley and C. M. Crawford, *Anal. Chem.*, **27**, 716 (1955).

involves the use of two reference standards, the more dilute one for setting the 100% transmittance and the more concentrated one for the zero transmittance setting; these concentrations should bracket the concentration of the unknown to be measured; the relative error is kept at a minimum if the two reference solutions have real transmittances closely bracketing 37% transmittance (absorbance, 0.434). In both trace analysis and maximum precision methods, a calibration curve should be constructed using photometer readings of known solutions. All of the differential methods have the effect of expanding the scale of the instrument.

APPLICATIONS

Single-Component Analysis

The applications of colorimetry and spectrophotometry are so numerous that no attempt is made here to list specific examples; several reference works are available.[12-15] Methods involving purely inorganic and purely organic systems, and the use of organic reagents in inorganic analysis, are numerous and more methods are being developed constantly.

Multicomponent Analysis

Solution of the multicomponent problem involves use of simultaneous equations; it is obvious that n components can be determined if n equations can be set up relating absorbance to concentration. Because of the complexity of the calculations, the method is rarely applied to systems of more than two components[16] unless the calculations are computerized. The following discussion is limited to two-component systems.

If two components in the same solution have spectral curves that do not overlap (and if the two components do not interact), the problem is merely one of two separate one-component analyses, each measurement being made at the characteristic wavelength. If there is a wavelength at which only one of the components absorbs, but its spectral curve overlaps that of the second component, the concentration of the first component is determined as usual from a calibration curve. From the known absorptivities of each component at the second wavelength, the measured absorbance at that wavelength is corrected by subtracting the contribution of the first component to obtain the absorbance due to the second component.

[12] J. H. Yoe, *Photometric Chemical Analysis*, vol. I (1928); J. H. Yoe and H. Kleinman, vol. II (1929), New York, Wiley.

[13] F. D. Snell and C. T. Snell, *Colorimetric Methods of Analysis*, Princeton, N.J., Van Nostrand, 1948, 1959, 3rd ed., 4 vols.

[14] E. B. Sandell, *Colorimetric Determination of Traces of Metals*, 3rd ed., New York, Interscience, 1959.

[15] D. F. Boltz, ed., *Colorimetric Determination of Nonmetals*, New York, Interscience, 1958.

[16] G. H. Ayres and S. S. Baird, *Talanta*, 7, 237 (1961).

When the spectral curves of the two components overlap one another, it is customary to select two wavelengths, λ_1 and λ_2, at which the ratios of the absorptivities of the two components, a_1/a_2 and a_2/a_1, are maximum. The absorptivity of each component at each of the chosen wavelengths must be determined accurately, either from measurements on solutions of several different concentrations or from the slopes of their absorbance vs. concentration plots. Test should also be made for additivity of absorbances by measuring solutions of mixtures of the two components at the two wavelengths. Also, it is important that all measurements be made at identical optical path lengths. The following equations, which are used, assume conformity of each component to Beer's law and additivity of absorbances; the two components and the two wavelengths are designated by the subscripts, and A is the measured absorbance of the mixture.

$$A_{\lambda_1} = (a_1)_{\lambda_1}c_1 + (a_2)_{\lambda_1}c_2$$

$$A_{\lambda_2} = (a_1)_{\lambda_2}c_1 + (a_2)_{\lambda_2}c_2$$

Simultaneous solution of these equations for concentrations gives

$$c_1 = \frac{(a_2)_{\lambda_2}A_{\lambda_1} - (a_2)_{\lambda_1}A_{\lambda_2}}{(a_1)_{\lambda_1}(a_2)_{\lambda_2} - (a_2)_{\lambda_1}(a_1)_{\lambda_2}}$$

$$c_2 = \frac{(a_1)_{\lambda_1}A_{\lambda_2} - (a_1)_{\lambda_2}A_{\lambda_1}}{(a_1)_{\lambda_1}(a_2)_{\lambda_2} - (a_2)_{\lambda_1}(a_1)_{\lambda_2}}$$

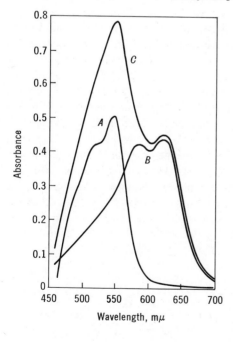

Fig. 31-17 Spectral curves of palladium and platinum with 2, 3-quinoxaline-dithiol. *A*, 1.60 ppm palladium + excess reagent. *B*, 3.20 ppm platinum + excess reagent. *C*, Mixture of 1.60 ppm palladium and 3.20 ppm platinum + excess reagent. From G. H. Ayres and H. F. Janota, *Anal. Chem.*, **36**, 138 (1964). (Used by permission of *Analytical Chemistry*.)

An example of this method is represented by the curves in Fig. 31-17 for the simultaneous determination of palladium and platinum with 2,3-quinoxaline-dithiol.[17] In this instance the analytical wavelengths chosen (where absorptivity ratios were maximum) coincided with the wavelengths of maximum absorption by the separate components, that is, 548 mμ (palladium maximum) and 624 mμ (platinum maximum). Equally good results were obtained by using 517 mμ, on the shoulder plateau of the palladium curve, instead of 548; although the absorbance due to palladium is less at 517 mμ, the contribution due to platinum is also less, and the ratio of the absorptivities at this wavelength is essentially the same as at 548 mμ. Analysis of mixtures of palladium and platinum, in the ppm region, was made with a relative error of less than 2%.

Determination of Composition of Complexes

1. Method of Continuous Variations.   Consider the reaction

$$M + nL \rightleftarrows ML_n$$

in which the complex ML_n is colored, and assume that neither M nor L is colored, or at least that they do not absorb appreciably at the absorption wavelength of the complex. Solutions of M and L of the same molar concentration are prepared, from which a series of solutions is made so that in each solution the total concentration of M + L is constant, but the ratio of M to L varies. For example, solutions are made containing one part of M plus nine parts of L; two parts of M plus eight parts of L; three parts of M plus seven parts of L; and so on. The absorbance of each solution is measured, at an appropriate wavelength (e.g., at the absorbance maximum of ML_n), and a plot is made of absorbance against mole fraction of L; mole fraction of L = $[L]/([M] + [L])$. The plot will maximize at a mole fraction corresponding to the composition of the complex formed. For example, absorbance maximizing at 0.5 mole fraction of L represents a 1 : 1 complex, ML; maximum at 0.67 mole fraction of L represents a 1 : 2 complex, ML_2; and so on.

This method was originated by Job,[18] who assumed the method was applicable only to a 1 : 1 ratio between reactants; Vosburgh and Cooper[19] showed that the method was applicable to higher order complexes. If more than one complex is formed, each with a characteristic absorption spectrum, measurements at the different appropriate wavelengths will give continuous variations curves that maximize at different mole fractions of reagent corresponding to the composition of the different complexes. If the formation of the complex ML_n is not quantita-

[17] G. H. Ayres and H. F. Janota, *Anal Chem.*, **36**, 138 (1964).
[18] P. Job, *Ann. Chim.* (Paris), (10) **9**, 113 (1928).
[19] W. C. Vosburgh and G. R. Cooper, *J. Am. Chem. Soc.*, **63**, 437 (1941).

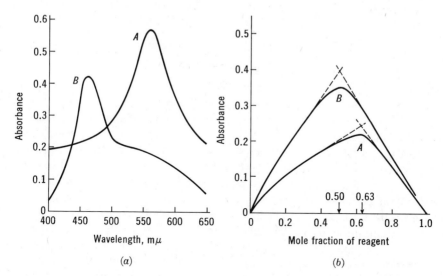

Fig. 31-18   (*a*) Spectral curves of osmium-anil solutions. *A*, excess anil; *B*, excess
osmium. (*b*) Continuous variations plots; total concentration of reactants,
$4.00 \times 10^{-5} M$. *A*, absorbance at 615 mμ; *B*, absorbance at 466 mμ. From
G. H. Ayres and C. W. McDonald, *Anal. Chim. Acta*, **30**, 40 (1964). (Used by
permission of *Analytica Chimica Acta*.)

tive when the stoichiometric amounts of M and L are used (i.e., if the complex is
dissociated), the plot of absorbance against mole fraction of ligand does not
peak sharply but is rounded; the greater the rounding, the more extensive is the
dissociation of the complex. Extrapolation of the first and last portions of the
curve (where dissociation of the complex is suppressed by the large excess of one
reactant) is then required to locate the position corresponding to the composition
of the complex. A typical plot is shown in Fig. 31-18, representing the reaction
of osmium in solution with *p*-(morpholino)-N-(4'hydroxy, 3'methoxy)benzyl-
idineaniline ("anil" for convenience).[20] It will be noted that in Fig. 31-18(*b*)
the curve at 615 mμ maximizes at 0.63 mole fraction of anil, rather than at 0.67
mole fraction, the correct value for a 1 : 2 complex; this is probably due to an
incomplete conversion of the 1 : 1 complex (which absorbs appreciably at 615
mμ, as shown in Fig. 31-18(*a*), curve *B*) to the 1 : 2 complex with stoichiometric
amounts of reactants. In any case, it is usually necessary merely to distinguish
between integral values of the reaction ratios.

Unambiguous deduction of the reaction ratio cannot be made by the method
of continuous variations when the ratio L : M is more than 4 : 1 (mole fraction

[20] G. H. Ayres and C. W. McDonald, *Anal. Chim. Acta.*, **30**, 40 (1964).

of L = 0.80); usually the data are not sufficiently exact to distinguish this composition from a 5 : 1 ratio (mole fraction of L = 0.83).

2. Mole Ratio Method.   Again, consider the reaction

$$M + nL \rightleftarrows ML_n$$

with the same assumptions as before. Yoe and co-workers[21,22] showed that if the complex is very little dissociated, a plot of absorbance against the mole ratio L/M, for a series of solutions in which [M] is kept constant and [L] is varied, rises steeply from the origin as a straight line for mole ratios below that corresponding to the composition of the complex formed, then breaks sharply to a constant absorbance at the mole ratio of L/M in the complex. Alternatively, [L] may be held constant and [M] varied; the break in the curve then indicates the ratio M/L. If the complex is appreciably dissociated, the mole ratio plot shows no sharp break, but a considerable curvature around the mole ratio corresponding to the composition of the complex, approaching asymptotically a constant absorbance at high mole ratios. In this case, extrapolation of the first and last portions of the curve to a point of intersection can often define the reaction ratio composition. Rounded curves can often be sharpened into breaks by working with solutions of high constant ionic strength.

Originally the mole ratio method was considered applicable only to systems in which a single complex was formed under a given set of conditions. However, if more than one complex is formed and the various complexes have different absorption characteristics and different formation constants, measurements at different wavelengths will often reveal their presence by breaks in the mole ratio plot; indeed, even at one given wavelength significant changes in slope of the mole ratio plot indicate the presence of different complexes. Using this method in a study of the color reaction between tin(II) and platinum(II) in hydrochloric acid solution, seven different mole ratios of Sn/Pt were found.[23] The mole ratio method applied to the color reaction between palladium and 2,3-quinoxalinedithiol (QDT)[24] is illustrated in Fig. 31-19. In Fig. 31-19(a), curve A is the absorption spectrum of the yellow solution formed by reaction of palladium and QDT in a 1 : 1 mole ratio; curve B is the spectrum of the red solution formed when QDT is present in excess, and corresponds to the 1 : 2 complex between palladium and QDT. The presence of both the 1 : 1 and the 1 : 2 complexes is clearly shown by the mole ratio plots in Fig. 31-19(b).

3. Slope Ratio Method.   Consider the reaction

$$xM + yL \rightleftarrows M_x L_y$$

in which, under a given set of conditions, only one complex is formed. A series of

[21] J. H. Yoe and A. L. Jones, *Ind. Eng. Chem., Anal. Ed.*, **16**, 111 (1944).

[22] J. H. Yoe and A. E. Harvey, *J. Am. Chem. Soc.*, **70**, 648 (1948).

[23] A. S. Meyer, Jr. and G. H. Ayres, *J. Am. Chem. Soc.*, **79**, 49 (1957).

[24] G. H. Ayres and H. F. Janota, *Anal. Chem.*, **31**, 1985 (1959).

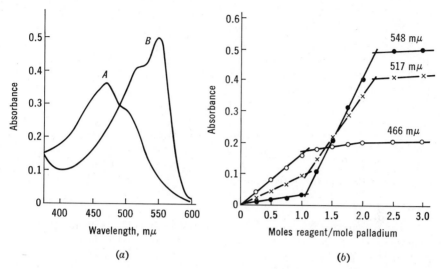

Fig. 31-19 (a) Spectral curves. A, palladium(II) and QDT, each at $3.0 \times 10^{-5} M$; B, palladium(II), $1.5 \times 10^{-5} M$ and excess QDT. (b) Mole ratio plots at significant wavelengths. From G. H. Ayres and H. F. Janota, *Anal. Chem.*, **31**, 1985 (1959). (Used by permission of *Analytical Chemistry*.)

solutions is prepared containing small increments of M and a constant concentration of L, which is so large that dissociation of the complex is suppressed to a negligible value. The equilibrium concentration of the complex, $[M_x L_y]$, is then proportional to the analytical concentration of M added; that is,

$$[M_x L_y] = C_M/x$$

and a plot of absorbance (which measures $[M_x L_y]$) against concentration of M is a straight line of slope inversely proportional to x. Similarly, if [M] is large and constant (and of the same molar concentration as L used previously) and L is added in small increments,

$$[M_x L_y] = C_L/y$$

and a plot of absorbance against concentration of L is a line of slope inversely proportional to y. The ratio of the slopes of the two plots is then the ratio y/x. See Fig. 31-20 for illustration.

The slope ratio method[25] has an advantage over the two previous methods for cases in which the complex is so much dissociated that the experimental plot in the continuous variations or the mole ratio method is so rounded that large extrapolation errors may preclude unambiguous determination of the composition of the complex. In the slope ratio method, each curve is in effect the first part of a mole ratio plot, one for fixed M and variable L, the other for

[25] A. E. Harvey and D. L. Manning, *J. Am. Chem. Soc.*, **72**, 4488 (1950).

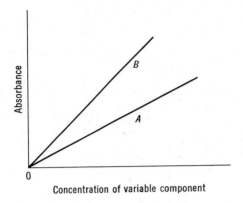

Fig. 31-20 Slope ratio plots for the complex ML_2. *A*, [M] large and constant, [L] varied; *B*, [L] large and constant, [M] varied.

fixed L and variable M. In each case the measurements are made in solution containing a large excess of one reactant, which suppresses the dissociation of the complex. The method is limited to conditions involving formation (or at least measurement) of a single complex; if more than one complex is formed between M and L, solutions containing excess M will be rich in the lowest complex and solutions containing excess L will be rich in the highest complex of the system, hence the same absorbing species would not be measured in the two series of solutions.

The three methods outlined above can be applied to the determination of the reaction ratio of two substances that form an absorbing product, which need not be a complex in the usual sense. For example, all three of these methods have been used to establish the reaction ratio of rhodium(III) with hypochlorite by measuring the absorbance of the blue oxidation product; all three methods confirmed a mole ratio of 1 : 1 in the reaction.[26]

Calculation of Formation Constant of a Complex.   Curvature of the mole ratio plot around the stoichiometric composition can be used for calculation of the formation constant of the complex. Suppose the complex formed by the reaction

$$M + nL \rightleftarrows ML_n$$

is appreciably dissociated, and that the complex is represented by the formula ML_2, as in Fig. 31-21. If the complex were very stable, the plot would consist of two straight lines intersecting at the point A_m (ordinate) and 2 (abscissa), as indicated by the extrapolation lines in the figure. Rounding of the curve is a qualitative indication of the degree of dissociation of the complex, and the measured absorbance near the stoichiometric composition can be used to calculate the dissociation or the formation constant of the complex, as follows.

If C_M is the analytical concentration of M taken, and if it were completely converted to the complex, then $[ML_2] = C_M$. The absorbance A_m would represent

[26] G. H. Ayres and H. F. Young, *Anal. Chem.*, **24**, 165 (1952).

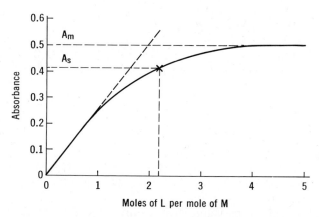

Fig. 31-21 Mole ratio plot, indicating data used for calculating the formation (or dissociation) constant of the complex ML_2.

the concentration of ML_2. A_m is also the limiting absorbance of a moderately unstable complex when measured in the presence of a large excess of ligand to suppress the dissociation of the complex. At any point where complex formation is incomplete,

$$[ML_2] = C_M \times \frac{A_s}{A_m}$$

where A_s is the measured absorbance of a solution of known concentration with respect to C_M and C_L used to prepare it. It follows that

$$[M] = C_M - [ML_2]$$

and

$$[L] = C_L - 2[ML_2]$$

and the formation constant of the complex is

$$K_f = \frac{[ML_2]}{[M][L]^2}$$

Most precise calculation of K_f is made from data at the stoichiometric composition of the complex, but data on either side of this point can also be used. In any case, K_f should be determined for several different values of C_M (bearing in mind that dissociation increases with increasing dilution) in order to get a reliable mean value.

In Fig. 31-21, assume $C_M = 1.50 \times 10^{-5}\ M$ and $C_L = 3.30 \times 10^{-5}\ M$; the mole ratio $L/M = 2.2$, slightly beyond the stoichiometric composition of the complex. A_s of this solution is 0.42; $A_m = 0.50$.

$$[ML_2] = 1.50 \times \frac{0.42}{0.50} = 1.26 \times 10^{-5}$$

$$[M] = 1.50 \times 10^{-5} - 1.26 \times 10^{-5} = 2.4 \times 10^{-6}$$

$$[L] = 3.30 \times 10^{-5} - 2(1.26 \times 10^{-5}) = 7.8 \times 10^{-6}$$

$$K_f = \frac{(1.26 \times 10^{-5})}{(2.4 \times 10^{-6})(7.8 \times 10^{-6})^2} = 8.7 \times 10^{10}$$

This method is limited to cases in which A_s is from about 0.7 to about $0.9A_m$. If the value of A_s is too close to that of A_m, the uncertainty in [M] and [L] becomes large. But if A_s is smaller than about $0.7A_m$, the curvature of the plot is so great that the stoichiometric composition of the complex cannot be established with certainty.

The same approach as used above can be applied to the continuous variations method [see Fig. 31-18(b), p. 471]. Indeed, calculations from the latter method are applicable to even weaker complexes than with the mole ratio method, because the first part of the curve (excess M) and the last part of the curve (excess L), both of which are approximately linear due to suppression of the dissociation by an excess of one reactant, approach one another at a sharper angle than in the mole ratio plot; an extrapolated intersection is therefore located more reliably.

Photometric Titrations

If, in the reaction

$$X \text{ (desired constituent)} + Y \text{ (titrant)} \rightarrow Z \text{ (product)}$$

at least one of the substances is colored, it is possible to determine the end point titrimetrically by measuring the absorbance of the solution after adding known increments of titrant, then plotting absorbance against volume of titrant.[27] Plots thus obtained consist of two straight-line segments, one before and one after the stoichiometric point, which are extrapolated to an intersection in order to locate the stoichiometric volume of titrant. If the reaction is quite incomplete, the plot of data around the end point has considerable curvature, and data points in this region are of little value. However, at points well removed from the end point, an excess of X (early in the titration) or an excess of Y (titrant) displaces the reaction toward completeness of formation of Z (product). Changes in absorbance are then essentially linear with volume of titrant, provided dilution effects are minimized by using a titrant solution about ten times more concentrated than the desired constituent; or, better, the measured absorbances are corrected by multiplying by the factor $(V + v)/V$, where V is the initial volume of the solution and v is the volume of titrant added up to that point. Accuracies of the order of 0.1 to 0.5% are attainable.

[27] J. B. Headridge, *Photometric Titrations*, New York, Pergamon Press, 1961.

The wavelength chosen for absorbance measurements should be one at which other solutes present do not interfere. It need not be at the absorption maximum of the absorbing species. Absorbances should be in a reliable range; but high accuracy of absorbances need not be achieved because the important feature is sharp *change* in absorbance with addition of titrant before and after the stoichiometric point. The sensitivity of the method can be changed by change in the analytical wavelength used, and frequently a wavelength on the side of an absorption band is used, especially if the titration involves substances of high absorptivity or at relatively high concentration.

Typical photometric titration curves are shown in Fig. 31-22. If foreign substances such as other solutes or suspensions are present that absorb somewhat at the chosen wavelength, the titration curve will lie at higher values on the absorbance axis, as shown by the dashed line in Fig. 31-22(a). This does not nullify the determination of the nonabsorbing solute. In addition to the types of curves shown in Fig. 31-22, other curve shapes are possible when two successive

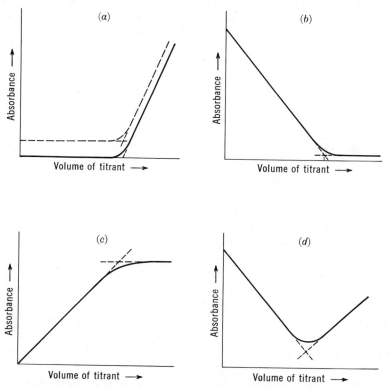

Fig. 31-22   Photometric titration curves. Reaction: $X + Y$ (titrant) $\rightarrow Z$. (*a*) Y absorbs, X and Z do not. (*b*) X absorbs, Y and Z do not. (*c*) Z absorbs, X and Y do not. (*d*) X and Y absorb, Z does not.

reactions form products of different absorptivities at the chosen wavelength, as in the formation of successive complex ions by use of the ligand as the titrant.

ATOMIC ABSORPTION SPECTROPHOTOMETRY

When a solution of a metallic salt is atomized into a high temperature flame, the solvent is evaporated, the salt is vaporized, and the molecules are dissociated into neutral atoms. Some of the atoms may be excited or ionized by the thermal energy of the flame; return to the ground electronic state may be accompanied by the emission of light, and this phenomenon is the basis of flame emission photometry (see p. 481). However, most of the atoms, probably 99%, are in the unexcited state and are in a favorable condition to absorb radiant energy of the characteristic frequencies of their resonance lines, by transition from the ground state to a higher energy level.

In atomic absorption photometry[28,29] the element of interest in the analysis is made the source of radiant energy, and is subjected to electrical excitation causing it to emit radiation of its characteristic frequencies; for example, if sodium is to be determined, the source may be a conventional sodium vapor lamp. For determination of elements other than the alkalies and mercury (for which vapor lamps are used), the source is a discharge tube or lamp in which the cylindrical cathode is made of the element under investigation; the sealed tube contains argon or helium carrier gas, at low pressure (1–2 mm). Application of a potential of several hundred volts across the electrodes causes the cathode to emit radiation characteristic of the cathode material. When this beam of energy is passed through the vaporized sample interposed between the source and the entrance slit of a monochromator, set at a wavelength to isolate the spectral line of interest, the atomic vapors of the sample absorb this energy and thus decrease the radiant power of the beam. The radiant power of the spectral line is measured with a photomultiplier tube and amplifier, first without and then with the sample vapor in the optical beam; the decrease in radiant power is proportional to the number of atoms of the element under investigation, in the beam. The method is calibrated with known amounts of the desired constitutent, and a calibration curve is constructed from the data. The principle of the method is analogous to conventional absorption spectrophotometry of solutions or liquids, except for the nature of the source and the physical state of the sample.

Burners used for vaporizing the sample usually have a long narrow slit orifice, the long dimension of which is below and parallel to the axis of propagation of the beam from the source; in this way many atoms capable of absorbing energy are placed in the beam. Additional sensitivity can be achieved by the use of reflecting mirrors to give several passes of the beam through the sample vapor before

[28] J. A. Dean, *Flame Photometry*, New York, McGraw-Hill, 1960, Chap. 10.
[29] H. H. Willard, L. L. Merritt, Jr., and J. A. Dean, *Intrumental Methods of Analysis*, Princeton, N.J., Van Nostrand, 1965, 4th ed., pp. 345–351.

measurement of the radiant power. For extension to high concentration ranges it may be desirable to measure a weaker spectral line.

Atomic absorption photometry, originated by Walsh,[30] has been applied to the analysis of some 50 elements in a wide variety of materials, and new applications are appearing in the current literature. Although flame absorption and flame emission photometry have several sources of error in common, some of these are easier to minimize or to avoid in absorption methods than in emission methods. The method is especially useful for the determination of elements that are vaporized by, but not appreciably excited in, the oxy-acetylene or similar high temperature flames. Commercial instruments are available, with several different hollow cathode tubes kept in warm-up condition and readily positioned for use.

EMISSION SPECTROMETRY

When atoms are subjected to sufficient thermal or electrical energy, such as by flames, arcs, or sparks, electrons are promoted from the ground state to higher energy levels, including complete expulsion of one or more electrons (ionization). The excited electrons tend to return to the ground state; in so doing, they emit the surplus energy as photons of radiant energy. Because the electrons can exist only in definite energy states or levels, the emission occurs at definite frequencies or wavelengths, and gives rise to a line spectrum that is unique for the excited atoms. Measurement of wavelength and intensity of the spectral lines serves for qualitative analysis of the sample. The greater the excitation energy, and therefore the energy emitted, the more numerous the lines in the resulting spectrum. With relatively low excitation energy, as from flames, the emission is mainly in the visible region of the spectrum; see Flame Photometry, p. 481. With higher excitation energy, such as with an arc or spark, the emission is often in the ultraviolet region. Photographic recording of the spectrum is used, and the method is known as **emission spectrography**. By suitable calibration, measurement of the radiant power of a characteristic spectral line is used for quantitative determination of the element under investigation.

Only a brief outline of principles and methods is possible here; reference works are available for details.[31-33]

The sources commonly used in emission spectrography are the dc arc, the ac arc, and the ac spark. Their function is to vaporize the sample and to promote electrons to higher energy levels. Temperatures up to about 8000°K are attainable. The dc arc is commonly used where very high sensitivity is desired, such as in the

[30] A. Walsh, *Spectrochim. Acta*, **7**, 108 (1955).

[31] W. R. Brode, *Chemical Spectroscopy*, 2nd ed., New York, Wiley, 1943.

[32] G. R. Harrison, R. C. Lord, and J. R. Loofbourow, *Practical Spectroscopy*, Englewood Cliffs, N.J., Prentice-Hall, 1948.

[33] C. E. Harvey, *Spectrochemical Procedures*, Glendale, Cal., Applied Research Laboratories, 1950.

identification of trace elements in samples; the wandering of the arc is a source of difficulty for quantitative work. The ac arc is more stable and reproducible. The ac spark gives higher excitation energies, is more stable and reproducible, and is generally preferred for quantitative analysis. A recent innovation is the use of an optical laser beam for vaporizing the sample.

Metallic elements can be used directly as electrodes. Powdered solids are placed in a shallow depression in the end of a carbon or graphite rod, which is usually made the positive electrode of an arc. Solutions may be evaporated to dryness on the electrode, which is then used as an arc or spark source; solutions may also be used by placing them in a " porous cup electrode " made by drilling out the center of a carbon or graphite rod, leaving a floor about 1 mm thick through which the solution seeps and is vaporized by the arc or spark.

The principal components of the spectrograph, besides the source unit, are a prism or diffraction grating to disperse the radiation from the source; a camera or other detection and measuring device, and the associated slits, lenses, and/or mirrors for directing the energy beam. Various types of mountings of the components are in use.

The spectrogram is recorded on a photographic plate or film. Exposure and processing of the photographic emulsion require adherence to rigid control of time, temperature, concentration of developing and fixing chemicals, etc., so that the density of the silver deposit has a definite relation to the exposure. Definite exposures are obtained by placing, in the optical beam, a step filter or a rapidly rotating step sector disc (less commonly, a log sector disc) that allows definite and known fractions of light to enter the spectrograph slit. A plot of density of silver deposit against the logarithm of the exposure is an S-shaped curve called the " characteristic curve " of the emulsion; the middle, nearly linear portion of this curve shows the useful range of the film. Most photographic emulsions are sensitive to short wavelength radiation, i.e., in the blue, violet, and ultraviolet regions; use of various dyestuffs in the emulsion can sensitize it for use with longer wavelengths.

For qualitative (identification) work, an iron spectrum is recorded adjacent to the spectrum of the unknown. Sometimes the spectrum of an element suspected to be present in the unknown is also recorded. The processed film is examined in a comparator, using the iron spectrum or the known spectrum of the element as a reference for wavelength; most comparators also have a standard plate showing the principal lines of many elements. Scales are provided for accurate measurement of the wavelengths of spectral lines. Tables of wavelength and relative intensities of spectral lines of the elements are available; the most complete collection is the M.I.T. Wavelength Tables, but abbreviated tables are found in several reference books. Positive identification of an element should involve observations of three or more sensitive lines of the element.

Quantitative emission spectrography requires careful control of all variables, such as excitation conditions, exposure time, film processing, etc. In order to eliminate, as much as possible, small variations in these factors it is customary to add an "internal standard" and measure the intensities of a "homologous line pair," one line of the element in question and the other line of the internal standard. Homologous line pairs should be closely adjacent in wavelength, and the two elements should have about the same vaporization characteristics and ionization potentials; slight variations in excitation conditions and/or film processing should then affect the two lines to the same extent, and the *ratio* of their intensities should be constant. The silver deposit resulting from the spectral line is measured in a densitometer (usually the densitometer and comparator are combined in a single instrument) by comparing the transmittance of the line with the transmittance of unexposed film adjacent to the line (background). Calibration is attained by using a series of known samples of varying content of the element under investigation and a fixed amount of internal standard element. If T_e is the transmittance of the element line and T_s is the transmittance of the internal standard line, a plot of log (T_e/T_s) against log concentration of the element is a straight line that is used as a calibration curve for translating measurements of unknowns into concentrations.

Direct reading spectrometers (sometimes called "quantometers") can be constructed in which the photographic film is replaced by photomultiplier tubes positioned at exit slits corresponding to wavelengths of lines of several elements. By means of associated electronic circuitry, direct read-out in terms of percent of the given element is accomplished. As many as 24 elements have been determined simultaneously, the analysis requiring only one to two minutes. Instruments of this kind are used in control laboratories in various industries.

Flame Photometry

The characteristically colored flames produced by compounds of sodium (yellow), strontium (red), and barium (green) are familiar qualitative tests for these elements. The mechanism of excitation and spectral emission serving as the basis of flame photometry[34,35] was given earlier (p. 478). Correlation of the radiant power emitted by an element with its concentration is the basis of quantitative analysis of unknowns.

The sample solution is sprayed under carefully controlled conditions into the flame, which is also carefully regulated with regard to pressure and flow rate of gases. Often the atomizer and burner are constructed into a single compact unit. Oxy-hydrogen and oxy-acetylene flames are used. Intensity of emission is influenced by several solution factors, such as viscosity, surface tension, size of spray droplets, presence of organic solvents, etc.

Light from the flame is directed onto the entrance slit of a monochromator, the wavelength scale of which is set to isolate a characteristic emission line of the

[34] J. A. Dean, *op. cit.*
[35] H. H. Willard, L. L. Merritt, Jr., and J. A. Dean, *op. cit.*, Chap. 11.

test element. (Filter photometers can also be used, but will not be discussed here.) The intensity (radiant power) of the line is measured by a photomultiplier or other type of photoconverter, and associated electronic circuitry. In measuring a line intensity, the instrument response includes the spectral emission plus any background emission. Correction for background is made by first measuring the intensity of line plus background by slowly scanning across the line and noting the peak reading, then slowly scanning to one side of the line and noting the minimum reading (background). The monochromator slit width should be as small as possible consistent with adequate sensitivity. The signal-to-background ratio should be as large as possible.

Qualitative analysis consists in identification of elements by means of the wavelengths of several characteristic lines. Attention needs to be given to possible interference of closely adjacent lines of two elements.

For quantitative analysis the method and instrument may be calibrated by the standard series method, as in solution absorption spectrophotometry. However, it is important to consider *all* the elements that may be present in the sample under test, so that any of the other elements that influence emission of the test element can be added to the standards. Because the effect of interfering substances reaches a maximum, "radiation buffers" consisting of high concentrations of the interfering elements are used in the standards and in the unknowns, to swamp the effects of these substances in the sample. For example, the interference of potassium in the measurement of sodium is blanked out by use of a high concentration of potassium in both standards and samples. The "method of standard addition" consists in measuring the emission of the unknown sample as well as the emission of the unknown sample to which has been added a known amount of the test element and converting the emission readings to concentrations by a calibration curve. If there are no interferences, the difference between the two concentrations should correspond to the amount of standard added. This method is useful for testing for suppression or enhancement by solution components; if these effects are present, methods of calculation for true content are available.

An effective means of compensating for variables such as fluctuating flame background and spray and burner variations is the internal standard method. The internal standard must be selected carefully; the factors to be considered are much the same as for selection of a suitable internal standard for emission spectrography (p. 481). The line intensity of each element, corrected for background, is measured, and the ratio of the test element to that of the internal standard element is plotted against concentration of the test element, on log-log coordinates. A straight line of about 45° slope is obtained for use as a calibration curve.

Common sources of error include interference due to close proximity or even overlap of another element line, superposition of a line on molecular band emission, self-absorption of the radiant energy by atoms of the same element in the ground state (see Atomic Absorption Spectrophotometry, p. 478), ionization of atoms of the test element, cation enhancement, and anion suppression of emission. Methods of coping with the various sources of error may be found in the literature.

PROBLEMS

31-1 0.2000 g of pure copper is dissolved in nitric acid; excess ammonia is added to form $Cu(NH_3)_4^{++}$, and the solution is diluted to one liter. A portion of the solution is placed in one cup of a Duboscq colorimeter and the depth of the solution is set at 28.00 mm. An unknown copper sample is prepared similarly; a portion of the solution is placed in the other colorimeter cup and the depth adjusted so that the color of the unknown matches that of the standard. Calculate the percentage of copper in the sample from the data in each part below.

Sample, g	Solution volume, ml	Depth at color match, mm
(a) 0.500	250.0	32.5
(b) 1.000	200.0	25.6
(c) 0.400	500.0	30.8
(d) 2.500	100.0	26.5

Ans. (a) 8.62.

31-2 (a) How many milliliters of $KMnO_4$ solution that is 0.0950 N against oxalate in acid solution are required to prepare 250.0 ml of solution containing 0.1000 mg of manganese per milliliter? *Ans.* 23.94.

(b) A 0.3000-g sample of manganese steel is dissolved, the manganese is oxidized to permanganate, and the solution is diluted to 100.0 ml. This solution is compared with a 1 : 10 dilution of the solution prepared in (a), using a Duboscq colorimeter; equal intensities are observed when the standard solution is set at 25.0 mm depth and the unknown is adjusted to 23.4 mm depth. Calculate the percentage of Mn in the steel.

Ans 0.356%.

31-3 A solution containing 10.0 ppm (1 ppm = 1 mg per liter) of a certain colored material, measured at 1.00 cm optical path, has the absorbance and the percent transmittance (% T) shown in the first line of the tabulation below. Calculate values to fill in the blanks in the tabulation, as indicated. Assume the system conforms to Beer's law.

	Conc., ppm	Optical path, cm	%T	Absorbance
Given:	10.0	1.00	38.9	0.410
(a)	4.2	1.00	—	—
(b)	12.7	1.00	—	—
(c)	18.0	2.00	—	—
(d)	—	1.00	—	0.861
(e)	—	5.00	22.1	—
(f)	10.0	—	19.2	—

Ans. (a) 67.3% T; A = 0.172.

31-4 A solution of $KMnO_4$ containing 1.00 mg of manganese per 100 ml has a transmittance of 12.9% when measured at 2.00 cm optical path.

(a) Calculate the absorbance of the solution.

(b) Calculate % T of the solution when measured at 1.00 cm optical path.

(c) A 0.2000-g sample of manganese steel is dissolved, oxidized to permanganate, and diluted to 500.0 ml. At 1.00 cm optical path the absorbance of the solution is 0.600. Calculate the percentage of Mn in the steel.

31-5 A solution of $KMnO_4$ containing 1.00 ppm of manganese has a transmittance of 90.4% at 1.00 cm optical path and 526 mμ.

(a) Calculate the % T of a solution containing 2.00 ppm of manganese when measured at 10.0 cm optical path.

(b) Calculate the molar absorptivity of *manganese* (measured as permanganate) at 526 mμ.

31-6 At 510 mμ a solution of $KMnO_4$ containing 20.0 ppm of manganese has an absorbance of 0.700 for 1.00 cm optical path. Calculate the molar absorptivity of $KMnO_4$ at 510 mμ.

31-7 At 565 mμ the molar absorptivity of $KMnO_4$ is 1430. Calculate the absorbance and the % T of a 0.00200% solution of $KMnO_4$ measured at 565 mμ and 2.00 cm optical path.

31-8 A 1.00-cm layer of 0.0200% solution of a compound of molecular weight 150 has a transmittance of 55.0%. Calculate the molar absorptivity of the compound.

31-9 The following data were obtained for measurement of a certain solute at 2.00 cm optical path:

Concentration, g/liter:	0.0105	0.0210	0.0280
percent transmittance:	44.8	20.0	11.7

(a) Does the system conform to Beer's law, within 1%?

(b) Calculate the average value of the specific absorptivity, per ppm-cm.

(c) Calculate the concentration of a solution having 28.7% T in a 2.00-cm cell.

(d) Calculate the concentration of a solution having 52.4% T in a 1.00-cm cell.

31-10 The following data were obtained in a standard series calibration for the determination of iron, by measuring the transmittance, at 506 mμ and 1.00 cm optical path, of solutions of iron(II) that were color developed with 1,10-phenanthroline.

Fe conc., ppm	% T	Fe conc., ppm	% T
0.20	90.0	3.00	26.3
0.40	82.5	4.00	17.0
0.60	76.0	5.00	10.9
0.80	69.5	6.00	7.0
1.00	63.5	7.00	4.5
2.00	41.0		

(a) On 2-cycle semilog graph paper, plot % T against concentration of iron. Does the system conform to Beer's law over the entire concentration range?

(b) Calculate the average molar absorptivity of iron, when it is determined by this method.

(c) On 2-cycle semilog graph paper, plot (100 − % T) against log concentration (Ringbom method). (1) What is the optimum concentration range, and the maximum accuracy (percent relative error per 1% photometric error) in this range? (2) In what concentration range will the relative analysis error, per 1% photometric error, not exceed 5%?

31-11 The following data were obtained in a standard series calibration for the determination of copper, as $Cu(NH_3)_4{}^{++}$, by measuring the transmittance in a filter photometer.

Cu conc., ppm	% T		Cu conc., ppm	% T
0.020	96.0		0.800	27.8
0.050	90.6		1.00	23.2
0.080	84.7		1.40	17.2
0.100	81.4		2.00	12.9
0.200	66.7		3.00	9.7
0.400	47.3		4.00	8.1
0.600	35.8			

(*a*) On 2-cycle semilog graph paper, plot % *T* against copper concentration. Does the system, measured under these conditions, conform to Beer's law over the entire concentration range? Is any deviation from the law of small, or of large magnitude? Suggest a plausible cause for any deviation.

(*b*) On 3-cycle semilog graph paper, plot $(100 - \% \, T)$ against log concentration (Ringbom method). (1) What is the concentration range for highest accuracy? (2) In this range, what is the percent relative error per 1% photometric error? (3) What is the concentration range within which the relative analysis error will not exceed 5%, 10%?

31-12 A solution of 5.00 mg of a certain solute in 50.0 ml measures 24.0% *T*, at optical path length of 1.00 cm; the molar absorptivity is 1200. Calculate the molecular weight of the solute.

31-13 5.00 ml of permanganate solution of unknown concentration is placed in an absorption cell and its absorbance, at a certain wavelength, is found to be 0.356. 1.00 ml of a standard $KMnO_4$ solution of concentration 5.00 ppm, is added; the absorbance is then 0.333. Another 1.00 ml of the same $KMnO_4$ solution is added, and the absorbance is then 0.318. Calculate the concentration of the unknown permanganate solution.

31-14 It is desired to calculate the volume of water in an irregularly shaped swimming pool. To the water, already containing cyanuric acid to stabilize the chlorine, is added 10 ounces of commercial calcium hypochlorite containing 20.0% of available chlorine. After thorough mixing, test with *o*-tolidine showed the water to contain 0.750 ppm chlorine. Calculate the volume of water, in U. S. gallons. (1 U. S. gallon = 3.785 liters; 1 ounce (avoir.) = 28.35 g.)

31-15 A spectrophotometer was set at 0% *T* with the light beam blocked, and to 100% *T* (zero absorbance) with a solution containing 140.0 ppm of an absorbing solute. A solution containing 160.0 ppm of the same solute had an absorbance measurement of 0.358. Calculate the concentration of an unknown solution of the same substance, having an absorbance of (*a*) 0.578; (*b*) 0.225. (All measurements were made at the same optical path length and the same wavelength.)

31-16 Using the "maximum precision method" of spectrophotometry, the 0% *T* of the scale was set with a 1.400 ppm solution, and the 100% *T* point was set with a 1.000 ppm solution of the same solute. Calculate the concentration of an unknown solution of the same solute which gave a reading of (*a*) 42.5% *T*; (*b*) 24.0% *T*.

31-17 Ni^{++} forms a blue complex with 2,3-quinoxalinedithiol (QDT) having an absorption peak at 650 mμ. Co^{++} reacts with QDT to form a red complex with an absorption maximum at 505 mμ. Both systems conform to Beer's law, and absorbances are additive. The specific absorptivities, in the dimensions (ppm-cm)$^{-1}$, are:

Ni complex: 0.257 at 650 mμ: 0.080 at 505 mμ
Co complex: 0.026 at 650 mμ; 0.610 at 505 mμ

(a) Calculate the molar absorptivity of each element at each of the two wavelengths.

(b) From the following measured absorbances, at 1.00 cm optical path, calculate the concentration of nickel and of cobalt in the unknown sample; give answer in ppm.

(1) Sample 1: 0.523 at 650 mμ; 1.638 at 505 mμ.
(2) Sample 2: 1.000 at 650 mμ; 0.664 at 505 mμ.

31-18 Palladium and platinum in solution can be determined simultaneously by color development with 2,3-quinoxalinedithiol (QDT) and measurement of absorbance at two characteristic wavelengths. Each system conforms to Beer's law, and absorbances are additive. Using 1.00-cm cells, the following data were obtained.

Sample	Absorbance at 625 mμ	Sample	Absorbance at 548 mμ
2.40 ppm Pd	0.013	2.00 ppm Pd	0.650
4.10 ppm Pt	0.555	2.05 ppm Pt	0.166
Unknown No. 1	0.285		0.950
Unknown No. 2	0.420		0.520

(a) Calculate the molar absorptivity of each element at each of the two wavelengths.

(b) Calculate the concentration, in ppm, of each element in the unknown solutions.

31-19 Platinum(II) solution reacts with tin(II) solution to form product(s) that can be measured spectrophotometrically. The following data were obtained by measuring the absorbance, at 350 mμ, of solutions containing the same total moles of platinum(II) and tin(II), but with the components in varying proportions.

Mole fraction of tin(II)	Absorbance	Mole fraction of tin(II)	Absorbance
0.10	0.42	0.65	0.25
0.20	0.32	0.75	0.44
0.30	0.22	0.80	0.51
0.40	0.12	0.85	0.43
0.50	0.04	0.90	0.32
0.55	0.08	0.95	0.20
0.60	0.15		

Plot absorbance against mole fraction of tin(II), and deduce the composition of the complex(es). [*Note:* tin(II) reduces platinum(II) to platinum(0).]

31-20 Osmium in solution reacts with a reagent having the trivial name "anil" to give products having strong absorption in the range 580–650 mμ, with sharp maximum at 615 mμ. The following data were obtained, using excess anil and measuring at 615 mμ in 1.00-cm cells.

Osmium conc., ppm	Absorbance	Osmium conc., ppm	Absorbance
0.76	0.142	3.80	0.687
1.52	0.280	4.56	0.798
2.28	0.424	5.32	0.923
3.04	0.559	6.08	1.007

(*a*) What is the visual color of the solutions?

(*b*) Plot absorbance against concentration; does the system conform to Beer's law?

(*c*) Calculate the molar absorptivity of osmium when determined by this method.

(*d*) Calculate the transmittance of each of the above solutions, and plot $(100 - \% T)$ against log concentration (Ringbom plot); use 2-cycle semilog graph paper. (If sufficient experimental points are not available from the above table, synthetic points can be generated from the plot in part (*b*) above.)

(*e*) Assuming an error of 0.5% (absolute) in measuring transmittance, what is the maximum accuracy, the optimum range, and the concentration range in which the relative error will not exceed 5%? Show how the answers are obtained.

31-21 A series of solutions containing a constant amount of osmium (3.80 ppm in the final solution) and increasing amounts of anil reagent gave the following data, with measurements at 615 mμ in a 1.00-cm cell.

Moles anil per mole Os	Absorbance	Moles anil per mole Os	Absorbance
0.40	0.093	2.40	0.384
0.80	0.173	2.80	0.396
1.20	0.247	3.20	0.403
1.60	0.312	3.60	0.411
2.00	0.343	4.00	0.414

(*a*) Plot absorbance against mole ratio of anil/osmium, and deduce the stoichiometric composition of the complex.

(*b*) Calculate the formation constant of the complex.

31-22 A series of solutions containing the same total concentration of reactants (osmium + anil = 4.00×10^{-5} mole per liter) gave the following data:

Mole fraction of anil	Absorbance At 615 mμ	At 466 mμ
0.10	0.063	0.108
0.20	0.104	0.185
0.30	0.143	0.257
0.40	0.175	0.317
0.50	0.203	0.352
0.60	0.218	0.327
0.70	0.188	0.236
0.80	0.132	0.144
0.90	0.065	0.065

(*a*) On the same graph paper, plot absorbance against mole fraction of anil, for each wavelength. Deduce the stoichiometric composition of the complexes formed.

(*b*) What is the visual color of the complex absorbing at 466 mμ? at 615 mμ?

(*c*) Calculate the formation constant of each of the complexes of osmium with anil.

(*d*) Outline an experimental procedure whereby the slope ratio method might be applied to this system to establish the stoichiometric composition of the two complexes. Include appropriate graphical representation.

31-23 Cobalt(II) reacts with QDT to form a red complex in solution. A solution containing 1.25 ppm of cobalt (and excess QDT) has 17.3% T at 1.00 cm optical path length.

(*a*) Calculate % *T* of a solution containing 0.50 ppm of cobalt, measured in a 4.00-cm cell.

(*b*) Calculate the molar absorptivity of cobalt, determined by the QDT method.

31-24   Ruthenium in solution forms a complex with dithiooxamide. A solution of the complex, containing 0.250 ppm of ruthenium, measured at 650 mμ in a 1.00-cm cell, has 33.1% *T*. Calculate the molar absorptivity of ruthenium in this method.

31-25   Rhodium(III) reacts with hypochlorite, at *p*H 6, to give a blue solution having an absorption maximum at 660 mμ. A solution containing 8.0 ppm of ruthenium, measured at 1.00 cm optical path length, has a transmittance of 50.6%. Calculate the molar absorptivity of ruthenium in this method.

31-26   A certain element, X, forms a colored complex with QDT having a molar absorptivity of 1.66×10^4 liter/mole-cm. A solution containing 2.00 ppm of X, measured at 1.00 cm optical path length, has 49.0% *T*. Calculate the atomic weight of the element X.

32

ELECTROANALYSIS

I. FUNDAMENTAL PRINCIPLES

Electrochemical Cells

A simple electrochemical cell consists of two metallic electrodes immersed in the same electrolyte solution, or in two different electrolytes in electrical contact (e.g., by means of a salt bridge). Two such cells are illustrated in Fig. 32-1.

Galvanic Cells. If the electrodes of cell 1 (Fig. 32-1) are short-circuited, spontaneous chemical reaction occurs: $Cu \rightarrow Cu^{++} + 2e$; electrons flow through the external conductor to the silver electrode: $Ag^+ + e \rightarrow Ag$. The cell emf generated is calculated as illustrated in Chap. 26. As the reaction $Cu + 2Ag^+ \rightarrow Cu^{++} + 2Ag$ proceeds, the concentration of Cu^{++} increases and the concentration of Ag^+ decreases; the emf therefore decreases and eventually becomes zero. Various type of galvanic cells are used to convert chemical energy to electrical energy.

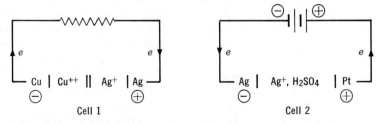

Fig. 32-1 Electrochemical cells. Cell 1, galvanic. Cell 2, electrolytic.

Electrolytic Cells.   These are cells in which chemical reactions are caused by imposing an external voltage greater than the reversible emf of the cell. In cell 2 (Fig. 32-1) the half-cell reactions are $Ag^+ + e \to Ag$, and $2H_2O \to 4H^+ + O_2 + 4e$, and the cell reaction is

$$4Ag^+ + 2H_2O \to 4Ag + 4H^+ + O_2$$

Commercial electroplating, electrolytic refining of metals, and electrolytic preparations (aluminum, chlorine, sodium hydroxide) utilize electrolytic cells.

The cathode is the electrode at which reduction occurs, and the anode is the electrode at which oxidation occurs; the "polarity" ($+$ or $-$) of the electrode is irrelevant to the definition.

In electrochemical phenomena,[1-4] interest is often centered on the reaction at only one electrode. The fundamental nature of electrode reactions is independent of whether the cell operates as a galvanic cell or as an electrolytic cell. In the cells illustrated above, the nature of the reaction $Ag^+ + e \to Ag$ is the same in both. If it is desired to plate out silver, this could be done either in the galvanic cell (by shorting the electrodes—i.e., by "internal electrolysis") or in the electrolytic cell.

Variables

In an electrochemical process, whether by galvanic or by electrolytic action, several types of variables are involved. A process is studied by holding certain variables at a constant value and observing the changes in other variables.

Solution variables include the concentration of the electroactive species, the concentration of other solute species (e.g., H^+), and the solvent.

Electrode variables include the material of the electrode, and its surface condition, area (A), and geometry.

Electrical variables include the potential (E), current (i), resistance (R), and quantity of electrical charge (Q); related to the latter is also time (t). Three of these variables are related by and defined in terms of Ohm's law: $E = iR$. The unit of potential is the **volt**, which is the emf required to pass a current of one **ampere** through a resistance of one **ohm**. (The reciprocal of resistance is **conductance**; its unit is the **reciprocal ohm** or **mho**.) Explicitly, the ohm is the resistance at 0°C of a column of mercury 106.300 cm long and weighing 14.4521 g; the cross section is approximately 1 mm². The quantity of electric charge, Q, is measured in **coulombs**; a coulomb is a current of one ampere flowing

[1] J. J. Lingane, *Electroanalytical Chemistry*, 2nd ed., New York, Interscience, 1958.

[2] I. M. Kolthoff and J. J. Lingane, *Polarography*, 2nd ed., New York, Interscience, 1952, vol. I.

[3] H. A. Laitinen, *Chemical Analysis*, New York, McGraw-Hill, 1960.

[4] L. Meites and H. C. Thomas, *Advanced Analytical Chemistry*, New York, McGraw-Hill, 1958.

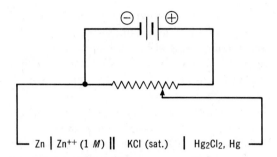

Fig. 32-2 Electrochemical cell. Reference electrode on the right is a saturated calomel electrode (S.C.E.).

for one second, and $Q = it$. The **faraday**, F (96,493 coulombs), is the quantity of electric charge associated with a chemical change of one gram equivalent weight of substance in an electrochemical process.

The mass transfer of the electroactive species between solution and electrode will be discussed in a later section.

Consider the cell represented in Fig. 32-2, in which the right-hand electrode is a saturated calomel reference electrode, S.C.E. (see p. 499). Neglecting activities and a small junction potential, the reversible, open circuit potential of the cell is $E^{\circ}_{cell} = E^{\circ}_{cal} - E^{\circ}_{Zn} = 0.242 - (-0.763) = 1.005$ v. If the externally applied emf, E_{app}, is just equal to E_{cell}, no current passes; that is, $i = 0$. When $E_{app} > E_{cell}$, the cell operates as an electrolytic cell. Suppose $E_{app} = 1.20$ v (i.e., the potential of the zinc electrode is made -1.20 v against S.C.E.); a question of interest is the amount of current that flows. Because i is the number of coulombs of electric charge flowing per second, or the number of electrons per second combining with Zn^{++}, i is a measure of the rate of the heterogeneous reaction $Zn^{++} + 2e \rightarrow Zn$.

$$i \text{ (amperes)} = \frac{dQ}{dt}\left(\frac{\text{coulombs}}{\text{seconds}}\right), \quad \frac{Q}{nF}\left(\frac{\text{coulombs}}{\text{coulombs/mole}}\right) = N \text{ (mole)} \quad (32\text{-}1)$$

$$\text{Velocity, } v \text{ (mole/sec)} = \frac{dN}{dt} = \frac{i}{nF} \quad (32\text{-}2)$$

Heterogeneous reaction rates usually involve area, hence

$$v \text{ (mole/sec/cm}^2) = \frac{i}{nFA} \quad (32\text{-}3)$$

Polarization, Overpotential

An *electrode* the potential of which deviates from its reversible (equilibrium) value is said to be **polarized**; the *amount* of the deviation is the **overpotential**;

i.e., $\eta = E - E_{eq}$. A *cell* is polarized if its emf departs from its reversible value; the overpotential of a cell is the sum of the overpotentials at the cathode and the anode. When considering either case of polarization, the ohmic voltage drop, iR, of the circuit is first subtracted before applying Ohm's law.

An **ideal polarized electrode** is an electrode the potential of which can be varied by any amount without the passage of current. The potential of an **ideal depolarized electrode** does not change from its equilibrium value upon passage of current. (Actually, passage of even a small current must cause a finite polarization; a current of a few microamperes may produce polarization of less than a millivolt, which is negligible for most purposes.) A **depolarizer** is a substance that decreases the amount of polarization. Often, the depolarizer acts by providing a preferential process of oxidation or reduction at the respective electrode.

Back EMF

When an external emf is applied to an electrolytic cell sufficient to produce reaction at the electrodes, the electrolytic products formed at the electrodes set up a galvanic action in opposition to the applied emf. The current, i, which flows is given by Ohm's law:

$$E_{app} = E_{back} + iR \qquad (32-4)$$

where R is the resistance of the entire circuit. With increasing current, E_{back} generally increases, and Ohm's law can be applied only after E_{back} is subtracted. The back emf consists of three components.

1. Reversible back emf is the reversible emf of the galvanic cell formed by passage of the electrolysis current; its magnitude depends upon the electrode and the solution components. For example, in Cell 2 of Fig. 32-1, the electrode reactions are

$$\text{at the cathode:} \quad Ag^+ + e \rightarrow Ag$$

$$\text{at the anode:} \quad 2H_2O \rightarrow O_2 + 4H^+ + 4e$$

If $[Ag^+] = [H^+] = 1$ M, the reversible back emf is the difference between the standard electrode potentials of the half cells:

$$E_{rev.\ back} = 1.23 - 0.80 = 0.43 \text{ v}$$

2. Concentration polarization or concentration overvoltage results from changes in concentration of the electroactive species at the surface of the electrode, compared with their concentration in the bulk solution. In the above example, increase in $[H^+]$ at the anode surface causes the reversible potential of that electrode to become more positive, and decrease in $[Ag^+]$ at the cathode surface causes the reversible potential of the silver electrode to become less positive. The combined effect is to increase the back emf. Concentration overvoltage is increased by increased current density (current per unit area), and is decreased by stirring.

Mass transfer. Transfer of material between solution and electrode can occur by one or more of the following processes:

a. Migration of a charged body under the influence of an electric field.

b. Diffusion of a species under the influence of a concentration gradient (chemical potential).

c. Convection, or hydrodynamic transport, by stirring, density gradients, etc.

The effects of concentration changes at either electrode during electrolysis can be monitored by introducing a reference electrode very close to the surface of the working electrode to be studied. Consider, for example, the cathode reaction

$$\text{Ox} + ne \rightarrow \text{Red}$$

If C_{ox} is the bulk concentration of Ox, and C_{Ox}° is its concentration at (i.e., in a thin layer adjacent to) the surface of the electrode because of depletion by reaction at the electrode, then $(C_{\text{Ox}} - C_{\text{Ox}}^{\circ})$ is the concentration gradient at the electrode. The flux at the electrode is given by $m_{\text{Ox}}(C_{\text{Ox}} - C_{\text{Ox}}^{\circ})$, where m_{Ox} is the mass transfer constant in cm/sec. In the absence of ionic migration, the rate of mass transfer of Ox to the electrode surface is

$$v_m = m_{\text{Ox}}(C_{\text{Ox}} - C_{\text{Ox}}^{\circ}) \tag{32-5}$$

The rate of the electrode reaction is equal to the rate of mass transfer of Ox to the electrode surface; hence,

$$\frac{i}{nFA} = m_{\text{Ox}}(C_{\text{Ox}} - C_{\text{Ox}}^{\circ}) \qquad \text{or} \qquad i = nFAm_{\text{Ox}}(C_{\text{Ox}} - C_{\text{Ox}}^{\circ})$$

or

$$i = k_{\text{Ox}}(C_{\text{Ox}} - C_{\text{Ox}}^{\circ}) \tag{32-6}$$

where $k_{\text{Ox}} = nFAm_{\text{Ox}}$. The maximum rate of mass transfer occurs when C_{Ox}° is negligible compared to C_{Ox}, whereupon a **limiting current** is attained:

$$i_{\text{lim}} = k_{\text{Ox}} C_{\text{Ox}} \tag{32-7}$$

This phenomenon is the basis of polarography (see section III). Dividing equation (32-6) by (32-7) gives

$$\frac{i}{i_{\text{lim}}} = \frac{C_{\text{Ox}} - C_{\text{Ox}}^{\circ}}{C_{\text{Ox}}} \qquad \text{or} \qquad C_{\text{Ox}}^{\circ} = C_{\text{Ox}} \frac{i_{\text{lim}} - i}{i_{\text{lim}}} \tag{32-8}$$

and C_{Ox}° decreases in direct proportion to the increase in current.

The concentration of the reduced form, Red, increases at the electrode surface by the electrode reaction, and

$$i = nFAm_{\text{Red}}(C_{\text{Red}}^{\circ} - C_{\text{Red}}) = k_{\text{Red}}(C_{\text{Red}}^{\circ} - C_{\text{Red}}) \tag{32-9}$$

where $k_{Red} = nFAm_{Red}$. If the reduced form is initially absent in the bulk solution, $C_{Red} = 0$, and

$$i = k_{Red} C_{Red}^{\circ} \qquad \text{or} \qquad C_{Red}^{\circ} = i/k_{Red} \tag{32-10}$$

Application of the Nernst equation.[5]   The values of C_{Ox}° and C_{Red}° are functions of the electrode potential, E; the functional relations depend upon the over-all kinetics of mass transfer. If the rate of electron transfer is so rapid that C_{Ox}° and C_{Red}° have their equilibrium values, application of the Nernst equation gives

$$E = E^{\circ\prime} - \frac{0.059}{n} \log \frac{C_{Red}^{\circ}}{C_{Ox}^{\circ}} \qquad \text{(at } 25°) \tag{32-11}$$

Introducing equations (32-8) and (32-10) into (32-11) gives

$$E = E^{\circ\prime} - \frac{0.059}{n} \log \frac{i}{i_{lim} - i} \cdot \frac{k_{Ox}}{k_{Red}}$$

$$= E^{\circ\prime} + \frac{0.059}{n} \log \frac{k_{Red}}{k_{Ox}} - \frac{0.059}{n} \log \frac{i}{i_{lim} - i} \tag{32-12}$$

When $i = i_{lim}/2$, the last term of equation (32-12) is zero, and

$$E = E^{\circ\prime} + \frac{0.059}{n} \log \frac{k_{Red}}{k_{Ox}} \tag{32-13}$$

The potential at this point is called the " half wave potential," $E_{1/2}$; that is,

$$E = E_{1/2} = E^{\circ\prime} + \frac{0.059}{n} \log \frac{k_{Red}}{k_{Ox}} \tag{32-14}$$

For any value of $0 < i < i_{lim}$, equation (32-12) becomes

$$E = E_{1/2} - \frac{0.059}{n} \log \frac{i}{i_{lim} - i} \tag{32-15}$$

When the reduced form is also initially present, equation (32-9) becomes

$$C_{Red}^{\circ} = \frac{i}{k_{Red}} + C_{Red} \tag{32-9a}$$

C_{Red}° increases by the electrode reaction, and

$$i_{lim} = -k_{Red} C_{Red} \qquad \text{or} \qquad C_{Red} = -\frac{i_{lim}}{k_{Red}} \tag{32-16}$$

---

[5] The treatment given above and to follow assumes the absence of activation overpotential—i.e., the current at all points is entirely diffusion controlled. When activation overpotential is considered, similar but more complicated relations are involved.

Combining equations (32-9a) and (32-16) gives

$$C_{\text{Red}}^{\circ} = \frac{i - i_{\lim}}{k_{\text{Red}}} \tag{32-17}$$

Subtracting equation (32-6) from (32-7) gives

$$C_{\text{Ox}}^{\circ} = \frac{i_{\lim} - i}{k_{\text{Ox}}} \tag{32-18}$$

Substitution of equations (32-17) and (32-18) into (32-11):

$$E = E^{\circ\prime} + \frac{0.059}{n} \log \frac{k_{\text{Red}}}{k_{\text{Ox}}} - \frac{0.059}{n} \log \frac{i - i_{\lim}}{i_{\lim} - i} \tag{32-19}$$

and

$$E = E_{1/2} - \frac{0.059}{n} \log \frac{i - (i_d)_a}{(i_d)_c - i} \tag{32-20}$$

which is a general equation for the current-potential relations.[6]

When $C_{\text{Red}} = 0$, $(i_d)_a = 0$, equation (32-20) is identical with equation (32-15), and the current-voltage relation gives a wave that is entirely cathodic, and the current is designated as positive, as in curve 1 of Fig. 32-3. When $C_{\text{Ox}} = 0$, $(i_d)_c = 0$, and

$$E = E_{1/2} - \frac{0.059}{n} \log \frac{i - (i_d)_a}{-i} = E_{1/2} + \frac{0.059}{n} \log \frac{i}{(i_d)_a - i} \tag{32-21}$$

The wave is then entirely anodic, and the current is designated as negative, as in curve 2 of Fig. 32-3. When both Ox and Red are initially present, equation (32-20) applies, and a composite anodic-cathodic wave (curve 3, Fig. 32-3) is obtained. For a composite wave of a reversible reaction, the value of E at $i = 0$ is the standard potential, E°, of the system as measured by a potentiometer. Furthermore, the value of $E_{1/2}$ is the same for the cathodic, anodic, or composite wave.

If the cathodic reaction involves plating out of a metal, e.g., $Ag^{+} + e \rightarrow Ag$, E at any point on the current-voltage curve should be given by (neglecting activities):

$$E = E^{\circ} + \frac{0.059}{n} \log C_{\text{Ox}}^{\circ} \tag{32-22}$$

where E° is the standard potential of the electrode reaction, and C_{Ox}° has its

---

[6] In the reaction Ox $+ ne \rightleftarrows$ Red, current in the forward direction (reduction) is designated *cathodic* and is given a positive sign; current in the reverse direction (oxidation) is designated *anodic* and is given a negative sign. Because the limiting currents are diffusion controlled, they are designated by $(i_d)_c$ and $(i_d)_a$ in equations.

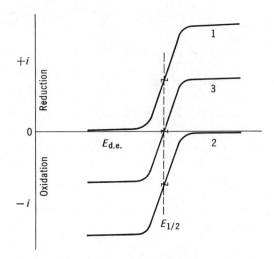

Fig. 32-3 Current-voltage curves (polarographic
waves) of reaction $Ox + ne \rightleftarrows$ Red. 1, cathodic wave (reduction); 2, anodic wave (oxi-
dation); 3, composite anodic-cathodic wave
of mixture of reduced and oxidized forms in
equal concentration.

usual significance. By considerations analogous to those developed previously,
it can be shown that the half wave potential, i.e., E when $i = (i_d)_c/2$, is given by

$$E_{1/2} = E^\circ + \frac{0.059}{n} \log \frac{C_{Ox}}{2} \qquad (32\text{-}23)$$

In this case $E_{1/2}$ is not constant, but becomes $0.059/n$ v more negative for each
ten-fold decrease in bulk concentration of metal ion. If, after some metal has
deposited, E_{app} is decreased below $E_{rev. back}$, the cell operates galvanically;
C_{Ox}° is then greater than C_{Ox}, and anodic concentration polarization increases
by $0.059/n$ volt for each ten-fold increase in C_{Ox}°/C_{Ox}. Unless C_{Ox} is very small,
concentration overpotential for metal dissolution is very small.

By definition, overpotential is the deviation of the electrode potential from its
reversible, equilibrium value, i.e., $\eta = E - E_{eq}$. For an electrode reaction in
which the reduced form is insoluble, as in the deposition of a metal, equation
(32-23) applies, and

$$\eta_{conc} = E - E_{eq} = \frac{0.059}{n} \log \frac{(i_d)_c - i}{(i_d)_c} = \frac{0.059}{n} \log \left(1 - \frac{i}{(i_d)_c}\right) \qquad (32\text{-}24)$$

When $0 < i < i_{lim}$, η_{conc} is negative (cathodic polarization) and increases without limit as i approaches i_{lim}. Expressions similar to equation (32-24) apply

when both Ox and Red are soluble. However, if either Ox or Red is initially absent, E_{eq} is not defined, therefore η_{conc} cannot be defined.

Because stirring increases the rate of mass transfer of the electroactive species, the value of i_{lim} increases and i/i_{lim} decreases, thus decreasing η_{conc}.

3. Activation Overpotential. After mass transfer (concentration polarization) effects have been taken into account, there still remains an overvoltage factor. If the cell reaction $Ox + ne \rightleftarrows Red$ is at equilibrium, "exchange current," i_0, is passing in each direction at the same rate, but no *net* current passes. If the electrode reaction is relatively slow (hence not reversible in the thermodynamic sense), more or less overpotential is required to initiate and maintain the reaction, i.e., to pass a net current. This so-called "activation overpotential" originates from a slow charge transfer process in the electrode reaction, or from a slow chemical reaction preceding or following the electron transfer. The slow reactions can influence the instantaneous concentrations of the electroactive species, hence the effect may be much the same as a concentration polarization. When activation overpotential is small, it is proportional to current, and is given by

$$\eta = \frac{RT}{nF} \cdot \frac{i}{i_{lim}} = \frac{0.0257}{n} \cdot \frac{i}{i_{lim}} \quad \text{(at 25°C)} \tag{32-25}$$

When η is large, it is proportional to the logarithm of current density.

This type of overpotential is especially large for reactions in which a gas is liberated at the electrode, such as cathodic generation of hydrogen or anodic liberation of oxygen. Activation overpotential is small for the metals silver, mercury, cadmium, zinc, etc., against their ions, but it is large for transition metals such as chromium, iron, cobalt, nickel, etc. Oxide film and adsorbed layers of organic substances on platinum electrodes increase the polarization.

II. ELECTROLYSIS AT ZERO CURRENT: POTENTIOMETRY

Chapter 26 presented the definition of electrode potential and the conventions to be used, and also calculations from the Nernst equation applied to the change of potential in redox titration systems due to change in concentration of electroactive species. This section is concerned with the measurement of potential and some applications of analytical importance.

Potentiometry consists in measuring the emf of a galvanic cell in such a way that the current passed is virtually zero, hence there is essentially no change in concentration of the electroactive species. Indeed, the usual variable of interest is the change of potential of a single electrode or half cell with change in concentration of one or both of its half-cell components. Because the potential of a single electrode cannot be measured directly, the electrode pair of the cell consists of a **reference electrode** that maintains a constant potential, and an **indicator electrode** the potential of which is dependent upon the composition of the electrolyte solution.

Reference Electrodes

If an electrode is to maintain a fixed potential, its composition must remain fixed, which requires that (virtually) no current be passed. This condition is provided by the circuitry and method of operation of the potentiometer used to measure the emf of the cell, and by the composition of the reference electrode, which will readjust to its original condition if only a minute amount of current is passed. Reference electrodes approach ideal depolarizability. The following half cells are used as reference electrodes. In each case the student should consider the way in which the electrode maintains or readjusts to its original composition by passing a *small* current in either direction.

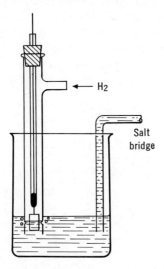

Fig. 32-4   Hydrogen electrode.

1. Hydrogen Electrode.   The arrangement of components is shown in Fig. 32-4; the platinized platinum foil is partly immersed in 1 M H^+ solution, and the exposed portion is surrounded with hydrogen gas. Connection to another half cell is made with a salt bridge. The half-cell formulation is

$$Pt \,|\, H_2 \,(1 \text{ atm}) \,|\, H^+ \,(1 \ M) \|$$

The standard potential, $E° = 0.00$ v, is arbitrarily chosen as the potential against which other half-cell potentials are referred. The hydrogen electrode is inconvenient to use, because it requires a source of pure hydrogen, which must be maintained at constant pressure; furthermore, the electrode is easily poisoned by traces of arsenic and sulfur compounds.

2. Calomel Electrode.   This electrode consists of a mixture of metallic mercury and mercury(I) chloride (calomel) in contact with a solution of potassium chloride:

$$Hg \,|\, Hg_2Cl_2(s) \,|\, KCl \text{ (known conc.)} \|$$

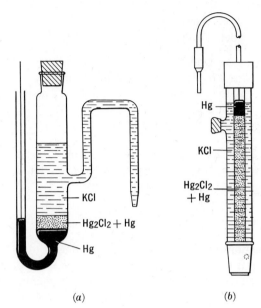

Fig. 32-5 Calomel electrodes. (*a*)
Side-arm type. (b) Sleeve type.

(a)   *(b)*

The half-cell reaction is

$$Hg_2Cl_2 + 2e \rightleftarrows 2Hg + 2Cl^-$$

Because Hg and Hg_2Cl_2 are at standard state, the potential of the half cell is dependent upon the concentration of chloride ion in solution:

$$E = E^\circ - \frac{0.059}{2} \log \frac{[Hg]^2[Cl^-]^2}{[Hg_2Cl_2]} = E^\circ - 0.059 \log[Cl^-]$$

Most calomel reference electrodes obtained commercially use a saturated solution of potassium chloride and excess solid KCl; the electrode is then known as a saturated calomel electrode (S.C.E.), for which $E^\circ = 0.2415$ v at 25°C. In the normal calomel electrode (N.C.E.) the potassium chloride is 1 *N*, and $E^\circ = 0.2812$ v.

In the early calomel electrode the salt bridge for making connection through a solution to another electrode was a U-tube side arm filled with potassium chloride solution, as shown in Fig. 32-5(*a*). In present commercial electrodes the salt bridging is accomplished either by a ground-glass sleeve covering a small hole through the glass near the bottom of the electrode, as in Fig. 32-5(*b*) or by a small fiber sealed through the glass; the ground-glass joint or the fiber is kept moist by the potassium chloride solution of the electrode, and the electrode assembly is dipped directly into the solution to be measured.

3. Quinhydrone Electrode. Although this electrode can serve as a reference electrode, it is somewhat inconvenient in that the quinhydrone and acid must be renewed every day or two. It is more often used as an indicator electrode for hydrogen ion, and is discussed in detail under that topic.

4. Silver Chloride Electrode. This electrode consists of a silver wire partly covered with a thin film of silver chloride; the concentration of chloride ion (and therefore of silver ion) is fixed by the solubility of silver chloride. The half reaction

$$AgCl + e \rightleftarrows Ag + Cl^-$$

has a standard potential $E° = 0.2222$ v at 25°C. The silver chloride electrode can also serve as an indicator electrode for chloride ion. Other silver halide electrodes are similar in action, but they have different $E°$ values.

Indicator Electrodes for Hydrogen Ions

A common application of potentiometry is the use of potentiometric data for end-point detection in acid-base titrations. The indicator electrode used for such measurements must exhibit a potential that varies in a definite manner with change in $[H^+]$ or pH.

1. Hydrogen Electrode. The hydrogen electrode can serve not only as a reference electrode, but also as an indicator electrode for H^+ concentration. At one atmosphere hydrogen gas pressure,

$$E = E° - \frac{0.059}{2} \log \frac{[H_2]}{[H^+]^2} = 0.00 + \frac{0.059}{2} \log [H^+]^2$$

$$= 0.00 + 0.059 \log [H^+] = -0.059 \, pH$$

The potential of the electrode is therefore a linear function of the pH of the solution.

2. Quinhydrone Electrode. Quinhydrone is a molecular compound of quinone and hydroquinone. It is moderately soluble in water, and the solution behaves like a mixture of the two compounds:

$$\underset{\text{Quinone, Q}}{C_6H_4O_2 \cdot C_6H_4(OH)_2} \rightleftarrows \underset{}{C_6H_4O_2} + \underset{\text{Hydroquinone, H}_2\text{Q}}{C_6H_4(OH)_2}$$

For the measurement of hydrogen ion concentration, the electrode consists of an inert metal (platinum or gold) dipping into the solution containing quinhydrone:

$$Pt \,|\, Q, H_2Q, H^+ \,(x\,M)\|$$

The two compounds constitute a redox half-reaction system:

$$C_6H_4O_2 + 2H^+ + 2e \rightleftarrows C_6H_4(OH)_2 \qquad E° = 0.700 \text{ v}$$

The Nernst expression for the half reaction is

$$E = 0.700 - \frac{0.059}{2} \log \frac{[H_2Q]}{[Q][H^+]^2}$$

But $[H_2Q] = [Q]$, hence the potential depends only upon $[H^+]$:

$$E = 0.700 + 0.059 \log [H^+] = 0.700 - 0.059 \, pH$$

As a reference electrode, it consists of a saturated solution of quinhydrone in 0.10 M hydrochloric acid in contact with excess solid quinhydrone.

The electrode has the disdavantage that hydroquinone in solution is slowly oxidized to quinone by air, and the electrode must be prepared fresh every one or two days. The quinhydrone indicator electrode cannot be used at pH above about 8 or 9 because of the formation of the hydroquinone ion, $C_6H_4O_2^{--}$. This decreases the concentration of the hydroquinone so that $[H_2Q]$ is no longer equal to $[Q]$, and there is then no simple basis for relating potential to $[H^+]$. Furthermore, this reaction consumes alkali that was not used in the titration of the acid being titrated. The electrode cannot be used reliably in solutions containing boric acid or borates because of the formation of strongly acidic complexes with hydroquinone. It is, however, a simple and convenient electrode for somewhat temporary use and it is not easily poisoned.

3. Glass Electrode. This electrode consists of a thin glass membrane in the form of a small bulb on the end of a glass tube filled with a buffer solution of known (or at least constant) pH. In commercial electrodes, external connection of the solution is made by a small calomel or silver chloride reference electrode built into the glass electrode assembly. When the electrode is placed in a solution containing hydrogen ions at a concentration different from that inside the membrane, a potential develops across the glass membrane. The electrode is in reality a concentration cell the potential of which depends upon the difference in concentration of hydrogen ion on the two sides of the membrane.

The action of the electrode appears to depend upon the permeability of the glass membrane; hydrogen ion, on account of its small size and high mobility, permeates the membrane more readily than other ions of the solution. The permeability of the glass membrane is highly dependent upon the composition of the glass. Special glasses have been developed for making electrodes that can be used continuously in solutions of high alkalinity (pH 13 or 14) and at high temperature. (Glasses are now available to serve as indicator electrodes also for various cations such as the alkali and alkaline earths.)

Glass electrodes cannot be used with conventional potentiometers, because the resistivity of the glass membrane is so great (of the order of megohms) that only a very feeble current can pass through at the low potential of the electrode. This current is too small to actuate the galvanometer of an ordinary potentiometer, but it can be passed through a vacuum-tube amplifier and balanced against a working potential. Glass electrodes are very versatile in that they are not affected by dissolved gases, reducing or oxidizing agents, organic matter, etc. They can be made in very small sizes and in combination with small reference electrodes for measurement of biological materials, and in rugged construction for continuous monitoring of plant streams in industrial processes. In systems of constant hydrogen ion concentration the glass electrode can be used as a reference electrode.

4. Metal–Metal Oxide Electrodes.   Certain metals, the surface of which is partly covered with a firmly adherent coating of their oxide, can serve as indicators for hydrogen ions. In this class of electrodes, the antimony electrode has been the most widely used. The half-cell reaction is

$$Sb_2O_3 + 6H^+ + 6e \rightleftarrows 2Sb + 3H_2O \qquad E° = 0.152 \text{ v}$$

The potential of the electrode is therefore dependent only upon the hydrogen ion concentration of the solution:

$$E = 0.152 + 0.059 \log[H^+] = 0.152 - 0.059 \ pH$$

The electrode is convenient, because no reagent (solid, gas) is needed; it is rugged, and suitable for continuous recording and control operation. Its useful range is about pH 2 to 8; it cannot be used at higher alkalinity on account of the solubility of antimony(III) oxide in alkali. Other metal–metal oxide electrodes that have been used are tellurium, tungsten, and passive iron.

Indicator Electrodes for Other Ions

By proper choice of materials, electrodes can be selected for indicating the change in concentration of certain ions, such as Cl^-, Ag^+, etc., and for indicating the change of concentration ratios of ions such as oxidized/reduced form in redox titrimetry. Some commonly used electrodes in this category are described below.

1. Silver–Silver Chloride Electrode.   This is not only a reference electrode (see p. 500) but also an indicator electrode for chloride ion concentration.

$$AgCl + e \rightleftarrows Ag + Cl^- \qquad E° = 0.2222 \text{ v}$$

$$E = E° - 0.059 \log \frac{[Ag][Cl^-]}{[AgCl]}$$

$$= 0.2222 - 0.059 \log[Cl^-]$$

The electrode is used as the indicator in the titrimetric precipitation of chloride ion by silver ion. A silver bromide electrode can be used similarly in the titration of bromide ion.

2. Metals.   A metal in contact with a solution of its ions can be used to indicate the concentration of the latter.

$$M^{n+} + ne \rightleftarrows M \qquad E = E^\circ + \frac{0.059}{n} \log[M^{n+}]$$

For example, a silver electrode dipping into a solution of silver ions indicates the concentration of the latter:

$$E = 0.7991 + 0.059 \log[Ag^+]$$

and can be used in the titration of silver ion by various reagents.

3. Inert Metals.   Platinum and gold are used in redox titrations to serve as a collector for the electrons involved in the reaction

$$Ox + ne \rightleftarrows Red$$

of the substance titrated (before the equivalence point) and of the titrant (after the equivalence point). The potential of the inert electrode is the potential of the half reaction involved, and is given by

$$E = E^\circ - \frac{0.059}{n} \log \frac{[Red]}{[Ox]}$$

The electrode indicates the ratio of the concentrations [Red]/[Ox] and therefore the progress of the titration reaction. Inert metal electrodes are often used in conjunction with the glass electrode (as a reference electrode) in redox titrimetry.

The Measurement of EMF

The essential functional components of a simple potentiometer circuit are shown diagrammatically in Fig. 32-6. A working cell, E_w, which may be a dry cell or a storage battery of voltage greater than is to be measured, is connected to a resistance wire AB to provide a uniform voltage drop along its length. The cell to be measured, E_x, is connected, with its polarity in opposition to that of E_w, to the same resistance wire with one fixed contact A and one movable or sliding contact C. The galvanometer G in the line shows whether or not current is flowing, and the voltmeter V across the unknown cell gives a rough reading of the voltage. In order to calibrate the instrument, the switch S is connected to a standard cell, E_s, the voltage of which is accurately known, and the contact C is moved to coincide with B. The tapping key K is closed momentarily (so that very little current is drawn) and any deflection of the galvanometer is noted. The resistance R in the circuit of the working cell is adjusted until no galvanometer deflection (i.e., a null point) is observed when the key is closed briefly. Under these conditions the voltage drop between A and B is the same as the

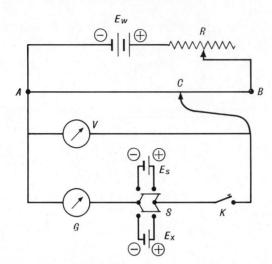

Fig. 32-6 Diagram of potentiometer circuit.

voltage of the standard cell E_s. The switch is then connected to the cell to be measured, E_x, and the contact C is moved until a point is found at which, on tapping the key K, a null point is registered by the galvanometer, showing that no current is flowing. At this point the voltage drop across AC from the unknown cell is the same as that across AC from the working cell, and represents a known fraction AC/AB of the voltage of the standard cell E_s used for calibration. Ordinarily, the slide wire resistance AB, mounted on a circular drum, carries a scale graduated in volts and millivolts, so that the position of the sliding contact or takeoff C can be read directly on the graduated scale. The instrument is calibrated by setting the scale at the exact voltage of the standard cell E_s and adjusting R to a galvanometer null. Any unknown voltage E_x is then read directly in volts or millivolts on the graduated scale.

For use in making pH measurements, the scale may be graduated directly in pH units, since a change of one pH unit corresponds to a change of 0.059 v (at 25°C) in the cell emf. The instrument is calibrated by the use of a buffer solution of known pH in the cell E_x, and by adjusting R to a null point on the galvanometer. The solution to be measured is placed in the cell, and the circuit is balanced by changing the contact C; pH is then read directly from the graduated scale. When a glass electrode is used in making pH measurements, a vacuum-tube amplifier is substituted for the galvanometer, and the circuit may be designed to actuate the needle of a sensitive voltmeter across a scale graduated directly in pH units. One form of commercial pH meter is shown in Fig. 32-7.

Potentiometric Titrations

The voltage developed in any titration cell will of course include the potential of the reference electrode. The changes in emf are then due to the changes in

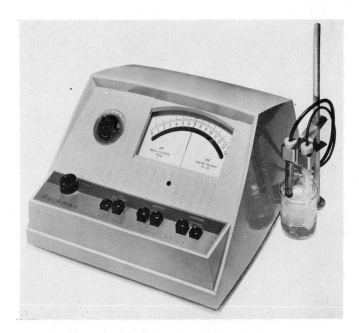

Fig. 32-7   Beckman Zeromatic *p*H meter. (Courtesy of Beckman
            Instruments, Inc.)

composition of the titration solution. The electrode pair to be used is selected
primarily on the basis of the system to be measured, although convenience
is also a consideration if several possibilities are presented. The following
examples illustrate several electrode pairs commonly used.

1. *Hydrogen and calomel electrodes*, for neutralization titration. The cell
formulation is

$$(-) \quad Pt\,|\,H_2\,(1\ atm)\,|\,H^+\,(x\ M)\,\|\,KCl\,(satd.)\,|\,Hg_2Cl_2\,|\,Hg \quad (+)$$

With the conventions previously adopted:

$$
\begin{array}{ll}
Hg_2Cl_2 + 2e \rightleftarrows 2Hg + 2Cl^- & E°_1 = 0.242\ v \\
\underline{2H^+ + 2e \rightleftarrows H_2} & \underline{E°_2 = 0.00\ v} \\
Hg_2Cl_2 + H_2 \rightleftarrows 2Hg + 2Cl^- + 2H^+ & E°_1 - E°_2 = 0.242\ v
\end{array}
$$

But Hg_2Cl_2, H_2, and Hg are at their standard states, and the constant concentration of Cl^- in saturated KCl is included in $E°_1$; hence,

$$E_{cell} = 0.242 - 0.059\ \log[H^+] = 0.242 + 0.059\ pH$$

The cell emf increases 0.059 v for each unit increase in *p*H.

2. *Glass and calomel electrodes*, for neutralization titration. It was stated
earlier that commercial glass electrodes may have a built-in saturated calomel

electrode in contact with the solution of known hydrogen ion concentration inside the membrane. Combination of a glass electrode with an external saturated calomel electrode for neutralization titrations can be represented as follows; the solution of known hydrogen ion concentration is assumed to be buffered at pH 7.

$$\underbrace{\text{Hg}\,|\,\text{Hg}_2\text{Cl}_2|\,\text{KCl (satd.)}\,\|\,\text{H}^+\,(x\ M)}_{\substack{\text{cell } r, \text{ titration solution}\\ \text{(external calomel)}}} \,|\text{glass}|\, \underbrace{\text{H}^+\,(10^{-7}\ M)\,\|\,\text{KCl (satd.)}\,|\,\text{Hg}_2\text{Cl}_2|\,\text{Hg}}_{\substack{\text{cell } i, \text{ glass electrode}\\ \text{(internal calomel)}}}$$

This cell can be considered as two separate hydrogen–calomel cells connected in series, through the glass membrane, so that electrons flow from one cell to the other as hydrogen ions migrate through the glass membrane on account of their concentration difference. The over-all voltage of the cell is the sum of the voltages of the two separate half cells, because they are in series connection, but the separate cell voltages have opposite signs because of the opposite direction of the reaction in the two parts. Hence, $E_{\text{total}} = E_i + E_r$

$$E_i = 0.242 + 0.059\ pH = 0.242 + (0.059 \times 7) = 0.655\ \text{v}$$

$$E_r = -(0.242 + 0.059\ pH) = -0.242 - 0.059\ pH$$

$$E_{\text{total}} = 0.655 - 0.242 - 0.059\ pH = 0.413 - 0.059\ pH$$

The discussion above would make it appear (and with some validity) that the glass electrode containing the buffered solution at constant pH is really the reference electrode, and that the external calomel electrode in the titration solution is the indicator electrode in the cell. However, the glass electrode is usually considered to include the external solution, because the electrode develops a voltage only when the hydrogen ion concentration is different on the two sides of the glass membrane.

The equation given above shows that the total cell voltage becomes zero at $pH = 7$, when the hydrogen ion concentration of the solution being titrated becomes equal to the hydrogen ion concentration inside the glass membrane, and that the voltage changes polarity in passing from pH less than 7 to pH greater than 7, and vice versa. For this reason, potentiometers to be used as pH meters have a reversing switch to change the polarity of the cell connections, and pH meters (until recently) are provided with two scales, one for the 0 to 7 pH range and the other for the 7 to 14 pH range. Several models of pH meters of recent manufacture have a single scale reading from 0 to 14 pH.

3. *Quinhydrone and calomel electrodes*, for neutralization titration. The entire cell may be formulated thus:

$$(-)\quad \text{Hg}\,|\,\text{Hg}_2\text{Cl}_2\,|\,\text{KCl (satd.)}\,\|\,\text{H}_2\text{Q, Q, H}^+\,(x\ M)\,|\,\text{Pt}\quad(+)$$

The cell reaction, derived in the usual way, is

$$\text{Q} + 2\text{H}^+ + 2\text{Hg} + 2\text{Cl}^- \rightleftarrows \text{H}_2\text{Q} + \text{Hg}_2\text{Cl}_2 \qquad E^\circ_{\text{cell}} = 0.458\ \text{v}$$

But $[Q] = [H_2Q]$, and Hg, Hg_2Cl_2, and Cl^- are at standard states; hence,

$$E_{cell} = 0.458 - \frac{0.059}{2} \log \frac{1}{[H^+]^2} = 0.458 + 0.059 \log [H^+]$$

$$= 0.458 - 0.059 \, pH$$

When this electrode combination is used in titrating an acid by a base, the cell emf decreases as pH increases, and the emf becomes zero when $pH = 0.458/0.059 = 7.9$. At higher pH the quinhydrone electrode would become negative with respect to the calomel electrode. For reasons mentioned earlier, the quinhydrone electrode is not stable above pH 8 or 9, hence this electrode can be used only for the titration of strong acids by alkali (never in the reverse direction), and the titration cannot be carried very far beyond the equivalence point.

4. *Silver and calomel electrodes*, for titration of silver ion. The cell formulation, reaction, and voltage relations are:

$$(-) \quad Hg\,|\,Hg_2Cl_2\,|\,KCl\,(satd.)\,\|\,KNO_3\,\|\,Ag^+\,(x\,M)\,|\,Ag \quad (+)$$

$$2Ag^+ + 2Hg + 2Cl^- \rightleftarrows Hg_2Cl_2 + 2Ag \qquad E^\circ_{cell} = 0.557 \text{ v}$$

$$E = 0.557 - 0.059 \log (1/[Ag^+]) = 0.557 + 0.059 \log [Ag^+]$$

The calomel electrode is not placed directly in the titration solution but is connected through a salt bridge containing potassium nitrate solution, to avoid reaction of the potassium chloride with the silver ion.

5. *Inert metal and calomel electrodes*, for redox titration. The relations will be illustrated by the titration of iron(II) with permanganate in acid solution. The cell formulation, cell reaction,[7] and voltage relations, up to the stoichiometric point, are:

$$(-) \quad Hg\,|\,Hg_2Cl_2\,|\,KCl\,(satd.)\,\|\,Fe^{+++}\,(y\,M),\,Fe^{++}\,(x\,M)\,|\,Pt \quad (+)$$

$$2Fe^{+++} + 2Hg + 2Cl^- \rightleftarrows 2Fe^{++} + Hg_2Cl_2 \qquad E^\circ_{cell} = 0.529 \text{ v}$$

$$E_{cell} = 0.529 - 0.059 \log \frac{[Fe^{++}]}{[Fe^{+++}]} = 0.529 + 0.059 \log \frac{[Fe^{+++}]}{[Fe^{++}]}$$

The voltage of the titration cell therefore increases during titration, as the ratio $[Fe^{+++}]/[Fe^{++}]$ increases. After the stoichiometric point the half reaction of the titrant ($KMnO_4$) becomes the half cell in combination with the calomel cell; the cell reaction and voltage relations are:

$$2MnO_4^- + 16H^+ + 10Hg + 10Cl^- \rightleftarrows$$
$$\qquad\qquad\qquad 2Mn^{++} + 8H_2O + 5Hg_2Cl_2 \qquad E^\circ_{cell} = 1.27 \text{ v}$$

Assuming $[H^+] = 1$ (e.g., solution buffered at pH 0),

---

[7] The *cell* reaction must not be confused with the *titration* reaction.

$$E_{cell} = 1.27 - \frac{0.059}{5} \log \frac{[Mn^{++}]}{[MnO_4^-]} = 1.27 + \frac{0.059}{5} \log \frac{[MnO_4^-]}{[Mn^{++}]}$$

and the voltage continues to increase beyond the stoichiometric point.

In a general way, then, for any redox half reaction measured with an inert electrode against a reference electrode, one may write

$$E_{cell} = E^\circ_{reactant} - E^\circ_{reference} - \frac{0.059}{n} \log K_{eq}$$

where n is the number of electrons transferred in the *cell* reaction and K_{eq} is the equilibrium constant for the *cell* reaction. Because the components of the reference electrode are at standard state, the above expression reduces to

$$E_{cell} = E^\circ_{reactant} - E^\circ_{reference} - \frac{0.059}{n} \log \frac{[Red]}{[Ox]}$$

where n is the number of electrons per molecule of reductant (or oxidant) in its half reaction.

Treatment of Data

In most potentiometric titrations the data consist of instrument readings, in volts (or millivolts) or in pH units, corresponding to measured increments of titrant added, and the end point of the titration is determined by plotting the first of these functions against the second. The end point corresponds to the position of the very steep (almost vertical) slope of the curve. The curves for neutralization titrations are exactly of the form shown by the figures in Chap. 23,

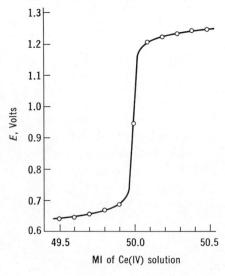

Fig. 32-8   Potentiometric titration of 50.0 ml of 0.100 N iron(II) with 0.100 N cerium(IV).

where the *pH* was calculated from the various equilibria involved. A curve for the titration of iron(II) by cerium(IV) is shown in Fig. 26-3, the voltages being calculated from the $E°$ values and the fraction titration; in that curve the voltages are based on $E° = 0.00$ for the standard hydrogen electrode.

Table 32-1   Potentiometric Titration. Iron(II) Solution Titrated with 0.1000 *N* Cerium(IV) Solution, Using Platinum and Saturated Calomel Electrodes

Ce(IV) Soln. Added, ml	E Measured, mv	$\Delta E/\Delta V$, mv/ml	$\Delta^2 E/\Delta V^2$
0.0	(Indeterminate)		
1.0	411		
		14	
5.0	467		
		4	
10.0	488		
		2	
25.0	524		
		3	
45.0	582		
		8	
48.0	606		
		18	
49.0	624		
		34	
49.5	641		
		60	
49.6	647		+ 20
		80	
49.7	655		+ 30
		110	
49.8	666		+ 60
		170	
49.9	683		+2440
		2610	
50.0	944		− 10
		2600	
50.1	1204		−2430
		170	
50.2	1221		− 50
		120	
50.3	1233		− 50
		70	
50.4	1240		− 20
		50	
50.5	1245		
		38	
51.0	1264		
		16	
52.0	1280		
		9	
55.0	1307		
		3	
60.0	1324		

Table 32-1 gives typical data for the potentiometric titration of iron(II) solution with cerium(IV) solution. Figure 32-8 is a plot of the measured voltage against the volume of titrant added, for the region around the equivalence point. In this case, which is a "symmetrical" titration (one electron change in each half reaction), the equivalence point is the point of inflection of the curve, that is, the point at which the curve has its maximum slope. It is not always easy to locate the equivalence point accurately by inspection of the curve. It can be located much more accurately by a differential plot, in which the difference in E values per unit volume of titrant, $\Delta E/\Delta V$, is plotted against the volume of

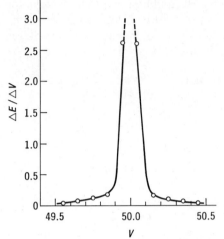

Fig. 32-9 First derivative curve of data of Fig. 32-8.

titrant. The term $\Delta E/\Delta V$ is merely the slope of the curve of Fig. 32-8 at any given value of V; the differential plot is therefore a means of locating more accurately the volume of titrant at the maximum slope of the ordinary titration curve. In Table 32-1, the figures in the third column are obtained by dividing the difference between adjacent E values by the corresponding difference in volumes. The differential plot for the region of the equivalence point is shown in Fig. 32-9; each $\Delta E/\Delta V$ point is located on the abscissa (volume) axis at the midvalue of the volumes for which $\Delta E/\Delta V$ was computed. The sharp peak in the curve locates the equivalence volume of the titrant.

Because of the very steep slope of the differential curve, it is sometimes difficult to locate the peak exactly; in this case the second differential, written $\Delta^2 E/\Delta V^2$, is used. At the exact stoichiometric point, the second differential is zero, that is, the slope of the first differential curve is zero. This condition occurs at the peak of the first differential curve, where the slope changes from positive to negative. In Table 32-1, the last column gives the second differential values for the data around the equivalence point. These values are plotted in Fig. 32-10.

The differential plots are especially advantageous for exact location of the end point in "unsymmetric" titrations, such as a redox reaction in which different numbers of electrons are involved in the two half reactions, or the titration of a weak acid (or base) with a strong base (or acid). In these cases the curve of E against V is not symmetrical around the equivalence point, and the position of maximum slope is not easily determined by inspection.

When differential plots are to be made from the data of a potentiometric titration there is a practical advantage, for simplifying the computations, in adding the titrant in definite equal increments, for example, 0.10 ml, as the end point is approached and passed.

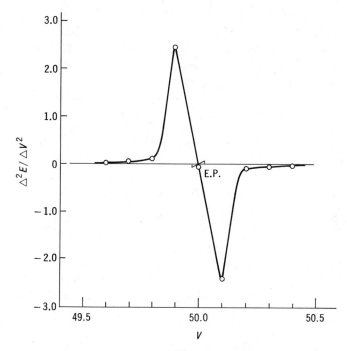

Fig. 32-10   Second derivative curve of data of Fig. 32-8.

Automation of the titration process can be accomplished by elaboration of the electric circuitry so that a valve, through which the titrant is delivered from a buret, is closed automatically at the end point of the titration. The Beckman Model K Automatic Titrator stops the titration when the voltage (or *p*H) reaches a value that is preset on the dial of the instrument; an "anticipation" circuit is provided so that the titrant is delivered more and more slowly as the end point is approached. The Sargent-Malmstat Automatic Titrator uses the second differential of the voltage of the titration cell to actuate the buret valve. The titration system therefore determines its own end point in the titration, and no presetting to a calculated end point voltage or *p*H is required.

ADDITIONAL APPLICATIONS OF POTENTIOMETRY

Determination of the Number of Electrons in a Half Reaction

The Nernst equation for a half reaction shows that as the ratio [Red]/[Ox] changes, the change in E is inversely proportional to n, the number of electrons involved in the half reaction. The slope of the titration curve, in which E is plotted against the fraction titrated, is smaller (the curve is flatter) the larger the number of electrons in the reaction. The curve is also symmetrical around the half-titration point for a considerable distance on either side. Reference to Fig. 26-3 shows that the titration curve for the oxidation of Fe^{++} to Fe^{+++} is symmetrical around the half-titration point, and has a constant slope from about 10–90% titration (5–45 ml of titrant).

If the electron transfer process is electrochemically reversible, the number of electrons involved in a half reaction can be deduced by determining the slope of the potentiometric titration curve, preferably at the 25% and the 75% titration points, between which the curve is linear. At 25% titration of a reductant, $[Red]/[Ox] = 3/1$, and

$$E = E° - \frac{0.059}{n} \log 3 = E° - \frac{0.059 \times 0.477}{n} = E° - \frac{0.028}{n}$$

For a one-electron change, the difference in the values of E from 25% to 50% titration, or from 50% to 75% titration, is 0.028 v. If the reaction involves two electrons in a one-step reaction (rather than two consecutive one-electron changes), the difference for these titration intervals is $0.028/2 = 0.014$ v; for a three-electron reaction, the E difference is $0.028/3 = 0.009$ v. An interpretation of the symmetry and the slope of potentiometric titration curves has been useful in deducing the number of electrons in redox reactions of organic compounds, and in determining whether reactions involving two or more electrons proceed in a single step or by successive one-electron reactions.

Determination of Ionization Constant of a Weak Ionogen

The hydrogen ion concentration of a solution can be determined by measuring the emf of a cell consisting of a hydrogen half cell and a reference half cell.

Consider the cell involving a known concentration of a weak acid, HA:

$$Pt \,|\, H_2 \,(1 \text{ atm}) \,|\, HA \,(0.10 \, M) \,\|\, KCl \,(1 \, M) \,|\, Hg_2Cl_2 \,|\, Hg$$

which is found to have an emf of 0.53 v. The right-hand half cell is the normal calomel reference electrode, for which $E° = 0.28$ v. Following the usual conventions,

$$0.53 = 0.28 - 0.059 \log [H^+]$$

$$\log [H^+] = \frac{0.28 - 0.53}{0.059} = -4.24 \quad \text{and} \quad [H^+] = 5.7 \times 10^{-5}$$

In the ionization of the weak acid, $HA \rightleftarrows H^+ + A^-$, $[H^+] = [A^-] = 5.7 \times 10^{-5}$ in the 0.10 M HA solution measured. Hence,

$$K_a = \frac{(5.7 \times 10^{-5})(5.7 \times 10^{-5})}{0.10} = 3.2 \times 10^{-8}$$

The dissociation constant (or the formation constant) of a complex ion can be determined in a similar manner, by setting up a cell in which one half cell is a reference electrode (e.g., a calomel electrode as above), and the other is a metal–metal ion half cell containing the complexing agent, as for example,

$$Ni\,|\,Ni^{++}\;(x\;M),\;KCN\;(y\;M)\|$$

From the measured emf of the cell, $[Ni^{++}]$ can be calculated; by starting with known amounts of Ni^{++} and CN^-, $[Ni(CN)_4{}^{--}]$ and $[CN^-]$ can be calculated. The equilibrium constant of the reaction $Ni(CN)_4{}^{--} \rightleftarrows Ni^{++} + 4CN^-$ is then calculated:

$$K_{\text{dissoc}} = \frac{[Ni^{++}][CN^-]^4}{[Ni(CN)_4{}^{--}]} \quad \text{and } K_f = 1/K_d$$

Determination of Solubility Product Constant

By a proper choice of half cells, the measured emf can be used to calculate the K_{sp} of a slightly soluble ionogen. Suppose it is desired to determine the K_{sp} of lead bromide; the cell to be used is set up as follows:

$$Pb,\,PbBr_2(s)\,|\,KBr\;(1\;M)\,|\,AgBr(s),\,Ag$$

and is found to have an emf of 0.36 v. The standard potentials of the two half cells, Pb^{++}, Pb and $AgBr$, Ag are known. Following the usual conventions,

$$\begin{array}{ll} AgBr + e \rightleftarrows Ag + Br^- & E^\circ{}_1 = 0.07\;v \\ \underline{Pb^{++} + 2e \rightleftarrows Pb} & \underline{E^\circ{}_2 = -0.13\;v} \\ 2AgBr + Pb \rightleftarrows 2Ag + 2Br^- + Pb^{++} & E^\circ{}_1 - E^\circ{}_2 = 0.20\;v \end{array}$$

But Pb, $AgBr$, and Ag are in standard state, and Pb^{++} and Br^- are in equilibrium with solid $PbBr_2$. Therefore

$$E_{\text{cell}} = E^\circ{}_1 - E^\circ{}_2 - \frac{0.059}{n}\log\{[Pb^{++}][Br^-]^2\}$$

$$= E^\circ{}_1 - E^\circ{}_2 - \frac{0.059}{n}\log K_{sp}$$

$$0.36 = 0.20 - \frac{0.059}{2}\log K_{sp}$$

$$\log K_{sp} = -\frac{0.36 - 0.20}{0.0295} = -5.42$$

$$K_{sp} = 3.8 \times 10^{-6}$$

III. ELECTROLYSIS AT SMALL ELECTRODES:
POLAROGRAPHY. AMPEROMETRIC TITRATION

The fundamental principles involved in reactions in electrochemical cells, and various mathematical formulations related thereto, were given in Section I. The present section deals with certain types of electrolysis cells, the interpretation of current-voltage data obtained from their operation, and some analytical applications.

Current-Voltage Curves

Unique current-voltage relations arise when electrolysis of a solute is conducted in a cell consisting of one depolarized electrode (a large, quiet surface, or a reference electrode) and another easily polarized electrode. The method is termed **polarography** (also, for obvious reasons, **voltammetry**), and the current-voltage curve is called a **polarogram**. The polarogram can be interpreted to deduce both the qualitative and the quantitative composition of the solution electrolyzed.

Consider an electrolysis cell consisting of a large-area reference electrode and a small, easily polarized electrode (e.g., a very short length of platinum wire) dipping into an electrolyte solution containing a low concentration of reducible metal ion, M^{n+}. The large electrode retains an almost constant potential (i.e., is depolarized) when small current passes; the potential of the small electrode can be changed over a certain range (is polarized) without causing continuous electrode reaction. If an external emf is applied so that the small electrode is made the cathode, essentially no current flows until the applied emf just exceeds the back emf of the cell. This condition is represented in Fig. 32-11 by the region AB. Further increase in E_{app} causes reduction at the cathode, $M^{n+} + ne \to M$, and if the solution is stirred to renew the supply of cation to the electrode surface, the current increases sharply (region BC) at a rate determined by

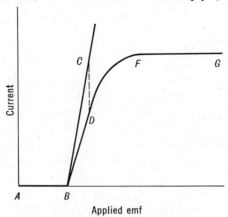

Fig. 32-11   Current-voltage curves. *ABC*, without polarization.

Ohm's law. (The slope of the line is inversely proportional to the cell resistance.) However, if the solution is not stirred, and E_{app} is held constant at the value corresponding to C, the current gradually decreases as the concentration of M^{n+} is decreased by reduction at the electrode surface, and eventually reaches a constant value, at D, determined by the rate of diffusion of M^{n+} to the electrode surface. As E_{app} is made more and more negative, the concentration of M^{n+} at the electrode surface becomes smaller and smaller until finally the concentration of M^{n+} at the electrode surface is negligible compared to its concentration in the bulk solution, and no further change in current can be produced by further change in E_{app}. The small electrode is then in a state of complete concentration polarization, and this part of the curve (FG) is called the **diffusion current region**. The current is determined by the rate of diffusion of M^{n+} from bulk solution to electrode, and because this rate is determined by the concentration difference in the two regions, the *diffusion current is proportional to the concentration* of M^{n+} in the bulk solution. This fact is the basis of quantitative polarography. The current passed is very small, usually less than about fifty microamperes, hence the concentration of the reducible substance is not appreciably changed in the bulk solution, and the polarogram can be exactly retraced in the reverse direction by decreasing E_{app}.

Electroactive solute ions can reach the electrode surface not only by diffusion, but also by ionic migration under the influence of the potential gradient in the solution between the electrodes. For reduction of cations, ionic migration increases the rate of mass transfer to the cathode, resulting in a larger limiting current; if anions are reduced at the cathode, ionic migration operates in opposition to diffusion, and a smaller limiting current is produced. The current is carried by *all* of the ions in the solution; the fraction carried by each ion depends upon its relative concentration in the solution and on its transference number. The migration current of the dilute electroactive species can be reduced to a negligible value by swamping it with a large amount of **supporting electrolyte**, which is inactive at the electrodes under the experimental conditions that prevail. There is an advantage in using as supporting electrolyte a salt solution in which the cation and anion have about the same transference number; for this reason, potassium chloride, at $0.1\ M$ or $1\ M$ concentration, is frequently used. (Other supporting electrolytes are also used, as the particular situation indicates.) The **limiting current** plateau of the **polarographic wave** is the resultant of two principal components, namely, the **diffusion current**, and a **residual current** (which increases gradually with increase in E_{app}), composed mainly of the **migration current**. (In the present treatment a very small nonfaradic "condenser" or "charging" current is ignored.) The diffusion current is obtained by subtracting out the (extrapolated) migration current.

If a small stationary platinum electrode is used as the polarizable electrode, there is a certain time lapse, after a change in E_{app}, before a steady current is established. If the electrode is rotated rapidly, a steady-state current is obtained immediately. However, the electrode surface characteristics (area, contamination, etc.) may be changed somewhat by deposition of even a minute amount of metal, and applicability of the platinum electrode to cathodic reductions is also somewhat limited because of the relative ease of reduction of hydrogen ion. As an anode, however, its range is limited only by the oxidation of water at about +1.7 v.

Many of the disadvantages of the small, solid electrodes are avoided by the use of the dropping mercury electrode (D.M.E.). The continuously renewed surface gives high reproducibility of the current-voltage relations, independent of the previous history of the solution. The small drops provide ideal conditions for concentration polarization; although current oscillations occur as drops form, grow, and separate from the capillary, they are so uniform that an average value is easily observed. A special advantage accrues, for cathodic currents, from the very high hydrogen overpotential on mercury and the low activity of the deposited metal by amalgamation with mercury, so that ions relatively difficult to reduce (those of aluminum, alkaline earths, and alkalies) can be determined without interference from reduction of hydrogen ion. Anodic oxidation at the D.M.E. is limited to quite easily oxidized substances because of the relative ease with which mercury is oxidized (about +0.6 v) to give unlimited anodic current.

Significance of the half-wave potential. The potential at which the current is one-half of the limiting value (after correcting both currents for the migration current) is called the **half-wave potential**, $E_{1/2}$. It was shown by equation (32-20) and related considerations that for a reversible reaction, $E_{1/2}$ has the same value as $E°$, the standard potential of the electrode reaction, whether the current is entirely cathodic, entirely anodic, or composite cathodic-anodic. The value of $E_{1/2}$ is therefore characteristic of the electrode reaction, and establishes the *identity* of the substance undergoing the electrode reaction. This is the basis for qualitative polarography.

Application of the dropping mercury electrode to analytical chemistry was first made in 1922 by Heyrovsky,[8] who also invented an instrument,[9] called a polarograph, by means of which the current-voltage curves were obtained automatically by photographic recording. The science of polarography has developed rapidly;[10] reliable, versatile polarographic equipment is commercially available. The Nobel prize in Chemistry was awarded to Heyrovsky some forty years after the method was first devised.

Apparatus

The essential components of a polarographic circuit are shown diagrammatically in Fig. 32-12. *A* is a mercury reservoir bulb connected by flexible tubing to

[8] J. Heyrovsky, *Chem. Listy*, **16**, 256 (1922).
[9] J. Heyrovsky and M. Shikata, *Rec. trav. chim.*, **44**, 496 (1925).
[10] I. M. Kolthoff and J. J. Lingane, *Polarography*, 2 vols., New York, Interscience, 1952.

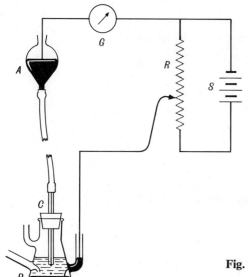

Fig. 32-12   Diagram of a simple polarographic circuit.

a glass capillary tube, *C*, of fine bore (e.g., 0.03 mm), from which the mercury
issues at the rate of one drop every 3 to 6 seconds. The end of the capillary
dips under the surface of the solution to be analyzed. *P* is a pool of mercury in
the cell containing the solution. The mercury in the quiet (pool) electrode and
in the reservoir (and hence in the dropping electrode) is connected to a source
of potential, *S*, usually about 3 v supplied by dry batteries, through a variable
resistor, *R*, and a galvanometer, *G*. Although the dropping electrode can be
given either polarity, positive or negative, it is more widely applied as the
reducing electrode or cathode. The galvanometer must have a period that is
long compared to the drop time of mercury from the capillary. By the use of a
motor-driven potential divider synchronized with a strip chart recorder, the
current-voltage curve can be recorded automatically; various sensitivities and
degrees of damping of periodic oscillations can be provided by incorporation of
appropriate electrical components, to give a very versatile instrument. A commercially available polarograph instrument is pictured in Fig. 32-13.

As a typical case, consider the analysis of zinc ion, in a solution of potassium
chloride serving as supporting electrolyte. After de-aeration with nitrogen (to
remove dissolved oxygen, which gives a polarographic wave), the potential
across the electrodes is gradually increased, that is, the dropping electrode is
made more negative. As a mercury drop forms and grows on the capillary tip,
the small current, carried by the supporting electrolyte, increases with the size
of the drop, and the galvanometer indicates this current by swinging to one
side. When the drop breaks away, the current drops momentarily to zero, then
again increases as another drop forms and grows, and so on. As the cathode

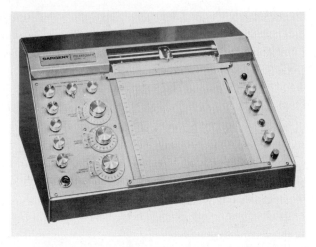

Fig. 32-13 Sargent model XV polarograph. (Courtesy of
E. H. Sargent and Co.)

is made more and more negative, eventually an applied potential is reached at
which the zinc ion of the solution begins to be reduced at the dropping electrode; simultaneously, mercury is oxidized at the quiet pool anode, and reacts
with the chloride ion of the supporting electrolyte to form mercury(I) chloride.

At cathode: $\quad Zn^{++} + 2e \rightarrow Zn$

At anode: $\quad 2Hg + 2Cl^- \rightarrow Hg_2Cl_2 + 2e$

When zinc ion begins to electrolyze there is a sharp rise in the current flowing
through the cell. This rise continues, with increasing potential applied to the
dropping electrode, until a limiting current is reached, which is dependent
upon the zinc ion concentration of the solution. Figure 32-14 represents the
case under discussion, for two different concentrations of zinc ion. The wave
height above the (extrapolated) residual current line [11] is the diffusion current;
see C_1 and C_2 in Fig. 32-14. Construction of the parallelograms in Fig. 32-14
shows one way in which the half-wave potential, $E_{1/2}$, may be derived from the
polarograms. If highly reproducible half-wave potentials are to be obtained in
polarography, a saturated calomel reference electrode is used as the stationary
electrode; most tables of half-wave potentials are given with reference to this
electrode.

A polarogram gives both the qualitative composition (by the half-wave
potential) and the quantitative composition (by the diffusion current) of the
solution measured. In order to determine the concentration of a given ion

---

[11] The term "wave height" used hereafter will assume that correction for residual current
has been applied.

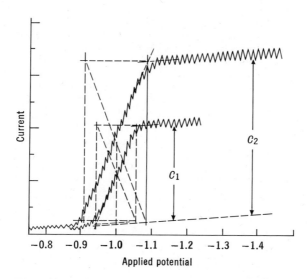

Fig. 32-14   Polarogram of zinc ion at two different concentrations.

in solution, it is necessary merely to obtain the polarograms of the unknown solution and of a standard solution of the same substance, and measure the wave heights, which are directly proportional to concentrations. If many samples containing the same component are to be analyzed, it is most practical to construct a calibration graph of wave height against concentration, from standard series measurements. An alternative method, called the "method of standard addition," is to make a polarogram of the unknown solution, then add to the sample a known amount of the same solute, and make a polarogram of this new solution. From the increase in wave height produced by the known amount of substance added, the concentration of the original solution is calculated by direct proportion. Still another method involves use of an internal standard or "pilot ion," and depends upon the fact that equal concentrations of two electroactive substances give a constant ratio of their wave heights in a given supporting electrolyte at the same temperature; details of the method are given in the literature.[10,12]

If a solution contains several ions of sufficiently different half-wave potentials, each ion will show its own polarographic wave at a characteristic half-wave potential, by means of which the ion is identified, and with a wave height proportional to its concentration in solution. Figure 32-15 represents a polarogram of a solution containing lead, cadmium, and zinc ions in a mole ratio of about $2:1:4$; the half-wave potentials that identify these ions, in 0.10 *M*

[12] H. H. Willard, L. L. Merritt, Jr., and J. A. Dean, *Instrumental Methods of Analysis*, 4th ed., Princeton, N.J., Van Nostrand, 1965, pp. 695–696.

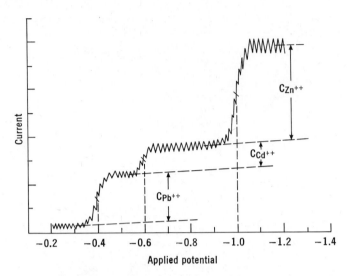

Fig. 32-15 Polarogram of solution containing lead, cadmium, and zinc ions in concentration ratio 2:1:4.

potassium chloride supporting electrolyte, are -0.40, -0.60, and -1.0 v (vs. S.C.E.), respectively. The wave height for one ion is independent of the presence of the other ions, and the concentration of each succeeding ion that is reduced as the cathode is made more negative is represented by the height of its wave above the last previous wave.

The theoretical considerations in polarography have been well worked out, and the relation of the average diffusion current to the various parameters is expressed by the Ilkovic equation:[13]

$$i_d = 607nD^{1/2}Cm^{2/3}t^{1/6}$$

where i_d = diffusion current in microamperes
n = number of faradays of electricity per mole of electroactive substance
D = diffusion coefficient of solute, in cm^2/sec
C = concentration of solute, in millimoles/liter
m = mass of mercury flowing, in mg/sec
t = drop time, in sec
607 = a combination of numerical constants that includes the geometry of the drop, and the faraday number in coulombs

The rate of mercury flow and the drop time are dependent upon the geometric characteristics of the capillary, the pressure of the mercury at the tip (height of mercury reservoir), the applied potential, and the temperature and composition

[13] D. Ilkovic, *Collection Czechoslov. Chem. Communs.*, **6**, 498 (1934).

of the solution. The diffusion coefficient is also influenced by temperature. Good temperature control is therefore essential to reproducible results.

For a given electrode reaction the terms 607, n, and $D^{1/2}$ are constant; the diffusion current, i_d, is proportional to the concentration C and to the product $m^{2/3}t^{1/6}$, where m and t are characteristic of the dropping mercury assembly. Rearrangement of the Ilkovic equation gives

$$\frac{i_d}{Cm^{2/3}t^{1/6}} = 607nD^{1/2} = I_d$$

The **diffusion current constant**, I_d, permits comparison and correlation of diffusion currents obtained with different capillaries or with the same capillary at different operating conditions.

Another fundamental relationship in polarography is the equation of the polarographic wave, derived by Heyrovsky and Ilkovic;[14] for a cathodic reduction,

$$E_{d.e.} = E_{1/2} - \frac{0.059}{n} \log \frac{i}{i_d - i} \qquad \text{(at 25°C)}$$

where $E_{d.e.}$ = potential of the dropping electrode during development of the polarographic wave

$E_{1/2}$ = half-wave potential of the reactant

n = number of electrons in the reaction

i_d = the diffusion current

i = current at any given value of $E_{d.e.}$

If the electrode reaction is reversible, a plot of log $i/(i_d - i)$ against $E_{d.e.}$ is a straight line the reciprocal slope of which is $0.059/n$ v at 25°C. Such a plot can be used to determine the number of electrons in the electrode reaction, as well as the half-wave potential, which is $E_{d.e.}$ where the log term becomes zero. A typical plot of this kind is shown in Fig. 32-16(b), along with the polarogram, Fig. 32-16(a), from which the data for (b) were derived.

Anodic and composite waves. When the dropping mercury electrode is made the anode in the circuit, oxidizable species are active at the dropping electrode and give polarographic waves of the same form as cathodic waves. In plotting polarograms it is conventional to give cathodic current a positive sign and anodic current a negative sign. For a metal ion that can exist in two different ionic oxidation states (e.g., Fe^{+++}, Fe^{++}), reduction of the oxidized form gives a cathodic wave, and oxidation of the reduced form gives an anodic wave, the equation of which has a positive sign before the log term. The form of the equation shows that the half-wave potential is the same for the cathodic and for the anodic wave. If the electrode reaction is reversible, a mixture of the

[14] J. Heyrovsky an d D. Ilkovic, *Collection Czechoslov. Chem. Communs.*, **7**, 198 (1935).

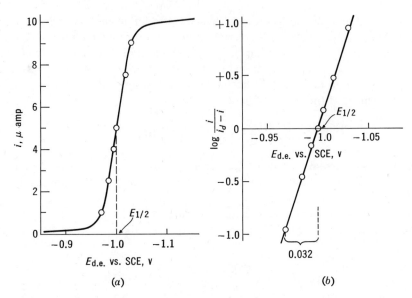

Fig. 32-16 (*a*) Polarogram of zinc ion. (*b*) Test of Heyrovsky-Ilkovic equation. Reciprocal slope $= 0.032$; $n = 0.059/0.032 = 2$ electrons per zinc ion. (Circles indicate data points.)

oxidized and reduced forms gives a composite anodic-cathodic wave having the same half-wave potential as the separate anodic and cathodic waves. See Fig. 32-3.

Applications

The applications of polarography are numerous and varied. Many simple inorganic ions can be determined by reduction at the dropping mercury electrode. If two ions have nearly identical half-wave potentials so that separate waves cannot be obtained, often one of the ions can be converted to a complex having a considerably different half-wave potential. Polarographic measurements are applicable to many complex ions. By changing the polarity of the dropping electrode, electro-oxidations of solutes can be effected. Many types of organic substances can be either reduced or oxidized at the dropping mercury electrode. The polarographic method is generally applicable to solutes in a concentration range of about 10^{-2} to 10^{-6} molar, with a reliability of about 2 to 5%. The method is nondestructive of the sample, for only an infinitesimal amount of solute undergoes chemical change at the electrode. If desired, the same solution may be polarographed over and over, with identical results. Microcells have been constructed that permit the use of a single drop of solution, which may be analyzed for several components if the half-wave potentials of the different species are sufficiently different (0.1 or 0.2 v).

Changes in concentration of a solute by reaction can be followed polarograph-ically; the method, known as amperometric titration, is discussed briefly in the following section.

Amperometric Titration

If the potential of a dropping mercury electrode is set at a value within the limiting current portion of a polarographic wave of a given solute, the current is proportional to the solute concentration. If now some reagent is added that lowers the concentration of the active solute, such as by neutralization or pre-cipitation, the polarographic current will decrease in proportion to the amount of solute removed from active condition. By adding the reagent titrimetrically up to and beyond the stoichiometric point of the reaction, the end point of the titration can be determined from a graph of current against volume of titrant added. Only a few experimental points are needed, and extrapolation of experi-mental segments of the plot to their intersection determines the end point.

Several different forms of amperometric titration curves are possible, depend-ing upon the value of the potential setting of the dropping electrode with respect to the electrode activity of the titrant and/or the substance titrated. Several different cases are illustrated below; in all instances the dropping electrode is the cathode.

1. Reducible Substance Titrated with Nonreducible Substance. Figure 32-17 illustrates the titration of lead ion with oxalic acid at a potential of -1.0 v. At this potential the limiting current of lead ion has been reached, but the potential is not sufficient to cause reduction of oxalic acid. As the oxalic acid is added, lead oxalate is precipitated and the polarographic current decreases as the lead ion concentration decreases. At the equivalence point the current is extremely small, on account of the very slight solubility of lead oxalate. With

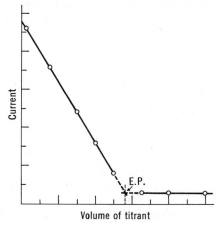

Fig. 32-17 Amperometric titration of lead ion with oxalic acid, at -1.0 v vs. S.C.E.

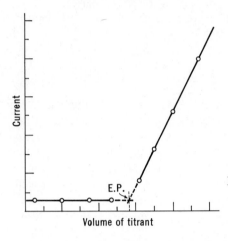

Fig. 32-18 Amperometric titration of lead ion in acetate buffer with dichromate ion, at zero potential vs. S.C.E.

addition of excess titrant, no change in current occurs, because the potential of the cathode is well below the decomposition potential of oxalic acid.

2. Nonreducible Substance Titrated with Reducible Substance. Figure 32-18 illustrates the titration of lead ion (in acetate buffer solution as the supporting electrolyte) by potassium dichromate:

$$2Pb^{++} + Cr_2O_7^{--} + H_2O \rightarrow 2PbCrO_4 + 2H^+$$

at an applied potential of zero, at which lead ion does not give a polarographic wave but dichromate does. The reaction of case 1 above, but titration in the reverse direction, gives a curve like that of Fig. 32-18. An important determination of this type is the titrimetric precipitation of sulfate ion by lead ion, at a potential of about -1.0 v.

3. Both Reactants Are Reducible. Figure 32-19 illustrates the amperometric

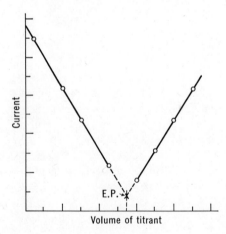

Fig. 32-19 Amperometric titration of lead ion with dichromate ion; potassium nitrate supporting electrolyte; applied potential -1.0 v vs. S.C.E.

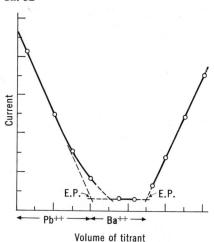

Fig. 32-20 Amperometric titration of a mixture of lead and barium ions with dichromate, at applied potential of −1.0 v vs. S.C.E.

titration of lead ion by dichromate ion, in potassium nitrate supporting electrolyte, at an applied potential of −1.0 v.

4. Titration of Mixture of Two Ions. In neutral solution, lead ion and barium ion can be titrated stepwise with potassium chromate or dichromate at a potential of −1.0 v at the dropping electrode. Lead ion is reducible, barium ion is not reducible, and dichromate ion is reducible at this applied potential. The titration curve is shown in Fig. 32-20. The less soluble lead chromate is precipitated first; the first end point comes somewhat after the stoichiometric point for lead ion because of coprecipitation of barium chromate with the lead chromate. Although the results for the individual ions are not very exact, the second end point is exact and gives a reliable measure of the sum of the two ions in solution.

Amperometric titrations have been applied to a wide variety of reactions, both inorganic and organic. Very dilute solutions can be titrated with high reliability.

IV. ELECTROLYSIS AT LARGE ELECTRODES: ELECTRODEPOSITION. ELECTROLYTIC SEPARATIONS

In electrolytic deposition methods, whether for the purpose of determining the amount of a constituent or for effecting separations, electrode reactions are produced by applying to the cell an external emf sufficient to cause electrolysis at an appreciable rate. Often the deposit is a metal that plates out on the cathode, but in some instances the desired constituent is deposited as its oxide on the anode, as in the cases of PbO_2 and MnO_2. If the amount of deposit is determined by increase in weight of the electrode, the method is called **electrogravimetry**. If the amount of constituent in a solution is determined by measuring the current and time (coulombs) and applying Faraday's law, the method is termed **coulometry**.

The total emf applied across the electrodes of an electrolytic cell is distributed among several factors:

$$E_{app} = E_a - E_c + iR = E_{back} + iR$$

where E_a and E_c are the potentials of anode and cathode, respectively, i is the current, and R is the cell resistance. Both E_a and E_c consist of a Nernstian or reversible potential plus an overpotential. In the absence of concentration over-potential and activation overpotential (charge transfer effects and/or slow reactions) the back emf is equal to the reversible emf of the galvanic cell set up by the electrolysis products formed by passage of the current. Concentration polarization can be largely eliminated by use of a large electrode surface and by stirring the solution to provide good transfer of electroactive species to the electrode.

Electrolysis Reactions

The reaction that occurs at an electrode during electrolysis depends, among other things, upon the material of the electrode, the kind of ions in solution (including H^+ and OH^- derived from water), and the ion concentrations. In the following illustrations, aqueous solutions are assumed.

1. Electrolysis between inert electrodes, such as platinum. Consider, for example, the following electrolysis cell:

$$(+) \quad Pt \,|\, Cu^{++} \,(1 \; M), \, SO_4^{--} \,(1 \; M), \, H^+ \,(1 \; M) \,|\, Pt \quad (-)$$

with the platinum electrodes connected to an external voltage source with the polarities shown. When the circuit is closed, chemical reactions occur at the electrodes, and current flows. But if E_{app} is less than a certain value, the current soon drops to zero, because electrolysis products generate a galvanic emf in opposition to E_{app}. Electrolysis cannot continue unless E_{app} is greater than the back emf. The theoretical or reversible emf can be calculated by use of the Nernst equation for each electrode. In the cell illustrated, the solutes are at standard state, and $E = E°$ for the electrodes. After a film of copper has deposited on the platinum, this electrode (cathode) behaves as a copper electrode. Cu^{++} is more easily reduced than H^+, and $E_c = E° = +0.34$ v. At the anode, water is more easily oxidized than is sulfate ion, and $E_a = E° = +1.23$ v. The reversible cell emf is $1.23 - 0.34 = +0.89$ v. But oxygen overpotential on a platinum electrode is about 0.5 v, and E_{app} has to be about 1.4 v to effect continuous electrolysis at a significant rate.

As electrolysis continues, the ratio [Red]/[Ox] increases at the cathode, and E_c changes in the negative direction and will eventually reach a value that initiates another reaction, often the reduction of hydrogen ion from an acid or from water. Similar changes occur at the anode; the potential of a platinum anode shifts in the positive direction until it is limited by oxidation of water, or of halide ion, etc.

2. Electrolysis of a solution containing cations of a relatively inactive element (Ag^+, Cu^{++}, etc.) between two electrodes of that element results in dissolution of the metal at the anode, and its deposition on the cathode. The cathode reaction is just the reverse of the anode reaction. This type of electrolysis is used in electrorefining of metals and in electroplating with metals.

3. Certain insoluble compounds can be used as electrode materials, or can be deposited on electrodes during electrolysis. If a solution of sodium chloride is electrolyzed using a silver anode, silver chloride is deposited at the electrode:

$$Ag + Cl^- \rightarrow AgCl + e$$

If a solution contains an ion that can be quite easily oxidized to a higher oxidation state the oxide of which is insoluble, the higher oxide may deposit on the anode. For example,

$$Pb^{++} + 2H_2O \rightarrow PbO_2 + 4H^+ + 2e$$

By this type of reaction PbO_2, MnO_2, and Co_2O_3 can be deposited anodically.

4. Ions that exist in more than one oxidation state may undergo changes at the electrodes without the "liberation" or deposition of products. For example, in the electrolysis of a solution containing Fe^{++} and Fe^{+++}, the latter is reduced at the cathode and Fe^{++} is oxidized at the anode. If the solution is well stirred during electrolysis, no net change in the concentration of these ions occurs.

5. In a solution containing a mixture of ions, the ion that reacts (at an appropriate voltage) at the cathode is the one most easily reduced—i.e., the one that requires the least negative (or most positive) potential. Similarly, the ion that reacts at the anode is the one that requires the least positive (or most negative) potential. These facts serve as the basis for separations by electrolysis. The generalized statement, however, must be modified by the restriction given in item 1 under Influence of Conditions on Separation, p.529.

6. The product liberated from a mixture also depends upon the concentrations of the ions in solution. In using a table of standard potentials for estimating what separations may be made, it must be remembered that the standard potentials are for the reactants at standard state (e.g., solutes at 1 M concentration), and the "working potential" of the electrode is markedly changed by large changes in concentration of the electroactive species. For example, $E°$ for the hydrogen ion–hydrogen electrode is 0.00 v. But if hydrogen ion is to be discharged from neutral solution ($[H^+] = 10^{-7}$), the cathode potential must be about -0.41 v. Continuous discharge of H^+ at the cathode from neutral solutions causes the solution in the region of the cathode to become increasingly alkaline; continuous oxidation of water (or of OH^- from water) causes the solution in the region of the anode to become increasingly acidic. These changes result in corresponding changes in the working potentials of the electrodes, as predicted by the Nernst equation.

Separations

In the light of the above considerations, the separations that can be accomplished by electrolysis are predictable from the activity series, that is, from the standard potentials of the half-cell reactions; see Table 32-2. Consider, for

Table 32-2   Activity Series of the Metals

	Metal	$E°$, v^a		
Very active; react with cold water, violent reaction with acids	Li	−3.045		Oxides not reduced by H_2 or CO, but only by electrolysis or by heating with more active metal
	K	−2.925		
	Ba	−2.90		
	Sr	−2.89		
	Ca	−2.87		
	Na	−2.714		
Less active; react with steam or with acids	Mg	−2.37		
	Al	−1.66		Oxides reduced by C or Al at high temperature
	Mn	−1.18		
	Zn	−0.762		
	Cr (to Cr^{+++})	−0.74		
	Fe (to Fe^{++})	−0.440		
	Cd	−0.403		
Moderately active; react with acids	Co	−0.277		
	Ni	−0.250		
	Sn (to Sn^{++})	−0.136		
	Pb	−0.126		
	HYDROGEN	0.000		
React only with oxidizing acids or other acids in presence of oxygen	Sb (to SbO$^+$)	+0.212		Oxides easily reduced by H_2 or CO at high temperature
	As (to As^{+++})	0.234		
	Bi (to BiO$^+$)	0.32		
	Cu (to Cu^{++})	0.337		
	Ag	0.799		
	Hg (to Hg^{++})	0.854		Oxides decomposed by heating
Dissolve only in aqua regia	Pt (to Pt^{++})	1.2		
	Au (to Au^{+++})	1.42		

^{a} $E°$ has a negative sign if the metal is a stronger reducing agent than hydrogen.

example, a solution that is 1 M in each of the ions Zn^{++}, H^+, and Cu^{++}, in solution as sulfates. What voltage must be applied across electrodes dipping into the solution in order to deposit copper on a bright platinum cathode without depositing zinc? Because water is more easily oxidized than is sulfate ion, the possible ion-electron half-cell reactions and their standard potentials are:

$$Zn^{++} + 2e \rightarrow Zn, \qquad E° = -0.76 \text{ v}$$
$$2H^+ + 2e \rightarrow H_2, \qquad E° = 0.00 \text{ v}$$
$$Cu^{++} + 2e \rightarrow Cu, \qquad E° = +0.34 \text{ v}$$
$$O_2 + 4H^+ + 4e \rightarrow 2H_2O \qquad E° = +1.23 \text{ v}$$

Combination of each of the first three half reactions in turn with the fourth reaction gives the (reversible) potentials 1.99, 1.23, and 0.89 v for the solutions of $ZnSO_4$, H_2SO_4, and $CuSO_4$, respectively. But oxygen overpotential on a platinum electrode is about 0.5 v. By neglecting the very small hydrogen over-potential on platinum (and also the resistance of the electrolyte solution), the potentials would be about 2.5, 1.7, and 1.4 v, respectively. If the applied emf is, for example, 1.5 v, only copper ion is reduced at and deposited on the cathode; oxygen is liberated at the anode. At an applied emf of 2.0 v, copper is deposited and some hydrogen is also liberated at the cathode, but zinc is not deposited.

The above illustration shows that the electrolytic separation of two ions can be accomplished if their half-cell potentials are sufficiently different. The separation of two cations whose standard potentials are of different sign is especially advantageous if electrolysis is made from acid solution, because of the intervening discharge of hydrogen ion to molecular hydrogen. Although the latter may influence the physical properties of the metal deposit, it effectively prevents the discharge of the ion of the more active metal.

Influence of Conditions on Separation. Several conditions influence the sharpness of separation by electrolysis. The explanations, given only briefly, are discussed in terms of cathodic reduction of metal ions.

1. *Concentration.* The Nernst equation relates potential of a half-cell reaction to the concentration of reactants. For a metal ion–metal half cell, $M^{n+} + ne \rightarrow M$, the metal is at standard state, and

$$E = E° + \frac{0.059}{n} \log[M^{n+}]$$

When $[M^{n+}]$ is very small, E is more negative than $E°$; consequently a more negative potential is required for the discharge of the ion. If a solution containing two ions, the standard potentials of which (against their metallic states) are not widely different, is subjected to electrolysis, the separation may not be very complete if the ion more readily reduced (more positive $E°$) is present in very small concentration relative to the concentration of the less reducible cation.

2. *Effect of pH.* Metals below hydrogen in the potential series may be deposited from acid solution, because the ions of the inactive elements are more easily reduced than is hydrogen ion. Metals above hydrogen in activity cannot be deposited from acid solution, except under conditions where the overpotential of hydrogen on the cathode is so high that the effective position of the hydrogen potential is shifted to a value more negative than that of the

metal to be deposited. For deposition of the more active metals, alkaline solution may be used. Under these conditions the concentration of hydrogen ion is so very small that the potential for its discharge is much more negative than the standard potential, and the more active metal can then be deposited. In the separation of copper from nickel, the solution containing Cu^{++}, Ni^{++}, and acid is electrolyzed and copper is deposited. The solution is then made ammoniacal and is electrolyzed again with a clean electrode; nickel is deposited. The quantitative determination of each metal is made by weighing the electrode before and after deposition of the metal.

3. *Stirring and elevated temperature.* After electrolysis has continued for a short time, the solution in the immediate vicinity of the cathode may become depleted in the reducible ion (concentration polarization), and the cathode potential then becomes more negative (less positive). As a result, other cations of more negative (less positive) $E°$ values may be discharged and contaminate the cathode deposit. Good stirring of the solution prevents the establishment of concentration gradients at the electrode and therefore gives a sharper separation of the ions of the solution. Heating sets up convection currents in the solution, which have much the same effect, qualitatively, as stirring. In addition, all reactions are more rapid at higher temperature, so the electrolysis can be completed in a shorter time at elevated temperature.

4. *Effect of current density.* High current density (high rate of electrolysis) may result in depletion of the reducible ion at the electrode surface, with the same results as in the absence of stirring.

5. *Depolarizers.* In much the same way that the presence of hydrogen ion limits the potential that may be applied to the cathode in the electrolysis of a copper ion solution, certain other substances can also provide a competitive reaction. Such substances are referred to as **depolarizers**. For example, nitrate ion is cathodically reducible to ammonium ion ($E° = +0.87$ v). The presence of nitrate ion in the electrolysis of copper is advantageous in that it largely prevents the discharge of hydrogen ion to hydrogen gas, and gives a bright, firmly adherent copper deposit. In the deposition of nickel, however, the presence of nitrate ion is a disadvantage because the nitrate ion is so much more easily reduced than is nickel ion, and nickel does not deposit well. If nitrate is unavoidably present in the solution to be electrolyzed, it can be destroyed by chemical reduction with urea or with sulfite. Ferric ion ($E°$ for the ferric–ferrous system $= +0.77$ v) acts as a depolarizer and interferes with the deposition of copper. On the other hand, the presence of both Fe^{+++} and Fe^{++} in solution constitutes an **electron buffer or a potential buffer**, and makes it possible to obtain a sharp separation of silver from copper without control of the applied potential. Presence of ferric ion in the solution prevents the cathode potential from attaining a value that will deposit copper. As ferric ion is reduced at the cathode, ferrous ion is oxidized at the anode and thus maintains an essentially constant ratio of the buffering components of the solution.

Nature of the Deposit. For quantitative determination of a metal by measuring the increase in weight of the electrode it is essential that the deposit be adherent and fine grained, so that it does not fleck off during handling of the electrode during weighing. There are several controlling factors.

1. *Concentration of ions.* Metals deposited from solutions of high concentrations of their ions are generally coarsely crystalline and adhere poorly to the electrode, whereas a satisfactory plating usually is obtained from dilute solution. Commercial electroplating is often done from solution containing complex ions of the metal, e.g., $Ag(CN)_2{}^-$, in which the cation concentration is low. However, there is evidence in some cases that direct reduction of the complex ion occurs.

2. *Nature of the metal of the electrode and the deposit.* Copper readily forms an adherent electrodeposit on most other metals; but silver, deposited under the same conditions, may be spongy and poorly adherent. Chromium adheres well to a copper or a cadmium surface, but not to iron; copper or cadmium is therefore used as an underplating for the chrome plating of iron and steel.

3. *Current density.* High current density, by depleting the solution of the ions being reduced at the electrode, promotes hydrogen evolution at the cathode and a brittle, poorly adhering deposit may result. With good stirring, high current density may often be used safely.

4. *Evolution of gas.* As just indicated, excessive gassing is undesirable. It can be prevented or minimized by stirring, elevated temperature, low current density, low acidity, and the use of depolarizers.

Methods and Applications

1. Constant Current Electrolysis. As electrolysis proceeds by this method, the ratio [Red]/[Ox] increases, causing the cathode potential to become more negative. This negative drift eventually reaches a value at which another cathode reaction is initiated (often, reduction of hydrogen ion). This method is therefore not very selective, and is usually applied for the deposition of metals whose reduction potentials are more positive than that of hydrogen. For example, silver or copper can be deposited from acid solution, but silver cannot be separated from copper unless an appropriate cathodic depolarizer is added.

2. Constant Applied Voltage Electrolysis. If the total applied emf is limited to a relatively small value, it is possible to complete the desired cathode reaction before the cathode potential drifts to a value at which an undesired reaction occurs. As electrolysis proceeds, E_{back} of the cell increases; hence, if E_{app} is held constant, the iR drop through the cell must decrease, and eventually the current also decreases. If E_a is kept constant at a value greater than E_{app} required for the desired electrolysis reaction, but less than that for the undesired reaction, eventually $E_{back} = E_a$, and electrolysis finally stops before the undesired cathode

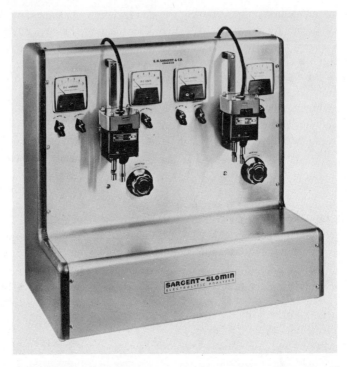

Fig. 32-21   Sargent-Slomin electrolytic analyzer. (Courtesy of
E. H. Sargent and Co.)

reaction can occur. In order to provide these conditions the initial current must
be small, hence completion of the electrolysis requires long electrolysis time;
however, some degree of selectivity is achieved.

A commercial electroanalyzer is shown in Fig. 32-21. Direct current is supplied
by a rectifier in the circuit from the regular alternating current supply. A cylindrical platinum gauze serves as the cathode, and a platinum wire loop anode is
motor driven to provide stirring. A rheostat adjusts the electrolysis circuit to
the desired voltage and/or current, registered by the voltmeter and ammeter.
An electric heater in the base supplies an elevated temperature if desired.
Detailed procedural directions for the electrodeposition of copper are given in
Exp. 40–3 (p. 652).

3. Controlled Cathode Potential Electrolysis.   The separation of two elements
of closely similar electrode potentials (a few tenths of a volt) can be effected by
controlling the cathode potential during the entire process at a value between
the deposition potentials of the two substances. The method, first introduced
by Sand in 1907, requires a separate means of measuring the potential of the
cathode with respect to the solution near it. A reference electrode, such as a

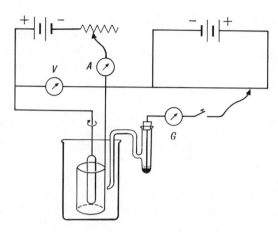

Fig. 32-22 Diagram of apparatus for controlled
cathode potential electrolysis.

calomel half cell, is placed very close to the working electrode; these two electrodes are connected to a potentiometer by means of which the potential of the
cathode is measured. A schematic diagram of the functional parts of the equipment is shown in Fig. 32-22. During electrolysis the cathode potential is measured
and the external resistance in the electrolysis circuit is changed as necessary to
keep the cathode potential from changing to a value that would initiate another
reaction at the cathode. By use of appropriate electronic circuitry, it is possible
to provide continuous and automatic control of the cathode potential.

During electrolysis the current decays from its initial value, i_0, to zero (or to
a very small value) when the electrode reaction is complete. If the potential of
the working electrode is controlled so that only a single cathode reaction occurs
with 100% current efficiency, current decay is exponential with time; the current,
i, at any time t, is proportional to the concentration of the electroactive species
remaining in solution, and i_t/i_0 is a measure of the completeness of the reaction.
If one observes the time required for i_0 to decay to $i_0/2$, that is, a "half-life"
of the electrolysis, then at three half-lives the reaction is 99.9% complete, and
little gain is attained by prolonged electrolysis. Usually a control potential
about 0.2 v greater than the deposition potential of the desired constituent is
adequate to obtain rapid electrolysis.

4. Mercury Cathode Separations. Deposition of many elements above
hydrogen in activity can be made from fairly acidic solutions by use of a mercury
cathode. The method is possible because of the very high overpotential of hydrogen on mercury, and also because the metal deposited on the mercury surface
is amalgamated (alloyed with mercury) so that the concentration or activity of
the metal.is much less than pure metal. The effect of the first condition is to
shift the hydrogen potential to a more negative value, and the effect of the

second condition is to shift the potential of the depositing metal to a less negative potential. The net effect, then, is a transposition of their relative positions on the potential scale so that the metal is more easily deposited than is hydrogen. Vigorous stirring is essential to keep a fresh surface of mercury exposed to the solution and to carry away the metal that is deposited. Metals up to and including zinc in activity are deposited in this way.

The method is used primarily for removing the less active elements that would interfere with the analysis for the more active ones. In the analysis of aluminum and magnesium alloys, elements such as iron, nickel, chromium, and copper are conveniently removed in this way. Equipment for mercury cathode electrolysis is available commercially; see Fig. 32-23. After the separation, the mercury containing the deposited metals is drawn off, and the remaining solution is analyzed for the more active elements. The used mercury is recovered by cleaning with nitric acid to dissolve the other metals, or by distillation under reduced pressure.

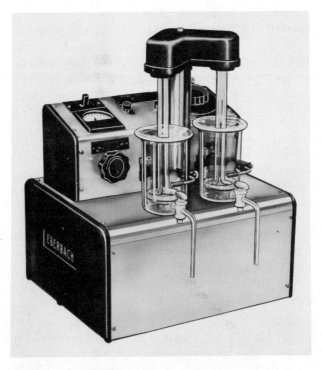

Fig. 32-23   Mercury cathode electrolysis apparatus. (Courtesy of Eberbach Corp.)

5. Displacement Deposition. The activity series of Table 32-2 is a displacement series, in that any element in the series will displace elements below itself from solution of their ions. This type of redox reaction is already familiar to the student from reactions such as the displacement of copper from solution by active metals such as zinc, or the displacement of hydrogen from acids by active metals. Displacement deposition methods are used in the precipitation of the platinum metals from solutions of their ions; zinc, magnesium, or aluminum is used as the active metal reducing agent. A displacement deposition is simply a specific case of a more general method of *chemical* reduction (as distinct from electrolytic reduction) to the metallic condition. Reducing agents, other than active metals, often employed for this purpose include hypophosphorous acid, hydrazine (either the free base or its salts), and hydroquinone.

Coulometry

When an electrode reaction takes place with 100% current efficiency, the quantity of substance reacting can be related to the quantity of electricity passed by applying Faraday's law. Specifically, the change of one gram-equivalent weight of substance is associated with 96,490 coulombs (1 faraday, commonly used as 96,500 coulombs except where highest precision is required); Q (coulombs) $= i$ (amperes) $\times t$ (seconds). Both current and time can be measured very accurately, and reliable electronic constant-current generators with simultaneous timers are available commercially. Even if current varies during the electrolysis time, the quantity of electricity can be determined by integrating the current with respect to time; this is done conveniently by determining the area under a current vs. time curve.

Instead of weighing a deposit at an electrode or measuring the volume of gas produced at an electrode, the amount of reactant is determined by measuring the current and time required to complete the reaction. This method is especially useful for accurate determination of very small amounts of material that cannot be measured accurately by other means. It has been used for determination of trace amounts (microgram quantities) of various cations, either by depositing the metal cathodically or by dissolving the metal anodically (" stripping ").

Coulometric generation of reagents. Electrolytic generation, either internally or externally, of a reagent that is brought into reaction with a desired constituent in solution, is a technique called **coulometric titration**. Instead of measuring the volume of solution of known concentration to complete the reaction, as in ordinary titration, the current and time are measured for generation of the amount of reagent required to reach the equivalence point. Various means, such as acid-base indicators, sharp changes in potential, or photometric detection, have been used to indicate the end point. In this way, chloride, bromide, or iodide can be precipitated by silver ion generated from a metallic silver anode. Iodimetric reactions can be carried out with iodine generated in

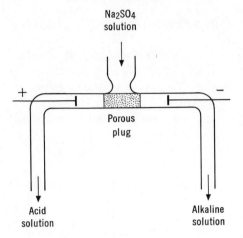

Fig. 32-24 Apparatus for generation of acid and alkali solution by electrolysis.

solution by anodic oxidation of iodide ion. Chlorine to be used as an oxidant can be generated externally by running a chloride solution through a specially constructed tube containing electrodes to effect the electrolysis.

A convenient method for preparing solutions of acid and base of known concentration consists in passing an aqueous solution of sodium sulfate through the arms of a T-tube, each arm of which contains a platinum electrode, one positive and the other negative in the emf source circuit; see Fig. 32-24. At the anode, oxidation of water liberates oxygen, leaving H^+ in solution; at the cathode, reduction liberates hydrogen, leaving OH^- in solution. If 100% current efficiency is attained and current and time are measured, the amount of H^+ and OH^- in the effluent solutions is known accurately. In any case, however, the method gives an acid solution and an alkaline solution that are exactly equivalent.

PROBLEMS

POTENTIOMETRY

See Appendixes I–V for constants needed for certain problems.

32-1 Calculate the emf of a cell consisting of a saturated calomel electrode (S.C.E.) and a hydrogen (1 atm) electrode dipping into the solution given.

(*a*) 0.0010 *M* HCl   (*e*) 0.020 *M* C_6H_5COOH
(*b*) 0.50 *M* CH_3COOH (*f*) 0.10 *M* HBO_2
(*c*) 0.040 *M* NH_3 (*g*) 0.0010 *M* NaOH
(*d*) 0.0050 *M* H_2SO_4 (*h*) 0.020 *M* $Ca(OH)_2$

Ans. (*a*) 0.419 v.   (*b*) 0.391 v.

32-2 Repeat the calculations of Problem 32-1, using S.C.E. and glass electrode.

32-3 Repeat the calculations of Problem 32-1, parts (*a*) through (*f*), using S.C.E. and quinhydrone electrode.

32-4 Repeat the calculations of Problem 32-1, parts (*a*) through (*f*), using S.C.E. and antimony–antimony oxide electrode.

32-5 Given the following cell formulation and the measured emf; calculate the hydrogen ion concentration of the acid solution. S.C.E. = saturated calomel electrode; N.C.E. = normal calomel electrode.

(*a*) S.C.E. $\|$ Q, H_2Q, H^+ (*x M*) $|$ Pt; 0.386 v.   *Ans.* 0.060 *M.*

(*b*) N.C.E. $\|$ Q, H_2Q, H^+ (*y M*) $|$ Pt; 0.356 v.

(*c*) N.C.E. $\|$ Q, H_2Q, HA (0.030 *M*) $|$ Pt; 0.254 v.

(*d*) Sb, Sb_2O_3 $|$ H^+ (*z M*) $\|$ S.C.E.; 0.150 v.

(*e*) Sb, Sb_2O_3 $|$ HX (0.25 *M*) $\|$ N.C.E.; 0.400 v.

(*f*) Sb, Sb_2O_3 $|$ H^+ (*x M*) $\|$ N.C.E.; 0.542 v.

32-6 A cell consisting of a S.C.E. and a hydrogen (1 atm) electrode dipping into the solution given, has the stated emf. Calculate the percent ionization and the ionization constant of the solute.

(*a*) 0.20 *M* acetic acid; 0.403 v.   *Ans.* 0.93%; 1.75×10^{-5}.

(*b*) 0.0010 *M* benzoic acid; 0.454 v.

(*c*) 0.020 *M* boric acid; 0.564 v.

(*d*) 0.10 *M* acid, "HA"; 0.478 v.

(*e*) 0.50 *M* nitrous acid; 0.348 v.

32-7 From $E°$ of the cation–metal couple and the K_{sp} of the slightly soluble compound, calculate E for the half cell given.

(*a*) Pb, $PbSO_4$(s) $|$ K_2SO_4 (0.20 *M*).   *Ans.* -0.335 v.

(*b*) Hg, Hg_2Cl_2(s) $|$ KCl (0.10 *M*).

(*c*) Cu, CuC_2O_4(s) $|$ $Na_2C_2O_4$ (1.0 *M*).

(*d*) Pb, $PbBr_2$(s) $|$ KBr (0.50 *M*).

(*e*) Zn, ZnS(s) $|$ Na_2S (0.40 *M*).

32-8 Given the cell formulation and the cell emf, and the K_{sp} of the other insoluble compound, calculate the K_{sp} of the compound stipulated.

(*a*) Tl, TlBr(s) $|$ KBr (1 *M*) $|$ AgBr(s), Ag; 0.733 v. Calculate K_{sp} of TlBr.

(*b*) Pb, PbI_2(s) $|$ KI (1 *M*) $|$ AgI(s), Ag; 0.217 v. Calculate K_{sp} of PbI_2.

(*c*) Cu, CuBr(s) $|$ KBr (0.1 *M*) $|$ Hg_2Br_2(s), Hg; 0.039 v. Calculate K_{sp} of Hg_2Br_2.

(*d*) Cd, CdS(s) $|$ Na_2S (0.1*M*) $|$ Ag_2S(s), Ag; 0.484 v. Calculate K_{sp} of CdS.

(*e*) Zn, $ZnCO_3$(s) $|$ Na_2CO_3 (0.50 *M*) $|$ $CuCO_3$(s), Cu; 1.141 v. Calculate K_{sp} of $ZnCO_3$.

32-9 From $E°$ of the simple cation–metal couple and the formation constant of the complex ion, calculate E of the half cell given. Assume that the simple cation is in equilibrium with the complex given and excess ligand, with no intermediate complexes present.

(*a*) Cd $|$ $Cd(CN)_4^{--}$ (0.10 *M*), CN^- (0.010 *M*).   *Ans.* -0.702 v.

(*b*) Cu $|$ $Cu(NH_3)_4^{++}$ (0.20 *M*), NH_3 (0.050 *M*).

(*c*) Ag $|$ $Ag(CN)_2^-$ (0.050 *M*), CN^- (0.10 *M*).

(*d*) Hg $|$ HgI_4^{--} (0.010 *M*), I^- (0.020 *M*).

(*e*) Zn $|$ $Zn(NH_3)_4^{++}$ (0.025 *M*), NH_3 (0.050 *M*).

32-10 Given the following cell formulation and the cell emf, calculate the formation constant of the complex. Assume a single equilibrium between cation plus ligand and the complex given, with no intermediate complexes.

(*a*) Ni | Ni^{++} (x M), Ni(CN)$_4$$^{--}$ (0.010 M), KCN (0.010 M) ‖ S.C.E.; 1.230 v.

Ans. 1.0×10^{31}.

(*b*) S.C.E. ‖ NH$_3$ (0.20 M), Ag(NH$_3$)$_2$$^+$ (0.10 M), Ag$^+$ (x M) | Ag; 0.166 v.

(*c*) Cd | Cd^{++} (x M), CdCl$_4$$^{--}$ (0.050 M), KCl (0.30 M) ‖ S.C.E.; 0.710 v.

(*d*) S.C.E. ‖ NH$_3$ (0.020 M), Hg(NH$_3$)$_4$$^{++}$ (0.010 M), Hg^{++} (x M) | Hg; 0.184 v.

(*e*) Ag | Ag$^+$ (x M), Ag(S$_2$O$_3$)$_2$$^{---}$ (0.040 M), Na$_2$S$_2$O$_3$ (0.020 M) ‖ S.C.E.; 0.119 v.

32-11 Given the following cell formulation and cell emf, calculate the percent of the ionic species in the reduced form.

(*a*) S.C.E. ‖ Fe^{+++}, Fe^{++} | Pt; 0.492 v.   *Ans.* 81.

(*b*) Pt | Sn^{4+}, Sn^{++} ‖ S.C.E.; 0.13 v.

(*c*) Pt | TiO^{++}, Ti^{+++}, H$^+$ (1 M) ‖ S.C.E.; 0.242 v.

(*d*) S.C.E. ‖ Ce^{4+}, Ce^{+++} (sulfate solution) | Pt; 1.29 v.

(*e*) Pt | Cr^{+++}, Cr^{++} ‖ S.C.E.; 0.73 v.

(*f*) Pt | V^{+++}, V^{++} ‖ S.C.E.; 0.38 v.

(*g*) Pt | VO^{++}, V^{+++}, H$^+$ (1 M) ‖ S.C.E.; 0.00 v.

32-12 The substance given is titrated potentiometrically with silver nitrate solution, using a titration cell consisting of a saturated calomel reference electrode connected through a potassium nitrate salt bridge, and a silver–silver salt indicator electrode, Ag–AgX, where X represents the anion being titrated. See Appendix V for the standard potential of the AgX–Ag half cell. Calculate the percent of the original solute that has been titrated when the emf of the cell has the value given. In each case assume a cell formulation with the S.C.E. on the right.

(*a*) 0.100 M KCl, Ag–AgCl indicator electrode; emf: (1) −0.039 v. (2) −0.057 v. (3) −0.140 v. (4) −0.268 v. (5) −0.437 v.

(*b*) 0.200 M KBr, Ag–AgBr indicator electrode; emf: (1) 0.13 v. (2) 0.09 v. (3) 0.05 v. (4) −0.19 v. (5) −0.44 v.

(*c*) 0.100 M KI, Ag–AgI indicator electrode; emf: (1) 0.33 v. (2) 0.31 v. (3) 0.26 v. (4) −0.08 v. (5) −0.38 v.

(*d*) 0.050 M Na$_2$S, Ag–Ag$_2$S indicator electrode; emf: (1) 0.91 v. (2) 0.90 v. (3) 0.87 v. (4) 0.45 v. (5) −0.39 v.

Ans. (*a*) 0, 50, 98, 100, 109 (9 % excess titrant).

32-13 The following data were obtained in the potentiometric titration of 25.00 ml of a weak acid, HA, with 0.1000 N NaOH, using a normal calomel electrode and a hydrogen (1 atm) electrode.

ml NaOH	emf, mv	ml NaOH	emf, mv
0.00	457	14.90	691
1.00	501	14.95	717
5.00	546	15.00	795
10.00	578	15.05	870
14.00	633	15.10	895
14.50	651	15.15	905
14.80	672	15.20	912
14.85	676	16.00	966

(*a*) Using the data for NaOH increments from 14.80 to 15.20 ml, calculate values of the first differential ($\Delta E/0.05$ ml) and the second differential ($\Delta^2 E/0.05$ ml), and plot the ordinary curve (E vs. ml), the first differential curve, and the second differential curve.

(b) Determine the normality of the original acid solution, and the pH at the stoichiometric point.

(c) Calculate the ionization constant of the acid HA, using (1) data at the stoichiometric point; (2) data for 5.00 ml of added NaOH.

32-14 The following data were obtained in a potentiometric titration of 25.00 ml of reducing agent by 0.1000 N solution of an oxidizing agent, using platinum and saturated calomel electrodes.

ml oxidant	emf, mv	ml oxidant	emf, mv
23.00	570	24.50	805
23.50	590	24.60	853
24.00	615	24.70	876
24.10	625	24.80	888
24.20	641	24.90	894
24.30	665	25.00	898
24.40	715	25.50	913

(a) Calculate values of the first differential ($\Delta E/0.1$ ml) and values of the second differential ($\Delta^2 E/0.1$ ml), and plot the ordinary, the first differential, and the second differential curves.

(b) From the curves, estimate the volume of oxidant and the emf at the stoichiometric point, and compare with values calculated (to the nearest 0.01 ml and nearest millivolt) from $\Delta^2 E$ values.

(c) Calculate the normality of the reducing agent.

(d) Use the value of emf at 23.00 ml of oxidant, and other information obtained above, and calculate $E°$ of the reductant, assuming it undergoes a one-electron change on oxidation.

32-15 A 0.2500-g sample of pure metal, M, is dissolved in dilute sulfuric acid to form M^{++}. This solution is titrated potentiometrically, using S.C.E. reference electrode and platinum wire indicator electrode. 40.00 ml of 0.1000 N Ce(SO_4)$_2$ is used to reach the end point. The emf at 25% titration is 0.184 v; the emf at 75% titration is 0.212 v; the titration curve is linear from 10% to 90% titration.

(a) Calculate $E°$ (vs. hydrogen electrode $= 0.00$ v) of the half cell of the substance titrated.

(b) Calculate the number of electrons involved in the oxidation of M^{++}.

(c) Calculate the atomic weight of the element M.

(d) Derive the *cell* reaction during titration, (1) before the stoichiometric point; (2) after the stoichiometric point.

POLAROGRAPHY

32-16 A solution containing two reducible substances, A and B, in 1 M KCl supporting electrolyte, gave the polarographic data tabulated below. The two substances have the same diffusion coefficient, and A is reduced at a more negative potential than is B.

E_{app}, v	i, μamp	E_{app}, v	i, μamp	E_{app}, v	i, μamp
0.00	0.0	−0.72	22.5	−1.20	40.5
−0.20	1.0	−0.76	28.5	−1.24	47.5
−0.40	2.0	−0.80	33	−1.28	53
−0.50	2.5	−0.84	34	−1.32	57
−0.54	2.7	−0.90	34.5	−1.40	57.5
−0.58	3.5	−1.00	35	−1.50	58
−0.60	5	−1.10	35.5	−1.60	58.5
−0.64	10	−1.14	36	−1.80	60
−0.68	16	−1.18	37.6		

(a) Plot current against applied potential, and determine the half-wave potential for A and for B.

(b) If the concentration of A is 4.0×10^{-4} M, what is the molar concentration of B?

32-17 (a) Make a labeled sketch of the polarogram that would be obtained from a solution that is 2.0×10^{-3} M in X^{++} ($E_{1/2} = -1.0$ v) and 1.0×10^{-3} M in Y^{++} ($E_{1/2} = -0.40$ v).

(b) The sulfate of Y^{++} is insoluble, but XSO_4 is soluble. The mixture of X^{++} and Y^{++} is titrated with Na_2SO_4 at $E_{app} = -0.70$ v. Sketch the titration diagram.

32-18 (a) Make a labeled sketch of the polarogram that would be obtained from a solution that is 0.010 M in the cation Q ($E_{1/2} = -0.20$ v) and 0.0040 M in the cation R ($E_{1/2} = -0.70$ v).

(b) The anion Z, which is reduced polarographically ($E_{1/2} = -1.0$ v) forms a precipitate with Q but not with R. The mixture of Q and R is titrated amperometrically with Z at -1.2 v. Sketch the titration diagram.

32-19 A solution containing Bi^{+++} in 1 M acid supporting electrolyte has a diffusion current constant, I, of 4.60. Using a capillary delivering 2.50 mg of mercury per second and a drop time of 3.00 seconds, the diffusion current, i_d, is 3.50 μamp. Calculate the concentration of bismuth ion in the solution.   *Ans.* 0.345 mM.

32-20 The diffusion current constant for a certain solution of Zn^{++} is 3.50. When $m = 3.00$ mg sec^{-1} and $t = 4.00$ sec, the diffusion current, i_d, is 7.00 μamp. Calculate the concentration of zinc ion in the solution.

32-21 Changing the height of mercury column, with a given capillary, changes m and t in such a way that the product mt is constant.

(a) With $m = 2.50$ mg/sec and $t = 3.40$ sec, a current of 6.70 μamp was obtained. The mercury column height was then changed so that the drop time was 4.00 sec. Calculate the current obtained under the new conditions. *Ans.* 6.16 μamp.

(b) With $m = 3.00$ mg/sec and $t = 3.50$ sec, a current of 5.65 μamp was obtained. The mercury column height was then changed to give a drop time of 4.00 sec. Calculate the current obtained under the new conditions.

(c) With $m = 2.13$ mg/sec and $t = 4.00$ sec, a current of 6.18 μamp was obtained. The mercury column height was then changed so that $m = 2.59$ mg/sec. Calculate the current obtained under the new conditions.

32-22 The diffusion coefficient of oxygen in dilute aqueous solution is 2.6×10^{-5} cm^2/sec. A 0.25 mM solution of oxygen in an appropriate supporting electrolyte gives a diffusion current, i_d, of 5.8 μamp, at an applied potential and with a capillary for which $m = 1.85$ mg sec^{-1} and $t = 4.09$ sec. To what product is the oxygen reduced under these conditions? (How many electrons are involved in the electrode reaction?)

32-23   The substances X, Y, and Z are reducible at a dropping mercury electrode; the half-wave potentials are, respectively, -0.20 v, -1.20 v, and -0.80 v. K_{sp} of XZ $= 10^{-12}$ and K_{sp} of YZ $= 10^{-6}$. Sketch the amperometric titration curve indicated in each part, and show how the equivalence point is obtained.

(*a*) Titration of a solution of X with a solution of Z at an applied potential of -0.50 v.

(*b*) Titration of a solution of X with a solution of Z at an applied potential of -1.0 v.

(*c*) Titration of a solution which is 0.0010 M in X and 0.0020 M in Y with a solution of Z at an applied potential of -1.0 v.

ELECTRODEPOSITION

In the following problems use 96,500 coulombs for the Faraday number. Assume that the applied emf is above the decomposition potential of the solution, and that current efficiency is 100% for the electrode reaction, unless the problem statement indicates otherwise.

32-24   Calculate the time required to deposit the stated weight of metal, from the electrolyte solution given, by electrolysis at the current specified.

Weight of metal	Electrolyte	Current, amp
(*a*) 0.3000 g of copper	$CuSO_4$	1.500
(*b*) 1.000 g of gold	$AuCl_3$	0.2500
(*c*) 0.5500 g of silver	$AgNO_3$	0.2000
(*d*) 0.4877 g of platinum	$PtCl_4$	0.2500
(*e*) 0.4877 g of platinum	$PtCl_2$	0.2500

Ans. (*a*) 607.3 sec.   (*b*) 5878 sec.

32-25   What weight of metal is deposited at the cathode in the electrolysis stated?

(*a*) $AgNO_3$ solution electrolyzed for 2 hours 20 minutes at 0.100 amp.

(*b*) $Hg(NO_3)_2$ solution electrolyzed for 40.0 minutes at 0.8000 amp.

(*c*) $Hg_2(NO_3)_2$ solution electrolyzed for 40.0 minutes at 0.8000 amp.

(*d*) $CuSO_4$ solution electrolyzed for 10.0 minutes at 1.500 amp.

(*e*) $PdCl_2$ solution electrolyzed for 10.0 minutes at 1.500 amp.

Ans. (*a*) 0.940 g.   (*b*) 1.995 g.

32-26   Calculate the current required for the electrolysis reaction stated.

(*a*) 0.4230 g of iodine (at the anode) from BaI_2 solution in one-half hour.

(*b*) 0.4800 g of iridium from $IrCl_4$ solution in 16.0 minutes.

(*c*) 0.2500 g of copper from $CuSO_4$ solution in 20.0 minutes.

(*d*) 0.3000 g of nickel from ammoniacal $NiCl_2$ solution in one hour.

(*e*) 0.1000 g of silver from $AgNO_3$ solution in ten minutes.

Ans. (*a*) 0.1787 amp.   (*b*) 1.004 amp.

32-27   A solution containing 0.2500 g of copper, as Cu^{++}, requires 20.0 minutes for complete deposition of the copper at 1.250 amp. Calculate the current efficiency.

Ans. 50.6%.

32-28   A nitric acid solution of $Pb(NO_3)_2$ is electrolyzed for 18.0 minutes at 0.400 amp.

(*a*) What weight of PbO_2 is deposited on the anode?

(b) If the volume of the solution is 200 ml, what is the gain in acid normality as a result of the electrolysis?

(c) What volume (STP) of hydrogen gas is liberated at the cathode?

Ans. (a) 0.536 g.   (b) 0.0224.   (c) 50.2 ml.

32-29 A dilute solution of sulfuric acid is electrolyzed at 3.00 amp. What electrolysis time is required to liberate a total of 450 ml of gas (oxygen plus hydrogen, STP)?

32-30 A solution containing 0.3500 g of rhodium, as $Rh_2(SO_4)_3$, is electrolyzed at 0.5000 amp.

(a) What electrolysis time is required for deposition of the rhodium?

(b) If electrolysis is continued for 20.0 minutes after the rhodium is deposited, what *total* volume of gas (STP) is liberated?

(c) What is the change (amount and direction) in acid normality at the end of the entire electrolysis, if the volume of the solution is 100 ml?

32-31 Calculate the weight of metal deposited by a constant current of 0.00500 amp passed for 24 hours through a solution of the ion given.

(a) Ag^+.   (b) Cu^{++}.   (c) Tl^{+++}.   (d) Pt^{4+}.

32-32 Calculate the volume of oxygen (STP) liberated at the anode during the deposition of 0.5000 g of silver at the cathode in the electrolysis of a solution of $AgNO_3$.

32-33 What volume of gas (hydrogen plus oxygen, STP) is evolved in a water coulometer by a current of 0.800 amp passed for 300 sec?

32-34 (a) What weight of copper can be deposited from $Cu(NO_3)_2$ by a current of 0.150 amp in a period of eight hours?

(b) If 1.1250 g of copper is deposited under the conditions of part (a), what is the current efficiency for copper deposition?

32-35 200.0 ml of solution containing 0.6567 g of gold in solution as $AuCl_3$ is electrolyzed at 0.5000 amp.

(a) What electrolysis time is required to deposit all the gold?

(b) What is the change in acid normality of the solution at the end of the gold deposition?

(c) What volume (STP) of oxygen is produced at the anode during deposition of the gold?

(d) If electrolysis were continued for 30.0 minutes after the gold is deposited, (1) what is the change in acid normality of the solution? (2) What *total* volume of gas has been liberated?

32-36 A solution made by dissolving 0.6300 g of lead and 0.1200 g copper in nitric acid is made up to 150.0 ml and electrolyzed.

(a) Which deposition, Cu on cathode, or PbO_2 on anode, is completed first? Show calculations.

(b) What is the change in acid normality at the end of the copper deposition?

(c) What volume of gas (STP) has been liberated at the end of the deposition of lead?

(d) If electrolysis is continued for 30.0 minutes at 0.4000 amp after all the lead is deposited, (1) what is the *total* change in acid normality, and (2) what is the *total* volume of gas evolved?

32-37 100.0 ml of solution that is 0.1000 M in Ag^+ and 0.1000 M in H^+ is electrolyzed at constant current and 100% current efficiency. Deposition of all the silver requires exactly one hour.

(a) What current was used for the electrolysis?

(b) If electrolysis is continued for 30 minutes at the same current, (1) what is the molar concentration of H^+ of the solution; and (2) what volume (STP) of hydrogen gas is liberated at the cathode?

32-38 A permanganate solution is reduced to manganous ion by ferrous ion generated coulometrically by a constant current of 2.500 milliamp acting for 10.50 min. Calculate the molar concentration of the permanganate if the initial volume is 50.00 ml.

32-39 The arsenic(III) from a certain spray residue requires 3 min, 30 sec for oxidation to arsenic(V) by bromine generated by a constant current of 0.0500 amp. Calculate the milligrams of As_2O_3 in the residue.

32-40 The chloride ion in a solution is precipitated as AgCl by Ag^+ generated coulometrically; a current of 3.000 milliamp for 15.00 minutes is required to complete the reaction. Calculate the milligrams of chloride in the solution.

32-41 A 100.0-ml sample of "sulfur water" is analyzed by coulometric titration with iodine generated by anodic oxidation of iodide ion. The reaction is complete when a current of 25.00 milliamp has been flowing for 15 minutes. Calculate the hydrogen sulfide concentration of the sample, in parts per million.

32-42 A solution of sodium sulfate is passed through the apparatus shown in Fig. 32-24, while a constant current of 0.600 amp is maintained. What is the normality of the acid and of the base formed, if 250.0 ml of solution is collected from each arm in 6.50 min?

32-43 Cobalt can be deposited anodically as Co_2O_3 from nitric acid solution of Co^{++}. 100.0 ml of solution containing 0.1473 g of Co^{++} is electrolyzed at constant current of 0.800 amp.

(a) What electrolysis time is required to deposit the cobalt?

(b) What is the change in hydrogen ion concentration of the solution at the end of the cobalt deposition?

32-44 200.0 ml of neutral aqueous solution containing 1.502 g of $Pd(NO_3)_2$ is electrolyzed for exactly one hour at 0.4000 amp.

(a) What volume (STP) of oxygen gas is evolved at the anode?

(b) What volume (STP) of hydrogen is evolved at the cathode?

(c) What is the acid normality of the solution at the end of the electrolysis?

32-45 A 0.6850-g sample containing alkali iodide (and inert matter) is dissolved in water containing a little dilute nitric acid. The solution is electrolyzed in a cell with silver electrodes, at a potential suitable for deposition of iodide on the anode by the reaction $Ag + I^- \rightarrow AgI + e$. A water coulometer in series with the electrolysis cell generates 10.84 ml of gas (at 25°C and 760 mm pressure) during the deposition of the iodide. The water coulometer generates 0.1739 ml (STP) of hydrogen-oxygen mixture per coulomb. Calculate the percent iodine in the sample.

32-46 A metal cube, 5.00 cm on an edge, is to be electroplated on all faces with copper deposited cathodically from solution of Cu^{++} (slightly acidified with HNO_3) by electrolysis at 2.000 amp. Density of copper $= 8.9$. Assume even deposition over the entire area.

(a) What is the thickness of the deposit produced by electrolysis for exactly one hour?

(b) What electrolysis time is required to produce a plating 0.0200 mm thick?

Part V □ Laboratory Experiments

33

TECHNIQUE OF COMMON
LABORATORY OPERATIONS

This chapter gives some general directions for the performance of laboratory work, and describes some of the common operations used in precipitation and titration methods. The general directions should be read carefully by the student before starting the laboratory work of the course. The sections on specific techniques should be studied in advance of the work requiring their use.

GENERAL DIRECTIONS

Conduct

The student is expected to be regular and punctual in attendance at the scheduled laboratory hours. It is essential to have a quiet, orderly environment if best results are to be achieved. Someone has devised the admonition, "In this LABORATORY use the first five letters, not the last seven." A student who has planned his work carefully will be busy during the laboratory period. When help or additional information is needed, *consult the laboratory instructor*.

Neatness and cleanliness are absolutely essential in quantitative work. The student's desk and balance and their surroundings, as well as his share of the general equipment, must be kept in good order. Apparatus should be arranged in the locker so that any item can be located immediately when needed. Insofar as practicable, items most frequently used should be placed near the front of the cabinet or drawer. A *clean* towel should always be at hand. Substances that have been spilled should be wiped up immediately with a wet sponge or cloth. At the close of the laboratory period, after all equipment is put away, the working space should be wiped with a damp sponge or cloth. Make sure that all utility taps (gas, water, air) are turned off.

Cleaning of Glassware

Glassware is best cleaned with a brush and water and soap or other detergent. Hot soap or detergent solution is preferable, and the use of scouring powder is occasionally required. Sulfuric acid-dichromate cleaning solution is sometimes recommended for removal of tarry substances; in ordinary quantitative work such residues are not encountered, and this cleaning solution is hazardous if spilled on clothing or on the person. Apparatus is washed with soap and tap water, rinsed thoroughly with *tap water*, and finally rinsed two or three times with *small* portions of distilled water from a wash bottle. **The washing or rinsing of apparatus at the distilled water tap is expressly forbidden.**

Glassware is much easier to clean if washed promptly after use. Properly washed beakers and flasks will drain clean and dry between laboratory periods if inverted on a clean towel in the locker; for many purposes dry inner surfaces are not required. Glass stopcock burets in which alkaline solutions have been used must be washed promptly after use, to prevent "freezing" of the plug in the stopcock.

Reagents

When reagents are being removed from a bottle with glass stopper, the stopper is held between the fingers; it must *not* be put on the desk or shelf. Stoppers from two reagent bottles should never be out at the same time, lest they be interchanged and both reagents contaminated. **Under no circumstances is an unused portion of a reagent to be returned to the reagent bottle.** Students can save time and chemicals by examining carefully the label on the reagent bottle to make sure the correct material is taken. Reagent bottles must not be taken away from the reagent shelves. The desired material should be obtained in a suitable receptacle—paper or watch glass for solids, test tube or beaker for liquids. After use, the reagent bottle should be returned to its proper place on the shelf.

Waste of reagents must be avoided; a conservative estimate should be made of the amount of reagent needed, and only that amount taken. More of the reagent can be obtained if necessary, but unused portions must not be returned to the reagent bottle. Undue waste of chemicals is a mark of carelessness on the part of the student. Proper use of reagents is a part of good laboratory technique. Waste of gas and distilled water must also be avoided. Distilled water is to be used only for making solutions, and in *small* amounts for rinsing apparatus after it has been washed in tap water.

Disposal of Waste Materials

Waste solids such as broken glassware, filter paper, and used matches are to be discarded into the waste jars provided for that purpose. Under no circumstances are such materials to be discarded into the troughs or sinks. Only liquids are to be poured into the troughs and sinks. Highly corrosive chemicals, such as concentrated acids and alkalies, should be poured directly into the *sink*, rather than into the trough, and flushed down with much water. Disregard of these instructions will result in damage to the plumbing, and inconvenience to all students.

Laboratory Safety

The student must not taste or smell substances promiscuously, nor stand unnecessarily close to apparatus in which material is being heated. In most industrial laboratories, the wearing of safety glasses is mandatory, and the practice has much merit for student laboratories. All accidents, no matter how trivial they may seem, should be reported immediately to the laboratory instructor. The best immediate treatment for strong acid, alkali, or other corrosive chemical spilled on the skin is to wash immediately with *large* amounts of water; then apply to the instructor for first aid if needed. Boric acid solution or sodium bicarbonate solution, after washing with water, is good to relieve stinging resulting from acid or alkali splashed into the eyes. Acid spilled on clothing may be sponged with *very dilute* ammonium hydroxide, the excess of which will evaporate as the cloth dries. For alkaline solutions spilled on clothing, sponge with *dilute* acetic acid, followed by *dilute* ammonium hydroxide. Corrosive or poisonous liquids should not be pipetted by direct mouth suction; a rubber suction bulb or a tube connected to an aspirator should be used. Evaporations that give corrosive fumes (strong acids, ammonia, bromine, etc.) should be made under a hood. Corrosive chemicals spilled on the desk or floor should be sponged up immediately. If a large amount of corrosive chemical is spilled, notify the laboratory instructor promptly.

The unauthorized use of chemicals and equipment for purposes other than the regularly assigned work is strictly forbidden.

Planning and Schedule

The required analyses are to be performed as rapidly as is consistent with intelligent, careful work. Efficient use of laboratory time is the result of careful planning. The student should have studied the text material and the laboratory directions and formulated an outline of the day's work before coming to the laboratory. By proper planning, two determinations often can be in progress simultaneously. A good student will never be idle during a laboratory period. While precipitates are being ignited or cooled, he will be preparing for the next operation, cleaning equipment, making calculations, etc. Rapid analytical work is the consequence of understanding exactly what is to be done and why, an estimate of about how long each step will take, a knowledge of points at which an analysis may be interrupted if necessary, and the productive use of all laboratory time. Mere rapid motions in doing laboratory work will likely result in spilled samples, broken equipment, and loss of time in general.

Some operations cannot be interrupted, and should not be started unless time is available for their completion. For example, a filtration should not be started unless sufficient time remains to complete the filtration *and washing* of the precipitate. In general, allowing a precipitate to stand in its mother liquor from one laboratory period to the next is advantageous. However, in the separation of calcium (as oxalate) from magnesium, the filtration must be made after one hour's digestion; in this separation, then, the precipitation, filtration, and washing of the precipitates must all be done in one laboratory period; careful planning and efficient performance are required.

Although accuracy should not be sacrificed for speed, it is important that the schedule of laboratory work be maintained and the analysis reports submitted when due. Students who plan their work carefully should have time to do more than the minimum number of required analyses.

Record Book

Different teachers have slightly different preferences for the form in which laboratory records are to be kept, but there is unanimous agreement on the following: **All data must be recorded in ink in a permanent (bound) record book[1] at the time of observation; the recording of data on loose pieces of paper or in a preliminary note book is expressly forbidden.** Violations of this rule will not be tolerated. Neatness in the recording of data is an important part of laboratory technique. The record should be such that it is intelligible not only to the student at the time or at any future date, but also to any trained analyst, who could if necessary repeat the work as a check or complete an unfinished analysis, without further information than appears in the record book. The value of a neat, permanent record made at the time of observation, cannot be over-emphasized.

Original data must not be altered by erasure. If, after an item has been recorded, it is discovered that an error has been made in the observation, the data are corrected by drawing a single line neatly through the erroneous figures and writing in the correct figures. Erasures or obliteration of original data, or removal of record book pages, will not be tolerated. If an entire analysis, or the analysis of one of a number of parallel samples, is to be discarded, a single line or an "X" may be drawn through the data, and a statement made as to the reason for doing so.

Record book pages should be numbered. The first two or three pages should be reserved for a table of contents, which should be kept up to date as the

---

[1] A Quantitative Analysis Record Book designed by the author is published by Hemphill's Bookstore, Austin, Texas.

work progresses. Each determination should be listed by title at the top of the page of data; for example, "Gravimetric Determination of Chloride." A *brief* outline of the method, with ionic equations for the reactions, should be written in the record book before starting the analysis; this may be done at the top of the summary data, or on a separate page immediately preceding the data of the analysis. Dates should accompany all records of data. In general, the left-hand page of the record book is used for detailed data, such as records of weighing operations if an equal-arm balance is used. The right-hand page is used for summarized data, such as weights of samples, weights of crucibles and contents, and titration data (buret readings). Brief comments regarding known slight errors and unusual observations are in order. Upon completion of the determination, the record should be dated and signed. The signature of the analyst in an analytical data book is considered to be his warranty that the entries are his own data and calculations based on those data.

The author has a preference for a record book about 6 by 9 inches, with faint quadrille rulings to keep the data aligned both in line and in column. Suggested forms for the recording of data are shown in the accompanying tables. Table 33-1 shows how details of weighing with an equal-arm balance are recorded; if only a few weighings are required, as for samples in titrimetric analysis, all weighings can be recorded on the left-hand page, opposite the titration data and calculations, which are tabulated on the right-hand page. In gravimetric analysis, where many weighings are made, the detailed weighing record may extend over two or three pages. The results are then summarized as shown in Table 33-2. Table 33-3 is a specimen record for a titrimetric method. When an equal-arm balance is used, the importance of recording the *details* of *all* weighing operations, as shown in Table 33-1, cannot be overemphasized. The detailed record permits checking for errors, whereas checking is impossible if only the total weight by mental summation is recorded. (This is one of the disadvantages of weighing with a single-pan balance.) A repetition of the analysis is often avoided by having a detailed record for checking.

Although the recording methods illustrated are not the only possible ones, experience has shown that they are among the best. Adherence to a set form of making records and calculations greatly facilitates checking of the record books by the instructor. Record books should be inspected frequently by the laboratory instructor, and the books may be called for at any time.

Calculations

As a general rule, calculations of the analyses should be made in the laboratory. This is especially true in titrimetric methods, where a certain precision is prescribed. Unless the calculations are made at the time, the student will not know whether the required precision has been attained. If calculations were reserved for homework and it turned out that the required precision had not been met, time is lost in preparing the solution in a buret for repeating the work. The saving of time, plus a normal curiosity to know the results of one's efforts, should be sufficient incentive to do the calculations in the laboratory.

All computations should be done with logarithms, which are to be tabulated neatly in the record book, so that at any time the student or the instructor can

Table 33-1 Specimen Record, Details of Weighing[a]

Gravimetric Determination of Sulfate

Oct. 11, 1967

Weighing bottle + contents					Weighing bottle, 1st sample			
90	120	20.	√√	88	132	20.	√√
93	118	5.	√√	90	130	5.	√√
95		3.	√√		127	3.	√√
93	119	1.	√√	89	130	0.500	√√
	93	0.200	√√		89	0.300	√√
	2)212	0.100	√√		2)219	0.010	√√
	106	0.030	√√		110	R 0.002	√√
0.033	R 0.006	√√	0.033		S 0.003	√√
× 6[b]	S 0.0002	√√	× 10			
0.198 mg	29.3362	g √	0.33 mg		28.8123	g √

Weighing bottle, 2nd sample					Weighing bottle, 3rd sample			
75	105	20.	√√	88	144	20.	√√
78	102	5.	√√	91	140	5.	√√
81		3.	√√		137	2.	√√
78	104	0.200	√√	90	140	0.500	√√
	78	0.050	√√		90	0.200	√√
	2)182	0.020	√√		2)230	0.050	√√
	91	R 0.007	√√		115	0.030	√√
		28.277				0.010	√√
0.033	S −0.0003	√√	0.033		R 0.002	√√
× 9			× 15		S 0.0005	√√
0.297 mg	28.2767	g √	0.495 mg		27.7925	g √

[a] Weighings were made with an equal-arm balance having a reciprocal sensitivity of 0.033 mg/div. When a single-pan balance is used, the dial readings are recorded directly in the summary table, as in Table 33-2 or 33-3.

[b] In weighing by difference during the same laboratory period, the zero point of the balance need not be determined; final adjustment of weight by calculation from the sensitivity is made by assuming the zero point of the balance to be 100. Since all weighings are referred to the same assumed zero point, any error due to this assumption cancels out when the weight difference is taken. However, when weighings that are to be compared are made during different laboratory periods, they must be referred to the true zero point of the balance at the time the weighing is made.

check the calculations with minimum effort. Generally, four-place logarithms are adequate, because the data seldom contain more than four significant figures. **All computations should be checked by slide rule.** Although a ten-inch slide rule is not sufficiently accurate for most original calculations of quantitative analysis, checking by this method will reveal any gross error in the logarithmic

Table 33-2　Specimen Summary Record

Gravimetric Determination of Sulfate

Method: The dried sample of soluble sulfate is weighed, dissolved in water, slightly acidified with HCl, and to the hot solution $BaCl_2$ is added dropwise to complete precipitation:

$$SO_4^{--} + Ba^{++} \rightarrow BaSO_4$$

The digested precipitate is filtered on paper, washed, dried, and ignited to constant weight as $BaSO_4$. Gravimetric factor for SO_3 is $SO_3/BaSO_4 = 80.06/233.40 = 0.34302$.

$$\text{percent } SO_3 = \frac{\text{g } BaSO_4 \times 0.34302 \times 100}{\text{g sample}}$$

Started Oct. 11, 1967

Samples	I	II	III	
Weigh. btl. + contents	29.3362	28.8123	28.2767	
Weigh. btl. − sample	28.8123	28.2767	27.7925	
g sample	0.5239	0.5356	0.4842	
Weight empty crucibles				
After 1st heating	16.3724	16.6536	14.0887	
After 2nd heating	16.3722	16.6534	14.0886	
Weight crucibles + $BaSO_4$				
After 1st heating	16.8848	17.1770	14.5600	
After 2nd heating	16.8840	17.1772	14.5600	
After 3rd heating	16.8838			
Wt. empty crucibles	16.3722	16.6534	14.0886	
Weight $BaSO_4$, g	0.5116	0.5238	0.4714	
Calculations				
Log g $BaSO_4$	$\bar{1}.7089$	$\bar{1}.7192$	$\bar{1}.6734$	
Log factor × 100	1.5353	1.5353	1.5353	
	1.2442	1.2545	1.2087	
Log g sample	$\bar{1}.7192$	$\bar{1}.7289$	$\bar{1}.6850$	
Log percent SO_3	1.5250	1.5256	1.5237	Average
Percent SO_3	33.50	33.55	33.40	33.48
Deviation, ‰	1	2	2	2

Completed Oct. 20, 1967

(Signed)　John Doe

calculations. Before reporting the results of an analysis, *all* calculations should be checked carefully, including the simple steps of additions and subtractions in the recorded data.

Table 33-3   Specimen Record of Titrimetric Method

Standardization of NaOH Solution

Method: Weighed samples of dry primary standard potassium acid phthalate (assay, 100.0%) are titrated with NaOH solution to the first pink color of phenolphthalein indicator:

$$HC_8H_4O_4^- + OH^- \rightarrow C_8H_4O_4^{--} + H_2O$$

Gme wt. of $KHC_8H_4O_4$ = mol. wt./1000 = 0.20423. Calculation:

$$N_{NaOH} = g\ KHC_8H_4O_4/(0.20423 \times ml\ NaOH).$$

Started Nov. 3, 1967

Samples[a]	I	II	III
Weigh. btl. + sample	21.5677	20.7512	19.9678
Weigh. btl. − sample	20.7512	19.9678	19.1345
g sample	0.8165	0.7834	0.8333
NaOH buret			
Final reading	39.87	36.68	39.16
Initial reading	0.70	0.28	0.65
ml NaOH added	39.17	36.40	38.51
HCl buret (back titrn.)			
Final reading	1.55		
Initial reading	0.15		
ml HCl added	1.40		
ml NaOH = HCl added[b]	1.30		
net ml NaOH added	37.87		
Calculations			
Log g sample	$\bar{1}.9120$	$\bar{1}.8940$	$\bar{1}.9208$
Log ml NaOH	1.5783	1.5611	1.5856
	$\bar{2}.3337$	$\bar{2}.3329$	$\bar{2}.3352$
Log gme	$\bar{1}.3100$	$\bar{1}.3100$	$\bar{1}.3100$
Log normality of NaOH	$\bar{1}.0237$	$\bar{1}.0229$	$\bar{1}.0252$	Average
Normality of NaOH	0.1056	0.1054	0.1060	0.1057
Deviation, ‰	1	3	3	2

Normality of HCl = 0.1057×0.9290^b = 0.09820

Completed Nov. 3, 1967
(Signed)   John Doe

---

[a] If an equal-arm balance is used, details of weighing are recorded, on the facing left-hand page, as shown in Table 33-1.

[b] From a previous comparison of the volume ratio of the two solutions, ml NaOH/ml HCl = 0.9290.

Reports

Results of analyses are to be submitted on report forms provided for this purpose[2] and must be submitted by the due date announced. If, after an analysis report has been graded, an error in calculation is discovered, a recalculated report may be submitted; however, a penalty may be imposed on the second grade. A recalculated report should be clearly marked as such, with remarks stating specifically what error was made in the original calculation; the record book should be submitted to the laboratory instructor for verification of the error and the corrections.

When an unsatisfactory grade is received on an analysis, a repeat determination must be made; a penalty will be assessed against the grade on the repeat analysis. More often than not, an unsatisfactory grade on an analysis is the result of calculation errors, although such errors can be avoided if the student checks carefully all record book entries, both data and calculations, as instructed previously. Before deciding that a repeat analysis is necessary, the student should recheck all items of the record. Reports on repeat analyses must be complete; if a new standard solution was used in a titrimetric analysis, the standardization report should be included with the analysis report. In other words, all reports, whether for original, recalculated, or repeat analysis, should be sufficiently complete that the report can be checked by the grader without access to further information.

Supplementary Equipment

A properly constructed wash bottle, Fig. 33-1, is required for very frequent use. A Florence flask of about 500-ml capacity is convenient. Bends in glass

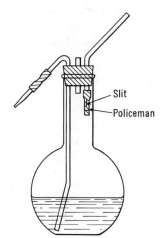

Slit

Policeman

Fig. 33-1   Wash bottle with Bunsen valve.

[2] Sample report forms are shown in Appendix VIII.

tubing should be smooth. The delivery tube should be positioned so the nozzle can be held between the fingers when the flask is grasped around the neck. The nozzle should have an orifice of about 0.5 mm, so it will deliver a *small* stream. For use with hot wash water, the neck of the flask should be covered with an insulating material; a cord such as is used on Venetian blinds or traverse curtains makes a suitable wrapping. Blow-back of steam into the mouth can be prevented by use of a Bunsen valve (see Fig. 33-1); delivery of water is controlled by thumb pressure on the short length of glass tubing in the third hole of the stopper.

Plastic "squeeze" bottles are very convenient in not requiring pressure by mouth; they have the disadvantage that they cannot be heated over flames or on hot plates for supplying hot wash water.

Several extra stirring rods of different lengths, for use with different size beakers, are desirable. A stirring rod should be about 5 cm longer than the diagonal height of the beaker in which it is to be used. Stirring rods fitted with policemen are furnished as desk equipment. The policeman end of a stirring rod should *never* be used in the solution during decomposition of the sample, nor used for stirring during precipitation and digestion. The policeman is used only during the last stages of transfer of a precipitate to the filter, to loosen precipitate particles from the glass surface.

Glass hooks, made from 5-mm glass rods bent at an acute angle and cut with legs of about 2 and 4 cm, are used to raise a watch glass above a beaker, to facilitate evaporation when desired.

PREPARATION OF SOLUTIONS FOR ANALYSIS

Regardless of the method of measurement finally used in the determination, most analyses require the same initial steps of drying, weighing, and dissolving the sample preparatory to separations and measurements. These steps are described below.

Samples

It is customary in elementary quantitative analysis courses to furnish samples that have been properly collected, ground, and sieved. If it is desired to have the final grinding, etc., done by the student, an agate mortar and pestle, and sieves of appropriate mesh size, must be available.

Drying of Samples

Most samples are analyzed and reported on the oven-dry (or merely "dry") basis. A sample is dried by placing it in a dry weighing bottle, then putting the *unstoppered* bottle along with its stopper in a small beaker, which is covered with a small watch glass and placed in the drying oven. The identity of the sample and its owner are indicated by writing *lightly* with a *lead pencil* (*not* with pen and ink) on the ground glass edge surface of the stopper and on the ground spot on the beaker. (The pencil marks are easily removed with an eraser.) For most samples a drying period of one hour at 110°C is adequate; if higher temperatures are required for certain samples, specific instructions are given in the analysis directions. At the end of the drying period, the unstoppered bottle and its stopper are put in a desiccator and allowed to come to room temperature (at least 20 minutes) before weighing. The weighing bottle may be stoppered at any time after it has reached room temperature, but this need not be done until the analyst is ready to weigh samples from it.

Drying operations should be started near the beginning of a laboratory period, so that samples may be removed to the desiccator before the end of the period. Samples must not be left in the oven from one laboratory period to the next; the oven space will be required for use in other laboratory sections.

Desiccator

Samples that have been oven dried, and ignited crucibles, either empty or containing ignited residues, are cooled and stored in an atmosphere of low, constant humidity, confined in a desiccator. Granular anhydrous calcium chloride is commonly used as the drying agent; a depth of about one-half inch of the solid in the bottom compartment is adequate. The calcium chloride should be replaced from time to time, and promptly so whenever there is evidence of caking. The ground rim of the desiccator and cover should be *lightly* greased with petroleum jelly (*not* with stopcock grease) to form an airtight seal and also to make for easy removal and replacement by *sliding* the cover off and on. Crucibles that have been ignited should be cooled in air for 30–60 seconds, until there is little radiated heat, before being placed in the desiccator. During the early part of the cooling period the desiccator cover should be slid carefully to one side momentarily, to equalize the pressure, otherwise it may be very difficult to remove the cover when room temperature is reached, and when opened the sudden inrush of air might sweep precipitates out of their crucibles. (This accident can be prevented by covering the crucibles in the desiccator.) The desiccator is carried to the balance for removal of objects for weighing. In carrying the desiccator the thumbs should be hooked over the edge of the cover so that it cannot possibly slide off.

Desiccators[3] of spun or cast aluminum have the advantage of light weight,

---

[3] A very inexpensive small desiccator can be made from a round plastic one-quart container with tightly fitting plastic lid. The plate, supported on three legs of small aluminum rod, is made of sheet aluminum with holes to support crucibles. Cost of materials is about 15–20 cents, depending upon the quantity of containers purchased. Silica gel desiccant is used.

rapid heat exchange, and no breakage, Many desiccants, especially calcium chloride, corrode the aluminum and must be placed in a glass or porcelain dish in the drier compartment; alternatively, aluminum oxide or silica gel desiccant may be used.

Weighing the Sample

Samples are usually weighed by difference from a weighing bottle. After the bottle (and contents) is weighed accurately, the bottle is unstoppered carefully over the vessel to which the sample is to be transferred, and the estimated amount of solid is removed by pouring slowly from the inclined bottle while imparting a rotary motion to it. The receiving vessel should be tilted so the solid slides down the inside. The weighing bottle is then raised to a vertical position, while holding its mouth over the receiver, and any particles adhering to the lip of the bottle are removed by gently tapping the bottle against the receiver. Any solid particles adhering to the ground surface of the bottle usually fall back into the bottle. The stopper is inserted carefully, and the bottle and contents are again weighed. A rough weighing is generally made first, and if insufficient sample was taken, more of it is transferred until the required amount is taken, then an accurate weighing is made. (If too much sample is taken, no attempt should be made to return any of it to the weighing bottle.) The difference in the two weighings gives the accurate weight of sample taken. The second weight serves as the initial weighing for a second sample, and so on. Handling of solids of very fine particle size and low density requires great care to prevent loss of material as fine dust in making the transfer and in opening and stoppering the weighing bottle.

One soon learns by practice how to estimate the amount of solid to be removed for a certain size sample. It is helpful in making this estimate if the approximate weight of the specimen in the weighing bottle is known. In most cases it is satisfactory if the sample weighed out is within $\pm 20\%$ of the sample size given in the procedure. For example, if the directions call for a 0.5-g sample, a sample weighing 0.4 to 0.6 g is satisfactory, weighed, of course, to 0.1 mg.

Occasionally it is necessary to weigh exactly specified amounts of solid, such as a primary standard for making a titrant solution by the direct method. A watch glass is weighed accurately. If a two-pan balance is used, a second watch glass, slightly lighter than the first and serving as a tare, makes for speed in weighing. Additional weights equal to the weight of solid to be taken are placed on the right pan and are exactly counterpoised by adding the desired solid to the watch glass on the left pan. When using a single-pan balance, dial in the additional larger weights required and note the final position required on the optical projection scale to give the desired weight of solid. In either case, final adjustment is made by transferring minute amounts of the solid by means of a small spatula or "scoopula." In transferring the solid to a receiving vessel, any solid that adheres to the watch glass is removed by a stream of distilled water from the wash bottle, with care to avoid splashing.

When multiplicate samples of a specimen are being worked, it is important that the vessels be numbered for identification with the record book data, as well as identity of sample. The etched spots on beakers and flasks are to be used for this purpose, the marking being done with an ordinary lead pencil; when no longer needed, these marks are simply erased. Porcelain crucibles and covers can be numbered permanently by marking *lightly* with a blue wax marking pencil (e.g., Blaisdell No. 168-T), then burning the mark into the glaze by heating to dull redness. Volumetric flasks, bottles of standard solutions, etc., should be identified by use of gummed labels showing contents, concentration, date of preparation, and owner's name.

Decomposition of Samples

Samples for gravimetric analysis are usually handled in beakers. The beaker is covered with a watch glass, which is moved slightly to one side while the reagent (water, acid, etc.) is poured carefully down the side of the beaker or down a stirring rod. If rapid effervescence occurs, the watch glass prevents loss of material. After rapid reaction subsides, the material on the underside of the cover glass is rinsed off into the main solution by a stream of water from the wash bottle. If prolonged heating is required to effect dissolution, additional reagent may have to be added to replace that lost by evaporation. Unless directions are given to the contrary, the mixture should never be allowed to evaporate to dryness. Samples for titrimetric analysis are frequently started in Erlenmeyer flasks in which the final titration is made. The tall form and narrow mouth are quite effective in preventing loss of material through effervescence, and if prolonged heating is required to cause dissolution, the upper part of the flask is a quite effective condenser for vapors and thus retards evaporation.

When it is desired to evaporate a solution, the cover glass should be raised, by glass hooks placed over the edge of the beaker, to permit better escape of vapors. (One form of watch glass is molded with ribs on the underside that raise the glass from the beaker.) Superheating of a liquid during evaporation may result in violent bumping and loss of sample even from covered beakers. A stirring rod left in the solution sometimes prevents bumping. Bumping is also less likely to occur when samples are heated on a hot plate than when heated over a free flame. Solutions that are evaporated to dryness may spatter near the end of the evaporation; gentle heating should be used at this stage of evaporation. Evaporation of large volumes of solution is a time-consuming process, and it cannot be hurried. When facilities are available, evaporations are best done by leaving the beakers or flasks on a steam bath or a *low*-temperature hot plate overnight or from one laboratory period to the next. Evaporation occurs below the boiling point, and bumping and spattering do not occur.

GRAVIMETRIC PRECIPITATION TECHNIQUES

Addition of Precipitant

The particles of a precipitate are larger and purer if formed slowly from solution reagents, that is, formed under conditions of low relative supersaturation (see Chap. 14). The precipitant solution is added slowly and with good stirring. Slow delivery is easily made by dropping the reagent from a pipet or a buret.

Digestion

Most, although not all, precipitates should be allowed to remain in contact with the mother liquor for some time before filtration; this process is called **digestion** of the precipitate. (The changes that occur during digestion are discussed in Chap. 14.) The digestion process is more rapid at high temperature, hence many digestions are made by keeping the precipitation mixture somewhat below the boiling point. Care must be taken not to reach the boiling point, because precipitates that have settled on the bottom of the beaker are conductive to bumping, possibly resulting in loss of material. A well-digested precipitate should settle rapidly when stirred, and leave a clear supernatant liquid. It is always necessary to test for complete precipitation by adding a little more of the reagent, noting whether any more precipitate is formed; even a slight turbidity indicates formation of more solid phase.

Filtration

A filter medium is selected on the basis of subsequent treatment to be applied to the precipitate. If the precipitate is to be ignited, filter paper is generally used. If the precipitate is to be oven-dried, filter crucibles having porous bottoms are used. Regardless of the filter medium used, it should be selected for proper porosity; the pores must be small enough to retain the precipitate particles, but not so small that excessive time is consumed in conducting the filtration and washing operations.

Filter Paper. Filter paper used for precipitates that are to be ignited must be ash-free; this is accomplished in the manufacture by washing with hydrofluoric and hydrochloric acids to remove inorganic constituents. The ash weight is stated on the package, and usually amounts to 0.1 mg or less per 9- or 11-cm circle. Each manufacturer markets many grades, differing in retentivity, hardness, wet strength, ash weight, etc. Paper of very high retentivity and wet strength usually filters slowly. Soft, loose texture papers are used for gelatinous precipitates such as the hydrous oxides. Barium sulfate usually requires a paper of quite high retentivity.

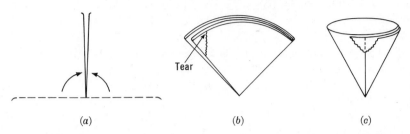

Fig. 33-2   Method of folding filter paper. (*a*) Edge view, flat (broken line) and folded in half (solid line). (*b*) Folded in quarters. (*c*) Opened to make the cone.

The time spent in properly folding a filter paper and fitting it to the funnel is well repaid by time saved in the filtration and washing. If a circle of filter paper is observed closely, it is noticed that the edge is very slightly turned by the cutting die. The paper is first folded in half so the turned edge curves to the outside of the fold, as in Fig. 33-2(*a*); it is then folded in quarters. About 2 cm away from the first fold, the single outside thickness of paper is torn diagonally down to the fold, as shown in Fig. 33-2(*b*). The paper is then opened on the opposite quadrant to form a cone, and the torn segment is carried across the fold, as shown in Fig. 33-2(*c*). The apex angle of the cone is 60°, which will exactly fit a properly made funnel. Holding the paper so that the folds do not spread, the paper is put into the funnel and held down with the forefinger while distilled water is poured into the funnel. The paper is pressed firmly against the funnel, with care taken to press the folds and the top edges down well; any bubbles under the paper may be worked up and out by finger pressure. If the funnel is of the proper angle, its stem is clean, and the paper fits snugly to the glass, the entire stem of the funnel should fill with liquid, no air bubbles should get past the edges or folds, and when the liquid has run through the paper, the stem should stay filled with liquid.

A well-made funnel has an angle of 60° and straight sides; if the angle of the funnel is more or is less than 60°, the second fold of the paper is made slightly different from a right angle; the larger or the smaller side is opened to make the cone, depending upon the angle of the funnel.

Funnels that have vertical flutings or channels molded on the inside face filter much more rapidly than plain funnels; the flutings allow the liquid that has passed through the paper to drain away quickly. Long stem funnels give more rapid filtration than those with short stems, because of the additional pull of a longer column of liquid below the paper.

Filter Crucibles.   Crucibles with porous bottoms are much used in filtrations. Pyrex crucibles have bottoms made of sintered ground glass; porcelain crucibles have bottoms of unglazed porcelain. Whether glass or porcelain, they are obtainable in different porosities for use with precipitates of different particle size. For certain special purposes crucibles having porous bottoms of aluminum oxide (alundum) or of platinum sponge (Munroe crucibles) are used. Before the sintered glass and porous porcelain filters were available, Gooch crucibles were much used, and they still find some applications; the filter medium is a compacted mat of asbestos fibers formed on the perforated bottom of the Gooch crucible.

Glass filter crucibles cannot be heated above about 500°C. If stronger heating of the precipitate is required, a porous porcelain or a Gooch crucible is used. For ignitions by burner, the filter crucible is usually placed in a larger porcelain crucible or a metal radiator. In all cases, whether oven-drying or ignition is used, the empty crucible is always prepared by heating under the same conditions as are to be used in drying or igniting the precipitate, until its weight is constant.

Filter crucibles are always used with suction, as illustrated in Fig. 33-3. The crucible is supported in a crucible holder or a funnel tube, which is fitted to a suction flask attached to a water aspirator pump or vacuum line. A trap (bottle or second flask) is placed between the suction flask receiver and the pump to prevent contamination of the filtrate if tap water should suck back from the aspirator.

Gravity filtration is almost always used with filter paper. Suction filtration is *not* used with gelatinous precipitates such as the hydrous oxides; suction tends to pull the gelatinous material into the filter pores, and clogs them so that passage of liquid through the filter is much retarded. Gravity filtration of gelatinous precipitates, sometimes slow at best, is nevertheless more rapid than when suction is used.

The size of filter paper to be used for a filtration is chosen on the basis of the

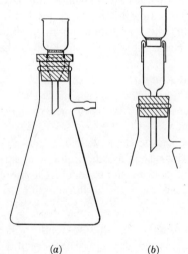

Fig. 33-3   Suction filtration with filter crucibles. (*a*) Walter crucible holder. (*b*) Gooch filter tube.

(*a*)   (*b*)

volume of liquid to be filtered and the bulk of the precipitate. Paper of 9- or 11-cm diameter, and funnels of 7.5-cm diameter, are most commonly used for routine work. The paper should come no closer than within 1 cm of the top edge of the funnel. The funnel is supported in a stand (preferably of wood) so that the ground tip of the stem touches the side of the receiver, to allow the liquid to flow into the receiver without splashing. Filtration of two to four samples can be carried on concurrently; the funnels and receivers should be clearly marked to correspond to the numbers of the samples being worked.

Filtration is expedited if the precipitate is well settled, so that most of the liquid can be decanted through the filter before much of the precipitate is brought onto it. If the solubility of the precipitate permits, the liquid should be hot, which makes for more rapid filtration. The liquid is poured down a stirring rod held against the pouring spout of the beaker and reaching nearly to the bottom of the filter, in order to avoid drips down the outside of the beaker and to avoid splashing of the liquid as it runs into the filter; see Fig. 33-4. The liquid level in the filter should not be allowed to rise above 1 cm from the top edge of the paper. Some precipitates creep in the liquid film; this action can be prevented by addition of a small amount of a surface active agent.

Washing

Effective washing of the precipitate is accomplished by adding a small amount of the required wash liquid to the precipitate, most of which is still in the beaker after the mother liquor has been poured off through the filter. The mixture is stirred well, and after the precipitate is well settled, the supernatant liquid is poured off through the filter; the operation is repeated several times. This process is known as **washing by decantation**. Finally, the precipitate is transferred completely to the filter. Much of this transfer can be made during the last decantation. The transfer is completed by holding the stirring rod across

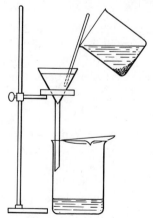

Fig. 33-4 Gravity filtration.

the beaker with the forefinger, and tilting the beaker to more than a horizontal position. The stirring rod directs the material into the funnel. A stream of water (or other specified wash liquid) from a wash bottle is then directed, around the entire inner surface of the beaker, progressively toward the spout, to flush all the solid particles into the funnel. The beaker is placed on the desk, a small amount of wash liquid is added, and solid particles adhering to the glass are scrubbed loose with a policeman. The suspension is poured through the filter, and the scrubbing is repeated as often as necessary to make a complete transfer of the precipitate.

The above operations accomplish most of the washing of the precipitate. Additional washing is done by a fine stream of liquid from a wash bottle, or by dripping the liquid down a stirring rod, always directing the liquid around the top edge of the paper. Several small portions of wash liquid in succession give a more efficient washing than the same total amount used in one or only a few portions. Each portion of wash liquid is allowed to drain through completely before the next portion is added. The washing operation is usually continued until a few drops of the last liquid to run through give a negative test for some component (usually the precipitant) of the main filtrate. By the time washing is completed, the precipitate is compactly collected in the apex of the filter, which can then be removed without danger of loss of precipitate.

The same general technique as described above is followed when filter crucibles are used. *Gentle* suction should be applied and the liquid should be transferred at such a rate as to keep not more than a few millimeters depth of liquid in the crucible; the liquid level should never rise to near the top of the crucible. When filtration and washing are complete, the vacuum in the receiver system should be broken by slowly removing the rubber tubing at a connection before the aspirator pump or vacuum is turned off.

Drying and Igniting

Precipitates in Filter Crucibles. The crucible containing the precipitate is placed in a small beaker, covered with a watch glass, and heated in a drying oven at the prescribed temperature, usually 110–135°C. An initial drying period of one to two hours is used, after which the crucible is cooled in a desiccator and weighed. Heating for an additional half hour, cooling, and weighing are repeated until constant weight is obtained.

Precipitates in Filter Paper. The *moist* paper is removed from the funnel, care being taken not to touch the inside of the paper. The cone is flattened and the top edge of the paper is folded over to make a good closure, then it is folded into smaller segments, keeping the three thicknesses of paper on the outside of the folds. Any precipitate that may have been spattered onto the funnel above the paper is wiped off with a small damp piece of ashless filter paper and added to the main precipitate. The paper containing the precipitate is put into a previously ignited and weighed crucible. The paper should be dried before it is charred. This is therefore a convenient point at which to interrupt the analysis if necessary; the crucibles and their precipitates are placed in a beaker, covered with a watch glass, and reserved until the next laboratory period.

The crucible containing the paper and precipitate is supported on a triangle made of nichrome wire, or of iron wire covered with clay or silica tubing. (When platinum crucibles are used, silica triangles must be used—never nichrome.) Heating is started *slowly* with a *small* flame from a Tirrill burner placed well below the crucible. If the paper is moist, it must be dried before it begins to char; the carbon formed by charring wet paper is very difficult to burn off later. The drying may be done by placing the crucible at an angle, and supporting its cover at the mouth of the crucible to serve as a reflector to direct the heat from the flame into the crucible, as shown in Fig. 33-5. Note that the bottom of the crucible is supported across one side of the triangle, with the mouth of the crucible toward the apex of the triangle.

After the paper is dry, the upright, uncovered crucible is heated at slowly increasing temperature to smoke off and char the paper. Active combustion by flame should not occur; if, by too rapid heating, the paper inflames, the crucible can be covered momentarily to smother the flames. The temperature is increased and all the carbon is burned off, which is best done by tilting the crucible on the triangle, as in Fig. 33-5, and applying the flame at the bottom of the crucible. This arrangement allows air to circulate into the crucible, to facilitate oxidation of the carbon. If the crucible were in a vertical position, heating with a strong flame would surround the mouth of the crucible with nonoxidizing gases, and removal of carbon would be very slow. When the residue from the paper is white or nearly so, change is made to a Meker or air-blast burner, and the bottom of the inclined crucible is heated at the full temperature of the burner for about ten minutes. Good access of air to the crucible is essential. The crucibles are cooled for about a minute, then placed in a desiccator, and weighed when cool. Ignition for another ten minutes, cooling, and weighing are repeated as required to bring the contents to constant weight.

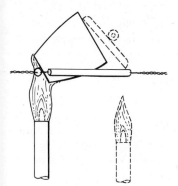

Fig. 33-5 Drying (dotted lines) and igniting a precipitate.

An electric muffle furnace, in which the temperature is easily regulated, is excellent for completing ignitions.

TITRATION TECHNIQUE

Testing the Buret

The buret stopcock, when properly greased, should appear transparent through the ground surfaces, it should turn easily and smoothly, and it must not leak. If the stopcock is operating properly, the plug should not be removed. However, if necessary to regrease the stopcock, the plug is removed from the barrel and all the old grease, from both plug and barrel, is wiped off with a clean, lintless cloth moistened with a little solvent such as carbon tetrachloride. A *thin* film of stopcock grease is applied in two rings near the ends of the plug, which is then inserted into the barrel and pressed firmly into it, while turning the plug back and forth to spread the grease evenly over the ground surfaces. An excess of grease is to be scrupulously avoided, because it will work into the bore of the plug and the barrel, from which it is very difficult to remove.

The inner walls of the buret must be clean. Any dirt or grease on the glass causes liquid to adhere in large drops when the liquid level is lowered and results in a substantial error in the measurement of the volume of liquid delivered. Soap or detergent solution and a buret brush are used for cleaning the buret, after which it is rinsed well with tap water. Testing for leakage and drainage is done with tap water. The buret is filled with water to a point slightly above the top (zero) mark, and the stopcock is opened briefly to fill the tip completely with liquid. The buret is allowed to stand for about fifteen minutes in the buret holder. If any water drips from the tip, or leaks out at the ends of the plug during this time, the stopcock must be cleaned and greased again more carefully. To test for drainage, the stopcock is opened to deliver a slow stream of liquid. The maximum delivery rate should be about 0.5 ml per second. If the orifice of the tip is of proper size, the correct delivery rate is given when the stopcock is opened full. However, this condition should not be assumed, and if the orifice is rather large, the flow should be controlled by partially closing the stopcock. As the liquid level in the buret falls, it should be observed carefully. The film of liquid adhering to the glass should not break at any point, for if it does, the drops formed will adhere to the glass above the meniscus. In this event the buret must be cleaned again. Burets require less frequent cleaning if they are left filled with distilled water when not in use.

Filling the Buret

The buret must be rinsed two or three times with *small* portions of the titrant solution. The transfer of solution should be made directly from the stock bottle (or volumetric flask) of standard solution to the buret, without the intermediate use of a beaker or a funnel. The buret is held in one hand while the stock bottle is manipulated with the other hand. A towel held around the buret will catch any drops of solution that might be spilled accidentally on the outside. After about 5 ml of solution have been transferred to the buret, it is held in a nearly horizontal position and rotated so that all portions of the wall are wet by the solution. The solution is wasted through the tip (to rinse it also), and the entire process is repeated with a second and a third small portion of the solution. Finally, the buret is filled to a point slightly above the zero mark and placed in the buret holder. No separate drops of solution should adhere to the glass above the liquid, because they might break loose after the reading is taken and give rise to error. The stopcock is opened, wide at first, to displace air completely from the tip, and the liquid is then drawn off slowly until the meniscus is at or preferably slightly below the zero mark. Opinions differ whether the level should be adjusted exactly to the 0.00 mark. Some analysts believe that a more accurate reading is possible if the meniscus does not exactly coincide with a graduation mark. It is the writer's opinion that nothing is gained in the accuracy of making the initial reading by adjustment exactly to the zero mark, and time is wasted in the process of making the adjustment.

Reading the Buret

The *bottom* of the meniscus (curved surface) is always read unless the solution is so deeply colored (as in the case of permanganate solution) that it cannot be seen sharply. Parallax in observing the liquid level can cause considerable reading error; the meniscus, the nearest graduation mark, and the eye should be on the same level; see Fig. 33-6. The reading is made directly to 0.1 ml, and

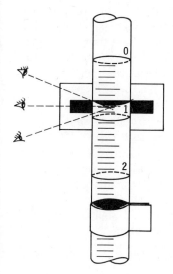

Fig. 33-6   Illustration of parallax in reading a buret; reading devices.

estimated to 0.01 ml. A small white card with a wide black line, or a card with the entire bottom half blackened, makes the curved meniscus more easily visible when the white-black division is near the meniscus level.

A number of devices to aid in avoiding parallax can be used for reading burets that have short graduation marks. One of the simplest aids is a straight strip of paper around the buret, to give a front and a back reference line for adjusting the eye level. The loop of paper is slid up until the back and front edges of the paper, the bottom of the meniscus, and the eye are all on the same level; the reading is then made. If the inner surface of the paper is blackened, reflection into the meniscus gives a good contrast with the solution. The best style of buret has *every* mark at least halfway around the barrel, from front to back, and the whole milliliter division marks extend all the way around. Parallax is easily avoided in reading a buret of this kind, by adjusting the eye level until the line nearest the meniscus is seen merely as a straight mark across the near face of the buret; the white-black reading card should be used to give the meniscus good contrast.

For the titration data, the reading, to 0.01 ml accuracy, is recorded as the "Initial Reading." Any small pendant drop of solution on the tip is removed by touching it to a towel, glass rod, or beaker. The buret is now ready for use.

Titration

The solution to be titrated is usually contained in an Erlenmeyer flask; efficient stirring is accomplished by *swirling* the contents. Burets are always made with the handle of the stopcock on the right-hand side when the graduation numbers are at the front. The stopcock is to be operated with the thumb and first two fingers of the *left* hand. The other fingers, held on the opposite side of the delivery tip just below the stopcock, serve to give some leverage against which the thumb and fingers can exert a slight "squeeze" on the plug to keep it well seated in the barrel of the stopcock. The novice may occasionally "push" instead of "pull," thus unseating the plug and ruining the titration, but with a little practice the stopcock can be operated smoothly and with perfect control.

The titration should be conducted in a good light against a white[4] background such as a porcelain-base buret stand, a porcelain tile, or a clean towel (the writer prefers the last), so the end-point change can be discerned easily. The titrant is run into the sample solution slowly, while the flask is swirled with the right hand. Too rapid delivery of the titrant not only increases drainage error, but increases the possibility of running past the end point. Generally, a warning of the approaching end point is observed as a momentary change of the indicator where there is a localized excess of titrant. This local end-point indication is discharged more and more slowly with the approach of the end point, until

---

[4] Titrations in which the end point is the first appearance of turbidity or the disappearance of a precipitate are conducted against a black background.

finally one drop, or even a fractional drop, gives the end-point indication. Fractional drops are taken by closing the stopcock when there is a small pendant drop on the tip; the drop is removed by touching the flask to the tip, then rinsing down with a stream of water from the wash bottle. Rinsing down near the end point is very important to bring into the mixture any unreacted sample solution that has splashed up on the side of the flask. If there is doubt whether or not the end point has been reached, the buret reading should be taken, then one more drop (or fractional drop) of the titrant is added and the mixture again observed. The procedure should be continued in this way until a positive one-drop end point is ascertained. It must be noted that any titrant solution hanging on the buret tip will be included in the measured volume of solution delivered even though it was not added to the sample solution. This condition should never be permitted.

After allowing 30 seconds for drainage, the buret is read, again to an accuracy of 0.01 ml. This "Final Reading" should be recorded above the "Initial Reading," for ease in subtraction to give the volume of solution delivered.

When multiplicate samples are being titrated and the student is not familiar with the end-point detection, it is helpful to save the titrated solution of the first sample for comparison in judging the end point in titrating subsequent samples.

Volumetric Flasks

Volumetric flasks are used principally for two purposes: (1) the preparation of standard solutions by the direct method and (2) the preparation of samples to a known volume for taking a definite fraction or aliquot. Because of the narrow neck, it is generally inadvisable to try to transfer weighed solids directly into the flask. Usually, the solid is first dissolved, then transferred by pouring the solution down a glass rod held in the mouth of the flask. The beaker must be rinsed well and the rinsings transferred to the flask. Finally, solvent is added up to the mark; the last few drops may be added with a dropper or a pipet. Separate drops of liquid must not adhere to the neck above the liquid surface. As liquid is added, from time to time the contents are mixed by swirling, and after dilution to the mark is completed, thorough mixing is accomplished by repeatedly (20 to 40 times) inverting the stoppered flask, each time shaking it well while in the inverted position.

Aliquots

If the weight of a sample appropriate for titration is so small that weighing errors are relatively large, the error can be avoided by weighing a larger sample, which is dissolved and made up to an exactly known volume in a volumetric flask. A definite fraction of the solution is then taken by a transfer pipet. Suppose, for example, that the weight of sample desired is about 0.1 g. A sample of about 0.5 g, accurately weighed, is dissolved and made up to the mark in a 250-ml volumetric flask; a 50-ml transfer pipet is then used to take one-fifth aliquots of this solution, corresponding to one-fifth portions of the original sample.

Obviously, multiplicate aliquots of a solution should require identical volumes of titrant. Care must be exercised to avoid prejudice in judging the end points (volumes delivered) in their titration. Furthermore, any error in weighing the original sample will not be revealed by lack of precision when aliquots are titrated.

Use of Pipet

The inner walls of the pipet must be clean, to allow proper drainage. During delivery the liquid film must not break and leave drops of liquid on the walls of the stem, bulb, or tip. Warm (*not* hot) soap or detergent solution is usually effective for cleaning.

A pipet is rinsed by sucking a small amount of the solution into it, then rotating the pipet while it is held in a horizontal position, so that the entire inner surface, including the upper stem to a point above the graduation mark, is wet with solution. The rinse solution is wasted through the tip, and the rinsing is repeated two or three times. The pipet is then filled by applying suction until the liquid is a few centimeters above the graduation mark. During this operation care must be taken to ensure that the tip of the pipet is below the surface of the liquid being transferred, otherwise air will enter and force the liquid ahead of it. The stem is then closed quickly with the index finger (*not* with the thumb); easing the pressure of the finger admits air slowly, and the flow of liquid from the tip is easily controlled to adjust the bottom of the meniscus exactly to the graduation mark.

The transfer is made by holding the pipet in a vertical position, removing the finger, and allowing the liquid to run under free flow through the tip. The orifice of the tip must be small enough that delivery is sufficiently slow to give proper drainage of the liquid film down the inner wall. The small amount of liquid remaining in the tapered part of the tip is *not* to be blown out or otherwise removed. The tip is touched to the liquid surface or against the wall of the receiver to remove any pendant drop, but any liquid not removed by this process is left in the tip. A transfer pipet is calibrated to deliver the specified volume when delivery is made as just described, and the same technique must therefore be followed in its use.

34

USE OF THE ANALYTICAL BALANCE

Reference: Chapter 2.

Almost every quantitative analysis, regardless of the method employed for the final measurement, requires the use of the analytical balance. In gravimetric methods *all* of the measurements are made by weighing. In most other methods, primary standards and samples for analysis must be weighed accurately. Accurate and rapid weighing, like any other skill, requires practice. It is useless to proceed to the analytical work until weighing can be done rapidly and with confidence in its reliability. Most of the weighings in quantitative analysis are made to the nearest 0.1 mg (0.0001 g). The analytical balance is a delicate instrument that will not stand abuse, but it will render long and excellent service under careful treatment.

Rules for Use of the Balance

The following rules apply to both the equal-arm and the single-pan types of balance. Additional rules and/or procedures applying only to a given type are stated in the appropriate part of Exp. 34-1.

1. Use only the balance to which you are assigned. Each student is held personally responsible for the proper care of the balance assigned.

2. When properly adjusted, the balance case is level, and the beam release and pan arrest operate smoothly; these latter mechanisms should be actuated slowly to avoid damage to the bearings.

3. The beam and pans should be supported when the balance is not in use, and when objects are placed on or removed from the pans. Objects are not to be left on the pans when the balance is not in use.

4. An object to be weighed must be clean, dry, and at room temperature. Crucibles that have been heated to redness require at least 30 minutes in a desiccator to come to room temperature. Objects that have been in the desiccator should be weighed as rapidly as possible, because they tend to take up moisture during weighing, especially if the air is quite humid. Carry the desiccator to the balance room, so the object is exposed as little as possible.

5. Only objects of glass, porcelain, plastic, or metal are to be placed directly on the balance pan. Powdered solids are weighed onto a watch glass or glazed weighing paper, or by difference from a weighing bottle; liquids are weighed only in small stoppered bottles or flasks. Any solids accidentally spilled on the pan or in the case should be removed immediately with a small soft brush.

6. Place the object to be weighed in the center of the pan, to prevent swinging when the pan is released.

7. Do not overload the balance. Student balances usually have a rated capacity of 100 to 200 g, but it is seldom that objects heavier than 50 g need to be weighed in ordinary analytical work.

8. Make all final adjustments and readings with the balance case closed, to avoid disturbance of the beam by air currents.

9. The student must *not* attempt to make adjustments of the balance mechanism; report any malfunction to the laboratory instructor.

10. Double check each weight value, and record the weight immediately in the permanent record book.

EXPERIMENT **34-1 PRACTICE WEIGHING**

Weighing with an Equal-Arm Balance

Reading the Pointer Scale. Although there are several methods for designating the marks on the pointer scale, the one preferred by the author is shown in Fig. 34-1.[1] The main marks, reading from left to right, are numbered 0, 50,

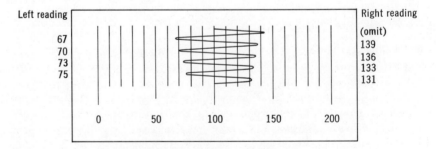

Fig. 34-1 Reading the pointer scale.

[1] It is recommended that instruction on the use of the equal-arm balance be given by the laboratory instructor as a demonstration to a small group of students. Many details, not given here, can be mentioned, with reasons and explanations.

100 (center), 150, and 200. Thus, the space between adjacent marks has a value of 10. Turning points of swings are always estimated to the nearest tenth of the space between marks, or units by this numbering designation.

The equilibrium position of the freely oscillating beam is calculated from the readings of five consecutive turning points, as illustrated in Fig. 34-1:

	Left	Right
	67	139
	70	136
	73	
	3)210	2)275
Average:	70	138
		70
		2)208
Equilibrium point:		104

The equilibrium point with no load on the balance is called the **zero point**; with any load on the pans or beam, it is called the **rest point**.

Determination of Zero Point. Determination of the equilibrium condition of the balance has been discussed in Chap. 2. With no weights on the pans, with the rider either raised from the beam or resting squarely on the zero mark (or, on a chainomatic balance, the chain carrier set at zero), and with the balance case closed, release the beam slowly by turning the knob in the center of the case counterclockwise; then slowly release the pan arrests, which should now allow the beam to oscillate slowly. If necessary to set the beam in motion, touch one pan *very lightly* with the tip of a camel's-hair brush. Sit squarely in front of the pointer scale to avoid parallax, and, omitting the first oscillation, record readings of the turning points or inflections of the pointer, using five *consecutive* inflections. Arrest the beam and pans (this must be done *only when the pointer is near scale center*), and calculate the equilibrium (zero) point. (On a magnetically damped balance, merely let the pointer come to rest and read the pointer position; the student should determine the minimum time for the pointer to come to rest with various amplitudes of original swing or thrust.) The equilibrium point of the empty balance is called the **zero point**. Repeat the determination of the zero point three or four times (or as many times as necessary to get concordant results), and record the average as the zero point of the balance for this day. Because the zero point of a balance may change from time to time, the zero point should be determined each day the balance is used, except when samples are weighed by difference on the same day. If the zero point is less than 80 or more than 120, ask the laboratory instructor to adjust the balance.

Determination of Sensitivity. The **sensitivity** of the balance is the pointer displacement, in divisions, produced by 1-mg overload on the right-hand balance arm. Because the sensitivity may vary with load on the pans, it is determined for various loads. The sensitivity remains constant over long periods of time if the center of gravity is not changed. The sensitivity, or its reciprocal, is used each time a weighing is made, hence it should be determined with great care. Place 10 g (integral weights) on each pan, take readings of swings, and calculate the rest point. (Because of slight inequalities of the weights, this rest point may not exactly coincide with the zero point.) Now add the rider (or chain) to the right-hand balance arm, at the 1-mg position, and again determine the rest point. The difference between the two rest points is the sensitivity for a 10-g load; it is more convenient to use the sensitivity reciprocal, which is the weight, in milligrams, required to produce a displacement of one scale division. The following will illustrate:

Rest point for 10-g load	104
Rest point with 10-g load + 1-mg overload	86
Sensitivity for 10-g load	18 div/mg

Sensitivity reciprocal for 10-g load = 1/18 = 0.056 mg/div

In the same way, determine the sensitivity and sensitivity reciprocal for a 20-, 30-, and 50-g load. Have the sensitivity determinations checked by the laboratory instructor before proceeding to the weighing exercise. Record the sensitivity reciprocal values in an easily accessible place such as on a small card pasted on the inside cover of the record book.

   Weighing an Object.   Place some small object, such as a crucible cr watch glass, on the left balance pan. Note that weights are to be handled only with ivory- or plastic-tipped forceps; care must be taken not to bend the fractional weights. Add weights to the right pan, applying them in the order in which they occur in the weight box, starting with a weight estimated to be slightly heavier than the object. After placing the weight on the pan, lower the beam *slowly*, and, if necessary, depress the pan arrests to note the direction in which the pointer starts to move (to the left, if weight is heavier than object). If the weight is heavier than the object, support the beam and pans, remove the weight, replace it with the next smaller weight in the set, and again test for direction of pointer movement. Continue in this way, working systematically from large to smaller weights, and using fractional weights and rider[2] until counterpoise within 1 mg is attained, so that the pointer swings approximately equal distances in each side of scale center. Take readings of swings and calculate the rest point. The divisions difference between the rest point and the zero point, multiplied by the sensitivity reciprocal gives the correction, in milligrams, to

---

   [2] A chain-weight balance requires no fractional weights of denominations less than 100 mg. After adding fractional weights in increments of 100 mg (0.1 g), final adjustment is made by adding the chain weight to the nearest milligram, and then determining the rest point in the usual way. If the balance also has a notched beam and dumbbell rider, no separate fractional weights are required. Increments of 0.1 g are added by the dumbbell rider on the beam, and weights below 100 mg are added by the chain.

be applied to the weights on the pan and rider (or chain); the correction is negative if the rest point is smaller than the zero point, and positive if the rest point is larger than the zero point.

Suppose, for example, that a crucible is being weighed on a balance the zero point of which is 104, and which has a sensitivity reciprocal of 0.056 mg/div. An approximate counterpoise is obtained with 13.730 g on the right pan and the rider at the 4-mg position. With this adjustment the rest point is 89, or 15 divisions smaller than the zero point; the weight corresponding to 15 divisions is $0.056 \times 15 = 0.84$ mg, or 0.0008 g. (Rounding to the first decimal place in milligrams, which is the fourth decimal place in grams, is done *after* the multiplication.) The weights used are 0.0008 g too heavy, and the correct weight is $13.734 - 0.0008 = 13.7332$ g. If, in weighing the crucible, the rider has been placed at the 3-mg position, giving a rest point of 107, the weights used are too light by $0.056 \times 3 = 0.168$ mg or (rounded) 0.0002 g, and the correct weight is $13.733 + 0.0002 = 13.7332$ g, the same as before. While the weights are still on the pan, record each denomination used, as well as the rider position, always recording from largest to smallest denomination; check the record by noting the empty spaces in the weight box, and check again as each piece is returned to its proper place in the weight box. See Table 33-1, p. 552, for method of making the weight record. (Most student errors are due to failure to make a proper *record* of the weights used.)

Weighing with a Single-Pan Balance

Check for Level.   Each time before using the balance,[3] check it for level. If the level bubble is not exactly centered in the circle inscribed on the glass, adjust the leveling screws on the base until the level bubble is exactly centered in the circle.

Check the Zero Position.   Turn the beam release knob (on the left side of the case) counterclockwise for full release, and observe the projection scale. If the zero mark is not exactly centered in the index fork, slowly rotate the zero adjust knob until the zero mark is centered in the fork. The zero point should be checked each time before using the balance.

Weighing an Object.   Make sure the beam is arrested, and place the object (crucible, watch glass, etc.) in the center of the pan. Turn the beam arrest knob clockwise for partial release. Rotate the knob controlling the largest estimated weight of the object until the projection scale changes direction with respect to the zero, then turn the knob back to the next lower position. For example, if the object is estimated to weigh about 15 g, rotate the "tens" knob to add 10 g

[3] The operating instructions given here are for a Mettler Type H5 or H6 balance. Other makes of single-pan balance may have the various control knobs located in different positions, or have a slightly different read-out method, but all operate on the same general principle. Consult the laboratory instructor for details.

(note the scale), then to the 20-g position; if now the scale moves in the opposite direction, turn back to the 10-g position. Then rotate the knob controlling the next lower decade of weights (1, 2, 3, etc.) until the scale reverses direction, and turn back one position. When the lowest weight that can be dialed in this way has been used, turn the beam arrest to its counterclockwise position (full release). If the index fork does not stand exactly on a scale mark, rotate the micrometer scale knob until the next lower graduation mark on the optical scale is brought exactly to center on the forked pointer. The weight of the object is then the sum of the weights indicated on the weight dials and the weight appearing on the projection scale and on the micrometer scale. Record the weight to the nearest 0.1 mg (0.0001 g). Arrest the beam, return all weight control knobs to zero, remove the object, and close the balance case. Note: The weight control knobs should be turned *slowly* from one weight increment to another; do *not* twirl the knobs rapidly—this might throw the weights out of their proper position on the beam.

Weighing Exercise

Regardless of the type of balance used, weigh accurately several small objects, recording each weight in the record book; also record the time required to make each weighing. (If an equal-arm balance is used, continue the practice weighing until an accurate weighing can be made in five minutes or less.) Then obtain from the laboratory instructor a numbered brass block. Wipe the block with a clean, dry towel, and weigh it accurately, recording the data as indicated previously; note also the time required to make the weighing. Return the brass block promptly upon completion of the weighing. Fill in the report form[4] for this experiment and submit it to the laboratory instructor.

Weighing from a Weighing Bottle

Place several grams of common salt in a clean weighing bottle. After inserting the stopper, carefully wipe away all adhering particles from the outside, and handle the bottle as little as possible during wiping. Weigh the bottle and contents accurately and record the data in the record book. (Note: when using an equal-arm balance for weighing samples by difference from a weighing bottle, the zero point may be assumed to be 100 for purposes of calculating the final weight adjustment; any error originating from this assumption is canceled when the subtraction is performed to calculate the weight of sample removed.) Hold the bottle over the top of a beaker and cautiously remove the stopper; make sure that no particles fall from it or from the bottle elsewhere than in the beaker. Pour from the bottle, by a rotary motion, an amount of solid estimated

---

[4] Blanks for reporting the results of laboratory work are obtained from the laboratory instructor.

to be about 1 g; carefully replace the stopper while holding the bottle over the beaker. Weigh the bottle and contents accurately, and record the details. In the same way transfer a second portion of the solid to another beaker, and weigh again; continue in this way until facility is acquired in weighing samples by difference from the weighing bottle. Summarize the results by tabulating the weights on the right-hand page of the record book, using the format shown near the top of Table 33-2, p. 553.

When the practice weighing has been completed, make certain that no objects or weights have been left on the balance pan, and that the beam and pans are supported and the balance case is closed. Any solids accidentally spilled in or around the balance must be removed.

35

GRAVIMETRIC
DETERMINATIONS

Reference: Chap. 14; Chap. 33, pp. 556–565.

The assigned determinations for the laboratory work of the course are to be performed in triplicate unless directions to the contrary are given. Report the individual results, their average, the deviation (in parts per thousand, ‰) of each result from the average, and the average deviation in ‰.

Before starting any laboratory work involving gravimetric precipitation, the student should read carefully the part of Chap. 33 dealing with the technique of carrying out precipitation, digestion, filtration, washing, and drying or igniting. Efficient use of laboratory time presupposes that the student has read the directions for the laboratory work and has planned a routine for the determination. The need for properly prepared, weighed crucibles must be anticipated, so they will be ready for use when required in the analysis. The text material covering the determination should be studied carefully, so that the principle of the method, the function of each reagent, and the possible sources of error are thoroughly understood.

EXPERIMENT 35-1 DETERMINATION OF WATER IN A HYDRATE

Reference: Chap. 16.

Several techniques are available for this determination; the choice of method is largely one of convenience and availability of equipment such as adequate oven space. The determination is to be done in triplicate; it is not necessary that all three samples be analyzed by the same method; different methods may be used and the results compared. The sample is to be analyzed *as received.*

Method 1: Heating in an Oven. If the weighing bottles and stoppers are not already numbered, mark them (Note 1) so they can be identified. Place the unstoppered weighing bottles and their stoppers in a beaker (marked with your initials) in the drying oven at 130°C for one-half hour or longer. Cool the bottles and their stoppers in the desiccator for 20 to 30 minutes, then weigh the stoppered bottles accurately. Transfer about one gram of the unknown to each bottle, and again weigh accurately. Lay the stopper on its side over the mouth of the weighing bottle, put the bottle in a beaker, and place the beaker in the oven; heat at 130°C for one hour. Cool the unstoppered bottles, contents, and stoppers in the desiccator for 20 to 30 minutes, then promptly (Note 2) weigh the stoppered bottles accurately. Again heat in the oven for one-half to one hour, cool, and weigh; repeat until the weight is constant to within 0.5 mg. Calculate and report the percent of water in the sample.

Method 2: Heating in an Air Bath (Note 3). Place the air baths on triangles supported on ring stands or tripods. Heat numbered crucibles and their covers (Note 1) in the air baths for one-half hour. Use very small flames; the tip of the flame should not touch the evaporating dish. Cool the covered crucibles in the desiccator for 30 minutes, then weigh accurately. Transfer about one gram of the unknown to each crucible, and again weigh accurately. Heat the samples in the air baths for about one hour. The crucible covers should be set slightly ajar to allow free escape of water vapor. Begin the heating slowly, to avoid possible loss of sample by decrepitation, and gradually increase the temperature. Cool the covered crucibles in the desiccator for 30 minutes, and weigh as soon as cool. Repeat the operation until constant weight within 0.5 mg is obtained. Calculate and report the percent of water in the sample.

Method 3: Direct Heating. Place numbered crucibles and their covers (Note 1) in triangles supported on tripods, and heat for 15 to 20 minutes with a *small* nonluminous flame waved back and forth across the bottom of the crucible, while the burner is held in the hand. Cool the crucibles and covers in the desiccator for 30 minutes, then weigh accurately. Transfer about one gram of the unknown to each crucible, and again weigh accurately. Place the crucibles containing the samples in triangles on tripods, set the covers slightly ajar, and heat for 15 to 20 minutes, very slowly at first, with the flame waved back and forth under the crucible. Care must be taken to raise the temperature gradually to avoid mechanical loss of sample by decrepitation as water is expelled. Use only a *very small flame* that should not touch the crucible; do *not* heat to redness nor to the melting point of the solid (Note 4). Cool the covered crucibles in the desiccator for 30 minutes, then weigh accurately as soon as cool. Repeat the process until constant weight, within 0.5 mg, is obtained. Calculate and report the percent of water in the sample.

Notes

1. See p. 557 for method of marking glassware. See p. 559 for method of marking porcelain.

2. If prompt weighing is not feasible, the bottles should be stoppered at the end of the cooling period.

3. An air bath for this experiment consists of a 3-inch porcelain evaporating dish covered with an asbestos board having in its center a hole just large enough to support a porcelain crucible near its upper rim.

4. If the sample consists of hydrated barium chloride, which is frequently used for this experiment, strong heating may volatilize some of the barium chloride.

EXPERIMENT **35-2 GRAVIMETRIC DETERMINATION OF CHLORIDE**

Reference: Chap. 17.

Prepare filter crucibles (Note 1) for use as follows: clean the crucible from surface contamination, then place it in a crucible holder in a suction flask (Fig. 33-3, p. 562). With gentle suction, draw several small portions of distilled water through the filter. Place three crucibles thus prepared in a beaker (marked with your initials), cover with a watch glass, and put the beaker and crucibles in the oven at 120–130°C for one to two hours. Using clean crucible tongs, transfer the hot crucibles to the desiccator, cool for 20–30 minutes, and weigh accurately. Repeat the heating for one-half hour, cool, and weigh; continue until weights constant within 0.3 mg are obtained.

Into numbered 400-ml beakers weigh accurately, by difference from a weighing bottle, triplicate samples of the dried unknown (Note 2) of about 0.5 g. Dissolve the sample in distilled water and dilute to about 150 ml. Add 1 ml of chloride-free nitric acid (Notes 3, 4, 5). The slow addition of silver nitrate to the solution is best accomplished by use of a buret. Wash the buret well with tap water, rinse with three or four small portions of distilled water, and finally fill with silver nitrate solution (Notes 6, 7). From this point on, avoid working in direct sunlight, or even in bright diffuse daylight or bright artificial light (Note 8). To the first sample add silver nitrate solution slowly and with good stirring until a slight excess is present; 40 ml of 0.25 M silver nitrate, or an equivalent volume of another concentration, should be sufficient for complete precipitation of a 0.5-g sample, although a test for complete precipitation must always be made. (The volume of silver nitrate solution need not be recorded.) Precipitate the other samples in the same way. Heat the suspensions nearly to boiling, with frequent or constant stirring, to coagulate the silver chloride (Note 9). Test for complete precipitation by carefully adding a few drops of silver nitrate to the clear supernatant liquid; if more precipitate or cloudiness appears, add a few more milliliters of silver nitrate solution, stir well, heat, let the precipitate settle, and again test. Continue in this way until precipitation is complete. Let the covered beakers with their contents stand in the desk, protected from light, for at least two hours before filtration; standing overnight, or from one laboratory period to the next, may be convenient.

In a beaker prepare a wash solution by adding 1 or 2 ml of chloride-free concentrated nitric acid (Note 10) to about 600 ml of distilled water. Decant the solution from the first sample through the first weighed filtering crucible, pouring the solution down a stirring rod, and using gentle suction. The precipitate should be disturbed as little as possible. To the precipitate in the beaker add about 25 ml of the wash solution, stir well, let the precipitate settle, and decant the solution through the filter crucible. Repeat the washing by decantation four times, and finally bring the precipitate onto the filter; use small portions of the wash solution for transfer. Remove with a rubber policeman any solid particles adhering to the beaker. Continue washing the precipitate in the crucible with the wash solution until the last portions of washings give a negative test for silver ion (Note 11). Ten or more washings may be required. Filter and wash the second and the third samples in the same way.

Place the crucibles containing the precipitates in a covered beaker in the oven at 120–130°C for two hours. Cool the crucibles in the desiccator, and weigh accurately. Reheat for one-hour periods as necessary to obtain weights constant within 0.3 mg. Calculate and report percent chlorine in the sample.

After completing the analysis, clean the crucibles as follows. Remove the cake of silver chloride, then put the crucibles in a beaker, pour about 5 ml of concentrated ammonium hydroxide into each crucible, and cover the beaker with a watch glass. After 10–15 minutes, transfer the crucible to the crucible holder in a suction flask, and wash with several portions of distilled water. If the filter plate is dark, treat in the same way with a few milliliters of concentrated nitric acid, then wash well.

Notes

1. See p. 561. Pyrex crucibles with sintered glass bottoms are most convenient; mark them for sample numbers (1, 2, 3) and with your initials; p. 559. If porcelain crucibles with porous bottoms are used, mark them as directed on p. 559.

2. Unless directions to the contrary are given, all samples for analysis must be dried before weighing; see p. 556 for the method.

3. Test a little of the nitric acid reagent by adding a few drops of silver nitrate solution. If any turbidity develops, the nitric acid contains chloride ion, and another supply of nitric acid must be obtained.

4. Instead of 1 ml of dilute nitric acid, about 10 drops (0.5 ml) of concentrated nitric acid may be used.

5. Nitric acid prevents the precipitation of silver salts of anions such as carbonate and phosphate, and it also aids in the coagulation of the silver chloride precipitate.

6. Silver nitrate is an expensive chemical; *do not waste it.*

7. Silver nitrate produces dark stains on the skin and on fabrics; avoid spilling it.

8. Silver chloride is light-sensitive, and undergoes decomposition when exposed to bright light.

9. Heating is conveniently done on a steam bath or a hot plate, and should be continued until the precipitate settles rapidly after stirring, leaving a clear supernatant liquid.

10. Nitric acid in the wash solution prevents peptization of the precipitate. If water were used for washing, the precipitate would start passing through the filter as the electrolytes are washed out.

11. Test by adding a few drops of dilute hydrochloric acid to the washings. Absence of a precipitate or turbidity shows that washing is complete.

EXPERIMENT 35-3   DETERMINATION OF SULFATE

Reference: Chap. 18.

Into numbered 400-ml beakers, weigh accurately by difference from a weighing bottle, triplicate 0.5-g samples of the dried unknown. To each sample add about 50 ml of distilled water. If the sample is completely soluble in water, add 1 ml of concentrated hydrochloric acid. If not completely soluble in water, add concentrated hydrochloric acid dropwise, with stirring, until the sample is completely dissolved, then 1 ml of the acid in excess (Note 1). In either case, after addition of the acid, dilute to about 200 ml with water. Heat the sample just to boiling (Note 2), and add 0.25 *M* barium chloride solution dropwise (Note 3), with constant stirring. After about 20 ml of the barium chloride solution have been added, let the precipitated barium sulfate settle (Note 4), and test the supernatant solution for complete precipitation by careful addition of a few drops more barium chloride. If more precipitate (cloudiness or turbidity) forms, add dropwise about 5 ml more barium chloride, stir well, let the precipitate settle, and test again. When precipitation is complete, cover the beakers with watch glasses, and keep the mixtures hot (Note 5) for one hour, or longer if necessary to obtain a perfectly clear supernatant liquid (Note 6).

Crucibles for receiving the precipitates are conveniently prepared while the precipitates are digesting. Make sure the crucibles are clearly marked for identification (Note 7). Support the crucibles, without covers, in triangles and heat to redness for 10 minutes by using the full temperature of the Meker burner. Let cool in air for a few minutes, until only moderate radiated heat is felt when the back of the hand is brought near the crucible, then transfer the crucibles to the desiccator. Leave the desiccator cover slightly ajar for about a minute before closing it completely. After 30 minutes or more, weigh the crucibles accurately. Repeat the heating, cooling, and weighing to weights constant within 0.3 mg.

At the end of the digestion period, again test for complete precipitation. If time permits the filtration during the same laboratory period, filter the hot solution as described below (Note 8). If samples must be carried over to another laboratory period, set them in the locker where they will not be disturbed, and filter at the next laboratory period. In this case it is best not to heat the samples before filtration, because of danger of bumping during heating.

Prepare funnels, marked with numbers to correspond to samples, with ashless filter paper, and test them for satisfactory operation (Note 9). Place a clean, numbered beaker under each funnel, the ground tip of which should touch the inside of the beaker. Filter by decantation through the filter paper, disturbing the precipitate as little as possible. Test the filtrate with a few drops of barium chloride solution. If no precipitate or turbidity results, discard the filtrate, rinse the receiving beaker, and replace it under the funnel (Note 10). Wash the precipitate by decantation three or four times with small portions of hot water, and finally bring the precipitate onto the filter with a jet of hot water from the wash bottle. At no time should the paper be more than half filled with liquid, because of the tendency of the precipitate to creep in the liquid film. From time to time discard the *clear* filtrate, so that if the precipitate begins to run through the filter, a large volume will not have to be refiltered. If at any time during the transfer or washing, any precipitate runs through the filter, as indicated by turbidity of the filtrate, heat and stir the turbid filtrate to coagulate the precipitate, and filter again through the same filter paper. A small amount of paper pulp, made by macerating part of a filter paper, is an efficient gathering agent for small amounts of precipitate. Use a rubber policeman to scrub loose any particles that adhere to the glass. Wash the precipitate on the filter several times with hot water, directing it around the top of the paper, and allowing the liquid to drain through completely before the next washing. After 8 to 10 washings, collect the last wash water in a test tube, and test for chloride ion by adding a few drops of silver nitrate solution. If a positive test is obtained, continue the washings until a negative test shows that soluble salts have been washed out.

Carefully remove the paper from the funnel (Note 11), flatten the paper, fold down the top edge, then fold into smaller segments, keeping the three thicknesses of paper on the outside. With a small damp piece of ashless filter paper wipe off any precipitate that may have spattered onto the funnel above the paper, and add it to the main precipitate. Place the paper containing the precipitate in a previously ignited and weighed crucible of corresponding sample number (Note 12).

Support the uncovered crucible on a triangle well above a *small* flame, and heat gently so that the paper dries before it begins to char (Note 13). Then gradually raise the temperature to char the paper; active combustion with a flame must be avoided (Note 14). Finally, increase the temperature and burn off all the carbon. During this and the remainder of the heating, incline the crucible in the triangle, and heat by applying the flame to the bottom of the inclined crucible so that gases from the flame do not surround the mouth of the crucible; *good access of air is essential* (Note 15). Cool the crucibles and contents as before, and after 30 minutes or more in the desiccator, weigh them accurately. Repeat the heating to redness for ten minutes, cool, and weigh, and continue to weights constant to within 0.3 mg.

Calculate and report percent SO_3 (Note 16) in the sample.

Notes

1. Acid used in the solution prevents precipitation of barium salts of other anions, such as carbonate, phosphate, etc.

2. Precipitation from hot solution gives larger and purer particles of precipitate.

3. The dropwise addition of barium chloride is best done by delivery from a buret.

4. Remove the flame during settling of the precipitate, to prevent bumping and possible loss of sample.

5. Hot digestion is best done by setting the beakers on a hot plate. The temperature should be below the boiling point, to avoid possible bumping.

6. Digestion of the precipitate is very important in obtaining coarse-grained precipitate free from contamination.

7. See p. 559 for method of marking porcelain crucibles.

8. Because hot liquids filter much more rapidly than cold ones, there is a time advantage in filtering immediately after digestion.

9. See p. 561 for the method of fitting a paper filter to a funnel.

10. If a precipitate or turbidity forms on the addition of barium chloride, precipitation was not complete, and the sample is to be discarded and a new one started.

11. Do not touch the inside of the paper with the fingers or any other object.

12. This is a convenient place at which the analysis may be interrupted if necessary; place the crucibles with their precipitates in a covered beaker and reserve until the next laboratory period.

13. If the paper chars before drying, a variety of carbon is formed that later burns off only with difficulty.

14. It is prudent to have at hand a crucible cover, so that if active combustion of the paper begins, the flame can be smothered immediately by covering the crucible momentarily.

15. If ignition has not been conducted properly, some barium sulfate may be reduced to barium sulfide by carbon and/or by reducing gases. Reoxidation to the sulfate is likely to be slow and incomplete. The barium sulfide can be converted to barium sulfate by adding one or two drops of dilute (6 N) sulfuric acid and heating *gently* with a *small* flame to drive off excess acid; dense fumes of SO_3 may appear near the end of the evaporation. Finally, heat the inclined

crucible at full burner temperature for 10 minutes. Cool and weigh, and repeat the ignition to constant weight.

16. Analysis of oxy-anions is usually reported in terms of the anhydride of the corresponding acid; thus, sulfate is reported as SO_3.

ANALYSIS OF LIMESTONE

The methods used in limestone analysis are characteristic of analysis of minerals and rocks in general. Although many minerals and rocks require drastic treatment to effect complete solution, limestone is quite easily put into solution for analysis. Limestone is chosen to illustrate the analysis of a complex sample also because it has wide commercial use, and analysis for the various components is likely to be met in industrial laboratories. Although the method of analysis for each constituent is in general the same as when it is present alone, the analysis is more difficult, because it involves quantitative separation of the constituents, and great care must be exercised to avoid loss or contamination of the sample, as well as to obtain sharp analytical separations. Any error in one determination may carry over into subsequent determinations on the sample. All beakers, funnels, crucibles, etc., used in carrying through the parallel samples should be clearly marked so there is no chance of confusing them.

For many purposes it is sufficient to make a partial or " proximate " analysis, which involves the determination of major constituents singly, and a combined determination of minor constituents, as for example the combined oxides or " R_2O_3." Some constituents, as for example sodium, potassium, and sulfur, may not be determined at all. The usual analysis of limestone includes the following determinations:

1. Loss on ignition, due mainly to loss of carbon dioxide.

2. Uncorrected silica, sometimes called "Silica and Insolubles."

3. Combined oxides, or "R_2O_3," including all substances precipitated by dilute ammonia.

4. Calcium, separated as calcium oxalate and determined by one of several methods.

5. Magnesium, separated as magnesium ammonium phosphate, which is usually ignited to and weighed as magnesium pyrophosphate. (The separation form may also be determined by EDTA titration.)

EXPERIMENT 35-4 **DETERMINATION OF LOSS ON IGNITION OF LIMESTONE**

Only one sample is to be analyzed for loss on ignition, using a portion of the sample *as received.* Heat a porcelain crucible and cover, supported on a triangle, to the full temperature of the Meker burner for 10 minutes. Let the crucible cool somewhat, transfer it to a desiccator, and after 30 minutes or more weigh crucible and cover accurately. Transfer about 1 g of the limestone sample to the crucible, cover it, and again weigh accurately, getting the sample weight by difference.

Support the covered crucible with its contents on a triangle, and heat with an ordinary burner, gently at first (Note 1) and gradually increasing the heat until at the end of about 15 minutes the full temperature of the burner is used. Then change to a Meker air-blast burner, and heat at the full temperature of the burner for about one hour. Cool (desiccator) and weigh within 30 to 40 minutes, *not longer* (Note 2). Repeat the ignition for one-half hour periods until the residue attains constant weight within 2 mg (Note 3). Calculate and report the percent loss on ignition (Notes 4, 5).

Notes

1. Very strong heating at first might result in mechanical loss of solid due to rapid expulsion of carbon dioxide.

2. The residue, principally calcium oxide, readily absorbs and reacts with water and with carbon dioxide at room temperature. Calcium oxide is a better desiccant than calcium chloride used in desiccators, and can take up moisture from it. The residue should therefore be weighed promptly after it has come to room temperature.

3. Some samples, after loss of carbon dioxide, show a slight increase in weight upon prolonged heating; the increase is usually due to oxidation of lower oxides of iron and/or manganese to the higher oxides.

4. The major constituent of limestone is calcium carbonate; more or less magnesium carbonate may be present, and perhaps also minor amounts of iron-(II) carbonate. The loss in weight when limestone is ignited is due mainly to volatilization of carbon dioxide. Obviously, all other weight changes are included, such as volatilization of moisture, sulfur dioxide, carbon dioxide from decomposition of organic matter, and oxidation of lower to higher metal oxides. All of these changes are of small magnitude compared with the loss due to carbon dioxide, and the loss on ignition can be used as an estimate of the amount of carbonate present.

5. The determination of carbon dioxide in a carbonate, by loss in weight on treatment with an acid, is given in Exp. 35–9.

EXPERIMENT 35-5   DETERMINATION OF UNCORRECTED SILICA

Reference: Chap. 19, I.

Weigh accurately, by difference from a weighing bottle, into numbered porcelain crucibles (which need not be previously weighed), triplicate 1-gram portions of the oven-dried limestone sample. Support the covered crucible in a triangle, and, heating slowly at first, gradually increase the temperature and finally heat for one-half hour at the full temperature of a Meker burner (Note 1). Let the sample cool in air, then transfer the solid without loss from the crucible to a correspondingly numbered 250-ml beaker. Place a few milliliters of 1 : 1 hydrochloric acid in the crucible, warm to dissolve any solid, and wash the solution into the beaker with the main sample, using a minimum amount of water for the transfer. To each sample add about 10 ml of distilled water, 15 ml of concentrated hydrochloric acid, and 1 ml of concentrated nitric acid (Note 2). Use a glass rod to break up any lumps of the sintered solid (Note 3), and warm to disintegrate the sample completely. Rinse down the sides of the beaker with a *small* amount of water. Cover the beaker with a watch glass supported on glass hooks to facilitate evaporation, and evaporate to dryness on the steam bath. Then bake the residue at 120°C for an hour or longer on an asbestos-covered hot plate, until the residue is entirely dry (Note 4). Add 10 ml concentrated hydrochloric acid (Note 5), warm the mixture, and break up any caked solids with the stirring rod. Add about 25 ml distilled water, scrub loose any solids adhering to the glass (use a rubber policeman), and heat nearly to boiling until soluble salts are dissolved, but do not prolong the heating unnecessarily (Note 6). Decant the solution through ashless filter paper, collecting the filtrate in a 400-ml beaker. To the residue in the original beaker add 20 ml of 1 : 9 hydro-chloric acid (Note 7), warm, and filter, bringing the precipitate onto filter paper. With a policeman, scrub off all silica particles adhering to the glass, and use 1 : 100 hydrochloric acid for transferring the precipitate to the filter. Wash the precipitate ten times with small portions of 1 : 100 hydrochloric acid; collect all the washings with the main filtrate (Note 8). *Reserve the filtrate and washings for the next determination* (Combined Oxides).

Place the filter paper containing the silica precipitate in a previously ignited and weighed porcelain crucible (Note 9); dry, smoke off, and char the paper, and finally ignite at the full temperature of a Meker air-blast burner for 10 minutes. Cool and weigh. Repeat the ignition for 10-minute periods, to constant weight (0.3 mg) of the precipitate (Note 10). Calculate and report the percent silica in the limestone.

Notes

1. See p. 227 for the reason for igniting the sample before adding acid.
2. Nitric acid oxidizes iron(II) to iron(III).
3. The stirring rod should be left in the beaker until the filtration operation that follows.
4. See p. 228 for explanation of the function of the baking operation, and the errors that may arise if the baking is not done at the proper temperature.
5. During baking of the residue, the chlorides of iron and aluminum, and to

some extent also calcium and magnesium, are converted to oxides or basic salts that are insoluble in water, but soluble in hydrochloric acid. The acid also prevents peptization of the silica.

6. Prolonged boiling increases the loss of silica in the separation.

7. Hydrochloric acid prevents peptization of the silica during washing.

8. For more accurate determination, evaporate the filtrate and washings nearly to dryness, add 5 ml of concentrated hydrochloric acid, evaporate to dryness, bake, take up the residue in hydrochloric acid, etc., as before. Filter the second silica precipitate on a new, small filter paper, and wash as before. Ignite the combined precipitates.

9. If "corrected silica" is to be determined by volatilization with hydrofluoric acid, ignite in a platinum crucible.

10. For the determination of corrected silica, add to the ignited residue in a platinum crucible, 5 ml of hydrofluoric acid and three or four drops of concentrated sulfuric acid. (Caution: If any hydrofluoric acid is spilled on the skin, wash *at once* with *much* water, then with *very dilute* ammonia.) Evaporate *slowly*, *under the hood*, taking care to avoid spattering. Finally, ignite at red heat for 10 to 15 minutes, cool, and weigh. Repeat the ignition to constant weight. The loss in weight represents silica. See p. 228 for the function of the hydrofluoric and sulfuric acids.

EXPERIMENT 35-6 DETERMINATION OF COMBINED OXIDES, R_2O_3

Reference: Chap. 19, pp. 233

To the filtrate and washings from the silica determination (Note 1), add 1 ml saturated bromine water (Note 2), and heat the mixture to boiling (Note 3). To the hot solution add slowly and with good stirring, dilute (1 : 1) ammonium hydroxide (Note 4); the yellow color due to excess bromine will disappear when the mixture is alkaline; use only a slight excess of ammonium hydroxide (Notes 5, 6). While stirring the mixture, boil for one or two minutes (Note 7), then allow the precipitate to settle for a few minutes (Note 8).

Without delay, filter by decantation through ashless paper and receive the filtrate in a 600-ml beaker. Immediately wash the precipitate several times with small portions of hot 1% ammonium nitrate solution (Note 9). Remove, temporarily, the beaker containing the filtrate and washings, and place the beaker in which the precipitation was just made under the funnel. Dissolve the precipitate from the filter by dropping around the top edge of the paper a boiling solution of 1 : 5 hydrochloric acid, using a total of about 25 ml for each sample. Wash the paper with three or four small portions of boiling 1 : 100 hydrochloric acid, and finally with hot water, until the solution and washings have a volume of about 75 ml. Do not discard the filter paper. Make the solution slightly alkaline with 1 : 1 ammonium hydroxide, boil for one or two minutes, let the precipitate coagulate and settle for a few minutes, then filter through the same paper used for the first filtration. Collect the filtrate and washings in the beaker containing the first filtrate. Wash the precipitate six to eight times with 1% ammonium nitrate solution, and combine the washings with the main filtrate (Note 10). Label the filtrates for calcium determination, add a few drops of methyl red indicator, neutralize the solution with hydrochloric acid (Note 11), and start the evaporation of the solution in preparation for calcium analysis.

Place the filter paper containing the hydroxide precipitate in a previously ignited and weighed porcelain crucible; dry, smoke off, and char the paper at a low temperature, then finally ignite at bright red heat for 10 minutes, with the crucible in an inclined position and the flame of the Meker burner applied on the bottom of the inclined crucible (Note 12). Cool and weigh. Repeat the ignition to constant weight (0.3 mg). Calculate and report the percent of combined oxides or R_2O_3 (Note 13).

Notes

1. The methods of this experiment can be applied to the determination of iron and/or aluminum in "soluble iron" or "soluble aluminum" samples for student analysis. In this case weighed samples of about 0.5 g are treated with 25 ml of 1 : 1 hydrochloric acid, warming as necessary to effect dissolution. The mixture should not be allowed to evaporate to less than 5 ml. More acid may be added to replace that lost by evaporation. Add 1 ml of nitric acid and boil the solution one or two minutes to oxidize any iron(II). If a silica residue remains, filter through a small filter, and wash the residue several times with 1 : 100 hydrochloric acid. Combine the washings and main filtrate, dilute to about 250 ml, and proceed to the addition of ammonium hydroxide.

2. The hydrous oxide of manganese(II) cannot be precipitated completely by ammonia in the presence of ammonium ion. The hydrous oxide of manganese-(IV), however, is extremely insoluble. Bromine is used to oxidize manganese-(II) to manganese(IV) so that its complete removal can be effected.

3. The precipitation, filtration, and washing of the precipitate should be done without interruption; the analysis should therefore be started at the beginning of a laboratory period.

4. The ammonium hydroxide solution must be perfectly clear; filter if necessary.

5. A large excess of ammonium hydroxide is to be avoided. Aluminum hydroxide, being amphoteric, is somewhat soluble even in the weak base.

6. The solution from the silica separation contains the equivalent of 10 ml of concentrated hydrochloric acid; neutralization with ammonia forms ammonium ion, which has the following functions:

a. By suppressing the ionization of ammonium hydroxide, the precipitation of magnesium is prevented.

b. By the same mechanism, ammonium ion prevents the dissolution of aluminum hydroxide.

c. Ammonium ion aids in the coagulation of the precipitate.

d. To some extent ammonium ion displaces other cations (Ca^{++}, Mg^{++}) that coprecipitate with the hydrous oxides.

7. Boiling removes any large excess of ammonia; see Note 5. After blowing away the steam from above the solution, the vapors should smell faintly of ammonia. Boiling also aids in coagulating the precipitate. Prolonged boiling, however, tends to give a slimy precipitate that is difficult to filter and wash. A little filter paper pulp is advantageous as a gathering agent.

8. The mixture should not stand more than 10 minutes before filtration, otherwise the alkaline solution may absorb enough carbon dioxide from the air to precipitate some of the calcium as carbonate.

9. Hydrous oxide precipitates are very readily peptized if washed with water. An electrolyte in the wash solution prevents peptization.

10. The first precipitate is usually quite impure because of coprecipitation of calcium and magnesium; reprecipitation is required.

11. The filtrate should be acidified to prevent absorption of carbon dioxide, which would precipitate calcium as carbonate. (If no subsequent analyses are to be made on the sample, the filtrate and washings are discarded.)

12. Good access of air is necessary to prevent reduction of Fe_2O_3 to Fe_3O_4 or FeO.

13. When a more complete analysis is desired, the R_2O_3 precipitate can be used for the determination of the individual components. If the amount of combined oxides is small, as is usually the case in limestone analysis, colorimetric or spectrophotometric methods are generally used for iron, manganese, titanium, and phosphorus, and aluminum is calculated by difference.

EXPERIMENT 35-7 DETERMINATION OF CALCIUM

Reference: Chap. 19, IV.

Evaporate the acidified filtrate from the combined oxides separation (Note 1) to about 200 ml. Add 5 ml concentrated hydrochloric acid (Note 2). To the hot solution add 50 ml of 4% ammonium oxalate solution (Notes 3, 4, 5), and a few drops of methyl red indicator. Keep the solution near the boiling point, and add, from a buret, 1 : 4 ammonium hydroxide (Note 6), rapidly at first until precipitation just begins, then dropwise over a period of 10 to 20 minutes until the indicator changes from pink to faint yellow. Let the precipitate settle and test for complete precipitation by adding more ammonium oxalate. When precipitation is complete, let the mixture stand for one hour; longer standing is to be avoided because of postprecipitation of magnesium oxalate. Filter by decantation and wash by decantation three or four times with cold 1% ammonium oxalate solution; leave as much of the precipitate as possible in the beaker (Note 7). To the filtrate and washings, containing most of the magnesium, add

50 ml concentrated nitric acid, and start the evaporation of the solution in preparation for the magnesium determination.

Place the beaker containing the main precipitate under the funnel. Heat about 25 ml of 1 : 4 hydrochloric acid to boiling and drip it around the top of the filter paper to dissolve the calcium oxalate on the filter. Wash the paper several times with hot 1% hydrochloric acid, and collect the washings with the main solution. If the precipitate in the beaker has not dissolved completely in the acid solution, warm the mixture, and if necessary add a few drops of concentrated hydrochloric acid. Dilute the solution to about 250 ml, add 5 ml of 4% ammonium oxalate solution, heat to boiling, and neutralize as before. Let stand for one hour then filter by decantation through a new filter. Wash three or four times by decantation with 10-ml portions of cold 1% ammonium oxalate solution, then add the filtrate and washings to the solution reserved for magnesium determination. Rinse the beaker twice with small portions of water after making the transfer of the solution. Transfer the calcium oxalate precipitate quantitatively to the filter paper, and wash the precipitate on the paper repeatedly with small portions of cold water (Note 8) until the last washing is free from oxalate ion (Notes 9, 10).

Remove the filter paper containing the precipitate, unfold it, and stick the damp paper on the inside wall of a 400-ml beaker, With a jet of water from the wash bottle, rinse the precipitate from the paper into the beaker. In a separate beaker prepare dilute sulfuric acid by pouring 20 ml of the concentrated acid into 200 ml of water (Note 11). Use about one-third of this dilute acid for each sample. Drip the *hot* dilute sulfuric acid down a stirring rod onto the filter paper to dissolve the remaining calcium oxalate from the filter. Wash the paper twice with distilled water, and then discard the paper (Note 12). Dilute the solution to about 200 ml and heat it nearly to boiling.

Meanwhile, rinse and fill a buret with standard potassium permanganate solution (Notes 13, 14). Record the initial buret reading to 0.01 ml, then titrate the hot oxalate solution with the permanganate. The reaction has an induction period, hence the first permanganate added may require several seconds for decolorization. Continue the slow addition of permanganate, finally approaching the end point dropwise, until the last added drop produces a faint pink tinge that lasts for 15 to 30 seconds. If during the titration the temperature of the solution falls below 60°C, heat again and continue the titration of the hot solution. When the end point is reached, record the final buret reading to 0.01 ml. Refill the buret, and titrate the additional samples in the same way (Note 15). Calculate and report the percent of calcium oxide, CaO, in the sample (Note 16).

Notes

1. If separate calcium samples containing no silica nor heavy metal ions are to be analyzed, weigh triplicate 0.5 g samples of the unknown into 600-ml

beakers. Add 25 ml water, cover the beaker with a watch glass, and carefully add 5 ml concentrated hydrochloric acid, a little at a time, by moving the watch glass slightly to one side and pouring the acid down the side of the beaker. Take care that no material is lost as spray from rapid effervescence. When vigorous action has subsided, warm the mixture if necessary to effect complete dissolution. Rinse down the cover glass and the sides of the beaker, and finally dilute to 200 to 250 ml. Continue as directed in the above procedure, starting with addition of ammonium oxalate to the hot solution.

2. The calcium oxalate precipitate must be filtered after a digestion period of one hour. The precipitation should therefore be started near the beginning of a laboratory period to allow sufficient time to complete the filtration.

3. If 4% ammonium oxalate solution is not supplied as a side-shelf reagent, add to each sample a solution made by dissolving 2 g of ammonium oxalate in 25 ml of distilled water.

4. The ammonium oxalate solution must be perfectly clear; filter the solution if necessary.

5. If the amount of calcium is large, some calcium oxalate may precipitate at this point, if so, add concentrated hydrochloric acid just to dissolve the precipitate.

6. As an alternative procedure, ammonia may be generated homogeneously in the solution to effect slow precipitation of the calcium oxalate. To the hot solution add 10 to 12 g of urea, and boil the solution gently until the indicator changes to its faint yellow color. One-half to one hour may be required. If by the end of one hour the indicator has not changed color, add 5 g more urea, and continue to boil the solution. Let the precipitate settle, and test for complete precipitation by adding more ammonium oxalate reagent. Digest the precipitate, etc., as in the regular procedure above.

7. If magnesium is known to be absent, or to be present only in small amount, reprecipitation of calcium oxalate is not necessary. Bring the precipitate onto the filter, and complete the analysis as described after the second precipitation.

8. When the determination is to be finished titrimetrically, as in this experiment, the final washing must be with water; if any ammonium oxalate were left on the precipitate, it would cause a positive error in the results. For a gravimetric finish all the washing is done with dilute ammonium oxalate, which is volatilized during ignition of the precipitate. See p. 235 for various methods of completing the determination gravimetrically.

9. Test with a few drops of calcium chloride solution.

10. If necessary, the analysis may be interrupted here; if the analysis is continued to the dissolution of the calcium oxalate precipitate, the solution must not be allowed to stand overnight before titration.

11. Concentrated sulfuric acid must always be poured into the water—never the reverse.

12. If a large amount of calcium is present, some insoluble calcium sulfate may form; it does not interfere with the subsequent titration.

13. See pp. 556–559 for method of filling and reading a buret, and the technique of making a titration.

14. For use in the determination of calcium in limestone, in which calcium content is high, the potassium permanganate should be about 0.4 N. A proportionally smaller normality should be used for samples of lower calcium content. If a standardized potassium permanganate solution is furnished, be sure to record its normality.

15. From the volume of permanganate solution used to titrate the first sample, the approximate volumes for the other samples can be estimated and the first part of the titrations of those samples made more rapidly. However, the end point should be approached slowly to avoid overstepping it.

16. Dissolution of calcium oxalate in strong acid gives bioxalate ion:

$$CaC_2O_4 + H^+ \rightarrow Ca^{++} + HC_2O_4^-$$

which is oxidized by the permanganate:

$$HC_2O_4^- \rightarrow 2CO_2 + H^+ + 2e$$

The gme of calcium oxide is therefore $CaO/2000 = 56.08/2000 = 0.02804$, and

$$\text{ml } KMnO_4 \times \text{normality of } KMnO_4 \times 0.02804 = \text{g } CaO$$

The metal content of samples containing their salts of oxy-anions (e.g., $CaCO_3$ in limestone) is often reported as the metal oxide.

EXPERIMENT 35-8 DETERMINATION OF MAGNESIUM

Reference: Chap. 19, V.

Evaporate the solution from the calcium separation (Note 1), to which 50 ml concentrated nitric acid (Note 2) have been added, to dryness. During evaporation, the beaker should be covered with a watch glass raised on glass hooks. The last part of the evaporation must be done carefully to avoid loss by spattering; a steam bath is convenient, and rapid evaporation without active boiling is preferred. If a large residue of salts remains, add 20 ml water, 10 ml concentrated hydrochloric acid, and 30 ml concentrated nitric acid; stir well, and again evaporate to dryness at as high a temperature as possible without spattering. To the dry residue add 2 ml concentrated hydrochloric acid and 40 to 50 ml water, warming to dissolve all soluble salts. A slight amount of insoluble matter is probably silica from the action of the alkaline solutions, previously used, on the glass. If the solution is not perfectly clear, filter through paper, receiving the filtrate in a 400-ml beaker (Note 3). Wash the precipitate several times with water, and combine the washings with the main filtrate.

To the solution add 5 ml concentrated hydrochloric acid and dilute to not more than 150 ml. Add 20 to 25 ml of clear 20% diammonium hydrogen phosphate solution, cool the mixture to room temperature or preferably in an ice bath (Note 4), add a few drops of methyl red indicator, then add clear ammonium hydroxide very slowly and with good stirring until the indicator just changes to yellow. Stir vigorously for a few minutes, but avoid scratching the beaker with the stirring rod (Note 3). Then add an excess of 5 ml concentrated ammonium hydroxide, and stir again. Let the mixture stand for four hours in the cold or overnight at room temperature (Note 5).

Filter the cold solution by decantation through ashless filter paper, and wash the precipitate in the beaker three times by decantation with small portions of 1 : 20 ammonium hydroxide. Bring as little as possible of the precipitate onto the filter (Note 6). Replace the filtrate beaker with the one in which precipitation was originally made and which still contains most of the precipitate. Heat to boiling 10 ml of 1 : 1 hydrochloric acid, and drip it around the top edge of the filter paper to dissolve the precipitate on the paper. Collect the filtrate in the beaker with the main precipitate. Wash the paper several times with *small* portions of hot 1 : 4 hydrochloric acid. Receive the washings with the acid filtrate. If necessary, warm to completely dissolve the precipitate in the acid. Add 1 ml of diammonium hydrogen phosphate solution, then reprecipitate the magnesium ammonium phosphate as before, by addition of ammonium hydroxide. After standing for four hours or longer, filter the cold solution by decantation through ashless paper, and wash twice by decantation with 1 : 20 ammonium hydroxide. Transfer the precipitate to the filter, and continue washing until the last wash is free, or nearly so, from chloride ion (Note 7). Transfer the paper and precipitate to a previously ignited and weighed porcelain crucible. Dry, smoke off, and char the paper at the lowest possible temperature (Note 8). Incline the crucible in the triangle, gradually increase the temperature, and finally heat to the full temperature of the Meker air-blast burner for 20 to 30 minutes. Cool and weigh. Repeat the ignition to constant weight of the magnesium pyrophosphate, $Mg_2P_2O_7$ (Note 9). Calculate and report the percent MgO in the sample.

Notes

1. For the analysis of separate magnesium samples, weigh accurately triplicate portions of 1 to 1.5 g. See Note 3. Add 100 to 150 ml distilled water and 5 ml concentrated hydrochloric acid, and warm if necessary to effect solution. Continue the analysis as directed above, starting with the addition of diammonium hydrogen phosphate.

2. Oxalate and ammonium ions, which interfere with the separation of magnesium, are destroyed by oxidation with nitric acid:

$$HC_2O_4^- + 2NO_3^- + 3H^+ \rightarrow 2CO_2 + 2NO_2 + 2H_2O$$

$$NH_4^+ + NO_3^- \rightarrow N_2O + 2H_2O$$

3. The beaker in which the magnesium is to be precipitated should be free from scratches on the inside surface. The magnesium ammonium phosphate

precipitate adheres tenaciously to scratched places on the glass and is very difficult to scrub loose.

4. Magnesium ammonium phosphate is one of the most soluble compounds commonly used as a precipitation form. Although the solubility is decreased by the presence of excess phosphate and ammonia, the volume of the solution and of wash liquids should be kept small and the solution should be cool to decrease solubility losses.

5. The magnesium ammonium phosphate readily forms supersaturated solutions, and even when some solid phase is present, attainment of solubility equilibrium is slow. Sufficient time must be allowed for complete precipitation before filtering.

6. The first precipitate is likely to be considerably contaminated by coprecipitated ammonium salts and/or by phosphates. These errors are largely eliminated by reprecipitation.

7. Test with silver nitrate and nitric acid.

8. In this determination it is especially important to *dry* the paper before it chars, otherwise the carbon may be very difficult to remove by ignition.

9. The correct ignition temperature, 1000–1100°C, may be difficult to attain with a burner, with the result that the residue comes to constant weight very slowly. An electric muffle furnace is much more satisfactory for ignition of the precipitate.

EXPERIMENT **35-9   DETERMINATION OF CARBON DIOXIDE IN A CARBONATE: ALKALIMETER METHOD**

Reference: Chap. 16, p. 209.

The apparatus to be used is the Schroedter alkalimeter, shown in Fig. 16-4 (Note 1). Make a sample tube by closing one end of a 10-cm length of 5-mm glass tubing; lightly fire polish the open end of the tube. Nearly fill the sample tube with the carbonate sample (Note 2), and weigh the tube and contents. Introduce the sample without loss through the side tube of the reaction chamber of the alkalimeter. Weigh the empty sample tube, to obtain the sample weight by difference.

Use a stream of water from the wash bottle to moisten the sample in the decomposition chamber. Nearly fill the dropper bulb of the alkalimeter with 2 N perchloric acid. Put concentrated sulfuric acid into the moisture trap to make it about one-third full. Insert the glass stoppers and exit tube, and close the exit tube of the trap with a short rubber tube and glass plug. Weigh the entire apparatus (Note 3).

Remove the stopper of the dropper bulb and the rubber tube and plug from the exit tube of the moisture trap. Carefully clamp the alkalimeter to a ring stand. Decompose the carbonate sample by slowly admitting a little perchloric acid into the reaction bulb; close the stopcock of the acid reservoir after each addition of acid. As the reaction subsides, admit more acid slowly; avoid a too rapid evolution of gas. The decomposition should take 15 to 20 minutes. When evolution of carbon dioxide has almost completely subsided (all of the perchloric acid having been added by this time), connect the exit tube of the moisture trap to an aspirator pump or vacuum line, using a trap between the pump or line and the alkalimeter. Also connect the top of the dropper bulb to a soda-lime tube (Note 4). Draw a slow current of air through the apparatus, while heating the reaction bulb *very gently* with a *small* flame; *do not boil*. The increased temperature will probably cause evolution of an additional quantity of carbon dioxide. Continue the gentle heating until there is no more effervescence, then allow the apparatus to cool to room temperature while air is still drawn through. Finally, stopper the acid reservoir and plug the exit tube as before, and weigh the entire apparatus again. Calculate and report the percent of carbon dioxide in the sample.

Notes

1. Obtain the alkalimeter from the laboratory instructor or from the storeroom; without fail, return it at the end of the laboratory period.

2. The method is applicable to any carbonate.

3. If the weighing is made on an equal-arm balance, a flask of about the same weight as the alkalimeter may be used as a tare or counterpoise.

4. Soda-lime removes carbon dioxide that may have accumulated in the air around the flask during the heating operation.

USE OF ORGANIC PRECIPITANTS

Reference: Chap. 10, pp. 145–150.

The use of organic precipitants for effecting analytical separations of inorganic ions is discussed briefly in the reference given above. Many of the precipitates are suitable weighing forms, after drying at oven temperatures. Two such determinations are given below.

EXPERIMENT 35-10 DETERMINATION OF MAGNESIUM WITH 8-QUINOLINOL

Weigh triplicate 0.5-g samples of the dried magnesium unknown (Notes 1, 2) into 400-ml beakers. Add 25 ml water and 5 ml concentrated hydrochloric acid, and warm if necessary to effect complete dissolution (Note 3). Dilute to about 100 ml, add 2 g of ammonium chloride (Note 4) and 0.5 ml (10 drops) of *o*-cresolphthalein indicator (Note 5). Add 1 : 1 ammonium hydroxide until the indicator changes to its violet color, then 5 ml in excess. Heat the solution to 60–80°C, and add 5% solution of 8-quinolinol reagent (Note 6) slowly from a buret (Note 7) and with good stirring, until the solution shows the yellow color of excess reagent; then add a 10% excess of reagent. Digest the precipitate for 20 to 30 minutes on a steam bath. Filter the hot solution through a previously weighed sintered glass filter crucible, and wash the precipitate with 50 ml of warm 1 : 50 ammonia, used in small portions (Note 8). Dry the precipitate in a 150–160°C oven to constant weight as $Mg(C_9H_6ON)_2$ (Note 9). Calculate and report percent MgO in the sample.

Notes

1. Student samples for this analysis usually contain magnesium sulfate. The directions given are for samples containing 5 to 10% MgO. The solution for precipitation should contain not more than 0.1 g of MgO per 100 ml.

2. Application of 8-quinolinol to the precipitation of magnesium requires the absence of the common cations except the alkalies. In the systematic analysis of limestone the interfering ions have been removed, and the filtrate from the separation of calcium, after evaporation with nitric acid, can be used for the determination of magnesium with 8-quinolinol.

3. If some undissolved residue (probably silica) remains, filter it off and wash it well with 1 : 100 hydrochloric acid, and combine the washings with the main filtrate.

4. Ammonium chloride suppresses the ionization of ammonium hydroxide, and thus prevents the precipitation of magnesium hydroxide.

5. Indicator solution: 0.02% in alcohol; pH range, 8.2 to 9.8, colorless to red-violet.

6. Reagent: 5 g of finely powdered 8-quinolinol, 12 ml glacial acetic acid, and about 75 ml distilled water. Heat to 60°C until dissolution is complete, filter, and dilute the filtrate to 100 ml. Store the solution in an amber bottle. The solution is not stable indefinitely, but will keep for several weeks.

7. Accurate measurement of the amount of reagent is not necessary. The approximate volume should be known, however, so that the appropriate amount of excess reagent can be added, and so the precipitation mixture can be maintained at the proper alkalinity. The reagent is approximately 2 M in acetic acid; if the amount of acid added in the reagent approaches the amount of excess ammonia in the solution before adding the reagent, more ammonia must be added to keep the solution alkaline.

8. Washing should be continued until there is no trace of the yellow color of the reagent in the washings.

9. The precipitate obtained is $Mg(C_9H_6ON)_2 \cdot 2H_2O$, which can be used as a weighing form by drying at 105–110°C. It is sometimes difficult to wash out the excess reagent, and some may be occluded. By drying at 150–160°C, the excess reagent is volatilized and the dihydrate is converted to the anhydrous salt for weighing.

EXPERIMENT **35-11** DETERMINATION OF NICKEL
WITH DIMETHYLGLYOXIME

The determination of nickel in ores and in steels differs mainly in the preparation of the solution for analysis. The following directions are for the determination of nickel in steel containing no cobalt.

Weigh triplicate samples (Note 1) of the steel, as received, into 400-ml beakers. Dissolve the sample in 30 ml concentrated hydrochloric acid (Note 2). When vigorous reaction has subsided add 1 : 2 nitric acid, a few drops at a time, until 10 ml have been added (Note 3). Evaporate the solution to moist solids, then add 30 ml concentrated hydrochloric acid and evaporate to about 15 ml (Note 4). Dilute with 50 ml water, and if any residue is present, filter immediately and wash the precipitate with 1 : 1 hydrochloric acid and then with water (Note 5). Dilute the solution to about 150 ml, and add 50 ml of 20% tartaric acid solution (Note 6). Heat the solution nearly to boiling and add 1 : 1 ammonium hydroxide slowly until the solution is alkaline (Note 7). If, during the addition of ammonia, any precipitate of ferric hydroxide appears, dissolve it by adding hydrochloric acid, add more tartaric acid solution, and again neutralize with ammonia (Note 8).

Make the solution slightly acidic with hydrochloric acid, heat to about 60°C, and slowly add 15 ml (Note 9) of 1% dimethylglyoxime reagent (Note 10). Add 1 : 1 ammonium hydroxide slowly, with good stirring, until the solution is ammoniacal. Digest the precipitate on the steam bath for an hour; cool to room temperature, and let stand for an hour (Note 11). Filter through a previously weighed sintered glass filter crucible (Note 12). Make sure the solution is alkaline, and test the filtrate for complete precipitation by adding a little more dimethylglyoxime. Wash the precipitate with cold water until the washings are free from chloride ion (Note 13). Dry the precipitate to constant weight in an oven at 110–120°C, and weigh as nickel dimethylglyoximate, $Ni(C_4H_7O_2N_2)_2$. Calculate and report the percent nickel in the sample (Note 14).

Notes

1. The weight of sample to be used is dependent upon its nickel content: for nickel in the range 0.1 to 1%, use a 2-g sample; for 1 to 3%, use 1-g sample; for 3 to 8%, use 0.5-g sample; for over 8%, use 0.25-g sample.

2. If reaction becomes so vigorous that loss of sample by frothing is imminent, moderate the reaction by adding cold water.

3. Iron(II) precipitates with nickel dimethylglyoxime; nitric acid oxidizes iron(II) to iron(III), which is then held in solution by complexing it with tartrate.

4. Evaporation with hydrochloric acid destroys excess nitric acid, which might oxidize the dimethylglyoxime reagent to be added.

5. The residue consists of silica and/or tungstic acid. If the residue is small, discard it after washing. If the residue is large, it should be treated with hydrofluoric acid and sulfuric acid to volatilize the silica, then fused with potassium pyrosulfate for recovery of any nickel. The melt is dissolved in water and added to the main solution.

6. Tartaric acid (tartrate ion) forms a stable complex with iron(III), from which the hydrous oxide does not precipitate when ammonia is added. Citric acid or ammonium citrate may be used for the same purpose.

7. During addition of ammonium hydroxide, the solution will go through a series of color changes: light green, dark orange, brown, yellow, and finally green again when the solution is alkaline. The final solution should smell distinctly of ammonia after blowing away the vapors from above the solution.

8. Any white or gray precipitate is probably silica, and should be removed by filtration.

9. Five ml of 1% dimethylglyoxime should be added for each 10 mg of nickel present, plus an excess of 10 ml of reagent.

10. The reagent is a 1% solution of dimethylglyoxime in 95% ethyl alcohol; the reagent is stable.

11. Longer standing does no harm, and is in fact advantageous if the amount of nickel is very small. This is a convenient place to interrupt the analysis if necessary.

12. The precipitate has a great tendency to creep in the liquid film. During filtration and washing, do not fill the crucible with liquid—keep the upper 1 cm of the filter crucible dry if possible.

13. The precipitate should be the characteristic bright red color; if not, dissolve it in a hot solution of 20 ml of 1 : 1 hydrochloric acid and 5 ml of nitric acid, wash the filter well, dilute the solution to 300 ml, add 10 ml tartaric acid solution, and reprecipitate by adding dimethylglyoxime and ammonia as before.

14. The crucible is cleaned, after use, by dissolving the precipitate in concentrated hydrochloric acid or nitric acid, followed by thorough washing with water.

36

TITRIMETRIC DETERMINATIONS: NEUTRALIZATION METHODS

References: Chaps. 20, 21, 22, 23.

In this and the next two chapters detailed directions are given for determinations illustrating the main classes of titrimetric methods. The determinations selected are analyses that might be met in practice, but the prime objective is instruction in the titrimetric method, the chemistry of the determinations, and calculations from laboratory data. In many of the methods, directions are given for the preparation of two standard solutions (acid and alkali; reductant and oxidant; etc.), each of which can be used for analysis of unknowns. If certain of the determinations are not to be performed in a given course of instruction, it may not be necessary to prepare both of the standard solutions. The bulletin board schedule and/or the laboratory instructor should be consulted for specific assignments of required determinations. Before starting titrimetric methods, the student should read carefully the references given.

EXPERIMENT 36-1 CALIBRATION OF BURETS

Reference: Chap. 20, p. 259.

Before starting the calibration, make sure that the buret to be calibrated is clean by testing it for drainage, and that the stopcock operates smoothly and does not leak. Then fill the buret with distilled water that has come to room temperature. Measure the temperature with a thermometer suspended near the buret. Either of two methods of calibration may be used.

Method 1: Use of a Calibrating Pipet. This method is recommended if a calibrating pipet is available; see p. 259.

Method 2: By Weight of Water Delivered. Weigh a clean 50-ml flask with stopper; a 50-ml volumetric flask is convenient. The flask need not be dry on the inside. All weighings in this calibration are to be made only to the nearest 10 mg. Weigh the empty flask. Adjust the bottom of the meniscus in the buret to a position at or slightly below the zero mark; record the buret reading to 0.01 ml. Then run water from the buret into the weighed flask until the meniscus in the buret is about at the 10.0 ml mark. It is not necessary to adjust exactly to the mark, but the liquid level must be read accurately (to 0.01 ml) and recorded. Weigh the stoppered flask and contents.

Without emptying the flask, run water from the buret into the flask until the meniscus in the buret is about at the 20-ml mark. Record the accurate buret reading, and the weight of the flask and contents. Continue in this manner, covering 10-ml intervals of the buret. For the last interval, be careful not to run past the 50-ml mark. The temperature should be noted when each 10-ml portion of water is removed, so that any significant changes in temperature during calibration can be taken into account in the calculations. Be sure to record any identifying number marked on the buret. If necessary, place an identification on the buret with a glass-marking stylus, or with a gummed label. Calibrate the second buret in the same way as described above.

The data and calculations should be summarized as indicated in Table 36-1.

Table 36-1 Calibration of Buret No. 435. Temperature, 30°C

Inter-val	Read-ing, ml	Diff. in Rdgs.	Weight, g	Diff. in Wts.	Volume Delivd., ml	Corrn., ml	Total Corrn., ml
40–50							
30–40							
20–30	etc.	etc.					
10–20	20.04	9.97	51.18	9.95	10.00	+0.03	+0.04
0–10	10.07	10.02	41.23	9.98	10.03	+0.01	+0.01
Initial	0.05		31.25				

It is convenient to make the tabulation in inverse order, to facilitate the necessary subtractions.

From the weight of water delivered for each interval, the volume delivered is computed by multiplying the weight in grams by the volume occupied by one gram of water at the calibration temperature. Table 36-2 shows, for various temperatures, the apparent specific volume of water, that is, the volume of one gram of water weighed in air with brass weights.

From the buret readings and the true volume of water delivered, compute the correction for each interval and the total corrections, as illustrated in Table 36-1; be sure to designate the sign of the correction. On graph paper, plot the nominal buret readings on the vertical scale (starting with 0 at the top) against total corrections on the horizontal scale (+ corrections to the right, − corrections to the left); draw a smooth curve (*not* a series of straight lines) through the plotted points. Calibration curves for both burets should be drawn on the same graph paper, preferably on the same coordinates. From the graph, read the total correction, to the nearest 0.01 ml, for each 2-ml interval, and tabulate these corrections neatly. Turn in the graph and tabulated corrections to the laboratory instructor. A duplicate graph and correction table for use by the student should be made a part of the notebook record, placed in a convenient location for ready reference.

Table 36-2 Apparent Specific Volume of Water

Temp.	Volume	Temp.	Volume	Temp.	Volume	Temp.	Volume
20	1.0028	24	1.0036	28	1.0046	32	1.0057
21	1.0030	25	1.0038	29	1.0048	33	1.0060
22	1.0032	26	1.0041	30	1.0051	34	1.0063
23	1.0034	27	1.0043	31	1.0054	35	1.0066

In titrimetric determinations, total corrections are used by simply adding them *algebraically* to the observed buret readings. The difference between the final corrected reading and an initial corrected reading is the true volume delivered from the buret. For elementary titrimetric analysis, use of burets at temperatures a few degrees above or below the calibration temperature introduces no significant error.

Details of calibration of pipets and volumetric flasks are given in Chap. 20.

EXPERIMENT **36-2 COMPARISON OF ACID AND ALKALI**[1]

References: for Exp. 36-2 to 36-7: Chaps. 23, 24.

Preparation of Solutions (Note 1)

Hydrochloric Acid. In a clean graduate, measure 9 ml of concentrated hydrochloric acid and transfer it to a clean 1-liter glass-stoppered bottle. Add distilled water up to the shoulder (*not* to the neck) of the bottle, stopper it, and *mix thoroughly* by repeatedly inverting and shaking. Assuming the concentrated hydrochloric acid to have a density of 1.18 g/ml and to contain 36% HCl by weight, what is the approximate normality of the dilute solution?

[1] If the equipment is available and the instructor so desires, any of the neutralization titrations can be performed with potentiometric detection of the end point. See Exp. 40-1 for apparatus and general method.

Sodium Hydroxide. On the laboratory platform balance weigh 4 to 5 g of sodium hydroxide pellets; the solid must *not* be weighed directly on the balance platform or pan—weigh it in a tared watch glass or small beaker. Any solid accidentally spilled must be taken up *immediately* and discarded. Make sure the side-shelf bottle of sodium hydroxide is tightly stoppered after use. Transfer the sodium hydroxide to a clean 400-ml beaker, add about 150 ml distilled water, and immediately stir well until the solid is completely dissolved (Note 2). Add about 150 ml more water, and transfer the solution to a clean 1-liter bottle. Rinse from beaker to bottle, add distilled water to fill the bottle to the shoulder, and close the bottle with a clean rubber stopper (Note 3). Mix the solution thoroughly by repeatedly inverting and shaking. What is the approximate normality of the solution?

Label the bottles for contents, date, your name, and leave space for writing in the normality when it has been determined accurately (Exp. 36-3).

Comparison of Solutions

By using the technique described on p. 566, rinse and fill one buret with the hydrochloric acid solution, and the other buret with the sodium hydroxide solution. Draw off liquid until the level is at or slightly below the zero mark (Note 4). Read the liquid level (bottom of meniscus) in each buret, estimating to the nearest 0.01 ml, and record the readings in the record book as "Initial Reading" of the respective burets. From the alkali buret run into a 250-ml Erlenmeyer flask about 35 ml of the sodium hydroxide solution. To the solution in the flask add about 40 ml of distilled water (which need not be measured accurately) and two drops of methyl purple indicator (Note 5). Place the flask under the acid buret, and run out hydrochloric acid solution slowly while the flask is rotated to mix the contents by gentle swirling. As the end point is approached (indicated by a localized change of color of the indicator), add the solution more slowly and finally dropwise until the solution changes color from green through neutral gray to the first permanent violet color. Rinse down the sides of the flask with a small stream of water from the wash bottle. Boil the solution for one minute (Note 6); cool to room temperature by running tap water over the outside of the flask. The solution may have changed back to the alkaline (green) color of the indicator. In that event, finish the titration by careful addition of more hydrochloric acid, taking half drops from the tip of the buret, until the first faint but permanent violet tinge appears in the solution. Just before the end point, rinse down the sides of the flask. If, through carelessness, the end point has been passed, run in a few drops of sodium hydroxide solution from the alkali buret, and adjust the end point more carefully, making sure that a one-drop end point is attained.

When the correct end point has been reached, read both burets to 0.01 ml, recording the values as "Final Reading" of the respective burets. The final reading should be recorded on the line above the initial reading, to facilitate subtraction to obtain the volume of solution used (Note 7). Calculate, to the proper number of significant figures, the acid/base ratio by dividing the milliliters of acid by the milliliters of base.

Refill the burets with their respective stock solutions, and carry out a second and a third comparison, *using somewhat different volumes* of the sodium hydroxide solution (Note 8). Calculate the acid/base ratio as before. The separate values of this ratio should agree with three or four parts per thousand (3 or 4‰); if they do not agree to this precision, titrate additional portions until the specified agreement is attained (Note 9). The average deviation of triplicates should not exceed 2‰. From the average value of the acid/base ratio compute its reciprocal, the base/acid ratio. Report the results on the appropriate report form.

Notes

1. If the course of instruction being followed uses only one standard solution, prepare that solution and proceed directly to its standardization, Exp. 36-3.

2. Sodium hydroxide tends to form a hard cake of solid if stirring is delayed or is insufficient.

3. Alkaline solutions tend to "freeze" glass stoppers.

4. No attempt should be made to adjust the meniscus exactly to the 0.00 mark.

5. Other indicators, the color change of which occurs in the pH range approximately 4 to 10, may be used in this titration, and the direction of titration may be reversed. When phenolphthalein is used as the indicator, it is customary to titrate the acid by the alkali, stopping at the first permanent pink color.

6. Boiling removes carbon dioxide from any carbonate in the alkaline solution.

7. If buret corrections are to be used, apply the corrections to the final and the initial readings before performing the subtraction to give the volume of solution delivered.

8. A common student tendency is to repeat the titration with identical volumes of solution; this practice defeats part of the purpose of performing multiplicate operations to establish a reliable value for use in subsequent calculations. Prejudiced (if not dishonest) end points often result from the use of identical volumes of sample solution titrated. Furthermore, there is no point in taking *exactly* 35.00 or *exactly* 40.00 ml of one solution; adjusting to exact values merely wastes time in performance of the work. If the first end point is overstepped and has to be readjusted, the original "whole-number" volume no longer prevails. The instructor will take a dim view of records and reports in which many initial readings are 0.00 and many volumes taken are "round numbers" such as 35.00 and 40.00. Perfect precision in triplicate samples can occur only *very* infrequently; some deviation is to be expected, if the measuring devices are sufficiently accurate.

9. The calculations should be done immediately, to learn if the required

precision has been reached. Additional samples can be titrated with a minimum of time while the burets are set up ready for use.

EXPERIMENT 36-3 STANDARDIZATION OF ACID AND ALKALI

The normality of both the acid and the alkali solutions can be determined by standardizing either solution against a primary standard, then calculating the normality of the other solution from the volume ratio of the two solutions determined in Exp. 36-2. The hydrochloric acid solution is to be used for the analysis of soda ash (impure sodium carbonate). A slight advantage results from standardization of the hydrochloric acid against pure sodium carbonate, because certain methodic errors (e.g., indicator error) cancel out. On the other hand, potassium acid phthalate, having a much higher equivalent weight than sodium carbonate, requires use of a larger sample, on which a given error in weighing is a smaller percentage error. Standardize by the method assigned on the laboratory schedule.

Standardization of Hydrochloric Acid

Into numbered 250-ml Erlenmeyer flasks weigh accurately, by difference from a weighing bottle, triplicate 0.2-g samples of primary standard sodium carbonate. Rinse and fill a buret with the hydrochloric acid solution. Dissolve the first sample of standard in about 75 ml distilled water. Add two drops of methyl purple indicator. Record the initial reading of the buret, then titrate the solution of sodium carbonate with the hydrochloric acid, following exactly the procedure given in Exp. 36-2 for comparison of solutions, including heating and cooling of the solution followed by careful adjustment of the end point (Note 1). Record the final buret reading. Dissolve and titrate the second and the third sample in the same way.

Calculate (Note 2) the normality of the acid solution. The average deviation of triplicates should not exceed 2‰. If the results do not agree to this precision, additional samples must be titrated. From the average normality of the acid and by the use of the acid/base ratio previously determined, compute the normality of the sodium hydroxide solution. (Alternatively, the sodium hydroxide solution may be standardized directly; see below.) Report the results on the form provided for this purpose. Write the normality of the solution on the label on the bottle.

Standardization of Sodium Hydroxide

Into numbered 250-ml Erlenmeyer flasks weigh accurately, by difference from a weighing bottle, triplicate 0.8-g samples of primary standard potassium acid phthalate, $KHC_8H_4O_4$. To each sample add about 75 ml distilled water (Note

3) and two drops of phenolphthalein indicator solution. Rinse and fill a buret with the sodium hydroxide solution, and read and record the initial buret reading. To the first sample add the sodium hydroxide solution to the first detectable pink tinge. Again read the buret and record the final reading. Titrate the second and third samples in the same way.

Calculate (Note 2) the normality of the sodium hydroxide solution. The average deviation of triplicate samples should not exceed 2‰. From the average normality of the sodium hydroxide and by the use of the base/acid ratio, calculate the normality of the hydrochloric acid solution. (Alternatively, the hydrochloric acid may be standardized directly, as described above.) Report the results on the form provided for this purpose. Write the normality of the solution on the bottle label.

Notes

1. If the end point is passed, back titration with the "opposite" solution is possible. However, time is saved both in procedure and in calculations by titrating directly to an exact end point.

2. Apply the purity factor or assay value of the primary standard to obtain the true weight of the primary standard in the sample taken.

3. If necessary, warm to hasten dissolution of the potassium acid phthalate.

EXPERIMENT 36-4 DETERMINATION OF ACIDITY OF VINEGAR

One laboratory period before the sample is needed, hand in to the laboratory instructor a small, dry, stoppered flask (a 50-ml volumetric flask is convenient) labeled with your name and laboratory section number. When the sample is obtained, do *not* dilute it, but use it as received.

Rinse a 5-ml pipet with small portions of the sample, then transfer exact 5.00-ml portions to three Erlenmeyer flasks. Add about 75 ml distilled water and two drops of phenolphthalein indicator, and titrate with standard sodium hydroxide solution to the first faint but permanent pink color. Assume the density of the sample to be 1.004 g/ml, and calculate and report the percent acetic acid, $HC_2H_3O_2$, in the sample.

EXPERIMENT 36-5 DETERMINATION OF ALKALINITY
OF SODA ASH

Reference: Chap. 24, pp. 318–321.

The term "soda ash" is used to designate commercial sodium carbonate; sodium bicarbonate and inert matter are usually present. The total alkalinity of soda ash is determined by titration with standard acid, using methyl purple indicator (or another indicator that changes color in the pH region 4 to 5). By this method, both bicarbonate and carbonate are titrated to carbonic acid. The analysis is reported as if due entirely to sodium carbonate. (By a double-indicator titration, or other special methods, it is possible to determine separately the amounts of bicarbonate and carbonate present; see Chap. 24.)

Into numbered 250-ml Erlenmeyer flasks weigh accurately, by difference from a weighing bottle, triplicate 0.4 g-samples of the dry unknown soda ash. Dissolve and titrate the samples exactly as described in Exp. 36-3 for standardization of hydrochloric acid against sodium carbonate. Calculate and report percent Na_2CO_3 in the sample.

Note: Save the standard solutions of hydrochloric acid and sodium hydroxide for Exp. 36-7 if it is to be performed; if not, the remainder of the solutions may be discarded *after* the analysis reports for Exp. 36-4 and 36-5 have been graded. A standard solution of a reagent should *never* be discarded until the student is certain that it is no longer needed.

EXPERIMENT **36-6** **DETERMINATION OF CARBON DIOXIDE IN AIR**

Preparation of Solutions

Standard Oxalic Acid Solution. On the rough balance weigh about 1.5 g of oxalic acid crystals. With a mortar and pestle grind the crystals to a fine powder, then expose the solid, in a thin layer on a large watch glass, to the air for several hours to allow it to come to the stable dihydrate composition, $H_2C_2O_4 \cdot 2H_2O$ (Note 1). Weigh out exactly 1.305 g of the oxalic acid dihydrate, dissolve it in recently boiled distilled water (Note 2), and make up to 500 ml in a volumetric flask (Note 3).

Barium Hydroxide. Using recently boiled distilled water and solid $Ba(OH)_2 \cdot 8H_2O$, prepare about 500 ml of barium hydroxide solution that is approximately equivalent to the oxalic acid solution prepared above.

The volume ratio of the solutions must be established by a comparison titration on the same day that the analyses are performed; this is best done during the carbon dioxide determination, as given below.

Collection of Samples

Triplicate samples of outdoor and of indoor air are to be analyzed. Obtain three 1-liter Erlenmeyer flasks, each fitted with a two-hole rubber stopper and short lengths of fire-polished glass rod for plugging the holes. Determine the volume of each flask as follows: insert the stopper (without the plugs) tightly in the neck of the flask, and mark the flask at the lower side of the stopper;

then fill the flask to the mark with tap water, and measure the volume of water with a graduated cylinder.

To obtain a sample of outdoor air, fill the flask with water, take it to the place where the sample is to be obtained, slowly pour out the water, and immediately insert the plugged stopper. Care should be taken that the flask is not warmed by the hand and that no air exhaled by the analyst enters the flask. To obtain a sample of indoor air, dry the sampling flask, and attach a two-hole rubber stopper one hole of which carries a glass tube extending almost to the bottom of the flask, and which is fitted with a rubber bulb pump. Take the flask to the place where the sample is to be obtained—preferably a laboratory where a number of students are working and a number of burners are in operation. Fill the flask with the laboratory air by pumping it through the flask long enough to displace all air originally present in the flask. Remove the stopper and pump and immediately insert the plugged stopper.

Titration

When the samples have come to room temperature, remove the plugs from the stopper, and deliver into the flask 25.0 ml (by pipet) of the barium hydroxide solution. Plug the stopper and allow the flask to stand for 15 to 20 minutes, with frequent shaking. During this time, determine the volume ratio of the oxalic acid to the barium hydroxide. For this purpose use *dry* 125- or 200-ml Erlenmeyer flasks, which are stoppered after displacing the air with tank nitrogen. From the acid buret, measure into the titration flask almost the required volume of standard oxalic acid (Note 4), then as quickly as possible add 25.0 ml (pipet) of barium hydroxide solution and two drops of phenolphthalein indicator, and titrate with the oxalic acid to the disappearance of the pink color. Repeat to appropriate checks.

By this time the reaction of the carbon dioxide, in the air samples, with the barium hydroxide should be complete. Determine the amount of excess barium hydroxide by titration with the oxalic acid. Remove one of the plugs from the stopper, and through the hole add two drops of phenolphthalein indicator; then insert the buret tip through the same hole and run in acid, at first rapidly and then dropwise toward the end. If necessary, relieve the pressure in the flask by removing the plug momentarily from the second hole of the stopper. Near the end, disconnect the buret, quickly remove the stopper, and rinse down the sides of the flask with distilled water. Again connect the stopper and buret and complete the titration.

Calculations

The calculations are based upon the following data:
(1) Volume of barium hydroxide solution added to sample.

(2) Volume of oxalic acid solution equivalent to the barium hydroxide added.

(3) Volume of oxalic acid to titrate the excess barium hydroxide.

(4) Difference (2) − (3) = volume of oxalic acid equivalent to the carbon dioxide in the sample.

(5) Volume of carbon dioxide equivalent to the oxalic acid in (4). (See Note 3.)

(6) Volume of air sample = volume of flask − volume of barium hydroxide solution added.

Calculate and report the volume of carbon dioxide in 10,000 volumes of air.

Notes

1. If desired, the properly prepared primary standard may be furnished as a side-shelf reagent or obtained from the storeroom.

2. Use of carbon dioxide-free water is mandatory in this determination. Boil the distilled water in a flask, which must then be stoppered promptly; cool to room temperature by running cold tap water around the flask.

3. The concentration of the reagents is such that 1 ml of the oxalic acid solution is approximately equivalent to 0.50 ml of carbon dioxide at most laboratory conditions. The exact value should be calculated from the room temperature and the barometric pressure.

4. The approximate volume ratio of the acid and alkali should be determined by a quick comparison, without taking the usual precautions.

EXPERIMENT **36-7 DETERMINATION OF NITROGEN: SEMIMICRO KJELDAHL METHOD**

In the method outlined below, the Hengar technique is used on a semimicro scale (Note 1) and is applied to the determination of crude protein in wheat flour. It could be used equally well for analysis of a wide variety of nitrogen compounds.

Preparation of Solutions

From the known normalities of the standard hydrochloric acid and sodium hydroxide prepared previously (Exps. 36-2 and 36-3), calculate the volume required to prepare 500 ml of 0.0200 *N* hydrochloric acid and 250 ml of 0.0200 *N* sodium hydroxide. From a buret, measure the required volume of standard hydrochloric acid, delivering it to a 500-ml volumetric flask. Make up to volume and mix thoroughly. In the same way, measure the required volume of standard sodium hydroxide, delivering it to a 250-ml volumetric flask, dilute to volume, and mix thoroughly (Note 2). Test the accuracy of the dilutions by running a volume ratio (comparison titration), using as indicator 10 drops of saturated aqueous solution of methyl red (Note 3).

Digestion of Sample

Analyze triplicate samples of whole wheat flour, and run a blank determination with the same weight of pure sucrose (Note 4). Press a waterproof paper disk into the glass weighing cup, with the plug provided for that purpose. Weigh the cup and disk accurately. Assume that the flour contains a maximum of 2% nitrogen, and calculate the approximate weight of sample to be taken so that about 15 ml of the standard acid will be required for reaction with the ammonia liberated. Weigh the sample into the weighing paper in the cup. Then gather the paper together at the top so the sample will not spill out, and drop it into a *dry* 100-ml Kjeldahl flask. Add 1–1.5 g of "low nitrogen" potassium sulfate (use the spoon provided), and a selenized granule. Measure into the flask 2.5 ml of pure concentrated sulfuric acid (Note 5). Insert the Hengar tube fitted with its paper tape into the neck of the flask and proceed with the digestion, using a flame about $\frac{3}{4}$ inch in height. At first, have the flask supported considerably above the flame, and slide the flask down in the clamp as digestion progresses. The digestion should be conducted with some care until streams of "oily" condensate are seen running back just above the body of the liquid. When the mixture is almost colorless, rotate the flask in the clamp every few minutes so the condensate will run back on all parts of the inside. The digestion is complete when the liquid is colorless and the walls of the flask are perfectly clean. Remove the Hengar tube, which will have acquired a sublimate of red selenium, and clean it as described at the end of the experiment.

Distillation

Cool the digestion flask, then add *carefully*, in *small* portions, a total of about 35 ml of water. Add the first portions down the wall of the flask, and mix by gentle swirling of the flask after the addition of each portion (Note 6). Cool the flask and contents to room temperature or below. Into a 100-ml beaker, deliver an accurately measured volume of 0.0200 N hydrochloric acid, using about 30 ml (or, if nitrogen is exceptionally high, 45 ml). Attach the delivery tube to the air condenser by means of a rubber sleeve. Place the beaker containing the acid beneath the delivery tube, then adjust the latter so that its upper end is in contact with the end of the condenser and its lower end is dipping just under the surface of the acid. For convenience at the end of the distillation, support the beaker about an inch above the desk level. Slip the second rubber sleeve over the short limb of the condenser. To the flask add two boiling chips, and 4–5 g (use the spoon provided) of sodium hydroxide pellets. Slide the pellets down the side of the inclined flask. *Immediately* connect the condenser system by means of the rubber sleeve; wetting the free end of the sleeve with distilled water facilitates making the connection. Swirl the flask gently to dissolve the sodium hydroxide and mix the solution. Distil over a *low* flame just touching the flask, until one-third to one-half of the liquid has passed over from the flask. The air condenser should be hot about one-half way down the vertical tube leading to the beaker, but not farther. When distillation is complete, disconnect the delivery tube from the condenser, and leave the delivery tube in the beaker.

Titration

With the 0.0200 N sodium hydroxide, titrate the excess acid in the receiver, using 10 drops of fresh (Note 3) saturated aqueous solution of methyl red as indicator. The delivery tube, which remains in the beaker during titration, is used for stirring. Titrate until the solution is water-white; the end point can be located within a fraction of a drop of titrant. Rinsing, if done at all, must be with *very small portions* of water. It is undesirable to lighten the already faint tint of the indicator by unnecessary dilution.

In calculating the results, take into account the amount of the blank. Report the percent nitrogen. Crude protein in flour is usually obtained by multiplying the nitrogen content by the factor 5.7.

After use, the Hengar tubes are prepared for re-use by heating to redness in a hot flame *in the hood*. Lay the hot tube on a clean asbestos board to cool. Return the apparatus immediately upon completion of the determination.

Notes

1. Equipment is available from Hengar Company, Philadelphia, Pa. Each Hengar outfit consists of a 100-ml Kjeldahl flask, an air condenser and delivery tube, two rubber sleeves, a Hengar tube for trapping sulfur trioxide, and a semimicro burner. One such outfit is required for each sample when multiplicates are to be run simultaneously. Additional equipment includes paper tape, glass weighing cup, paper weighing disks, selenized granules, boiling chips, and measuring spoons.

2. For the most accurate work, the air from the flask to contain the sodium hydroxide solution should be displaced with nitrogen. If the solutions are transferred to bottles, the air should be displaced by nitrogen in the bottle to receive the sodium hydroxide solution.

3. The indicator should be either freshly prepared, or, if kept from day to day, the container should *not* be stoppered. because the solution would spoil and lose its red color. When not in use, the indicator should be protected from contamination by keeping it under a glass cover.

4. The blank determination is for the purpose of correcting for any nitrogenous material present in the reagents used.

5. The sulfuric acid for this use must be protected from contamination by ammonia vapors in the laboratory atmosphere by keeping the bottle under a glass cover (e.g., bell jar) when not in use. If the sample being analyzed contains much water (e.g., a milk sample), fuming sulfuric acid should be used.

6. Mixing water and concentrated sulfuric acid generates much heat. When water is added to the acid, the reaction may become so vigorous that the water is raised almost immediately to its boiling point, and may be spattered out of the mixture. Great care must be exercised in making this dilution to avoid danger of personal injury, as well as loss of sample. The mouth of the flask should be pointed away from the operator and any other person nearby; safety glasses must be worn.

37

TITRIMETRIC
PRECIPITATION
AND COMPLEXATION

Reference: Chap. 25.

Reference: Chap. 25.

EXPERIMENT 37-1   STANDARD SOLUTIONS OF SILVER NITRATE AND POTASSIUM THIOCYANATE

Preparation of Solutions

Silver Nitrate.   Dry a clean weighing bottle and stopper in the oven at about 110°C for one-half hour. Cool the unstoppered bottle and its stopper in the desiccator for 20 minutes, then weigh the stoppered bottle accurately. Obtain a sample of 6–7 g of pure, dry silver nitrate (Note 1); transfer the solid to the weighing bottle, and weigh bottle and contents accurately. Transfer the weighed silver nitrate without loss to a small beaker; rinse the weighing bottle thoroughly with distilled water and add the rinsings to the beaker. Dissolve the silver nitrate completely in about 100 ml distilled water. Transfer the solution quantitatively to a 500-ml (Note 1) volumetric flask. Rinse well from beaker to flask with several small portions of water. Make the solution to volume and mix it thoroughly. Calculate the normality of the solution.

An alternate method is to standardize a solution, of the nominal concentration desired, against weighed samples of primary standard sodium chloride, following the directions given in Exp. 37-3, Determination of Chloride.

Potassium Thiocyanate.   On the laboratory balance weigh about 2.5 g of potassium thiocyanate. Transfer the solid to a 500-ml bottle, add distilled water to the shoulder, and mix the solution thoroughly. What is the approximate normality of the solution for reaction with silver ion?

Comparison of Solutions

To about 30 ml of silver nitrate solution, accurately measured from a buret (Note 4), add about 25 ml of distilled water, 10 ml of 6 *M* nitric acid, free from chloride and from oxides of nitrogen (Notes 2, 3), and 5 ml of ferric alum indicator. Titrate with the thiocyanate solution to the first faint red tinge in the solution above the precipitate. Titrate additional portions of the silver nitrate, of somewhat different volumes, to triplicate checks (Note 5). Calculate and report the normality of the potassium thiocyanate.

Notes

1. If the silver nitrate furnished is not already dried, place it in the weighing bottle and dry it in a 100°C oven for at least an hour; cool and weigh. If Exp. 37-3, Determination of Chloride, is not to be performed, use only about 3 g of silver nitrate and make it up to 250 ml.

2. Test the nitric acid with a few drops of silver nitrate solution; no opalescence or turbidity should appear.

3. Oxides of nitrogen interfere with the indicator action in the titration of silver ion by thiocyanate. If the chloride-free 6 *M* nitric acid is not perfectly colorless, boil about 40 ml of the acid in an Erlenmeyer flask until the solution is colorless, and keep it in the dark (laboratory locker) until it is needed.

4. Nearly all the silver nitrate solution prepared will be required for subsequent titrations. Rinse the buret with no more than two 5-ml portions of the solution.

5. Silver residues are usually saved for silver recovery. In this experiment, as well as in Exps. 37-2 and 37-3, upon completion of the titrations, pour off most of the supernatant liquid, then discard the residues into a side-shelf bottle marked for "Silver Residues."

EXPERIMENT 37-2 DETERMINATION OF SILVER IN AN ALLOY

Transfer triplicate weighed samples (Note 1) to 250-ml Erlenmeyer flasks. Add 10 ml of 6 *M* nitric acid (Note 2) and warm *gently* to dissolve the metal completely (a *small* amount of dark residue may be ignored). Boil the solution to expel oxides of nitrogen. When the solution has cooled, rinse down the sides of the flask, then add 10 ml of 6 *M* nitric acid (see Note 3, Exp. 37-1), 5 ml ferric alum indicator, and about 50 ml distilled water. Titrate with standard potassium thiocyanate solution to the first faint red tinge in the solution, exactly as in Exp. 37-1. Calculate and report the percent silver in the alloy.

Alternate Determination of Silver. The concentration of an unknown solution of silver nitrate is to be determined. One laboratory period before the sample is needed, hand in to the laboratory instructor a 100-ml volumetric flask labeled with your name and section number. Dilute the sample received to exactly 100 ml. Titrate portions of the solution, of somewhat different volumes measured from a buret, with standard potassium thiocyanate solution exactly as in Exp. 37-1. Calculate and report the total grams of silver in the sample received.

Notes

1. The sample weight should be of such size as to contain 0.15–0.20 g of silver; consult the laboratory instructor regarding the weight of sample to be taken; analyze in triplicate. U.S. ten-cent coins minted before 1965 make excellent samples for analysis; clean the coin surface with scouring powder, rinse well, and dry thoroughly with a clean towel. Weigh the coin accurately, dissolve it (in a beaker) in 15 ml of 6 M nitric acid (Note 2), warming gently as required. Cool the solution, rinse down the sides of the beaker, and transfer the solution quantitatively to a 250-ml volumetric flask; add distilled water to the mark, and mix the solution thoroughly. Titrate 25.0-ml aliquots of the coin solution (or somewhat different volumes measured from a buret), using the same amounts of nitric acid, ferric alum, and water as given in the above directions. Report percent silver. Jeweler's alloy, often obtainable locally, may be used as the sample. Silver alloys (containing 20–50% silver) for student analysis may be obtained from Thorn Smith, 1847 N. Main Street, Royal Oak, Michigan.

2. The nitric acid must be free from chloride ion; see Note 2, Exp. 37-1.

EXPERIMENT **37-3 DETERMINATION OF CHLORIDE**

Chloride can be determined titrimetrically with silver nitrate by any of the following methods. The Mohr method is restricted to nearly neutral solutions. The Fajans method can be used for solutions that are slightly acidic to slightly alkaline (pH about 5 to 9). The Volhard method is applicable in the presence of nitric acid.

Fajans Method (Adsorption Indicator). Into Erlenmeyer flasks weigh triplicate 0.15–0.17-g samples of the dry unknown chloride (Note 1). Dissolve the sample in about 75 ml distilled water, add 5 ml of 5% dextrin solution (Note 2) and 10 drops of 0.1% dichlorofluorescein indicator. Titrate, in diffuse light (Note 3), with standard silver nitrate solution to the first permanent change from yellowish to salmon pink tinge in the suspension and the settled precipitate. No blank test is possible. Calculate and report the percent chlorine in the sample.

Mohr Method. Into Erlenmeyer flasks weigh triplicate 0.15–0.17-g samples (Note 1) of the dry unknown chloride. In another flask place about

0.3 g (roughly weighed) of chloride-free calcium carbonate. To each flask add about 75 ml distilled water and 1 ml of 5% potassium chromate indicator solution. To the calcium carbonate suspension add standard silver nitrate solution *dropwise* from a buret until a permanent faint red-orange tinge is produced, just noticeably different from the yellow color of chromate ion (Notes 4, 5). Titrate the first sample of chloride with silver nitrate solution to the first permanent red-orange tinge, and match the color with that of the titrated blank. Titrate the second sample and match the color with that of the first sample. Shake both samples to suspend the precipitate when observing for color comparison. To one of these titrated samples add a minute crystal of sodium chloride or potassium chloride to restore the yellow color. This procedure now gives two comparison samples, one which is just past the equivalence point, and one that is just prior to the equivalence point. Titrate the third sample, and use the two previous samples for comparison in judging the end point. Correct the titration volumes for the amount of the blank, and calculate and report the percent chlorine in the sample.

Volhard Method: Caldwell Modification. Weigh triplicate 0.15–0.17-g samples of the dry unknown chloride into flasks or bottles that can be glass-stoppered (Note 6). Dissolve the sample in about 75 ml distilled water, add 10 ml recently boiled chloride-free 6 *M* nitric acid. From a buret add standard solution of silver nitrate until it is present in excess. Near the equivalence point the precipitate will coagulate. After this occurs, shake well, allow the precipitate to settle, and add a little more silver nitrate to the supernatant liquid. If precipitation is complete, no further precipitation or cloudiness will occur. Continue until it is certain that silver nitrate is in excess. Add about 2 ml of nitrobenzene, stopper the container, and shake vigorously. Add 5 ml ferric alum indicator, and titrate the excess silver ion with standard potassium thiocyanate solution. When the first permanent red tinge appears in the solution, swirl the contents well, then let the precipitate settle. If the red tinge has disappeared, add more thiocyanate solution dropwise, to develop the red tinge again. Continue in this way until, after good mixing, the supernatant liquid has a faint but permanent red color.

From the total volume of silver nitrate solution added, subtract the volume of silver nitrate equivalent to the potassium thiocyanate used in the back titration, to obtain the net volume of silver nitrate required for precipitation of the chloride (Note 7). Calculate and report the percent of chlorine in the sample.

Notes

1. The weights indicated are for high-chloride samples. For lower chloride content, take proportionally larger samples.
2. In the use of adsorption indicators it is essential that the precipitate be

kept well dispersed in small particle size so the solid presents a large specific surface. Dextrin prevents the coagulation of the silver chloride precipitate.

3. If, before the equivalence point is reached, the precipitate darkens considerably because of photochemical action, an exact end point cannot be determined. In this event, titrate a new sample in more subdued light, and conduct the titration more rapidly almost to the end point, then finish dropwise.

4. The end point in the Mohr titration is much more sharply detected if the titration is done under a yellow light.

5. Only a *few drops* of silver nitrate should be required. This blank test is necessary to determine the amount of titrant required to react with the chromate indicator to give a visible amount of silver chromate. The calcium carbonate is used to simulate the precipitate that will be obtained in the chloride titration.

6. The titration is best carried out in a glass-stoppered flask or bottle, so that vigorous shaking can be accomplished after the nitrobenzene is added. In the back titration step, however, vigorous shaking is to be avoided, although good mixing of the titration sample is required.

7. Alternatively, subtract the number of gme of thiocyanate from the number of gme of silver nitrate to obtain the number of gme of chloride in the sample.

EXPERIMENT **37-4** **DETERMINATION OF MAGNESIUM WITH EDTA**

Reference: Chap. 25, pp. 346–350.

Preparation of Solutions

EDTA. Dissolve 4–5 g of disodium dihydrogen ethylenediaminetetraacetate dihydrate in about 250 ml distilled water (Note 1); mix thoroughly. What is the approximate molar concentration of the EDTA solution, and what is its magnesium titer?

Buffer, pH 10. (Note 2). Dissolve 6.8 g of ammonium chloride in 20 ml distilled water, add 57 ml concentrated ammonium hydroxide, and dilute to 100 ml.

Standardization

Accurately weigh triplicate 0.10–0.12-g samples (Note 3) of pure calcium carbonate into Erlenmeyer flasks. Add about 10 ml distilled water, then 1 *M* hydrochloric acid dropwise until the solid is just dissolved (Note 4). Dilute to about 75 ml, add 1 ml of 6 *M* sodium hydroxide, and about 0.2 g of murexide indicator (Note 5). Titrate the solution with EDTA solution to the change in color from pink to violet. Calculate and report the molarity of the solution (Note 6), and also its magnesium and magnesium oxide titer.

Determination of Magnesium

Weigh triplicate 0.6–0.8-g samples of the dry unknown (Note 7). Dissolve the sample in about 75 ml distilled water (Note 8). Add 10 ml of *p*H 10 buffer solution, and five or six drops of eriochrome black T indicator (0.4% solution in alcohol). Titrate with standard EDTA solution until the wine-red color of the magnesium-indicator complex changes to the blue color of the indicator in alkaline solution. No trace of purple color remains at the end point (Note 9). Calculate and report percent of magnesium oxide in the sample.

Determination of Hardness of Tap Water

1. Total Hardness.   Transfer exactly 10 ml (pipet) of the standard EDTA solution to a 100-ml volumetric flask and dilute it to the mark with distilled water; mix thoroughly. Allow city water to run from the tap for about 30 seconds, then measure triplicate exact 100-ml samples of the tap water into Erlenmeyer flasks (Note 10). Add 10 ml of the *p*H 10 buffer, five or six drops of eriochrome black T indicator, and titrate with the diluted EDTA solution. Calculate and report the hardness as magnesium in parts per million (ppm), and also as grains per U.S. gallon (Notes 11, 12).

2. Magnesium Hardness.   Take triplicate samples of tap water as in part 1 (Note 10), add about 5 ml each of dilute hydrochloric acid and ammonium oxalate solution. Add four or five drops of methyl red indicator, heat the solution nearly to boiling, and precipitate the calcium oxalate by slowly neutralizing the solution with ammonium hydroxide. Allow the mixture to stand for one-half hour, then filter promptly. Wash the precipitate with several small portions of water, and collect the washings with the main filtrate. Add 10 ml of buffer solution, five or six drops of eriochrome black T indicator, and titrate with the dilute standard EDTA solution to the color change from wine-red to blue. Calculate and report calcium and magnesium (Note 13) as parts per million (ppm) (Note 14).

Notes

1. If all parts of this experiment are to be performed, prepare twice the above amount of EDTA solution.

2. The buffer solution may be furnished as a side-shelf reagent. If not, and if all parts of this experiment are to be performed, prepare 150 ml of buffer solution.

3. As an alternative, weigh 0.5–0.6 g of calcium carbonate, dissolve it in the least possible amount of 1 *N* hydrochloric acid, added dropwise, and make up the solution volumetrically to 250 ml. Take 50-ml aliquots (pipet) for titration.

4. A large excess of acid must be avoided. Why?

5. Murexide in solution is not stable in storage. The indicator consists of murexide mixed with a relatively large amount of sodium chloride as a diluent. The indicator should be used sparingly to get the sharpest end point. Alternatively, "calcon" indicator (eriochrome blue black R) may be used; the end point is the disappearance of the last pink tinge, changing to the blue color of the uncomplexed indicator in the buffered solution.

6. Because EDTA forms 1 : 1 complexes with all metal ions, molarity is more meaningful than normality if the EDTA solution is used for titration of metal ions of different oxidation numbers.

7. Student samples of hydrated magnesium sulfate make convenient unknowns. Such samples should be dried at 160°C for two hours in preparation for weighing. As an alternative, solution unknowns can be furnished, in which case the analysis is reported as total grams of magnesium and also as total grams of magnesium oxide in the sample received.

8. Water-insoluble samples are first dissolved in the least possible amount of 1 N hydrochloric acid, then diluted to about 75 ml.

9. There is very little warning of the approach of the end point; it comes suddenly, and care must be taken not to run past it.

10. If desired, a synthetic solution sample, containing calcium chloride and magnesium chloride, can be issued for student analysis. In this case, obtain the sample in a 250-ml volumetric flask, and dilute the sample received to the mark with distilled water; mix well. Take 25-ml aliquots (pipet) for titration.

11. This titration gives both calcium and magnesium, but the results are reported as magnesium. See a handbook for conversion factors needed to convert to grains per U.S. gallon.

12. If a synthetic solution sample is analyzed, calculate the results to total milligrams of magnesium in the sample received. The calcium is calculated as magnesium for reporting total hardness.

13. Calcium is obtained by difference in the titration for total hardness and the titration for magnesium hardness.

14. If a synthetic solution sample is analyzed, report milligrams of magnesium and milligrams of calcium in the sample received.

EXPERIMENT 37-5   OPTIONAL DETERMINATIONS WITH EDTA

See Chap. 25, pp. 346–350, and the references given there, for various applications of EDTA titrations. The student may propose a determination, outlining the procedure and the reagents needed, and check with the instructor for approval of the determination and to make arrangements for the reagents and the sample required.

38

REDOX METHODS

Reference for Exps. 38-1 to 38-5: Chap. 28.

Preparation of Solution

Weigh, to the nearest 0.1 g, 3.2 g of potassium permanganate crystals. Stir the solid into about 1 liter of distilled water. Heat the mixture, with frequent stirring, until the solid has dissolved, then cover the beaker with a watch glass and heat just below the boiling point for at least 30 minutes. Let the solution stand in the covered beaker for at least 24 hours, preferably longer. Filter the solution by decantation through a sintered glass filtering crucible or funnel, by using gentle suction. Take care to disturb the precipitated manganese dioxide *as little as possible*. Discard the last 50 to 75 ml of solution containing most of the precipitate. Transfer the filtered solution to a clean amber bottle with glass stopper (Note 1).

Prepare about 1 liter of 5% sulfuric acid solution by pouring 50 ml of concentrated sulfuric acid *slowly and with good stirring* into 950 ml distilled water. Cover the beaker with a watch glass and set it aside while the samples of standard are being weighed.

Standardization

Accurately weigh triplicate 0.25-g samples of primary standard sodium oxalate, $Na_2C_2O_4$, into 500-ml Erlenmeyer flasks or 600-ml beakers. To each sample add about 250 ml of 5% sulfuric acid, and stir until the solid has dis-

620

solved. Heat the solution nearly to boiling. Titrate (Note 2) the hot solution with the potassium permanganate solution, adding it slowly enough that a large localized excess does not accumulate (Note 3). Finish the titration by dropwise addition, and allow each drop to become decolorized before adding the next drop. Good mixing is essential, but vigorous stirring is to be avoided (Note 4). The end point is the first detectable pink tinge that persists for at least 30 seconds. If the temperature drops below 60°C before the end point is reached, heat again and complete the titration in hot solution. Titrate the second and third samples in the same way.

Determine the blank as follows: Heat 250 ml of 5% sulfuric acid to about 70°C, and add permanganate solution from the buret, in fractional drops, to the appearance of the first pink tinge that persists for at least 30 seconds.

Correct the titration volumes for the amount of the blank, then calculate and report the normality of the potassium permanganate solution; triplicates should agree within 2‰ average deviation.

Do *not* return used permanganate solution from the buret to the stock supply. After the analyses requiring permanganate have been completed, *save the remainder of the stock solution* for use in Exp. 39-2, Determination of Manganese in Steel.

Notes

1. The manganese dioxide on the filter can be removed readily by treatment with a small volume of hydrogen peroxide containing a few drops of nitric acid, followed by rinsing well with water. If it becomes necessary to clean the filter before all the solution has been filtered, the filter must be washed *very* thoroughly to remove all traces of hydrogen peroxide before continuing the filtration.

2. The permanganate solution is so deeply colored that it may be necessary to read the top of the meniscus.

3. The oxidation of oxalate ion by permanganate has an induction period that may last for many seconds. Although the reaction is slow at first, as soon as a little manganous ion is formed, it catalyzes the redox reaction and the reduction of permanganate then proceeds very rapidly.

4. Some hydrogen peroxide may be formed as an intermediate in the oxidation of oxalate ion to carbon dioxide. Any hydrogen peroxide must be titrated also, but stirring must not be so vigorous as to decompose the peroxide by disproportionation.

EXPERIMENT **38-2   ANALYSIS OF HYDROGEN
                      PEROXIDE SOLUTION**

One laboratory period before the unknown sample will be needed, hand in to the laboratory instructor a clean 100-ml volumetric flask labeled with your name and laboratory section number. The unknown must be analyzed on the same day the sample is received (Note 1).

Prepare about 200 ml of 10% sulfuric acid by pouring 20 ml of concentrated acid slowly and with good stirring into about 180 ml of distilled water. Cool the solution to room temperature before using it in the analysis.

Dilute the hydrogen peroxide sample to exactly 100 ml and mix it thoroughly, but *avoid violent agitation* of the solution (Note 2). Rinse and fill one buret with the unknown peroxide solution and the other buret with standard potassium permanganate solution. Measure accurately from the buret about 25 to 30 ml of the unknown peroxide into an Erlenmeyer flask, add about 50 ml of 10% sulfuric acid, and titrate at once with standard permanganate solution to the first pink tinge that lasts for at least 30 seconds. In the same way, titrate a second and a third portion of the unknown solution, using somewhat different volumes; if the first portion required less than 15 ml or more than 45 ml of the permanganate, measure a correspondingly larger or smaller volume of the peroxide solution for the second and third titrations.

Determine the amount of the blank by using 30 ml of water and 50 ml of 10% sulfuric acid. Add fractional drops of permanganate to a pink tinge stable for at least 30 seconds. Correct the titration volumes for the amount of the blank, and calculate and report the total grams of hydrogen peroxide in the unknown received. Triplicates should agree within 3‰ average deviation.

Notes

1. Even though the hydrogen peroxide solution contains a stabilizer, the concentration of the solution changes slowly; comparison of student results with the true peroxide content requires that the student samples be analyzed on schedule.

2. Violent shaking may result in decomposition of some of the hydrogen peroxide: $2H_2O_2 \rightarrow 2H_2O + O_2$.

EXPERIMENT **38-3 DETERMINATION OF IRON IN ORE: ZIMMERMANN-REINHARDT METHOD**

Accurately weigh triplicate 0.5-g samples of the dry iron ore into 500-ml Erlenmeyer flasks. To each sample add 10 ml concentrated hydrochloric acid and 3 ml stannous chloride solution (Note 1). Place the flasks on the steam bath or hot plate (Note 2) and heat until any residue is white or only slightly gray (Note 3). Do not allow the samples to evaporate to dryness. Add hydrochloric acid, if necessary, to replace that lost by evaporation. Frequent mixing by rotating the flask to swirl the contents will hasten dissolution.

From this point on, each sample must be handled separately through the remainder of the procedure. If the solution is colorless because of an excess of stannous chloride, add *small* crystals of potassium chlorate just to restore the yellow color. Heat the sample nearly to boiling, and to the hot solution add stannous chloride solution *dropwise*, with good stirring. When the solution is nearly decolorized, rinse down the sides of the flask with a *very small amount* of water, again heat nearly to boiling, and continue the dropwise addition of stannous chloride until the solution is *just decolorized* (Note 4), then add not more than two drops of excess stannous chloride. Sharp detection of the end of the reduction requires that the solution be of small volume, containing sufficient hydrochloric acid, and nearly boiling. If, through error, more than two drops of excess stannous chloride are added, or if in doubt regarding complete reduction of the iron(III), add a *small* crystal of potassium chlorate, heat again to restore the yellow color, then decolorize more carefully. Immediately cool the sample to room temperature and rapidly add 10 ml of saturated mercuric chloride solution, and mix well. A small amount of white, silky precipitate should form (Note 5). After addition of mercuric chloride, allow the mixture to stand not more than three minutes.

Dilute the solution with about 250 ml of water, add 25 ml of Zimmermann-Reinhardt solution (Note 6), and titrate immediately (Note 7) with standard potassium permanganate to the first detectable pink tinge that persists for at least 30 seconds.

Determine the blank as follows: In a flask place 5 ml of concentrated hydrochloric acid and 5 ml water. Add two drops of stannous chloride solution and 10 ml saturated mercuric chloride solution, then proceed with all steps as in the determination above. The blank should not exceed a few drops.

Correct the titration volumes for the amount of the blank, and calculate and report the percent iron in the ore.

Notes

1. The ore is more quickly dissolved if some stannous chloride is present during the acid attack.

2. *Gentle* heating with a burner is permissible; the heating *must be done in the hood.*

3. The time required to decompose the sample may vary from several minutes to an hour or more, depending on the nature of the sample, the temperature, frequency of stirring, etc.

4. The reduced solution may have a very faint greenish tinge, but all yellow color of ferric ion must be discharged.

5. If no precipitate forms within one or two minutes, insufficient stannous chloride was used. The white precipitate that forms is mercurous chloride, Hg_2Cl_2. If too much stannous chloride was used, or if the mercuric chloride

solution was added too slowly, some reduction to free mercury (black) may occur. If no precipitate forms, or if a gray to black precipitate forms, the sample must be discarded and more care taken with subsequent samples.

6. Refer to p. 399 for explanation of the function of each component of the Zimmermann-Reinhardt solution.

7. The solution should be titrated immediately because of the ease with which ferrous ion is oxidized by air.

EXPERIMENT 38-4 DETERMINATION OF CALCIUM OXIDE IN CALCIUM CARBONATE

Weigh triplicate 0.5-g samples of the dry unknown into 600-ml beakers. Add 25 ml of water, cover the beaker with a watch glass, and cautiously add 5 ml of concentrated hydrochloric acid, a little at a time. When vigorous action has subsided, warm the sample if necessary to effect complete dissolution. Rinse down the cover glass and the sides of the beaker, and finally dilute to about 200 ml. Then proceed with the analysis exactly as described in Exp. 35-7, p. 590, for the determination of calcium in limestone, starting with "To the hot solution add 50 ml of 4% ammonium oxalate solution . . ." Note, however, that double precipitation of calcium oxalate is not required in the present analysis; the calcium oxalate precipitate is filtered, washed free from oxalate ion, dissolved in sulfuric acid, and titrated. Calculate and report percent calcium oxide in the sample.

EXPERIMENT 38-5 DETERMINATION OF AVAILABLE OXYGEN IN PYROLUSITE (MnO$_2$)

Weigh triplicate 0.4-g samples of the dry ore into Erlenmeyer flasks. On the assumption that the ore is pure MnO$_2$, calculate the weight of arsenious oxide, As$_2$O$_3$, required for reduction of the sample to manganous ion. Allow a 0.2-g excess, and weigh accurately the required amount of primary standard As$_2$O$_3$ into the flasks containing the pyrolusite (Note 1). Add about 50 ml water and 10 ml concentrated sulfuric acid; observe the usual precautions in adding the acid. Boil gently to decompose the sample completely, as indicated by disappearance of black or brown particles.

To the cool solution add about 50 ml water, one drop of 0.002 M potassium iodate solution (catalyst), and titrate the excess arsenite with standard permanganate. From the amount of arsenious oxide (Note 1) added, and the amount of its excess as determined by the back titration with permanganate, calculate and report percent of "available oxygen" (Note 2) in the sample.

Notes

1. Alternatively, the sample can be reduced by the addition of a standard arsenite solution if this is available. To the weighed ore sample add 20% more than the calculated volume of arsenite solution, accurately measured by buret or pipet; then add sulfuric acid, and proceed as described above.

2. "Available oxygen" is calculated as if oxygen were the oxidizing agent in the reaction with arsenite.

EXPERIMENT **38-6 PREPARATION OF STANDARD SOLUTIONS OF POTASSIUM DICHROMATE AND FERROUS AMMONIUM SULFATE**

Reference for Exps. 38-6 to 38-8: Chap. 30.

Preparation of Solutions

Potassium Dichromate. Calculate the weight of potassium dichromate, $K_2Cr_2O_7$, required to make exactly 500 ml of 0.1000 N solution; take into account any purity factor that may be indicated. Accurately weigh a small watch glass; then weigh out exactly the amount of potassium dichromate required. Transfer the weighed solid without loss to a beaker; rinse any solid adhering to the watch glass into the beaker with a jet of water from the wash bottle. Add about 100 ml distilled water, stir to dissolve the solid, and transfer the solution without loss to a 500-ml volumetric flask. Rinse several times from beaker to flask, and finally dilute to the mark. Mix the solution thoroughly.

Ferrous Solution (Note 1).   On the laboratory balance weigh 20 g of ferrous ammonium sulfate crystals, and transfer the solid to a beaker. Add 15 ml 6 N sulfuric acid (Note 2), dissolve the solid by adding distilled water, transfer the solution to a glass-stoppered bottle, and make up to about 500 ml. Mix the solution well.

Comparison of Solutions (Note 1)

Prepare a solution of sulfuric acid and phosphoric acid by pouring 15 ml of each concentrated acid into about 225 ml of distilled water. Cool the solution before use. Fill one buret with the potassium dichromate solution and the other buret with the ferrous solution. Into an Erlenmeyer flask measure from the buret about 40 ml of the ferrous solution. Add about 75 ml of the sulfuric-phosphoric acid mixture and 5 to 10 drops of barium diphenylamine sulfonate indicator. Titrate the solution with the standard potassium dichromate solution. As the dichromate ion is reduced, the solution acquires the green color of chromic ion. The end point is the appearance of the first permanent blue-violet color of the oxidized indicator. If the end point is overstepped, run back with several drops of ferrous solution, then finish the titration more carefully. Titrate a second and a third portion of the ferrous solution, taking somewhat different volumes. From the volumes of potassium dichromate solution used, subtract 0.05 ml as a blank correction (Note 3), and calculate the normality of the ferrous solution. Triplicates should agree within 2‰ average deviation.

Notes

1. If the determination of chromium in Exp. 38-8 is to be done by Method 2, preparation of the ferrous solution and its comparison with the dichromate solution are unnecessary.

2. The acid serves to prevent hydrolysis and retard atmospheric oxidation of ferrous ion. The ferrous solution should be used within a few days of its standardization.

3. The amount of the blank cannot be determined directly.

EXPERIMENT **38-7 DETERMINATION OF IRON**

In Iron Ore

Accurately weigh triplicate 0.5-g samples of the dry iron ore into 500-ml Erlenmeyer flasks. Dissolve and reduce the samples exactly as described in the first two paragraphs of Exp. 38-3, through the addition of mercuric chloride; see also Notes 1–5 in that experiment. Then continue as directed below.

Add about 250 ml water, 5 ml concentrated phosphoric acid, and 5 to 10 drops of barium diphenlyamine sulfonate indicator. Titrate at once with standard potassium dichromate solution to the first permanent blue-violet color of the oxidized indicator. Approach the end point carefully, and finally adjust dropwise, allowing a few seconds after each addition, because the oxidation of the indicator is not instantaneous. Reduce and titrate the second and then the third sample in the same way. Correct the titration volumes by subtracting a blank correction of 0.05 ml. Calculate and report the percent iron, and also the percent ferric oxide, Fe_2O_3, in the ore.

In Soluble Iron Samples

If desired, the determination of iron by dichromate may be made on water-soluble ferrous salts, for example, ferrous ammonium sulfate. "Soluble iron" samples are usually hydrates, and they must *not* be dried before weighing. Take about 1-g samples, treating them individually for the dissolution and titration.

Dissolve the sample in about 200 ml water, add 5 ml each of concentrated sulfuric acid and phosphoric acid, and 5 to 10 drops of barium diphenylamine sulfonate indicator. Titrate with the potassium dichromate to the blue-violet end point. Subtract 0.05 ml for the blank, and calculate and report the percent iron and also the percent ferric oxide, Fe_2O_3, in the sample.

EXPERIMENT 38-8 DETERMINATION OF CHROMIUM IN A SOLUBLE CHROMATE

This determination is the converse of the method for the determination of ferrous iron. However, the end point is often unsatisfactory when titration is done in this direction. It is better to add a known excess of ferrous ion to the sample, then determine the amount of the excess ferrous ion by titration with standard dichromate. For the determination of chromium, the ferrous solution should be recently standardized, preferably on the same day that it is used for the determination. Instead of using a measured volume of standard ferrous solution (Method 1), an accurately weighed excess of pure ferrous ammonium sulfate can be added (Method 2) and the excess then titrated. If it is not practical to standardize the ferrous solution on the same day the determination of chromium is to be made, use of the weighed amount of ferrous ammonium sulfate is recommended.

Method 1. If the sample for analysis is a chromate solution, obtained in the usual way, take triplicate 25-ml aliquots (pipet) of the solution as received. If the sample is a solid chromate, accurately weigh triplicate 0.5-g samples. In either case, to each measured portion add about 75 ml water, 5 ml concentrated sulfuric acid, and 5 ml phosphoric acid. Cool the mixture. Then run in, from a buret, about 45 ml of standard ferrous solution. If this amount is insufficient to cause complete reduction of the dichromate (orange) to chromic ion (green), add more ferrous solution from the buret. Record the total volume of ferrous solution added. Add 5 to 10 drops of barium diphenylamine sulfonate indicator, and titrate the excess ferrous ion with standard dichromate. If a solution sample is analyzed, calculate and report the grams of chromium and also the grams of chromic oxide, Cr_2O_3, per liter of solution analyzed. If a solid sample is analyzed, calculate and report percent chromium and also percent chromic oxide, Cr_2O_3, in the sample.

Method 2. Take the solution or solid sample as in Method 1. To each sample add, without loss, an accurately weighed quantity of pure ferrous ammonium sulfate hexahydrate (Mohr's salt), $FeSO_4 \cdot (NH_4)_2SO_4 \cdot 6H_2O$, in the amount of 1.5 to 1.8 g. Stir well to dissolve the ferrous salt. If the amount of ferrous salt added is insufficient to cause complete reduction of the dichromate (orange) to chromic ion (green), an additional accurately weighed quantity of the ferrous salt must be added. Add the indicator and titrate with potassium dichromate as in Method 1. Calculate and report the results as in Method 1.

EXPERIMENT 38-9   COMPARISON OF SODIUM THIOSULFATE AND IODINE SOLUTIONS

Reference for Exps. 38-9 to 38-13: Chap. 29.

Preparation of Solutions

Sodium Thiosulfate.   On the laboratory balance weigh 25 g sodium thiosulfate crystals, $Na_2S_2O_3 \cdot 5H_2O$, and 1 g sodium carbonate. Transfer the solids to a clean one-liter bottle, and add recently boiled distilled water (Note 1) to make about one liter. Shake well to dissolve the solids and mix the solution thoroughly.

Iodine.   On the laboratory balance weigh 6.5 g of iodine crystals and 20 g potassium iodide. Grind the iodine in a mortar with repeated small portions of potassium iodide and water, pouring off the solution frequently into a bottle, until the solids are completely dissolved. Dilute the solution to about 500 ml and mix the solution thoroughly (Note 2).

Comparison of Solutions (Note 3)

Into an Erlenmeyer flask measure from a buret about 40 ml of the iodine solution. Dilute to about 100 ml with recently boiled distilled water, add 1 ml glacial acetic acid, and from the other buret run in thiosulfate solution until the yellow color of the solution is almost discharged. Then add 2 ml starch solution and continue the titration until the blue color just disappears. Titrate a second and a third sample of the iodine solution in the same way, using some-what different volumes. Calculate and report the volume ratio iodine/thiosulfate.

Notes

1. Water to be used in making sodium thiosulfate solution and for use as a diluent in the determinations must be recently boiled in a flask, which is then stoppered and the water cooled to room temperature. The need for recently boiled water should be anticipated so it will be available when required.

2. It is desirable to let the solution stand one or two days, with occasional shaking, to make sure all the iodine has dissolved.

3. If both the sodium thiosulfate and the iodine solutions are to be standardized directly, the comparison titration of the solutions is unnecessary, although it serves as a cross-check on the standardizations.

EXPERIMENT **38-10** **STANDARDIZATION OF SODIUM THIOSULFATE AND IODINE SOLUTIONS**

Standardization of Thiosulfate

Into Erlenmeyer flasks weigh triplicate 0.12–0.17-g samples of dry primary standard potassium iodate, KIO_3 (Note 1). Dissolve the samples in about 50 ml of recently boiled water. From this point, handle each sample individually through the titration. To the first sample add 2 g potassium iodide, weighed on the laboratory balance, swirl to hasten dissolution, then add a solution consisting of 1 ml concentrated hydrochloric acid in about 15 ml water. Titrate the liberated iodine at once with thiosulfate until the yellow color is almost discharged, then add 2 ml starch solution and continue the titration just to disappearance of blue color. Titrate the second and the third samples in the same way. Determine the blank by use of the same amount of potassium iodide and hydrochloric acid in the same volume of water. Correct the volume of thiosulfate for any blank, apply any necessary purity factor for the potassium iodate standard, and calculate the normality of the thiosulfate solution. From the volume ratio of the solutions determined in Exp. 38-9, calculate also the normality of the iodine solution (Note 2). Report the results.

Standardization of Iodine

Into Erlenmeyer flasks accurately weigh triplicate 0.15–0.20-g samples of dry primary standard arsenious oxide, As_2O_3. Dissolve in 10–20 ml of 1 M sodium hydroxide solution, add 1 M hydrochloric acid until the solution is *just acidic* (Note 3) to a small piece of litmus paper placed in the solution. Add 1 g of sodium bicarbonate (weighed on the laboratory balance), dilute to about 100 ml, add 2 ml starch solution, and titrate with the iodine solution to the first permanent tinge of blue. Calculate the normality of the iodine solution. Also calculate the normality of the thiosulfate solution from the results of the comparison titration, Exp. 38-9 (Note 4). Report the results.

Notes

1. An alternative method is to weigh a single sample of 0.7–0.8 g of potassium iodate, dissolve it in water and make to volume in a 250-ml volumetric flask; 50-ml aliquots of the solution are taken for titration, as described in the procedure.

2. If desired, iodine solution may be standardized directly against arsenious oxide.

3. Care must be taken not to add an excess of hydrochloric acid, otherwise

it would consume much of the bicarbonate added next, and an indistinct end point would result. If the latter should occur, add more sodium bicarbonate.

4. If desired, the sodium thiosulfate solution may be standardized directly against potassium iodate as described above.

EXPERIMENT 38-11   ANALYSIS OF BLEACHING SOLUTION

One laboratory period before the sample is needed, hand in to the laboratory instructor a clean 250-ml volumetric flask (Note 1) labeled with your name and laboratory section number. The sample is to be analyzed on the same day it is received.

Dilute the sample received to exactly 250 ml with recently boiled distilled water; mix thoroughly but avoid violent shaking. Rinse and fill a buret with the bleaching solution, and another buret with standard thiosulfate solution. Run into an Erlenmeyer flask about 40 ml of the bleaching solution, add about 25 ml of recently boiled water, 2 g of potassium iodide, and 10 ml of 6 N sulfuric acid. At once, titrate the liberated iodine with thiosulfate until the yellow color is almost discharged, then add 2 ml starch solution and complete the titration to disappearance of blue color. If the end point should be overrun, add a little more of the bleaching solution and approach the end point more carefully. Titrate a second and a third sample of the bleaching solution, using somewhat different volumes. Calculate and report the total grams of available chlorine (Note 2) in the sample received.

Notes

1. The flask need not be dry, since the solution is to be diluted to volume.

2. Calculation to the basis of available chlorine is made as if chlorine were the oxidizing agent that reacted with iodide to liberate the iodine that is titrated.

EXPERIMENT 38-12   DETERMINATION OF COPPER IN AN ORE

Weigh triplicate 1-g samples of the dry copper ore into 250-ml beakers. Add 10-15 ml concentrated nitric acid, cover the beaker with a watch glass, and heat below the boiling point until the ore is decomposed. Do not evaporate to less than 5 ml. If necessary, replace the acid lost by evaporation. When the ore is completely decomposed and any residue is white or nearly so (Note 1), evaporate to a volume of about 5 ml. Add about 30 ml water, and warm to dissolve soluble salts. Cool and add 10 ml bromine water (Note 2), then boil until bromine odor is no longer detected in the vapors. If the residue (silica) is nearly white and of small amount, filtration is unnecessary (Note 3); otherwise, filter off the residue, receiving the filtrate in an Erlenmeyer flask. Wash the filter several times with small portions of very dilute nitric acid (1 : 100), and collect the washings with the main filtrate. Concentrate the solution to about 25 ml; cool, then add dilute (1 : 1) ammonium hydroxide slowly and with good stirring, just to the formation of a blue-white precipitate of cupric hydroxide, or the first permanent formation of the deep blue cupric-ammonia complex (Notes 4, 5, 6). After blowing away the vapors from above the solution, it should smell faintly of ammonia. If an excess of ammonia has been added inadvertently, boil the mixture to expel the excess. From this point on, handle the samples individually through the titration.

On the laboratory balance weigh, to the nearest 0.1 g, 2.0 g ammonium bifluoride, NH_4HF_2, 2.0 g potassium acid phthalate, and 3.0 g potassium iodide. Add the solids, in the order stated, but wait until the first has dissolved before adding the next. Titrate without delay with standard thiosulfate solution until the yellow color is almost discharged; add 2 g potassium thiocyanate and 2 ml starch solution, and complete the titration dropwise just to disappearance of blue color, which should not return within several minutes (Note 7). Complete the analysis of the second and the third sample in the same way. Calculate and report percent copper in the ore.

Notes

1. If the ore is not readily decomposed by the nitric acid, add also 5 ml concentrated hydrochloric acid and heat just below the boiling point (hood!) until any residue is white or only slightly gray. Cool, add 10 ml concentrated sulfuric acid, and evaporate in the hood to copious evolution of dense white fumes of sulfur trioxide. Cool, and proceed with the dilution, etc.

2. Bromine water completes the oxidation of any arsenic and/or antimony.

3. If filtration is unnecessary, go directly to the addition of ammonium hydroxide.

4. Ammonium hydroxide neutralizes the excess acid in the solution, so that careful adjustment of pH can be made later.

5. Owing to the presence of ammonium salt formed by the neutralization, the blue-white precipitate may fail to appear. Formation of the first deep blue color in the solution indicates that the free acid has been neutralized.

6. If much iron is present, ammonium hydroxide should be added to complete precipitation of hydrous ferric oxide.

7. A rapid return of blue color may be due to insufficient buffer and a high pH, at which the oxidation of iodide ion by cupric ion is somewhat slow; or it may be due to insufficient fluoride to complex all the ferric ion.

EXPERIMENT **38-13** DETERMINATION OF
ANTIMONY IN STIBNITE

Into dry 250-ml beakers weigh triplicate 1.5-g samples of the dry stibnite (antimony sulfide) ore. Add about 0.3 g finely powdered potassium chloride (Note 1), nearly cover the beaker with a watch glass, and carefully add 10 ml concentrated hydrochloric acid by pouring it down the side of the beaker. Place the covered beaker on the steam bath or low temperature hot plate (hood), and warm (*do not boil*) until the ore is decomposed; the mixture should no longer give an odor of hydrogen sulfide, and any residue (silica) should be white or only slightly gray. Do not allow the solution to evaporate to dryness, which might result in loss of antimony trichloride; add more hydrochloric acid if necessary. When decomposition is complete, add 3 g finely powdered tartaric acid and continue the heating for 10–15 minutes. Add water in portions of about 5 ml with good stirring until the solution is diluted to about 100 ml. If, during dilution, a red-orange precipitate (Sb_2S_3) appears, heat gently until the precipitate has dissolved before continuing the dilution. If a white precipitate of basic salts forms, discard the determination (Note 2). When dilution is completed, boil the solution for one minute.

Rinse off the watch glass into the solution, and carefully neutralize the solution with 6 N sodium hydroxide solution, using methyl red indicator. Then add 6 N hydrochloric acid *dropwise* until the solution is just acidic, carefully avoiding an excess.

In 600-ml beakers or 500-ml Erlenmeyer flasks prepare solutions containing 3 g sodium bicarbonate in 200 ml water. Pour the sample solution into the sodium bicarbonate solution; avoid loss by effervescence, and rinse several times with a stream of water from the wash bottle to obtain complete transfer of the solution. Add 2 ml starch solution, and titrate with standard iodine to the appearance of the first permanent blue color (Note 3). Calculate and report percent antimony in the ore.

Notes

1. Addition of potassium chloride prevents volatilization loss of antimony trichloride.
2. If insufficient tartaric acid is added, an excessively large amount of hydrochloric acid would be required to redissolve the insoluble basic salt (SbOCl); it is best to discard the sample.
3. A fading or indistinct end point is due to insufficient buffer; in that event add 1 g additional sodium bicarbonate, and complete the titration.

39

COLORIMETRIC METHODS

Reference: Chap. 31.

EXPERIMENT 39-1   COLORIMETRIC DETERMINATION OF pH

Reference: Chap. 23, pp. 306–307.

One method of determining the pH of a solution is to treat the sample with an appropriate indicator, and compare the color with a series of standard buffer solutions varying by small increments of pH, to which the same amount of indicator has been added. This method is somewhat tedious, because it requires the preparation of several buffer solutions.

Within the color change interval of an indicator, both the acid and the alkaline forms are present, but in different relative amounts depending upon the pH. The observed color is therefore a composite of the colors of the two forms, and depends upon their relative amounts. In Chap. 23 it was shown that

$$pH = pK_{ind} + \log([\text{alkaline form}]/[\text{acid form}])$$

By the method of Gillespie[1] the pH of a solution can be determined without the use of buffer solutions. The method depends upon the fact that the observed color of light passing successively through two solutions, one containing a measured amount of a two-color indicator all in the acid form and another containing a measured amount of the indicator all in the alkaline form, is the same as if the two colored forms were both in the same solution. A series of comparison tubes containing varying amounts of the indicator, all in the acid

[1] L. J. Gillespie, *J. Am. Chem. Soc.*, **42**, 742 (1920).

form, is paired with a series of tubes containing varying amounts of the indicator, all in the alkaline form, the pairing being done in such a way that the *total* amount of indicator in each pair is the same. When the pairs of tubes are observed by transmitted light, they show a gradation of color from the acid to the alkaline color of the indicator. An unknown sample, to which the same amount of indicator has been added as used in the standards, is then matched against the comparison tubes in order to determine the ratio of the concentration of the alkaline form to the acid form of the indicator. From this ratio and the value of the indicator constant, the pH is calculated by use of the above equation. The method is accurate to 0.2 pH unit, or even to 0.1 pH unit by careful preparation and matching of the sample and standards, if the indicator is so chosen that the final matching falls about in the middle of the color change interval of the indicator. Near the extremes of the color change interval, poor matching of sample with standards results in rather large errors. A careful judgment of color between adjacent standards will reduce the error.

Procedure

One laboratory period before the determination is to be performed, hand in to the instructor two stoppered test tubes labeled with your name and section number; these tubes will be used for issuing the sample (Note 1) and the indicator.

Table 39-1 Indicators for Gillespie Method

No.	Indicator	$pK_{ind}{}^a$	Acid Required[b]	Alkali Required[b]
1.	Thymol blue (acid)	1.6	1 ml 2.5 N HCl	5 ml 2% KH_2PO_4
2.	Methyl orange	3.5	2 ml 0.05 N HCl	0.1 ml 0.05 N NaOH
3.	Bromphenol blue	3.8	1 ml 0.05 N HCl	0.1 ml 0.05 N NaOH
4.	Bromcresol green	4.7	0.1 ml 0.05 N HCl	0.1 ml 0.05 N NaOH
5.	Methyl red	5.0	0.1 ml 0.05 N HCl	0.1 ml 0.05 N NaOH
6.	Chlorphenol red	6.0	0.1 ml 0.05 N HCl	0.1 ml 0.05 N NaOH
7.	Bromcresol purple	6.1	0.1 ml 0.05 N HCl	0.1 ml 0.05 N NaOH
8.	Neutral red	6.8	0.1 ml 0.05 N HCl	0.1 ml 0.05 N NaOH
9.	Bromthymol blue	7.1	0.1 ml 0.05 N HCl	0.1 ml 0.05 N NaOH
10.	Phenol red	7.8	0.1 ml 0.05 N HCl	0.1 ml 0.05 N NaOH
11.	Cresol red[c]	8.1	5 ml 2% KH_2PO_4	1 ml 0.2 N Na_2CO_3
12.	Metacresol purple[c]	8.3	5 ml 2% KH_2PO_4	1 ml 0.5 N Na_2CO_3
13.	Thymol blue[c]	8.9	5 ml 2% KH_2PO_4	1 ml 0.5 N Na_2CO_3

[a] pK_{ind} values are given only to the first decimal figure, because the method is no more accurate than to 0.1 pH unit.

[b] These amounts of reagents are required, per final volume of 10 ml, for conversion of the indicator all to the acid or all to the alkaline form, respectively.

[c] Alkaline range of the indicator. These indicators have another color change interval in the low pH range.

The indicator issued will be identified by a number corresponding to the serial number of the indicator listed in Table 39-1. Obtain, on temporary order from the storeroom, a set of Gillespie pH equipment, consisting of a 10-hole comparator block (20 holes arranged in pairs), 20 test tubes, two 1-ml graduated pipets, and one 10-ml graduated pipet.

Prepare about 250 ml of carbonate-free water by boiling distilled water in a flask, then stoppering the flask and cooling the water without access to air. The test tubes to be used must be scrupulously clean, and as nearly dry as can be attained by shaking out after rinsing with distilled water.

Using small labels placed near the top of the test tubes, number a set of tubes from 1A to 9A, and another set of tubes from 9B to 1B. Arrange the tubes in the comparator block in pairs as follows: 1A and 9B; 2A and 8B; 3A and 7B; etc. Use a clean 1-ml graduated pipet that has been rinsed once with a small amount of the indicator solution; add 0.1 ml of indicator to tube 1A, and 0.9 ml to tube 9B; 0.2 ml to tube 2A and 0.8 ml to tube 8B; etc., for all tubes. Refer to Table 39-1 for the amount of acid and alkali required to convert the indicator in use all to the acid and all to the alkaline forms, respectively. To each of the tubes of set A, add the required amount of acid with the second 1-ml graduated pipet. Rinse the pipet, then add to each tube of set B the required amount of alkali. By means of a buret, or a 10-ml graduated pipet, add recently boiled distilled water to make the total volume of liquid in each test tube 10 ml; mix the contents well. To another similar test tube add 1.0 ml of the indicator and 9.0 ml of the unknown solution, and pair this tube with distilled water.

Use the comparator block containing the pairs of tubes having alkaline and acid forms of the indicator in known ratio, and match the color of the pair containing sample and water (Note 2). Keep the paired tubes together, and shift the tubes in the comparator block in order to get the unknown pair adjacent to the standard pair most similar in color. If a decision cannot be made, at first, between two standards, try shifting the order of standards and unknown, making sure to keep matched pairs of tubes together in the holes of the comparator block. Record the value of the [alkaline]/[acid] ratio (number of tube B/number of tube A) of the indicator that most nearly matches the color of the unknown (Note 3). From this ratio and the pK_{ind} for the indicator used (see Table 39-1), calculate and report the pH of the unknown.

Rinse the test tubes and pipets with tap water and then with distilled water, and return the apparatus to the storeroom. Under no circumstances shall the apparatus be retained by the student from one laboratory period to another.

Notes

1. For good results, buffered solutions should be used as samples. Samples for student analysis are conveniently issued in the form of buffered solutions, prepared by the method of Clark and Lubs, *J. Biol. Chem.*, **25**, 479 (1916), or from commercially available buffer solids such as Harleco Parstains buffer salts.

2. The tubes should be observed by transmitted light, preferably light from a bright sky, but not in direct sunlight.

3. If the unknown is darker than one pair (for example, 4B/6A) but lighter than the next pair (for example, 5B/5A), record an intermediate value (for example, 4.5B/5.5A). Estimation closer than 0.5 unit in B and A is probably impossible, and at any rate is not demanded by the accuracy of the determination.

EXPERIMENT 39-2 DETERMINATION OF MANGANESE IN STEEL

Small amounts of manganese in ores and steels are best determined colorimetrically as permanganate. Among the various reagents that will oxidize lower oxidation states of manganese to permanganate, the periodate method of Willard and Greathouse[1] is the most satisfactory. The concentration of acid may be varied within wide limits; prolonged boiling after development of the color does no harm, and the color is stable indefinitely if an excess of periodate is present. The method is satisfactory in the presence of titanium, where the peroxydisulfate method is of no value.

In the analysis of steel, components other than manganese contribute some color to the solution; the color of ferric ion is removed with phosphoric acid by formation of the colorless phosphato complex. The color contributed by small amounts of chromium, vanadium, nickel, and cobalt can be compensated by having these components present in the blank or reference standard against which the unknown is compared. Interference by other colored components is also largely eliminated by using incident light (by a narrow band-pass color filter or by a spectrophotometer) of the wavelength most strongly absorbed by the component being determined. Maximum absorbance of permanganate occurs at 526 mμ, which is in the yellow-green region of the spectrum.

Time may be saved in the analysis that follows by first weighing the steel samples and adding the nitric acid, allowing the samples to dissolve while the calibration is being made.

Calibration

Preparation of Color Standards. By appropriate dilution of a previously standardized solution of potassium permanganate (Note 1), prepare 250 ml of solution containing exactly 0.100 mg of manganese per milliliter (Note 2). From this stock standard a series of more dilute standards containing 0.200, 0.500, 1.00, 1.50, and 2.00 mg of manganese per 100 ml is prepared, as follows. Rinse and fill a buret (Note 3) with the stock permanganate; measure 2.00 ml of the solution into a 100-ml volumetric flask, make up to volume with distilled water,

[1] H. H. Willard and L. H. Greathouse, *J. Am. Chem. Soc.*, **39**, 2366 (1917).

and mix thoroughly. Prepare the additional diluted standards in the same way
by the use of appropriate volumes of the stock solution (Note 4).

Measurement of Absorbance and/or Transmittance (Note 5).   Because of the
variety of photoelectric colorimeters and spectrophotometers in use in different
laboratories (Note 6), no attempt is made here to describe in detail the construction and the operating procedure for any specific instrument. There are,
however, some features of construction and operation that most of these
instruments have in common. Study the operating procedure for the instrument
to be used, and consult the laboratory instructor, as necessary. The absorption
cells (tubes or cuvettes) must be scrupulously clean. With the wavelength
control set at 526 mμ (Note 7) and the light beam shuttered or blocked, adjust
the meter reading to zero transmittance (infinity absorbance). Fill two absorption cells with distilled water, and wipe the outside surface carefully with soft
cleansing tissue. Insert one cell in the light beam of the instrument, and adjust
the controls to give a reading of 100% transmittance (zero absorbance) on the
meter or scale. Insert the second cell in the light beam and note the meter reading
(Note 8). Check back and forth from one tube to the other several times, and
record the absorbances and transmittances.

Rinse the sample cell with two or three small portions of the solution to be
measured (Note 9); distilled water in the other cell serves as the blank (Note 10).
Place the blank solution in position, and adjust to read 100% T (absorbance =
zero). Then put the sample solution in position, and read and record percent
transmittance and also absorbance. Check back and forth several times between
blank and sample, recording individual readings and their average. Measure
each of the solutions in the series of standards in the same way. Record the
serial number of the instrument used (Note 11).

Data Plots.   Prepare graphs, as indicated below, and submit them with the
analysis report for manganese in steel.

1. *Transmittance vs. concentration.*   On semilog graph paper (Note 12) plot
percent transmittance *on the log scale as ordinate* against concentration, in
milligrams of manganese per 100 ml of solution, as abscissa. Draw a smooth
curve to give the best fit to the experimental points (Note 13); the extrapolated
curve should pass through 100% transmittance at zero concentration.

2. *Absorbance vs. concentration.*   On linear coordinate paper plot absorbance as ordinate against concentration (in milligrams of manganese per 100 ml)
as abscissa. Draw a smooth curve to give the best fit to the experimental points
(Note 13); the extrapolated curve should pass through the origin. Either of these
plots serves as a calibration curve for determining the concentration of manganese
in the unknown.

3. *Ringbom plot.*[2]   On two-cycle semilog graph paper, plot (100 − percent T)

[2] A. Ringbom, *Z. anal. Chem.*, **115**, 332 (1939). See also G. H. Ayres, *Anal. Chem.*, **21**, 652
(1949).

as ordinate against log concentration (log scale) as abscissa. Draw a smooth curve for best fit to the experimental points. From this plot, evaluate (*a*) the optimum concentration range; and (*b*) the relative analysis error, per 1% *T* error, within this range (Note 14).

Analysis of Steel

The unknown is *not* to be oven-dried. Accurately weigh steel samples (duplicate or triplicate as directed by the instructor) of 0.25 to 0.30 g. Transfer the sample to a 250-ml beaker, add 25 ml of dilute (1 : 3) nitric acid, cover with a watch glass, and simmer until the sample is dissolved, or only a small amount of carbon residue remains; as necessary, add water to replace that lost by evaporation. Boil for one or two minutes, remove from the heat, and add, a little at a time, about 0.5 g of ammonium peroxydisulfate. Boil gently for 10 minutes to oxidize carbon compounds. If a purple color of permanganate develops or a dark precipitate of manganese dioxide forms, add a few grains of sodium bisulfite to reduce these compounds, then boil for three to five minutes longer if sodium bisulfite was added (Note 15). Dilute with about 25 ml water (Note 16), add 5 ml syrupy phosphoric acid and about 0.2 g potassium periodate (Note 17). Boil the solution gently for about five minutes to develop the color; if the color does not develop readily, or is very faint, add more potassium periodate to make sure the oxidation of manganese is complete. Cool the solution and transfer it quantitatively to a 100-ml volumetric flask; dilute to the mark and mix thoroughly. Transfer about 20 ml of the sample solution to a small beaker, add several drops of concentrated hydrochloric acid, warm if necessary to reduce the permanganate, and use the reduced solution as a blank (Note 18), exactly as in the measurement of the standards. If the sample shows less than about 20% transmittance (0.7 absorbance) or if the transmittance falls on a part of the calibration curve that is nonlinear (Note 19), make an accurate dilution (1 : 1, 1 : 2, 1 : 3, as appropriate) and again measure the transmittance (or absorbance) (Note 20). If the measured transmittance is more than about 60% (absorbance less than 0.2), more accurate results could be obtained by the use of a larger sample or a smaller volume.

From the calibration graph, read the concentration corresponding to the transmittance (absorbance) of the sample solution. Calculate and report the percent manganese in the steel (Note 21).

Notes

1. The potassium permanganate solution prepared and standardized in Exp. 38-1 may be used, provided it has been properly stored and is used for the present experiment without undue delay. If desired by the instructor, a standard solution of potassium permanganate may be furnished by the storeroom; in

this case, the stock standard should be stabilized by the addition of sulfuric acid and potassium periodate.

2. This solution will contain a total of 0.0250 g of manganese. In the standardization of permanganate against oxalate, the gme of manganese is $54.94/5000 = 0.01099$. The volume of standard permanganate required is computed from the relation:

$$ml \times N \times 0.01099 = 0.0250$$

3. Pipets of appropriate capacities, e.g., 2, 5 and 10 ml, may be used instead of the buret if desired.

4. Unless several 100-ml volumetric flasks are provided in the locker equipment, transfer the first diluted standard to another *dry* container, such as a small bottle, Erlenmeyer flask, or large test tube, which is then stoppered to prevent evaporation. If cork or rubber stoppers are used, care must be taken that the solution does not contact the stopper and result in reduction of the permanganate. Rinse the volumetric flask with water, prepare the second dilute standard, and so on. Most efficient use is made of the instrument and of the student's time if all the solutions are prepared so they can be measured in succession when the student goes to the instrument room. Because of possible traces of reducing substances in the distilled water, the diluted permanganate solutions may not be stable for more than a few hours. The color standards must be measured during the same laboratory period in which they are prepared. However, the permanganate in the steel sample solutions is stable (why?), and can be kept indefinitely.

5. The dials or meters of most instruments have a dual scale, one reading percent transmittance, the other reading absorbance (also called "optical density"). Read and record both percent transmittance and absorbance. Either function may be used for constructing the calibration curve. If the scale reads only in percent transmittance, these readings can be converted to absorbances through the relation $A = -\log T$, where $T = \%T/100$.

6. In the author's laboratory, Bausch and Lomb Spectronic 20 instruments (see Fig. 31-6) are used for this experiment. Various makes of filter photometers are also satisfactory. Beckman spectrophotometers Models B, DU, DB, and DK-1 are also available, but are generally reserved for more advanced instruction and research. It is suggested that the student be furnished mimeographed operating instructions for the instrument to be used.

7. If a filter photometer is used, insert the green or yellow-green filter.

8. Fluctuations in line voltage may cause some fluctuations of the meter needle. Checking back and forth and taking the average of several readings gives greater reliability of the data. The cells should match within $1\% T$ or less. If they differ by more than 1%, use the cell having the higher transmittance for the blank, adjust the instrument to read $100\% T$ (zero absorbance), then insert the other cell—to be used for the sample solutions to be measured—and read

its *absorbance*. Apply this value as a subtractive correction to subsequent *absorbance* readings. (Why is the correction made in terms of absorbance rather than transmittance?) It is important that the cells be placed always in the same position in the instrument, and (unless the cells match perfectly) that the blank solution always be placed in the same cell and that all samples are measured in the other cell of the pair.

9. If there is no sink or trough near the instrument, use a large beaker for discarding rinsings and solutions after measurement. Take extreme care not to spill or splash any liquid on the instrument.

10. For more careful work in spectrophotometry the blank usually contains all the reagents used in preparation of the colored solution, but of course none of the desired constituent. In the calibration procedure of this method, the reagents used have no appreciable absorption at the wavelength of the measurement to be made, hence use of a water blank is permissible.

11. Because different instruments, even of the same make and model, have somewhat different response characteristics, it is mandatory that the calibration standards and the unknown solutions be measured on the same instrument and with the same absorption cells. A record of the serial number of the instrument on the analysis report also aids the instructor in making certain that all instruments are operating satisfactorily.

12. Semilog graph paper has logarithmically spaced rulings along one axis and linearly spaced rulings on the other axis. If any transmittance reading is less than 10%, use two-cycle paper; otherwise, one-cycle paper is satisfactory.

13. When filter photometers, rather than spectrophotometers, are used, the transmittance (absorbance) at high concentrations usually changes less rapidly with concentration than is demanded by Beer's law, and the curves flatten out in the high concentration region. In the present experiment, good linearity is obtained, even with filter photometers, up to about 1.5 mg of manganese per 100 ml of solution. The Spectronic 20 instrument gives a linear plot over the entire concentration range of this experiment.

14. The Ringbom method of plotting is discussed in Chap. 31 and is illustrated in Figs. 31-14 and 31-15. This type of plot can also be used as a calibration curve, but more experimental points would be needed to get an exact location of the curve.

15. Additional boiling expels sulfur dioxide and oxides of nitrogen.

16. In some samples a black residue remains after the peroxydisulfate treatment. If the residue is in small amount, it may be ignored except where greater accuracy is required. If there is more than a trace of black residue, filter it off and wash it with four or five portions of water. Collect the washings with the filtrate. Then proceed to the addition of phosphoric acid, etc.

17. Obtain potassium periodate from the laboratory instructor. The reagent is an expensive chemical; do not waste it.

18. The iron(III) in solution has been converted to a colorless complex by

the phosphoric acid; other components that may be present, such as chromium, nickel, cobalt, etc., contribute color and may interfere to some extent, especially if they are present in relatively large amounts. By reducing the permanganate, the blank contains all other components that might contribute to the absorbance of the sample.

19. There is no fundamental reason for avoiding a curved part of the calibration curve for analysis of unknowns if the exact location of the curve has been determined by measurement of a sufficient number of standards. In the present experiment this is hardly the case in the range 1.0 to 2.0 mg of manganese per 100 ml of solution. On the other hand, when experimental points follow a linear relation in the functions plotted, only a few experimental points are required to establish the calibration curve (straight line).

20. If it becomes necessary to dilute the sample solution to get it into an appropriate range for measurement, the blank solution should be diluted in the same ratio as the sample.

21. For samples containing a few tenths up to 1 or 2% of manganese, triplicates should agree within a few hundredths of a percent of manganese.

EXPERIMENT 39-3 SPECTROPHOTOMETRIC ANALYSIS OF A MIXTURE

Reference: Chap. 31, pp. 468–470.

Apparatus and Reagents

Spectrophotometer and absorption tubes or cells.
Manganese stock solution: 4.0×10^{-3} M $KMnO_4$ in 0.5 M sulfuric acid, stabilized with KIO_4.
Chromium stock solution: 1.00×10^{-2} M $K_2Cr_2O_7$ in 0.5 M sulfuric acid.
Diluent: 0.5 M sulfuric acid.

Preparation of Solutions

Prepare the following solutions by volumetric dilution, starting with the appropriate stock solution.
Solution A: In a 50-ml volumetric flask, prepare 4.0×10^{-4} M solution of $KMnO_4$ in 0.5 M sulfuric acid.
Solution B: Dilute a portion of Solution A with an equal volume of 0.5 M sulfuric acid.
Solution C: Dilute a portion of Solution B with an equal volume of 0.5 M sulfuric acid.
Solution D: In a 50-ml volumetric flask, prepare 1.00×10^{-3} M solution of $K_2Cr_2O_7$ in 0.5 M sulfuric acid.

Solution E: Dilute a portion of Solution D with an equal volume of 0.5 M sulfuric acid.

Solution F: Dilute a portion of Solution E with an equal volume of 0.5 M sulfuric acid.

Solution G: In a 50-ml volumetric flask prepare a solution that is 2.0×10^{-4} M in $KMnO_4$, 5.0×10^{-4} in $K_2Cr_2O_7$, and 0.5 M in sulfuric acid.

In a 50-ml volumetric flask obtain, from the laboratory instructor, an unknown solution containing $KMnO_4$ and $K_2Cr_2O_7$; make the solution to volume with 0.5 M sulfuric acid. (Note 1.)

Measurement

Measure the absorbance of each of the above solutions, A through G, and also the unknown solution, against a 0.5 M sulfuric acid blank, at 526 mμ and at 440 mμ (Note 2).

Calculations

From the measured absorbances of Solutions A, B, and C, calculate the molar absorptivity of $KMnO_4$, and the average of the three values, at both 526 and 440 mμ.

From the measured absorbances of Solutions D, E, and F, calculate the molar absorptivity of $K_2Cr_2O_7$, and the average of the three values, at both 526 and 440 mμ.

For Solution G, compare the measured absorbance at each wavelength with the sum of the absorbances of the separate components at the same concentrations; are the absorbances additive, within experimental error?

Calculate the concentration of each component in the unknown (after dilution to 50 ml for measurement); report the results in terms of molar concentration of $KMnO_4$ and of $K_2Cr_2O_7$, and also as ppm manganese and ppm chromium.

See Note 3 for an optional experiment using Solutions A through F.

Notes

1. A wide variety of unknowns can be prepared by the instructor (or by storeroom personnel) by using accurately measured volumes of the stock solutions, and keeping within the concentration ranges of the solutions measured. The method is applicable to the determination of manganese and chromium in steel. In this case, weighed steel samples, about 1 gram, are dissolved in a mixture of sulfuric and phosphoric acid, and the chromium and manganese oxidized first with peroxydisulfate (with Ag^+ catalyst) and then with periodate. The solution is made to known volume, and the absorbance measured at 526 and at 440 mμ. Calculations are made, as with the solution unknown, by solving

the appropriate simultaneous equations; results should be reported as percent manganese and percent chromium in the steel.

2. If desired, the appropriate wavelengths for measurement may be determined by the student from the spectral curve of Solution A and of Solution D. If a recording spectrophotometer is available, record the absorbance of Solution A over the wavelength region 700 to 400 mμ; roll back the recorder chart and record the absorbance of Solution D over the same wavelength region. Point-by-point scanning, although tedious, can be done on other spectrophotometers (e.g., B. and L. Spectronic 20, Beckman Model B or DU). Measure the absorbance over the range 600 to 400 mμ at 10-mμ intervals, except where absorbance is changing rapidly with wavelength, in which case measure at 5- or even at 2-mμ intervals. (Note that the zero and infinity absorbance points on the instrument must be adjusted each time a wavelength setting is changed.) Plot, on a single graph, absorbance against wavelength for both solutions. What two wavelengths are the most suitable for analysis of permanganate and dichromate mixtures? Explain.

3. An interesting and important method of plotting spectrophotometric data can be illustrated with the solutions prepared above. A recording spectrophotometer should be used—point-by-point scanning of the six spectral curves is time consuming. Record the absorbance of Solution A over the wavelength region 700 to 400 mμ. Roll back the recorder chart, and record the absorbance of Solution B over the same wavelength region. Repeat with Solution C. On a new portion of chart paper record, in the same way and over the same wavelength region, the absorbance of Solutions D, E, and F. Are the curves for a given solute superimposable by translation along the absorbance axis? On a sheet of semilog graph paper, plot absorbance on the log scale as ordinate against wavelength as abscissa, for the three permanganate solutions. Make a similar plot for the three dichromate solutions. Are the curves for a given solute superimposable by translation along the absorbance axis? Explain, How could plots of log absorbance against wavelength be used to determine the concentration of an unknown solution of the solute?

EXPERIMENT **39-4 COMPOSITION OF A COMPLEX**

Reference: Chap. 31, pp. 470–472.

Apparatus and Reagents

Spectrophotometer and absorption tubes or cells.

Stock solution A: Ferrous ion, 0.0100 M. Dissolve 3.92 g of reagent grade $FeSO_4 \cdot (NH_4)_2 SO_4 \cdot 6H_2O$ in water, add 1 or 2 ml 6 M sulfuric acid, and dilute to 1 liter.

Stock solution B: 1,10-phenanthroline, 0.0100 *M*. Dissolve 1.98 g of the monohydrate in the smallest amount of ethanol, and dilute with water to one liter.

Hydroquinone, 1% aqueous solution.

Hydrochloric acid, 0.1 *M*.

A. METHOD OF CONTINUOUS VARIATIONS

Preparation of Solutions

Using volumetric flasks (Note 1), prepare an exact 1 : 10 dilution of stock solution A and of stock solution B; label these solutions C and D, respectively. Using burets or measuring pipets for delivering solutions C and D, prepare each of the following mixtures in a 50-ml volumetric flask:

1. 8.0 ml of C + 2.0 ml of D
2. 6.0 ml of C + 4.0 ml of D
3. 4.0 ml of C + 6.0 ml of D
4. 3.0 ml of C + 7.0 ml of D
5. 2.5 ml of C + 7.5 ml of D
6. 2.0 ml of C + 8.0 ml of D
7. 1.5 ml of C + 8.5 ml of D
8. 1.0 ml of C + 9.0 ml of D
9. 2.5 ml of C + 20.0 ml of D (Note 2)

To each solution add 1 ml of 1% hydroquinone and 0.5 ml of 0.1 *M* hydrochloric acid (small graduate), and dilute with water to 50 ml. Mix each solution thoroughly, and allow the solutions to stand for one hour at room temperature.

Measurement

Set the wavelength scale of the spectrophotometer at 508 mμ, and follow the usual procedure to set the absorbance reference points on the spectrophotometer dial or meter. Measure the absorbance of each of the above solutions, using water as a blank.

Plotting and Calculations

On linear graph paper, and using the data for solutions 1 through 8, plot absorbance as ordinate against mole fraction of D as abscissa. (Note 3.) Draw a smooth curve through the experimental points (best fit). Extrapolate the segments of the curve to a point of intersection, and note the value of the absorbance at this point; how does it compare with the measured absorbance of solution 9? Deduce the composition of the complex in terms of the number of moles of 1,10-phenanthroline that react with one mole of Fe^{++}

Use the absorbance of solution 9 and the absorbance of the solution in the above series corresponding to the composition of the complex to calculate the formation constant of the ferrous–phenanthroline complex. Compare the calculated value with a value obtained from the literature. [See I. M. Kolthoff, T. S. Lee, and D. Leussing, *Ind. Eng. Chem., Anal. Ed.*, **20**, 985 (1948).] Speculate on the cause of any discrepancy.

B. MOLE RATIO METHOD

Preparation of Solutions

Into each of nine 50-ml volumetric flasks deliver 2.0 ml of solution C and, to the respective flasks, 2.0, 4.0, 5.0, 6.0, 7.0, 8.0, 10.0, 12.0, and 15.0 ml of solution D. To each flask add 1.0 ml of 1 % hydroquinone and 0.5 ml of 0.1 *M* hydrochloric acid (small graduate), then dilute to the mark with distilled water, mix the solutions well. Let the solutions stand at room temperature for one hour.

Measurement

Measure the absorbance of each solution at 508 mμ, against a water blank.

Plotting and Calculations

On linear graph paper plot absorbance against the number of moles of 1,10-phenanthroline per mole of Fe^{++}. (For this purpose, volume of solution D taken, per unit volume of solution C taken, can be used in lieu of actual molar concentrations; why?) From the graph, deduce the number of moles of 1,10-phenanthroline that react with one mole of Fe^{++} to form the complex.

Use the absorbance of the last solution (15 ml D/2 ml C) and the absorbance of the solution corresponding to the mole ratio in the reaction to calculate the formation constant of the complex. Compare this value with the value determined in part A and with the literature value.

Notes

1. If both parts A and B of this experiment are to be performed, prepare 100 ml of solution C, and 200 or 250 ml of solution D. If only part A of the experiment is to be performed, prepare 50 ml of solution C and 100 ml of solution D.

2. The absorbance of solution 9, containing a large excess of 1,10-phenanthroline, represents complete conversion of Fe^{++} to the complex. Locate its position on the graph for part A.

3. Mole fraction of $D = [D]/([C] + [D])$; the volumes taken for preparation of the solutions can be used as if they were concentrations.

SUGGESTIONS FOR FURTHER WORK

Many systems can be used to illustrate the above methods for determining reaction ratios. In several instances, more than one complex is formed; in such cases, the spectral curves for the different complexes should be determined, and absorbance measurements for the method of continuous variations and for the mole ratio method made at appropriate wavelengths. Sometimes the formation of successive complexes is pH dependent, so that pH control and measurement of absorbances at different pH values is necessary. Some of the systems that are suitable for measurement are:

Iron(III) and sulfosalicylic acid.
Iron(III) and thiocyanate.
Palladium(II) or platinum(II) and 2,3-quinoxalinedithiol.
Platinum(II) or (IV) and tin(II) in hydrochloric acid.
Iron(III) and "tiron" (catechol disulfonic acid, sodium salt) at different pH values.

Literature on the above methods should be consulted for proper preparation of solutions with respect to various additives such as acid, organic solvent, etc.

40

ELECTROMETRIC METHODS

Reference: Chap. 32, II.

Apparatus and Reagents

pH meter, with glass and calomel electrodes.
Stirring motor and glass stirrer or magnetic stirrer and bar.
50-ml buret, preferably with offset delivery tip.
Standard solution of oxalic acid, 0.100 M: dissolve 12.6 g of reagent grade oxalic acid dihydrate and make to 1 liter.
Approximately 0.1 M sodium hydroxide.
Approximately 0.1 M ammonium hydroxide.
Buffer solution, pH 7.0 for standardizing the pH meter.

Procedure

Study the operating instructions for the pH meter to be used. Consult the laboratory instructor regarding preparation of the electrodes and assembly of the apparatus. Standardize the pH meter with a small amount of pH 7.0 buffer.

1. Titration with Sodium Hydroxide.   (Before proceeding with the titration, it is recommended that the student estimate the approximate end-point pH from the ionization constants of oxalic acid.) Transfer exactly 20.0 ml (pipet) of the standard oxalic acid solution to a 250-ml beaker, and add 80 ml (graduate) distilled water. Immerse the electrodes in the solution in such a position that there is no danger of contact with the stirring bar or paddle. Rinse and fill a 50-ml buret with the 0.1 *M* sodium hydroxide. Adjust the meniscus exactly to zero; for facilitating subsequent calculations it is convenient to add the titrant in "whole number" increments, such as 5.00, 1.00, 0.50, 0.10 ml. Stir the solution in the beaker at a moderate rate to avoid splattering; record the buret reading and the *p*H reading. Add 5.00 ml of titrant, stir for about 30 seconds or until the *p*H becomes constant, and record the buret and the *p*H readings. Repeat with another 5.00-ml portion of titrant, and continue in the same way. The stoichiometric point is the point of greatest rate of change of *p*H with addition of titrant. Some indication of the approach of the stoichiometric point is given by the value of ΔpH per unit volume of titrant; it is useful, therefore, to calculate and record, for each increment of titrant, the value of ΔpH per 0.10 ml of titrant (these values will also be needed later). Be careful not to overstep the stoichiometric point by the addition of a large increment of titrant; if this happens, the titration must be started anew. As the stoichiometric point is approached, add the titrant in smaller increments, for example, 0.50 and finally 0.10 ml. Continue the titration to about 20% beyond the stoichiometric point; the increments of titrant added may be increased as the titration progresses farther beyond the stoichiometric point.

Discard the solution, and rinse the beaker and the buret in preparation for the next titration.

2. Titration with Ammonium Hydroxide.   Repeat the titration, using the same amount of oxalic acid sample and water, and titrating with the 0.1 *M* ammonium hydroxide. Around the stoichiometric point, use 0.10 ml increments of titrant, and carry the titration to about 20% excess titrant.

Plotting

1. On graph paper, plot *p*H as ordinate against ml of titrant as abscissa, for the entire titration by both titrants. Draw a smooth curve to fit the experimental points, and estimate, as closely as possible by inspection, the stoichiometric *p*H and titrant volume, for each curve.

2. For the region of a few milliliters on each side of the equivalence point, calculate ΔpH per 0.10 ml of titrant, and plot these values as ordinate against the volume of titrant as abscissa. The curves for both titrations may be put on the same sheet of graph paper, although it may be necessary to use different ordinate units for the two curves. The equivalence point on this first derivative plot is the point where the ΔpH function is maximum. Locate, as closely as possible, the stoichiometric volume of each titrant.

3. From the ΔpH/0.10 ml values obtained in 2 above, calculate the *change* in ΔpH per 0.10 ml of titrant (the second derivative function is written $\Delta^2 p$H$/\Delta V^2$); plot these values as ordinate against volume of titrant as abscissa. The second derivative becomes zero at the equivalence point. Locate the exact stoichiometric volume of each titrant.

Calculations

1. Is potentiometric detection of the end point suitable for *stepwise* titration of the two protons of oxalic acid? Explain.

2. Calculate the normality of the NaOH and of the NH_4OH solution.

3. Compare the observed and the calculated pH at the initial point (before any base has been added).

4. For each titration: from the observed pH and the concentration of oxalate ion at the stoichiometric point, calculate pK_2 of oxalic acid, and compare with the known value.

5. For each titration: from the observed pH at $3/4$ the stoichiometric volume of titrant, calculate pK_2 of oxalic acid; compare with the value found in item 4 above, and with the known value.

6. For each titration: from the observed pH at $1/2$ the stoichiometric volume of titrant and the known value of pK_2, calculate pK_1 of oxalic acid, and compare with the known value.

SUGGESTIONS FOR FURTHER WORK

Titration of 0.10 M phosphoric acid with 0.1 M sodium hydroxide; calcula- , tion of K_1, K_2, and K_3 of phosphoric acid.

Precipitation and redox titrations, using appropriate indicator electrodes and a potentiometer.

Determination of formation constants of complexes, and K_{sp} of slightly soluble ionogens, from the measured emf of an appropriately constructed cell with respect to electrodes and solution.

For details on the above and similar methods of potentiometry, consult the references cited below.[1-3]

EXPERIMENT **40-2 POLAROGRAPHY**

Reference: Chap. 32, III.

Apparatus and Reagents

Polarograph, preferably automatic recording; however, a manually operated instrument is entirely satisfactory.

Capillary and mercury reservoir assembly.

[1] H. H. Willard, L. L. Merritt, Jr., and J. A. Dean, *Instrumental Methods of Analysis*, 4th ed., Princeton, N.J., Van Nostrand, 1965.

[2] C. E. Meloan and R. W. Kiser, *Problems and Experiments in Instrumental Analysis*, Columbus, Ohio, Merrill, 1963.

[3] C. N. Reilley and D. T. Sawyer, *Experiments for Instrumental Methods*, New York, McGraw-Hill, 1961.

H-form polarographic vessel, with saturated calomel electrode in one side and salt-agar bridge in the cross-arm.

Stop watch.

Cadmium chloride solution, 0.100 *M*.

Potassium chloride solution, 2.5 *M* (for supporting electrolyte).

Tank nitrogen for de-aeration of solutions.

Procedure

Study carefully the operating instructions for the instrument to be used. Consult the laboratory instructor as may be necessary.

Solution 1.   Into a 100-ml volumetric flask pipet 5.0 ml of 0.100 *M* cadmium chloride solution; add 40 ml (graduate) of 2.5 *M* potassium chloride, and dilute with distilled water to the mark.

Solution 2.   In a 100-ml volumetric flask obtain from the instructor an unknown cadmium chloride solution (Note 1). Add 5.0 ml (pipet) of the 0.100 *M* cadmium chloride stock solution and 40 ml of 2.5 *M* potassium chloride, and dilute to the mark.

Thoroughly rinse the solution side of the H-cell with distilled water, then with two small portions of Solution 1, and finally fill the cell with the solution to above the cross-arm and to a depth that will receive the capillary. De-aerate the solution for 15 minutes with a slow stream of nitrogen. Record the polarogram (Note 2). Also make a record of the various operating control settings, such as bridge voltage, sensitivity or current multiplier setting, galvanometer sensitivity, etc.

On completion of the measurements with Solution 1, and without disturbing the cell and capillary assembly, set the voltage at a value on the plateau of the polarographic wave. Using a stop watch, accurately measure the time for 20 drops to fall, and calculate the drop time, *t*, in seconds.

Through the stopcock of the polarographic vessel draw off the mercury into the bottle for waste mercury, then discard the solution; rinse and fill the cell with Solution 2, and start its de-aeration. Meanwhile, accurately weigh a clean, dry weighing bottle. Dry the dropping mercury capillary tube with cleansing tissue, and clamp the capillary at the same level as when used for recording the polarogram, so as to give the same head of mercury. In the weighing bottle, collect the mercury that drops from the capillary in three or four minutes, accurately timed with a stop watch. Weigh the bottle and mercury, and calculate *m*, the weight of mercury flowing per unit time, expressed in milligrams per second.

Record the polarogram of Solution 2 (Note 2). Upon completion, remove the mercury from the H-cell, discard the solution, rinse the cell, and replace the equipment exactly as found. *Any spilled mercury must be cleaned up immediately*; consult the instructor for the method.

Plotting

Conversion of instrument readings to current in microamperes need not be made for plotting purposes; however, actual current will be needed for certain calculations.

Graph 1. For each of the cadmium solutions plot, on the same sheet of graph paper, galvanometer readings (or current) as ordinate against applied voltage as abscissa. If automatic recording was used, draw a smooth curve through the mid-point of the oscillatory trace, and read off current-voltage points for this graph.

Graph 2. For Solution 1, determine i and $i_d - i$ from Graph 1 as follows: extrapolate the residual current line and the limiting current line (plateau) to cover the voltage range of the rising portion of the polarographic wave. The vertical distance from the (extrapolated) residual current line to the wave line is i; the vertical distance from the wave line to the (extrapolated) limiting current line is $i_d - i$. For several (six or eight) values of applied voltage in the *ascending part of the wave*, read off the values and tabulate under the following headings:

$$E_{d.e.} \quad i \quad i_d - i \quad \frac{i}{i_d - i} \quad \log \frac{i}{i_d - i}$$

Plot log $[i/(i_d - i)]$ as ordinate against $E_{d.e.}$ as abscissa.

Calculations

1. From the wave heights in Graph 1, and operating conditions, as applicable, determine the diffusion current, i_d, in microamperes, for each of the two solutions.

2. From the i_d values (Note 3) and the known concentration of Solution 1, calculate the concentration of Solution 2 and then of the unknown received; report in terms of millimoles and also in grams of cadmium per liter of the solution measured.

3. On each curve of Graph 1, construct for the determination of the half-wave potential, $E_{1/2}$; compare with the literature value.

4. From Graph 2, what is the value of the half-wave potential? Compare with the value from 3 and with the literature value. How many electrons are gained, per cadmium ion, in the electrode reaction? Show method.

5. Use the i_d value (in microamperes) for Solution 1 and the concentration of cadmium, in millimoles per liter, and calculate the **diffusion current constant,** I_d.

6. Use I_d calculated in 5 and i_d for solution 2, and calculate the concentration of cadmium in Solution 2. Compare with the value determined directly from the diffusion current values of the two solutions.

Notes

1. The instructor can easily prepare unknowns by using accurately measured volumes of the stock 0.100 *M* cadmium chloride solution, delivered directly into the 100-ml flask and followed by the addition of several milliliters of water.

2. If a manually operated instrument is used, after each new setting of the applied voltage, read and record the *average* position of the galvanometer oscillation.

3. Use either the linear measurements from Graph 1, or the i_d values, in microamperes, calculated in item 1, for calculation of concentrations.

EXPERIMENT **40-3** ELECTROLYTIC DETERMINATION OF COPPER

Reference: Chap. 32, IV.

Accurately weigh duplicate 1-g samples of the dried copper unknown (Notes 1, 2). Prepare a 1 : 2 sulfuric acid solution by *carefully* pouring 10 ml of concentrated sulfuric acid, with good stirring, *into* 20 ml of cold distilled water. (Caution! Much heat is generated.) Add 15 ml of the diluted sulfuric acid to each sample. Cover the beaker with a watch glass, and warm the mixture to dissolve the sample completely, or until only a white residue remains (Note 3). Cool the solution to room temperature (Note 4), then cautiously add 50 ml distilled water, in small portions and with good stirring, and cooling if necessary. If any insoluble material is present, filter it off (Note 5), wash it well with small portions of hot water, and collect the washings with the main filtrate. Add 1 ml of *freshly boiled* concentrated nitric acid (Notes 6, 7). The volume of solution for electrolysis should be 100 to 150 ml.

Meanwhile, obtain the platinum electrodes, and prepare the gauze cathodes for use. Clean the electrodes by immersing them for a short time in warm 1 : 1 nitric acid; then rinse well with tap water and distilled water, and finally with 95% ethyl alcohol or with acetone. *Do not touch the gauze surface* with the fingers at any time after the nitric acid treatment, otherwise the copper deposit may not adhere to the electrode. Place the electrodes in a 100°C oven for *not more than two minutes*, cool in the desiccator, and weigh the electrodes accurately. The stirring loop anodes should be clean, but no special precautions are required (Note 8).

Connect the stirring anode to the chuck of the stirring motor. This chuck makes connection to the positive terminal of the direct-current source. Connect the weighed gauze cathode to the negative terminal so that the anode centers inside the gauze cylinder. Take care not to touch the gauze with the fingers. Test the anode for free rotation by turning the motor shaft *by hand*—not by starting the motor. It is imperative that the electrodes be positioned so there is absolutely no possibility of their coming in contact. Raise the beaker containing the sample under the electrodes, and adjust the height so the gauze cathode is almost covered with the solution; about 1 cm of the cathode should be above the liquid surface. Cover the beaker with a split watch glass to prevent loss of solution by spray from possible evolution of gas during the electrolysis.

Start the stirring motor, which should run at a speed that will give good stirring, but no danger of splashing. Turn on the direct current to the electrodes, and adjust the rheostat to give a current of 1–3 amp; the voltage across the electrodes should be 2–4 v (Note 9). Electrolyze for about 45 minutes, or longer if the solution still has any trace of blue color. When electrolysis is judged to be complete, rinse off the cover glass into the beaker, and if necessary add more water to the beaker to raise the liquid level about 5 mm above its former level. Continue the electrolysis for another 15 minutes. If no copper deposit has appeared on the fresh surface of the cathode, electrolysis is complete; otherwise, continue the electrolysis for another 15 to 30 minutes, and again test for complete deposition. Without turning off the current to the electrodes (the stirring motor may be turned off), slowly lower the beaker away from the electrodes, *at the same time rinsing the cathode* with a stream of water from the wash bottle, until finally the electrodes are entirely out of the solution (Note 10). Then turn off the current to the electrodes.

Disconnect the cathode from its terminal, immerse the gauze in distilled water to make sure all soluble substances are removed, then rinse it with alcohol or acetone and place it in a 100°C oven for *not more than two minutes*. Cool the cathode in a desiccator, and weigh it as soon as it has come to room temperature (Note 11). Calculate and report the percent copper in the sample.

Notes

1. Samples for student analysis generally contain copper oxide (and inert matter), easily soluble in warm 1 : 2 sulfuric acid. Other suitable student samples are: (1) mixtures of copper sulfate pentahydrate and potassium sulfate, which must *not* be dried before weighing; (2) copper-nickel alloys such as Monel metal; the alloy is dissolved in nitric acid, the excess of which is then expelled by fuming down with sulfuric acid.

2. Duplicate (rather than triplicate) samples are used in this analysis as a matter of convenience and economy of apparatus. Commercially available electrolysis equipment is often supplied in two-place models, permitting two samples to be electrolyzed simultaneously. In many laboratories the equipment (including platinum electrodes) for electrodeposition is somewhat limited, and its use must be carefully scheduled by the laboratory instructor.

3. The residue may be silica, and/or lead sulfate if any lead is present in the sample.

4. Do *not* add water to the *hot* sulfuric acid solution, because of danger of spattering, resulting in loss of sample and possible personal injury.

5. The electrolysis is best done in tall-form beakers, in order to have maximum depth of solution for a given volume. The filtrate may be collected directly in a tall-form beaker. If filtration is unnecessary, transfer the solution quantitatively to the electrolysis beaker.

6. Boiling destroys nitrite ion and removes oxides of nitrogen; the freshly boiled solution should be completely colorless. If nitrite ion is present in the solution, the deposition of copper may be retarded; or sometimes the copper deposits satisfactorily at first, then rather suddenly redissolves from the cathode.

7. Nitric acid (i.e., nitrate ion in solution) acts as a cathodic depolarizer; see p. 530. By preventing the evolution of hydrogen at the cathode, the copper deposit is bright and adheres firmly to the electrode. A large amount of nitric acid is to be avoided on account of its solvent action on metallic copper.

8. The directions given are for the Fisher or the Sargent-Slomin apparatus, using a stirring anode. If the equipment at hand does not provide for a stirring anode, a plain platinum wire anode can be used, and stirring can be provided by an inexpensive electric or air-driven motor and a glass stirrer, or by a magnetic stirrer. If electrolysis is performed without stirring, electrolysis for three to four hours, or preferably overnight, may be required for complete deposition.

9. If nickel is present, the potential across the electrodes should not exceed 4 v. A current higher than 3 amp can be used without harm when electrolysis is made with stirring. It is advisable, however, to start the electrolysis at a low current and then gradually increase it if desired.

10. It is very important that the current not be interrupted while the electrodes are still in contact with the solution, otherwise some of the copper will redissolve.

11. Clean the copper deposit from the cathode by immersing it in warm 1 : 1 nitric acid for a short time. Rinse thoroughly with water and then with alcohol or acetone. Return all electrodes to the laboratory instructor or to the storeroom immediately upon completion of the determination. Under no circumstances shall the platinum electrodes be retained by the student from one laboratory period to another.

41

ANALYTICAL SEPARATIONS

EXPERIMENT **41-1** **SEPARATION OF IRON(III) FROM CHROMIUM(III) BY SOLVENT EXTRACTION**[1]

Reference: Chap. 12.

To the sample solution (Note 1) add concentrated hydrochloric acid and water as necessary to give a final volume of not more than 50 ml of solution which is 7 M in hydrochloric acid (Note 2). Transfer the solution to a 250-ml Squibb-form separatory funnel, using a minimum of 7 M hydrochloric acid for rinsing in transfer. Add an equal volume of 1 : 1 mixture of methyl isobutyl ketone (4-methyl-2-pentanone) and amyl acetate. Stopper the funnel, and shake it for 15 seconds. Allow the phases to separate, then draw off the aqueous (lower) layer directly into a second separatory funnel (Note 3). To the aqueous solution, in a separatory funnel, add an equal volume of the organic solvent mixture, and again shake for 15 seconds, let stand for separation of phases, then draw off the aqueous layer into an Erlenmeyer flask (Note 4). Combine the two organic extracts into one separatory funnel; add 50 ml of 7 M hydrochloric acid, shake for 15 seconds, and after separation of phases, draw off the aqueous layer (Note 5). Shake the acid solution with 5–10 ml of the organic solvent to recover any traces of iron that may have back extracted. Combine the organic layers and measure the total volume (Note 6).

Spectrophotometric Determination of Iron in the Extract. Large amounts of iron can be determined directly on the organic extract; the $HFeCl_4$ solute in

---

[1] Adapted from A. Classen and L. Bastings, *Z. anal. Chem.*, **160**, 403 (1958). The method is also applicable to the separation of iron(III) from many other elements, such as aluminum, lead, manganese, nickel, cobalt, copper, titanium, thorium, etc.

this solvent mixture has maximum absorbance at 532 mμ. Measure the absorbance of the solution against a blank consisting of the organic solvent mixture that has been equilibrated with 7 M hydrochloric acid, and compare the absorbance against a calibration curve prepared from measurements of known amounts of iron(III) carried through the procedure. Calculate and report the milligrams of iron in the sample received.

Small amounts (microgram quantities) of iron are best determined spectrophotometrically on the aqueous solution after back extraction (see next paragraph) and reduction, using 1,10-phenanthroline as the color reagent (see Exp. 39-4).

Back extraction and titrimetric determination of iron. This method is applicable to relatively large amounts of iron. In a separatory funnel, shake the organic solution with 25 ml of distilled water (Note 6). Draw off and retain the aqueous layer. Repeat the back extraction of the organic solution with two more 25-ml portions of distilled water; combine the aqueous solutions. Acidify the solution with 5 ml of 6 M sulfuric acid, pass the solution through a Jones reductor (Note 7), and titrate the iron(II) with standard permanganate, dichromate, or cerium(IV) solution. Calculate and report the milligrams of iron in the sample received.

Determination of chromium. It is suggested that the analysis for chromium in the original aqueous phase be given to the student as a "library problem," to outline at least two distinctly different methods of determination that would be applicable. If desired, and a method is approved by the instructor, the student could perform the analysis.

Notes

1. Solution samples, issued by the storeroom or prepared by the instructor, are conveniently prepared by dissolving known weights of chromium(III) chloride and iron(III) chloride (or ferric alum) in water, adding hydrochloric acid, and making to known volume. Different measured small volumes of the solution can be issued as unknowns. Adjustment, by the student, of the final solution to 7 M in hydrochloric acid is simplified if the unknown solution is also 7 M in hydrochloric acid; the unknown may then be merely diluted, as desired, with 7 M hydrochloric acid.

2. Maximum extractability with the organic solvent is attained from solution that is 7 M in hydrochloric acid.

3. If a second funnel is not available, draw off the aqueous layer into a flask or beaker, and then the organic layer into another similar vessel; reserve both solutions for further treatment as directed.

4. If the aqueous layer is not to be analyzed for chromium, it may be discarded.

5. This layer would contain small amounts of cobalt, copper, and titanium, if present, that are extracted to a slight extent by the organic solvent.

6. The volume of organic extract is required for the calculation of iron content, if iron is determined by measuring the absorbance of the organic solution. If the iron is determined titrimetrically, the volume of the organic extract, and the volume of water used in the back extraction, need not be known.

7. Other methods of reducing the iron(III) to iron(II) may be used; see Chap. 27.

EXPERIMENT **41-2 DETERMINATION OF TOTAL CATION
CONTENT OF A SOLUTION BY ION EXCHANGE
(COLUMN OPERATION)**

Reference: Chap. 13, pp. 173–175.

Preparation of Ion Exchange Column

The glass column to be used is similar to the one used for making a Jones reductor, Fig. 27-1. Alternatively, a 50-ml buret from the student's desk equipment may be used. Place a glass-wool plug in the bottom of the tube. Add about 5 ml distilled water, fill the tip below the stopcock with water, and leave the glass-wool plug covered with a small amount of water. Place about 40 g of cation exchange resin (Note 1) in a beaker, cover it with 6 *M* hydrochloric acid (Note 2) and allow the mixture to stand for several minutes, with occasional stirring (Note 3). Decant the solution, and wash the resin several times by decantation to remove the acid (Note 4). Hold the column on a slant, and carefully pour in the resin slurry until the settled resin reaches a depth of 20–25 cm (or, if a buret is used for the column, until the resin reaches to about the 40-ml mark). Draw off water as necessary, but always leave 2 or 3 cm of water on top of the resin; make certain there are no air pockets in the resin bed. Place a glass-wool plug on top of the resin.

Analysis of Sample

By means of a pipet, introduce a measured volume of sample solution onto the column (Note 5). Slowly draw off 5.0 ml (graduate) of liquid (Note 6) and test it with one drop of methyl purple indicator. If the solution is not acidic, discard it. Continue collection of the effluent in 5.0-ml fractions, without loss, as distilled water is added to the top of the column. Transfer the first and all subsequent 5.0-ml fractions that show acidic reaction to *separate* Erlenmeyer flasks (Note 7); rinse the collection graduate with several small portions of distilled water, and add the rinsings to the fraction of effluent collected. Continue until a fraction collected does not give acidic reaction. Titrate each fraction with standard sodium hydroxide, about 0.1 *N* (Note 8). Calculate the number of milliequivalents of H^+ (and therefore of cation that displaced it) in each fraction, and plot this value as ordinate against the *cumulative* volume of effluent, from the start of the collection to complete elution of acid. Calculate and report the milliequivalents of cation per milliliter of sample analyzed.

Regeneration of Resin

Ion exchange resins can be used repeatedly for long periods of time if properly regenerated. **Do not discard the resin** into the waste jar, trough, or sink. When finished with the resin (see alternative experiments below), run 25 ml of 6 *M* hydrochloric acid through the resin column, followed by distilled water until the effluent is no longer acidic to methyl purple. Remove the glass-wool plug from the top of the resin column, and transfer the resin slurry to the side shelf bottle marked for "used cation exchange resin."

ALTERNATIVE EXPERIMENTS

Mineral Content of Raw Water

The procedure is generally the same as that described above. Owing to the wide variation in mineral content of natural water in different localities, specific directions on the volume of water sample and quantity of distilled water for elution covering all situations cannot be given. Details covering the local situation can be worked out by the instructor. All fractions of effluent giving acidic reaction when tested with indicator are combined for the titration; for most situations, the standard alkali for the titration should be about 0.01 *N*.

Preparation of Standard Acid by Ion Exchange

Dissolve a weighed amount (Note 9) of pure, dry sodium chloride or potassium chloride in a small amount of distilled water. Transfer the solution quantitatively onto a cation exchange column prepared as described earlier, and elute the acid with distilled water; collect the effluent in a volumetric flask of appropriate size. Finally, add distilled water to the mark on the volumetric flask, and mix the solution thoroughly. If desired, an aliquot of the solution can be titrated with standard alkali as a check on the preparation, or an aliquot of the acid solution can be used to standardize an alkaline solution.

Notes

1. Amberlite IR-120, or Dowex 50W-2X, is recommended. Other varieties of Amberlite or Dowex cation exchange resins may be used.

2. If it is known that the cation exchange resin is already in the hydrogen-ion form, treatment with acid is unnecessary. In this case, stir the resin with water,

decant, repeat two or three times, and allow the mixture to stand for several minutes before transferring the slurry to the column.

3. Ion exchange resins, as received, swell considerably in water or aqueous solutions, and might break the glass if swelling took place in the column.

4. Test with indicators such as methyl orange or methyl purple (a masked indicator) must show the "alkaline" color of the indicator; if a *p*H meter is used for the subsequent titration, the *p*H should be 6 or higher.

5. Convenient sample solutions for student unknowns contain alkali or alkaline earth chlorides, either singly or mixed. Add 5.0 or 10.0 ml (pipet) of sample solution, depending on the concentration of the unknown solution. See Note 9.

6. A flow rate of about 3 ml per minute should be used. When the liquid level has fallen to within 1 or 2 cm above the top of the resin, rinse down the wall of the column with distilled water, draw off more solution at the bottom, and nearly fill the column with distilled water. Continue in this manner during collection of the fractions of effluent.

7. If a plot of the elution curve is not desired, all of the fractions showing acidic reaction are combined for a single titration. If a plot is to be made, a record should be kept of the number of 5.0-ml portions of effluent, at the start of the collection, that do not show acidic reaction, so these can be included in the cumulative volume to be used in the plot.

8. The first and last acidic fractions may contain only a very small amount of acid; take care not to overstep the end point of the titration.

9. The resins specified have an exchange capacity of about 2 milliequivalents per milliliter of wet resin. Obviously, the amount of cation taken in the sample must be less than the total exchange capacity of the quantity of resin used.

EXPERIMENT **41-3 ANALYSIS OF AN INSOLUBLE SALT BY CATION EXCHANGE (BATCH OPERATION)**

Most insoluble salts, such as $BaSO_4$, $PbSO_4$, $AgCl$, $CaHPO_4$, etc., can react with sulfonic type resins in the acid form; for example,

$$2RSO_3H + BaSO_4 \rightarrow (RSO_3)_2Ba + SO_4^{--} + 2H^+$$

Titration of the acid liberated is a measure of the amount of insoluble salt transposed.

Prepare the cation exchange resin (Note 1) by the acid wash, followed by rinsing with distilled water, as described in Exp. 41-2, until the rinsings are no longer acidic. Place the sample to be analyzed (Note 2) in a 250-ml Erlenmeyer flask with about 50 ml distilled water, and add about 10 g of the prepared cation exchange resin. Also prepare a blank, using the same amount of water and resin. Heat the mixture on a steam bath or *low*-temperature hot plate, with frequent stirring, for one hour or until the sample has disappeared (Note 3). Decant the solution through a course filter paper; collect the filtrate in an Erlenmeyer flask. Transfer the resin to the filter with small portions of distilled water, and wash it thoroughly with small portions of distilled water; collect the washings with the main filtrate. Add an appropriate indicator (Note 4) and titrate the solution with standard alkali. Subtract the amount of the blank, and calculate and report the assay of the insoluble salt being analyzed.

Regenerate and save the used resin as described in Exp 41-2, unless the following additional experiment is to be performed.

Additional experiment. The resin from the above transposition contains the cation of the original insoluble salt. The cation can be displaced by treatment with strong acid, and then titrated with EDTA under suitable conditions and with an appropriate indicator. It is suggested that the student outline the details of such a method and submit them to the instructor; if the method is approved, the student may proceed with the determination.

Notes

1. Prepare 10 g of resin for each sample to be analyzed, plus 10 g for a blank. Amberlite IR-120 or Dowex 50W-2X is recommended.

2. As a finish method for the determination of sulfate, Exp. 35-3, the barium sulfate precipitate, after thorough washing with hot water, is transferred from the filter paper to an Erlenmeyer flask by puncturing the filter paper and flushing off the precipitate with a jet of water from the wash bottle, using a total of about 50 ml of water. If an original sample containing the insoluble material is to be analyzed, weigh samples of about 0.5 g.

3. Insoluble impurities such as silica will remain unaltered.

4. For strong acids, such as sulfuric or hydrochloric, use methyl orange or methyl purple indicator; for weak acids, such as phosphoric, use phenolphthalein indicator.

EXPERIMENT **41-4 THIN LAYER CHROMATOGRAPHY**

Materials for performing separations by thin layer chromatography (TLC), including "starter" kits, are available commercially (Note 1). Consult the laboratory instructor regarding the materials to be used, and the operational procedure to be followed if the thin layer plate is to be prepared by the student. Whatever the type, plate, film, or sheet, to be used, activate it by heating in the oven at 100°C for 15 to 30 minutes (Note 2).

The method will be illustrated by the separation of the components of ballpoint inks, and the identification of an unknown ink (Note 3). For each of the numbered "standard" inks and the unknown, select a portion of the writing where the ink is thick and heavy. Place this portion of the paper on a watch glass, or in the depression of a white spot plate, and extract the ink with a *small* amount of pyridine (*work in the hood*). Remove the paper, and allow the solvent to evaporate, without disturbance, nearly to dryness.

Pick up the concentrated extract in a clean capillary tube. Spot the extract from the standards and the unknown on the activated TLC plate in a straight line about 2 cm from the bottom of the plate, with the different spots about 2 cm apart. Keep the spots as small as possible; more of the same sample can be added to a spot if the solvent is allowed to evaporate completely between additions. Allow the solvent from all spots to evaporate before starting development of the chromatogram. Consult the laboratory instructor for any additional directions, such as the preparation of a "sandwich" developing chamber by use of a cover plate separated a short distance from the TLC material.

The developing solvent is a mixture of butyl alcohol, ethyl alcohol, and water, in the volume ratio 50 : 10 : 50. A narrow trough for containing the solvent can be fashioned from aluminum foil; place the trough in a jar or large beaker, and add the solvent to the trough to a depth of a few millimeters (Note 4). Immerse the lower edge of the prepared plate in the solvent mixture, and allow the chromatogram to develop to a distance of about 7 cm, or more if the size of the plate permits.

Measure the positions of the spots and the solvent front, and report the R_f values of the components of the various samples, and identify the pen that was used to make the unknown sample. Turn in the developed TLC plate to the laboratory instructor with the report.

Notes

1. The Mallinckrodt Chroma-Kit contains materials for preparation of a thin layer of hydrated silica adsorbent on a glass plate. (These materials have been used in our laboratory, hence the reference to "plate" in the directions.) Eastman chromatogram sheets, ready for use except for activation, consist of a layer of adsorbent silica gel on a flexible support film. Gelman instant thin layer chromatography (ITLC) sheets consist of special fiber glass impregnated with the absorbent.

2. If the activated TLC material is not to be used promptly, store it in a desiccator until ready to use it.

3. The laboratory instructor should provide several different brands of ball-point pens of the same nominal color, preferably blue, numbered for identification. Samples of the ink may be obtained by the student by making a thick, heavy mark with the pen on a piece of bond paper. The unknown is conveniently issued by the instructor in the form of a piece of paper on which the student's name or initials is written with the ink to be identified.

4. The solvent level must be below the position of the spotted samples when the plate is placed on edge in the trough.

Appendixes

APPENDIX I

Solubility Product Constants

Compound	Equilibrium	K_{sp}	pK_{sp}
Aluminum			
Hydroxide	$Al(OH)_3 \rightleftarrows Al^{+++} + 3OH^-$	2×10^{-32}	31.7
Phosphate	$AlPO_4 \rightleftarrows Al^{+++} + PO_4^{---}$	6.3×10^{-19}	18.20
Barium			
Arsenate	$Ba_3(AsO_4)_2 \rightleftarrows 3Ba^{++} + 2AsO_4^{---}$	8×10^{-51}	50.1
Carbonate	$BaCO_3 \rightleftarrows Ba^{++} + CO_3^{--}$	5.1×10^{-9}	8.29
Chromate	$BaCrO_4 \rightleftarrows Ba^{++} + CrO_4^{--}$	1.2×10^{-10}	9.93
Fluoride	$BaF_2 \rightleftarrows Ba^{++} + 2F^-$	1.0×10^{-6}	6.00
Hydroxide	$Ba(OH)_2 \rightleftarrows Ba^{++} + 2OH^-$	5.0×10^{-3}	2.30
Iodate	$Ba(IO_3)_2 \rightleftarrows Ba^{++} + 2IO_3^-$	6.5×10^{-10}	9.19
Manganate	$BaMnO_4 \rightleftarrows Ba^{++} + MnO_4^{--}$	2.5×10^{-10}	9.61
Oxalate	$BaC_2O_4 \rightleftarrows Ba^{++} + C_2O_4^{--}$	1.5×10^{-8}	7.82
Phosphate	$Ba_3(PO_4)_2 \rightleftarrows 3Ba^{++} + 2PO_4^{---}$	6×10^{-39}	38.2
Sulfate	$BaSO_4 \rightleftarrows Ba^{++} + SO_4^{--}$	1.0×10^{-10}	10.0
Sulfite	$BaSO_3 \rightleftarrows Ba^{++} + SO_3^{--}$	9.5×10^{-10}	9.02
Bismuth			
Arsenate	$BiAsO_4 \rightleftarrows Bi^{+++} + AsO_4^{---}$	4×10^{-10}	9.4
Hydroxide	$Bi(OH)_3 \rightleftarrows Bi^{+++} + 3OH^-$	4.3×10^{-31}	30.37
Phosphate	$BiPO_4 \rightleftarrows Bi^{+++} + PO_4^{---}$	1.3×10^{-23}	22.89
Sulfide	$Bi_2S_3 \rightleftarrows 2Bi^{+++} + 3S^{--}$	1×10^{-96}	96.0
Cadmium			
Arsenate	$Cd_3(AsO_4)_2 \rightleftarrows 3Cd^{++} + 2AsO_4^{---}$	2×10^{-33}	32.7

Compound	Equilbrium	K_{sp}	pK_{sp}
Cadmium			
Carbonate	$CdCO_3 \rightleftarrows Cd^{++} + CO_3^{--}$	5.2×10^{-12}	11.28
Hydroxide	$Cd(OH)_2 \rightleftarrows Cd^{++} + 2OH^-$	1.2×10^{-14}	13.93
Oxalate	$CdC_2O_4 \rightleftarrows Cd^{++} + C_2O_4^{--}$	1.8×10^{-8}	7.74
Sulfide	$CdS \rightleftarrows Cd^{++} + S^{--}$	7.1×10^{-27}	26.15
Calcium			
Arsenate	$Ca_3(AsO_4)_2 \rightleftarrows 3Ca^{++} + 2AsO_4^{---}$	6.4×10^{-19}	18.2
Carbonate	$CaCO_3 \rightleftarrows Ca^{++} + CO_3^{--}$	4.8×10^{-9}	8.32
Fluoride	$CaF_2 \rightleftarrows Ca^{++} + 2F^-$	4.0×10^{-11}	10.40
Hydroxide	$Ca(OH)_2 \rightleftarrows Ca^{++} + 2OH^-$	5.5×10^{-6}	5.26
Iodate	$Ca(IO_3)_2 \rightleftarrows Ca^{++} + 2IO_3^-$	7.1×10^{-7}	6.15
Oxalate	$CaC_2O_4 \rightleftarrows Ca^{++} + C_2O_4^{--}$	1.3×10^{-9}	8.89
Phosphate	$Ca_3(PO_4)_2 \rightleftarrows 3Ca^{++} + 2PO_4^{---}$	2.0×10^{-29}	28.70
Sulfate	$CaSO_4 \rightleftarrows Ca^{++} + SO_4^{--}$	1.2×10^{-6}	5.92
Cerium(III)			
Hydroxide	$Ce(OH)_3 \rightleftarrows Ce^{+++} + 3OH^-$	6.3×10^{-21}	20.2
Iodate	$Ce(IO_3)_3 \rightleftarrows Ce^{+++} + 3IO_3^-$	3.2×10^{-10}	9.50
Chromium(III)			
Hydroxide	$Cr(OH)_3 \rightleftarrows Cr^{+++} + 3OH^-$	6×10^{-31}	30.2
Phosphate	$CrPO_4 \rightleftarrows Cr^{+++} + PO_4^{---}$	2.4×10^{-23}	22.62
Cobalt(II)			
Carbonate	$CoCO_3 \rightleftarrows Co^{++} + CO_3^{--}$	8×10^{-13}	12.1
Hydroxide	$Co(OH)_2 \rightleftarrows Co^{++} + 2OH^-$	2.5×10^{-16}	15.60
Sulfide	$CoS \rightleftarrows Co^{++} + S^{--}$	5×10^{-22}	21.3
Copper(I)			
Bromide	$CuBr \rightleftarrows Cu^+ + Br^-$	5.9×10^{-9}	8.23
Chloride	$CuCl \rightleftarrows Cu^+ + Cl^-$	1.9×10^{-7}	6.73
Iodide	$CuI \rightleftarrows Cu^+ + I^-$	1.1×10^{-12}	11.93
Sulfide	$Cu_2S \rightleftarrows 2Cu^+ + S^{--}$	1×10^{-49}	49.0
Thiocyanate	$CuCNS \rightleftarrows Cu^+ + CNS^-$	1.9×10^{-13}	12.73
Copper(II)			
Arsenate	$Cu_3(AsO_4)_2 \rightleftarrows 3Cu^{++} + 2AsO_4^{---}$	8×10^{-36}	35.1
Carbonate	$CuCO_3 \rightleftarrows Cu^{++} + CO_3^{--}$	2.5×10^{-10}	9.60
Chromate	$CuCrO_4 \rightleftarrows Cu^{++} + CrO_4^{--}$	3.6×10^{-6}	5.44
Hydroxide	$Cu(OH)_2 \rightleftarrows Cu^{++} + 2OH^-$	2.2×10^{-20}	19.66
Oxalate	$CuC_2O_4 \rightleftarrows Cu^{++} + C_2O_4^{--}$	2.9×10^{-8}	7.54
Sulfide	$CuS \rightleftarrows Cu^{++} + S^{--}$	6×10^{-36}	35.2

Compound	Equilibrium	K_{sp}	pK_{sp}
Iron(II)			
Carbonate	$FeCO_3 \rightleftarrows Fe^{++} + CO_3^{--}$	3.5×10^{-11}	10.46
Hydroxide	$Fe(OH)_2 \rightleftarrows Fe^{++} + 2OH^-$	1.4×10^{-15}	14.84
Sulfide	$FeS \rightleftarrows Fe^{++} + S^{--}$	5.0×10^{-18}	17.30
Iron(III)			
Arsenate	$FeAsO_4 \rightleftarrows Fe^{+++} + AsO_4^{---}$	6×10^{-21}	20.2
Hydroxide	$Fe(OH)_3 \rightleftarrows Fe^{+++} + 3OH^-$	4.5×10^{-37}	36.35
Phosphate	$FePO_4 \rightleftarrows Fe^{+++} + PO_4^{---}$	1.4×10^{-22}	21.87
Lead			
Arsenate	$Pb_3(AsO_4)_2 \rightleftarrows 3Pb^{++} + 2AsO_4^{---}$	4×10^{-36}	35.4
Bromide	$PbBr_2 \rightleftarrows Pb^{++} + 2Br^-$	3.9×10^{-5}	4.41
Carbonate	$PbCO_3 \rightleftarrows Pb^{++} + CO_3^{--}$	1×10^{-13}	13.0
Chloride	$PbCl_2 \rightleftarrows Pb^{++} + 2Cl^-$	1.6×10^{-5}	4.79
Chromate	$PbCrO_4 \rightleftarrows Pb^{++} + CrO_4^{--}$	1.8×10^{-14}	13.75
Fluoride	$PbF_2 \rightleftarrows Pb^{++} + 2F^-$	2.7×10^{-8}	7.57
Hydroxide	$Pb(OH)_2 \rightleftarrows Pb^{++} + 2OH^-$	1.2×10^{-15}	14.93
Iodate	$Pb(IO_3)_2 \rightleftarrows Pb^{++} + 2IO_3^-$	2.6×10^{-13}	12.58
Iodide	$PbI_2 \rightleftarrows Pb^{++} + 2I^-$	6.5×10^{-9}	8.19
Oxalate	$PbC_2O_4 \rightleftarrows Pb^{++} + C_2O_4^{--}$	8.3×10^{-12}	11.08
Phosphate	$Pb_3(PO_4)_2 \rightleftarrows 3Pb^{++} + 2PO_4^{---}$	8.0×10^{-43}	42.10
Sulfate	$PbSO_4 \rightleftarrows Pb^{++} + SO_4^{--}$	1.6×10^{-8}	7.80
Sulfide	$PbS \rightleftarrows Pb^{++} + S^{--}$	7.1×10^{-29}	28.15
Magnesium			
Ammonium phosphate	$MgNH_4PO_4 \rightleftarrows Mg^{++} + NH_4^+ + PO_4^{---}$	2.5×10^{-13}	12.60
Arsenate	$Mg_3(AsO_4)_2 \rightleftarrows 3Mg^{++} + 2AsO_4^{---}$	2×10^{-20}	19.7
Carbonate	$MgCO_3 \rightleftarrows Mg^{++} + CO_3^{--}$	1×10^{-5}	5.0
Fluoride	$MgF_2 \rightleftarrows Mg^{++} + 2F^-$	6.4×10^{-9}	8.19
Hydroxide	$Mg(OH)_2 \rightleftarrows Mg^{++} + 2OH^-$	2.4×10^{-11}	10.63
Oxalate	$MgC_2O_4 \rightleftarrows Mg^{++} + C_2O_4^{--}$	8.6×10^{-5}	4.07
Manganese(II)			
Arsenate	$Mn_3(AsO_4)_2 \rightleftarrows 3Mn^{++} + 2AsO_4^{---}$	2×10^{-29}	28.7
Carbonate	$MnCO_3 \rightleftarrows Mn^{++} + CO_3^{--}$	1.8×10^{-11}	10.74
Hydroxide	$Mn(OH)_2 \rightleftarrows Mn^{++} + 2OH^-$	1.9×10^{-13}	12.72
Oxalate	$MnC_2O_4 \rightleftarrows Mn^{++} + C_2O_4^{--}$	1.1×10^{-15}	14.96
Sulfide	$MnS \rightleftarrows Mn^{++} + S^{--}$	1.1×10^{-15}	14.96
Mercury(I)			
Acetate	$Hg_2(Ac)_2 \rightleftarrows Hg_2^{++} + 2Ac^-$	3.6×10^{-10}	9.44
Bromide	$Hg_2Br_2 \rightleftarrows Hg_2^{++} + 2Br^-$	5.8×10^{-23}	22.24
Carbonate	$Hg_2CO_3 \rightleftarrows Hg_2^{++} + CO_3^{--}$	8.9×10^{-17}	16.05

Compound	Equilibrium	K_{sp}	pK_{sp}
Mercury (I)			
Chloride	$Hg_2Cl_2 \rightleftarrows Hg_2^{++} + 2Cl^-$	1.3×10^{-18}	17.88
Chromate	$Hg_2CrO_4 \rightleftarrows Hg_2^{++} + CrO_4^{--}$	2.0×10^{-9}	8.70
Cyanide	$Hg_2(CN)_2 \rightleftarrows Hg_2^{++} + 2CN^-$	5×10^{-40}	39.3
Hydroxide	$Hg_2(OH)_2 \rightleftarrows Hg_2^{++} + 2OH^-$	1.8×10^{-24}	23.74
Iodate	$Hg_2(IO_3)_2 \rightleftarrows Hg_2^{++} + 2IO_3^-$	2.0×10^{-14}	13.70
Iodide	$Hg_2I_2 \rightleftarrows Hg_2^{++} + 2I^-$	4.5×10^{-29}	28.35
Sulfate	$Hg_2SO_4 \rightleftarrows Hg_2^{++} + SO_4^{--}$	7.1×10^{-7}	6.15
Sulfide	$Hg_2S \rightleftarrows Hg_2^{++} + S^{--}$	1×10^{-48}	48.0
Thiocyanate	$Hg_2(CNS)_2 \rightleftarrows Hg_2^{++} + 2CNS^-$	3.0×10^{-20}	19.52
Mercury(II)			
Hydroxide	$Hg(OH)_2 \rightleftarrows Hg^{++} + 2OH^-$	3.0×10^{-26}	25.52
Iodide	$HgI_2 \rightleftarrows Hg^{++} + 2I^-$	8.8×10^{-12}	11.06
Sulfide	$HgS \rightleftarrows Hg^{++} + S^{--}$	1.6×10^{-54}	53.8
Nickel(II)			
Carbonate	$NiCO_3 \rightleftarrows Ni^{++} + CO_3^{--}$	6.6×10^{-9}	8.18
Hydroxide	$Ni(OH)_2 \rightleftarrows Ni^{++} + 2OH^-$	6.2×10^{-16}	15.21
Sulfide	$NiS \rightleftarrows Ni^{++} + S^{--}$	3×10^{-21}	20.5
Silver			
Acetate	$Ag(Ac) \rightleftarrows Ag^+ + Ac^-$	2.3×10^{-3}	2.64
Arsenate	$Ag_3AsO_4 \rightleftarrows 3Ag^+ + AsO_4^{---}$	1×10^{-23}	23.0
Bromate	$AgBrO_3 \rightleftarrows Ag^+ + BrO_3^-$	5.5×10^{-5}	4.26
Bromide	$AgBr \rightleftarrows Ag^+ + Br^-$	5.0×10^{-13}	12.30
Carbonate	$Ag_2CO_3 \rightleftarrows 2Ag^+ + CO_3^{--}$	8.1×10^{-12}	11.09
Chloride	$AgCl \rightleftarrows Ag^+ + Cl^-$	1.8×10^{-10}	9.75
Chromate	$Ag_2CrO_4 \rightleftarrows 2Ag^+ + CrO_4^{--}$	1.3×10^{-12}	11.89
Cyanide	$AgCN \rightleftarrows Ag^+ + CN^-$	1.6×10^{-14}	13.80
Hydroxide	$AgOH \rightleftarrows Ag^+ + OH^-$	2.6×10^{-8}	7.59
Iodate	$AgIO_3 \rightleftarrows Ag^+ + IO_3^-$	3.1×10^{-8}	7.51
Iodide	$AgI \rightleftarrows Ag^+ + I^-$	8.3×10^{-17}	16.08
Nitrite	$AgNO_2 \rightleftarrows Ag^+ + NO_2^-$	1.6×10^{-4}	3.80
Oxalate	$Ag_2C_2O_4 \rightleftarrows 2Ag^+ + C_2O_4^{--}$	1.1×10^{-11}	10.96
Phosphate	$Ag_3PO_4 \rightleftarrows 3Ag^+ + PO_4^{---}$	1.3×10^{-20}	19.89
Sulfate	$Ag_2SO_4 \rightleftarrows 2Ag^+ + SO_4^{--}$	1.7×10^{-5}	4.77
Sulfide	$Ag_2S \rightleftarrows 2Ag^+ + S^{--}$	3.3×10^{-52}	51.48
Thiocyanate	$AgCNS \rightleftarrows Ag^+ + CNS^-$	1.0×10^{-12}	12.00
Strontium			
Arsenate	$Sr_3(AsO_4)_2 \rightleftarrows 3Sr^{++} + 2AsO_4^{---}$	1×10^{-18}	18.0
Carbonate	$SrCO_3 \rightleftarrows Sr^{++} + CO_3^{--}$	1.1×10^{-10}	9.96
Chromate	$SrCrO_4 \rightleftarrows Sr^{++} + CrO_4^{--}$	3.6×10^{-5}	4.44

Compound	Equilibrium	K_{sp}	pK_{sp}
Strontium			
Fluoride	$SrF_2 \rightleftharpoons Sr^{++} + 2F^-$	2.5×10^{-9}	8.61
Iodate	$Sr(IO_3)_2 \rightleftharpoons Sr^{++} + 2IO_3^-$	3.3×10^{-7}	6.48
Oxalate	$SrC_2O_4 \rightleftharpoons Sr^{++} + C_2O_4^{--}$	5.6×10^{-10}	9.25
Phosphate	$Sr_3(PO_4)_2 \rightleftharpoons 3Sr^{++} + 2PO_4^{---}$	1×10^{-31}	31.0
Sulfate	$SrSO_4 \rightleftharpoons Sr^{++} + SO_4^{--}$	3.2×10^{-7}	6.49
Thallium(I)			
Bromide	$TlBr \rightleftharpoons Tl^+ + Br^-$	3.9×10^{-6}	5.41
Chloride	$TlCl \rightleftharpoons Tl^+ + Cl^-$	1.7×10^{-4}	3.76
Iodate	$TlIO_3 \rightleftharpoons Tl^+ + IO_3^-$	3.1×10^{-6}	5.51
Iodide	$TlI \rightleftharpoons Tl^+ + I^-$	6.5×10^{-8}	7.19
Sulfide	$Tl_2S \rightleftharpoons 2Tl^+ + S^{--}$	1×10^{-21}	21.0
Thallium(III)			
Hydroxide	$Tl(OH)_3 \rightleftharpoons Tl^{+++} + 3OH^-$	6.3×10^{-46}	45.20
Tin(II)			
Hydroxide	$Sn(OH)_2 \rightleftharpoons Sn^{++} + 2OH^-$	3.2×10^{-26}	25.50
Sulfide	$SnS \rightleftharpoons Sn^{++} + S^{--}$	1×10^{-26}	26.0
Zinc			
Arsenate	$Zn_3(AsO_4)_2 \rightleftharpoons 3Zn^{++} + 2AsO_4^{---}$	1.3×10^{-28}	27.89
Carbonate	$ZnCO_3 \rightleftharpoons Zn^{++} + CO_3^{--}$	2.1×10^{-11}	10.68
Hydroxide	$Zn(OH)_2 \rightleftharpoons Zn^{++} + 2OH^-$	3.3×10^{-17}	16.48
Phosphate	$Zn_3(PO_4)_2 \rightleftharpoons 3Zn^{++} + 2PO_4^{---}$	1×10^{-32}	32.0
Sulfide	$ZnS \rightleftharpoons Zn^{++} + S^{--}$	8×10^{-25}	24.1

APPENDIX II

Ionization Constants of Weak Acids

Acid	Equilibrium	K_a	pK_a
Acetic	$HC_2H_3O_2 \rightleftharpoons H^+ + C_2H_3O_2^-$	1.8×10^{-5}	4.74
Arsenic	(1) $H_3AsO_4 \rightleftharpoons H^+ + H_2AsO_4^-$	6.0×10^{-3}	2.22
	(2) $H_2AsO_4^- \rightleftharpoons H^+ + HAsO_4^{--}$	1.1×10^{-7}	6.98
	(3) $HAsO_4^{--} \rightleftharpoons H^+ + AsO_4^{---}$	3.0×10^{-12}	11.53
Arsenious	$HAsO_2 \rightleftharpoons H^+ + AsO_2^-$	6×10^{-10}	9.2
Benzoic	$HC_7H_5O_2 \rightleftharpoons H^+ + C_7H_5O_2^-$	6.6×10^{-5}	4.18
Boric	$HBO_2 \rightleftharpoons H^+ + BO_2^-$	6.0×10^{-10}	9.22
Carbonic	(1) $H_2CO_3 \rightleftharpoons H^+ + HCO_3^-$	4.6×10^{-7}	6.34
	(2) $HCO_3^- \rightleftharpoons H^+ + CO_3^{--}$	5.6×10^{-11}	10.25
Chromic	(2) $HCrO_4^- \rightleftharpoons H^+ + CrO_4^{--}$	3.2×10^{-7}	6.50
Citric	(1) $H_3C_6H_5O_7 \rightleftharpoons H^+ + H_2C_6H_5O_7^-$	8.3×10^{-4}	3.08
	(2) $H_2C_6H_5O_7^- \rightleftharpoons H^+ + HC_6H_5O_7^{--}$	2.2×10^{-5}	4.66
	(3) $HC_6H_5O_7^{--} \rightleftharpoons H^+ + C_6H_5O_7^{---}$	4.0×10^{-7}	6.40
Cyanic	$HCNO \rightleftharpoons H^+ + CNO^-$	2.2×10^{-4}	3.66
EDTA	(1) $H_4Y \rightleftharpoons H^+ + H_3Y^-$	1×10^{-2}	2.0
	(2) $H_3Y^- \rightleftharpoons H^+ + H_2Y^{--}$	2.1×10^{-3}	2.67
	(3) $H_2Y^{--} \rightleftharpoons H^+ + HY^{---}$	6.9×10^{-7}	6.16
	(4) $HY^{---} \rightleftharpoons H^+ + Y^{4-}$	5.5×10^{-11}	10.26
Formic	$HCOOH \rightleftharpoons H^+ + HCOO^-$	1.7×10^{-4}	3.77
Fumaric	(1) $H_2C_4H_2O_4 \rightleftharpoons H^+ + HC_4H_2O_4^-$	9.6×10^{-4}	3.02
	(2) $HC_4H_2O_4^- \rightleftharpoons H^+ + C_4H_2O_4^{--}$	4.1×10^{-5}	4.39
Hydrazoic	$HN_3 \rightleftharpoons H^+ + N_3^-$	1.9×10^{-5}	4.72
Hydrocyanic	$HCN \rightleftharpoons H^+ + CN^-$	4.9×10^{-10}	9.31
Hydrofluoric	$HF \rightleftharpoons H^+ + F^-$	2.4×10^{-4}	3.62

Acid	Equilibrium	K_a	pK_a
Hydrosulfuric	(1) $H_2S \rightleftarrows H^+ + HS^-$	1.0×10^{-7}	7.00
	(2) $HS^- \rightleftarrows H^+ + S^{--}$	1.2×10^{-13}	12.92
Hypobromous	$HBrO \rightleftarrows H^+ + BrO^-$	2.5×10^{-9}	8.60
Hypochlorous	$HClO \rightleftarrows H^+ + ClO^-$	3.0×10^{-8}	7.53
Hypoiodous	$HIO \rightleftarrows H^+ + IO^-$	5×10^{-13}	12.3
Malic	(1) $H_2C_4H_3O_5 \rightleftarrows H^+ + HC_4H_3O_5^-$	3.5×10^{-4}	3.46
	(2) $HC_4H_3O_5^- \rightleftarrows H^+ + C_4H_3O_5^{--}$	8.9×10^{-6}	5.05
Nitrous	$HNO_2 \rightleftarrows H^+ + NO_2^-$	5.1×10^{-4}	3.29
Oxalic	(1) $H_2C_2O_4 \rightleftarrows H^+ + HC_2O_4^-$	5.6×10^{-2}	1.25
	(2) $HC_2O_4^- \rightleftarrows H^+ + C_2O_4^{--}$	5.2×10^{-5}	4.28
Phenol	$C_6H_5OH \rightleftarrows H^+ + C_6H_5O^-$	1.3×10^{-10}	9.89
Phosphoric	(1) $H_3PO_4 \rightleftarrows H^+ + H_2PO_4^-$	7.5×10^{-3}	2.12
	(2) $H_2PO_4^- \rightleftarrows H^+ + HPO_4^{--}$	6.2×10^{-8}	7.21
	(3) $HPO_4^{--} \rightleftarrows H^+ + PO_4^{---}$	4.7×10^{-13}	12.33
Phthalic	(1) $H_2C_8H_4O_4 \rightleftarrows H^+ + HC_8H_4O_4^-$	8.0×10^{-4}	3.10
	(2) $HC_8H_4O_4^- \rightleftarrows H^+ + C_8H_4O_4^{--}$	4.0×10^{-6}	5.40
Succinic	(1) $H_2C_4H_4O_4 \rightleftarrows H^+ + HC_4H_4O_4^-$	6.5×10^{-5}	4.19
	(2) $HC_4H_4O_4^- \rightleftarrows H^+ + C_4H_4O_4^{--}$	3.3×10^{-6}	5.48
Sulfuric	(2) $HSO_4^- \rightleftarrows H^+ + SO_4^{--}$	1.0×10^{-2}	2.00
Sulfurous	(1) $H_2SO_3 \rightleftarrows H^+ + HSO_3^-$	1.3×10^{-2}	1.89
	(2) $HSO_3^- \rightleftarrows H^+ + SO_3^{--}$	6.3×10^{-8}	7.20
Tartaric	(1) $H_2C_4H_4O_6 \rightleftarrows H^+ + HC_4H_4O_6^-$	3.0×10^{-3}	2.52
	(2) $HC_4H_4O_6^- \rightleftarrows H^+ + C_4H_4O_6^{--}$	6.9×10^{-5}	4.16

Ionization Constants of Weak Bases

Base	Equilibrium	K_b	pK_b
Ammonia[a]	$NH_3 + H_2O \rightleftarrows NH_4^+ + OH^-$	1.8×10^{-5}	4.74
Aniline[b]	$C_6H_5NH_2 + H_2O \rightleftarrows C_6H_5NH_3^+ + OH^-$	4.6×10^{-10}	9.34
Ethylamine	$C_2H_5NH_2 + H_2O \rightleftarrows C_2H_5NH_3^+ + OH^-$	5.6×10^{-4}	3.25
Hydrazine[c]	$N_2H_4 + H_2O \rightleftarrows N_2H_5^+ + OH^-$	3×10^{-6}	5.5
Hydroxylamine	$NH_2OH \rightleftarrows NH_2^+ + OH^-$	6.6×10^{-9}	8.18
Methylamine	$CH_3NH_2 + H_2O \rightleftarrows CH_3NH_3^+ + OH^-$	5×10^{-4}	3.3
α-Naphthylamine	$C_{10}H_7NH_2 + H_2O \rightleftarrows C_{10}H_7NH_3^+ + OH^-$	9.9×10^{-11}	10.01
β-Naphthylamine	$C_{10}H_7NH_2 + H_2O \rightleftarrows C_{10}H_7NH_3^+ + OH^-$	2×10^{-10}	9.70
Phenylhydrazine	$C_6H_5N_2H_3 + H_2O \rightleftarrows C_6H_5N_2H_4^+ + OH^-$	1.6×10^{-9}	8.80
Pyridine	$C_5H_5N + H_2O \rightleftarrows C_5H_5NH^+ + OH^-$	2.3×10^{-9}	8.64
Quinoline	$C_9H_7N + H_2O \rightleftarrows C_9H_7NH^+ + OH^-$	1×10^{-9}	9.0
Triethylamine	$(C_2H_5)_3N + H_2O \rightleftarrows (C_2H_5)_3NH^+ + OH^-$	2.6×10^{-4}	3.58

[a] "Ammonium hydroxide" is a water solution of ammonia; the ionization equilibrium is often written $NH_4OH \rightleftarrows NH_4^+ + OH^-$.

[b] The organic amines may be considered to be ammonia from which hydrogen has been replaced by an organic radical. For example, aniline (phenylamine) can be considered to be formed from NH_3 by replacement of a hydrogen atom by the C_6H_5- group. By analogy to ammonia, the organic amine may be considered to form "anilinium hydroxide" or "phenylammonium hydroxide," which is weakly ionized to give anilinium (phenylammonium) ion and hydroxyl ion. Similarly for the other organic amines.

[c] Hydrazine may be considered to be derived from NH_3 by replacement of a hydrogen atom by the NH_2 group, forming NH_2—NH_2.

APPENDIX **IV**

Formation (Stability) Constants of Complexes

The tabular value is the *logarithm* of the formation (stability) constant. Stepwise constants are designated by $k_1, k_2, \ldots, k_n$. The cumulative constant is the product of the stepwise constants, i.e., $K_{cum} = k_1 k_2 \cdots k_n$, hence $\log K_{cum} = \log k_1 + \log k_2 + \cdots + \log k_n$. Where values of the stepwise constants are not given, the parenthetical number before $\log K_{cum}$ indicates the value of n for the overall reaction $M + nL \rightleftarrows ML_n$.

Ligand	Cation	$\log k_1$	$\log k_2$	$\log k_3$	$\log k_4$	$\log K_{cum}$
NH_3	Ag^+	3.20	3.83			7.03
	Cd^{++}	2.51	1.96	1.30	0.79	6.56
	Co^{++}	1.99	1.51	0.93	0.64	5.07
	Cu^{++}	3.99	3.34	2.73	1.97	12.03
	Hg^{++}	8.8	8.7	1.00	0.78	19.3
	Ni^{++}	2.67	2.12	1.61	1.07	7.47
	Zn^{++}	2.18	2.25	2.31	1.96	8.70
CN^-	Ag^+					(2) 19.85
	Cd^{++}	5.18	4.42	4.32	3.19	17.11
	Co^{++}					(6) 19.09
	Cu^+	$\log (k_1 k_2) = 24$		4.59	1.70	30.3
	Fe^{++}					(6) 24
	Fe^{+++}					(6) 31
	Hg^{++}	18.00	16.70	3.83	2.98	41.52
	Ni^{++}					(4) 31.0
	Pb^{++}					(4) 10
	Zn^{++}					(4) 16.76

Ligand	Cation	$\log k_1$	$\log k_2$	$\log k_3$	$\log k_4$	$\log K_{cum}$
CNS^-	Fe^{+++}	3.03				
	Hg^{++}	9.48	10.30	1.70		(4) 21.9
F^-	Al^{+++}	6.13	5.02	3.85	2.74	(6) 19.84
	Fe^{+++}	5.17	3.92	2.91		(6) 15.3
Cl^-	Ag^+	3.04	2.00	0.0	0.26	5.30
	Cd^{++}	2.00	0.60	0.10	0.30	3.00
	Cu^+					(2) 5.54
	Hg^{++}	6.74	6.48	0.85	1.00	15.07
	Pd^{++}	6.1	4.6	2.4	2.6	15.7
	Zn^{++}					(4) 0.20
Br^-	Cd^{++}	2.23	0.77	−0.17	0.10	2.93
	Hg^{++}	9.05	8.28	2.41	1.26	21.00
I^-	Cd^{++}	2.28	1.64	1.08	1.10	6.10
	Hg^{++}	12.87	10.95	3.78	2.23	29.83
$S_2O_3^{--}$	Ag^+	8.82	4.64			13.46
$EDTA^a$	Ba^{++}	7.78				
	Ca^{++}	11.00				
	Cd^{++}	16.59				
	Cu^{++}	18.79				
	Fe^{++}	14.3				
	Fe^{+++}	24.23				
	Mg^{++}	8.69				
	Mn^{++}	13.6				
	Na^+	1.66				
	Ni^{++}	18.56				
	Pb^{++}	18.3				
	Zn^{++}	16.26				

		Equilibrium[b]		
OH^-	Al^{+++}	$Al(OH)_3 + OH^- \rightleftarrows Al(OH)_4^-$		2.60
	Cr^{+++}	$Cr(OH)_3 + OH^- \rightleftarrows Cr(OH)_4^-$		−2.0
	Pb^{++}	$Pb(OH)_2 + OH^- \rightleftarrows Pb(OH)_3^-$		−1.70
	Sn^{++}	$Sn(OH)_2 + OH^- \rightleftarrows Sn(OH)_3^-$		−3.30
	Zn^{++}	$Zn(OH)_2 + 2OH^- \rightleftarrows Zn(OH)_4^{--}$		−1.0

[a] EDTA forms only 1:1 complexes with the cations.
[b] The values given for the various cations with OH^- as the ligand are for the equilibrium between the solid amphoteric hydroxide and the anionic complex.

V

Standard Electrode (Half-Cell) Potentials

The direction of the half-reaction equation and the sign of the potential conform to the IUPAC (Stockholm) conventions.

Ion-Electron Half Reaction	$E°$, volts[a]
$F_2 + 2H^+ + 2e \rightleftarrows 2HF$ (aq).	+3.06
$H_2N_2O_2 + 2H^+ + 2e \rightleftarrows N_2 + 2H_2O$	2.85
$O_3 + 2H^+ + 2e \rightleftarrows O_2 + H_2O$	2.07
$S_2O_8^{--} + 2e \rightleftarrows 2SO_4^{--}$	2.01
$Ag^{++} + e \rightleftarrows Ag^+$	1.98
$Co^{+++} + e \rightleftarrows Co^{++}$	1.842
$H_2O_2 + 2H^+ + 2e \rightleftarrows 2H_2O$	1.77
$Ce^{4+} + e \rightleftarrows Ce^{+++}$ (perchlorate solution)	1.70
$IO_4^- + 2H^+ + 2e \rightleftarrows IO_3^- + H_2O$	1.70
$MnO_4^- + 4H^+ + 3e \rightleftarrows MnO_2 + 2H_2O$	1.695
$PbO_2 + 4H^+ + SO_4^{--} + 2e \rightleftarrows PbSO_4 + 2H_2O$	1.685
$Ce^{4+} + e \rightleftarrows Ce^{+++}$ (nitrate solution)	1.61
$NaBiO_3 + 6H^+ + 2e \rightleftarrows Na^+ + Bi^{+++} + 3H_2O$, or $Bi_2O_4 + 4H^+ + 2e \rightleftarrows 2BiO^+ + 2H_2O$	1.59
$BrO_3^- + 6H^+ + 5e \rightleftarrows \frac{1}{2}Br_2 + 3H_2O$	1.52
$MnO_4^- + 8H^+ + 5e \rightleftarrows Mn^{++} + 4H_2O$	1.51
$Mn^{+++} + e \rightleftarrows Mn^{++}$	1.51

[a] Numerical values taken from W. M. Latimer, *The Oxidation States of the Elements and Their Potentials in Aqueous Solution*, 2nd ed., Tables 84, 85. Copyright 1952, by Prentice-Hall, Inc., Englewood Cliffs, N.J. Used by permission of the publisher.

Ion-Electron Half Reaction	$E°$, volts[a]
$HClO + H^+ + 2e \rightleftarrows Cl^- + H_2O$	1.49
$ClO_3^- + 6H^+ + 5e \rightleftarrows \frac{1}{2}Cl_2 + 3H_2O$	1.47
$PbO_2 + 4H^+ + 2e \rightleftarrows Pb^{++} + 2H_2O$	1.455
$HIO + H^+ + e \rightleftarrows \frac{1}{2}I_2 + H_2O$	1.45
$ClO_3^- + 6H^+ + 6e \rightleftarrows Cl^- + 3H_2O$	1.45
$Ce^{4+} + e \rightleftarrows Ce^{+++}$ (sulfate solution)	1.44
$BrO_3^- + 6H^+ + 6e \rightleftarrows Br^- + 3H_2O$	1.44
$Cl_2 + 2e \rightleftarrows 2Cl^-$	1.3595
— $Cr_2O_7^{--} + 14H^+ + 6e \rightleftarrows 2Cr^{+++} + 7H_2O$	1.33
$Ce^{4+} + e \rightleftarrows Ce^{+++}$ (chloride solution)	1.28
$Tl^{+++} + 2e \rightleftarrows Tl^+$	1.25
$MnO_2 + 4H^+ + 2e \rightleftarrows Mn^{++} + 2H_2O$	1.23
$O_2 + 4H^+ + 4e \rightleftarrows 2H_2O$	1.23
$IO_3^- + 6H^+ + 5e \rightleftarrows \frac{1}{2}I_2 + 3H_2O$	1.195
$ClO_4^- + 2H^+ + 2e \rightleftarrows ClO_3^- + H_2O$	1.19
$Br_2 \text{ (liq.)} + 2e \rightleftarrows 2Br^-$	1.065
$HNO_2 + H^+ + e \rightleftarrows NO + H_2O$	1.00
$VO_2^+ + 2H^+ + e \rightleftarrows VO^{++} + H_2O$	1.00
$HIO + H^+ + 2e \rightleftarrows I^- + H_2O$	0.99
$NO_3^- + 4H^+ + 3e \rightleftarrows NO + 2H_2O$	0.96
$NO_3^- + 3H^+ + 2e \rightleftarrows HNO_2 + H_2O$	0.94
$2Hg^{++} + 2e \rightleftarrows Hg_2^{++}$	0.920
$ClO^- + H_2O + 2e \rightleftarrows Cl^- + 2OH^-$	0.89
$NO_3^- + 10H^+ + 8e \rightleftarrows NH_4^+ + 3H_2O$	0.87
$Cu^{++} + I^- + e \rightleftarrows CuI$	0.86
$Hg^{++} + 2e \rightleftarrows Hg$	0.854
$NO_3^- + 2H^+ + e \rightleftarrows NO_2 + H_2O$	0.80
$Ag^+ + e \rightleftarrows Ag$	0.7991
$Hg_2^{++} + 2e \rightleftarrows 2Hg$	0.789
$Fe^{+++} + e \rightleftarrows Fe^{++}$	0.771
$BrO^- + H_2O + 2e \rightleftarrows Br^- + 2OH^-$	0.76
$C_6H_4O_2 + 2H^+ + 2e \rightleftarrows C_6H_4(OH)_2$ (quinhydrone)	0.700
$O_2 + 2H^+ + 2e \rightleftarrows H_2O_2$	0.682
$UO_2^+ + 4H^+ + e \rightleftarrows U^{4+} + 2H_2O$	0.62
$BrO_3^- + 3H_2O + 6e \rightleftarrows Br^- + 6OH^-$	0.61
$MnO_4^- + 2H_2O + 3e \rightleftarrows MnO_2 + 4OH^-$	0.60
$Sb_2O_5 + 6H^+ + 4e \rightleftarrows 2SbO^+ + 3H_2O$	0.581
$MnO_4^- + e \rightleftarrows MnO_4^{--}$	0.564
$H_3AsO_4 + 2H^+ + 2e \rightleftarrows HAsO_2 + 2H_2O$	0.559
$I_3^- + 2e \rightleftarrows 3I^-$	0.5355
$Cu^+ + e \rightleftarrows Cu$	0.521
$IO^- + H_2O + 2e \rightleftarrows I^- + 2OH^-$	0.49
$Fe(CN)_6^{---} + e \rightleftarrows Fe(CN)_6^{4-}$	0.36

Ion-Electron Half Reaction	$E°$, volts[a]
$Cu^{++} + 2e \rightleftarrows Cu$	0.337
$Hg_2Cl_2 + 2e \rightleftarrows 2Hg + 2Cl^-$ (tenth-normal calomel)	0.3341
$UO_2^{++} + 4H^+ + 2e \rightleftarrows U^{4+} + 2H_2O$	0.334
$VO^{++} + 2H^+ + e \rightleftarrows V^{+++} + H_2O$	0.31
$Hg_2Cl_2 + 2e \rightleftarrows 2Hg + 2Cl^-$ (normal calomel)	0.2812
$IO_3^- + 3H_2O + 6e \rightleftarrows I^- + 6OH^-$	0.26
$Hg_2Cl_2 + 2e \rightleftarrows 2Hg + 2Cl^-$ (saturated calomel)	0.2415
$AgCl + e \rightleftarrows Ag + Cl^-$	0.2222
$SO_4^{--} + 4H^+ + 2e \rightleftarrows H_2SO_3 + H_2O$	0.20
$Cu^{++} + e \rightleftarrows Cu^+$	0.153
$Sb_2O_3 + 6H^+ + 6e \rightleftarrows 2Sb + 3H_2O$	0.152
$Sn^{4+} + 2e \rightleftarrows Sn^{++}$	0.15
$S + 2H^+ + 2e \rightleftarrows H_2S$	0.14
$TiO^{++} + 2H^+ + e \rightleftarrows Ti^{+++} + H_2O$	0.10
$S_4O_6^{--} + 2e \rightleftarrows 2S_2O_3^{--}$	0.08
$AgBr + e \rightleftarrows Ag + Br^-$	0.07
$UO_2^{++} + e \rightleftarrows UO_2^+$	0.05
$2H^+ + 2e \rightleftarrows H_2$	0.000
$HgI_4^{--} + 2e \rightleftarrows Hg + 4I^-$	−0.04
$Hg_2I_2 + 2e \rightleftarrows 2Hg + 2I^-$	−0.04
$2H_2SO_3 + H^+ + 2e \rightleftarrows HS_2O_4^- + 2H_2O$	−0.08
$Pb^{++} + 2e \rightleftarrows Pb$	−0.126
$Sn^{++} + 2e \rightleftarrows Sn$	−0.136
$AgI + e \rightleftarrows Ag + I^-$	−0.15
$CuI + e \rightleftarrows Cu + I^-$	−0.19
$Ni^{++} + 2e \rightleftarrows Ni$	−0.250
$V^{+++} + e \rightleftarrows V^{++}$	−0.26
$PbCl_2 + 2e \rightleftarrows Pb + 2Cl^-$	−0.268
$Co^{++} + 2e \rightleftarrows Co$	−0.277
$PbBr_2 + 2e \rightleftarrows Pb + 2Br^-$	−0.280
$Tl^+ + e \rightleftarrows Tl$	−0.34
$PbSO_4 + 2e \rightleftarrows Pb + SO_4^{--}$	−0.36
$PbI_2 + 2e \rightleftarrows Pb + 2I^-$	−0.37
$Cd^{++} + 2e \rightleftarrows Cd$	−0.403
$Cr^{+++} + e \rightleftarrows Cr^{++}$	−0.41
$Fe^{++} + 2e \rightleftarrows Fe$	−0.440
$2CO_2 \,(gas) + 2H^+ + 2e \rightleftarrows H_2C_2O_4 \,(aq.)$	−0.49
$S + 2e \rightleftarrows S^{--}$	−0.51
$U^{4+} + e \rightleftarrows U^{+++}$	−0.61
$HgS + 2e \rightleftarrows Hg + S^{--}$	−0.70
$Ag_2S + 2e \rightleftarrows 2Ag + S^{--}$	−0.71
$Cr^{+++} + 3e \rightleftarrows Cr$	−0.74
$Zn^{++} + 2e \rightleftarrows Zn$	−0.763

Ion-Electron Half Reaction	$E°$, volts[a]
$2SO_3^{--} + 2H_2O + 2e \rightleftarrows S_2O_4^{--} + 4OH^-$	-1.12
$Mn^{++} + 2e \rightleftarrows Mn$	-1.18
$ZnO_2^{--} + 2H_2O + 2e \rightleftarrows Zn + 4OH^-$	-1.22
$Al^{+++} + 3e \rightleftarrows Al$	-1.66
$H_2 + 2e \rightleftarrows 2H^-$	-2.25
$Al(OH)_4^- + 3e \rightleftarrows Al + 4OH^-$	-2.35
$Mg^{++} + 2e \rightleftarrows Mg$	-2.37
$Na^+ + e \rightleftarrows Na$	-2.714
$Ca^{++} + 2e \rightleftarrows Ca$	-2.87
$Sr^{++} + 2e \rightleftarrows Sr$	-2.89
$Ba^{++} + 2e \rightleftarrows Ba$	-2.90
$K^+ + e \rightleftarrows K$	-2.925
$Li^+ + e \rightleftarrows Li$	-3.045

VI

Approximate Density of
Some Common Substances

Substance	Density, g/cc	Substance	Density, g/cc
Air	0.0012	Lead	11.3
Alcohol	0.90	Mercury	13.6
Aluminum	2.7	Nickel	8.9
Brass	8.4	Platinum	21.4
Copper	8.9	Porcelain	2.4
Glass	2.6	Silver	10.5
Gold	19.3	Stainless steel	8.0
Iron	7.9	Water	1.0

The Use of Logarithms

Large and Small Numbers. For many purposes there is an advantage in expressing numbers as factors of appropriate powers (exponents) of 10.

EXAMPLE 1

2,730,000	may be written 2.73×10^6
2,730	may be written 2.73×10^3
0.273	may be written 2.73×10^{-1}
0.000273	may be written 2.73×10^{-4}

This exponential form of notation is especially convenient for expressing very large or very small numbers. It is customary, for reasons set forth below, to write one figure to the left of the decimal point, whereupon the magnitude of the number is found at a glance by observing the power of 10. The exponent represents the number of times 1 must be multiplied or divided by 10, depending on whether the exponent is positive or negative. Thus,

$$10^3 = 1 \times 10 \times 10 \times 10 = 1000$$

$$10^{-4} = \frac{1}{10 \times 10 \times 10 \times 10} = 0.0001$$

The common logarithm (abbreviated " log ") of a number is the power (exponent) of 10 that will give the number.

EXAMPLE 2

log	10,000	$=$	4, because 10^4	$=$	10,000
log	100	$=$	2, because 10^2	$=$	100
log	10	$=$	1, because 10^1	$=$	10
log	1	$=$	0, because 10^0	$=$	1
log	0.1	$= -1$, because 10^{-1}	$=$		0.1
log	0.0001	$= -4$, because 10^{-4}	$=$		0.0001

It is obvious from the above that any number between 1 and 10 has a log between 0 and 1; any number between 10 and 100 has a log between 1 and 2, etc. Because most numbers are incommensurable powers of ten, a common logarithm consists of an integer, called the **characteristic**, and a decimal fraction, called the **mantissa**. The mantissa is obtained by the use of a table of logarithms, and the characteristic is obtained by inspection, by noting the position of the decimal point with respect to the first significant figure in the number.

The logs of all numbers expressed by the same digits in the same sequence, with the decimal point in different positions, have the same mantissa but different characteristics.[1]

EXAMPLE 3

$$\log 2,730,000 = 6.4362$$
$$\log \quad\;\; 2,730 = 3.4362$$
$$\log 0.273 \quad\;\; = \bar{1}.4362, \text{ or } 9.4362 - 10, \text{ or } 0.4362 - 1$$
$$\log 0.000273 = \bar{4}.4362, \text{ or } 6.4362 - 10, \text{ or } 0.4362 - 4$$

Note that the mantissa is always a positive number, whereas the characteristic may be either positive or negative, depending on the position of the decimal point in the number the log of which is taken. A negative characteristic may be designated by placing the minus sign above the characteristic; or in the "$N - 10$" form (e.g., $-1 = 9 - 10$; $-4 = 6 - 10$); or by writing the negative characteristic after the mantissa. The last method has many advantages in the use of logarithms for carrying out various mathematical operations.

Note, from Examples 1 and 3 above, that the exponent of 10 in Example 1 is identical with the characteristic of the logarithm in Example 3; this fact is one of the principal advantages of the exponential form of notation, because it expedites the use of logarithms.

EXAMPLE 4

$$22,400 = 2.24 \times 10^4 \qquad \log = 4.3502$$

$$0.000018 = 1.8 \times 10^{-5} \qquad \log = \bar{5}.2553, \text{ or } 0.2553 - 5$$

USE OF FOUR-PLACE LOG TABLE

To Find the Log of a Number. For a number of three figures, take out the tabular mantissa on the *line* of the first two figures of the number and in the *column* under its third figure. Thus, $\log 6.06 = 0.7825$. For a number of less than three figures, supply zeros to make a three-figure number and take the

---

[1] By the rules for use of significant figures, there should be carried in the mantissa of the logarithm the same number of significant figures as in the quantity the log of which is taken. By this rule, $\log 2.730 = 0.4362$; $\log 2.73 = 0.436$; $\log 2.7 = 0.44$. In illustrating, for the beginner, the use of a four-place log table and the mathematical operations performed by logs, this rule has not been applied, the emphasis being on the mechanics of using logarithms. The rule has been applied, however, in the illustrations involving negative logarithms for interconversion of $[H^+]$ and pH, etc.

mantissa as before; thus, log $4 = $ log $4.00 = 0.6021$. For a number of four figures, take the tabular value of the mantissa for the first three figures, as indicated above, and add to it the number of units designated under the fourth figure in the right-hand column of proportional parts. Thus, log $2.004 = 0.3010 + 0.0008 = 0.3018$; log $2.007 = 0.3010 + 0.0015 = 0.3025$: etc. Most of the data of analytical chemistry have four significant figures, hence a four-place log table is adequate. However, a five-place table is convenient to use for analytical calculations, since the tabular mantissa is for a four-digit number and no interpolation or proportional parts need to be used. To find the characteristic of the log: if the decimal point stands after the first significant figure of a number, counting from the left, the characteristic is 0; if after two figures, it is 1; if after three figures, it is 2, etc. If the decimal point stands before the first significant figure, the characteristic is -1; if there is one zero between the decimal point and the first significant figure, the characteristic is -2, and so on. See Examples 2 and 3 for illustration.

To Find the Number Corresponding to a Given Log. (i.e., to find the antilogarithm). If the mantissa is found exactly in the table, join the figure at the top of the *column* in which the mantissa appears to the two figures on the *line* (at the left) in which the mantissa appears. If the mantissa is not found exactly in the table, obtain the first three figures of the number by using the tabular mantissa next lower than the given one, and get the fourth figure by use of the proportional parts columns at the right. Thus, antilog $2.4362 = $? The mantissa .4362 is found in column 3 on line 27, hence the sequence of digits in the number is 273. The characteristic, 2, fixes the decimal point after the third figure; antilog $2.4362 = 273$. Antilog $1.8654 = $? The mantissa .8654 is not found exactly in the table; the next lower mantissa, .8651, corresponds to the digits 733; the difference between .8654 and .8651 is 3 units, and this difference appears in the right-hand part of the table under column 5; the sequence of digits is therefore 7335; the characteristic, 1, fixes the decimal point after the second figure; hence, antilog $1.8654 = 73.35$. Antilog $\bar{1}.2440$ (or $0.2440 - 1) = 0.1754$.

MATHEMATICAL OPERATIONS WITH LOGARITHMS

Logarithms are commonly used for the operations of multiplication, division, powers, and roots. Each of these operations is illustrated below.

Multiplication

To multiply numbers, add their logarithms, then find the antilog. The sum of the logs of numbers is the log of their product; in general terms, log $ab = $ log $a + $ log b.

EXAMPLE 5

$43.26 \times 0.1016 \times 0.05301 = ?$ (*Ans.* 0.2330)

log 43.26	$= 1.6361$		1.6361
log 0.1016	$= \bar{1}.0068$	or	$0.0068 - 1$
log 0.05301	$= \bar{2}.7244$	or	$0.7244 - 2$

log product $= \overline{\bar{1}.3673}$ or $\overline{2.3673 - 3}$ or $0.3673 - 1$

antilog $0.3673 - 1 = 0.2330$

Division

To divide numbers, subtract the log of the divisor from the log of the dividend to get the log of the quotient, then find the antilog. In general terms: log $a/b =$ log $a -$ log b.

EXAMPLE 6

$0.8436/0.2042 = ?$ (*Ans.* 4.131)

log 0.8436	$= \bar{1}.9261$	or	$0.9261 - 1$
log 0.2042	$= \bar{1}.3100$	or	$0.3100 - 1$

log quotient $= \overline{0.6161}$ or $\overline{0.6161}$

antilog $0.6161 = 4.131$

It is obvious that the operations of multiplication and division can be combined.

EXAMPLE 7

$$\frac{36.48 \times 0.1224 \times 5.584}{0.5235 \times 0.1000} = ?$$ (*Ans.* 476.3)

log 36.48	$=$	1.5621
log 0.1224	$=$	$0.0878 - 1$
log 5.584	$=$	0.7469
		$\overline{2.3968 - 1}$

log 0.5235	$= 0.7189 - 1$	
log 0.1000	$= 0.0000 - 1$	
	$\overline{0.7189 - 2}$	$0.7189 - 2$

log answer $=$ $\overline{1.6779 + 1}$ or   2.6779

antilog $2.6779 = 476.3$

Powers

To raise a number to a given power, multiply the log of the number by the power expressed, then find the antilog. In general terms: log $a^n = n(\log a)$.

EXAMPLE 8

$$32.5^3 = ?$$ (*Ans.* 3.433×10^4)
$$\log 32.5 = 1.5119 \qquad 3(1.5119) = 4.5357$$
$$\text{antilog } 4.5357 = 3.433 \times 10^4$$

EXAMPLE 9

$$0.725^4 = ?$$ (*Ans.* 0.2762)

$$\log 0.725 = \bar{1}.8603 \qquad \text{or} \qquad 0.8603 - 1$$
$$\underline{\times 4} \qquad\qquad\qquad\qquad \underline{\times 4}$$
$$\overline{1}.4412 \qquad\qquad 3.4412 - 4 \quad \text{or} \quad 0.4412 - 1$$
$$\text{antilog } 0.4412 - 1 = 0.2762$$

Roots

To take roots, divide the logarithm of the number by the root to be taken, then find the antilog. In general terms: $\log \sqrt[n]{a} = (\log a)/n$.

EXAMPLE 10

$$\sqrt[5]{924} = ?$$ (*Ans.* 3.918)

$$\log 924 = 2.9657 \qquad (2.9657)/5 = 0.5931$$

$$\text{antilog } 0.5931 = 3.918.$$

When the characteristic is negative and not evenly divisible by the root to be taken, modification of the logarithm expression is necessary, because the mantissa is a positive number.

EXAMPLE 11

$$\sqrt[5]{0.000924} = ?$$ (*Ans.* 0.2472)

$$\log 0.000924 = \bar{4}.9657 \quad \text{or} \quad 0.9657 - 4 \quad \text{or} \quad 1.9657 - 5$$

Adding 1 to and subtracting 1 from the characteristic does not change the value of the logarithm, but now the negative part of the logarithm is evenly divisible by 5, the root to be taken. Then $(1.9657 - 5)/5 = 0.3931 - 1$, and antilog $0.3931 - 1 = 0.2472$.

An alternative method of performing the above operation is to put the number into the conventional exponential form, then readjust so that the power of 10 is evenly divisible by the root:

$$\sqrt[5]{0.000924} = \sqrt[5]{9.24 \times 10^{-4}} = \sqrt[5]{92.4 \times 10^{-5}}$$

Multiplying the coefficient by 10 and dividing the exponential by 10 does not change the value of the number. Now take the fifth root of the coefficient by the use of logarithms:

$$\log 92.4 = 1.9657 \qquad (1.9657)/5 = 0.3931 \qquad \text{antilog} = 2.472$$

The fifth root of the exponential factor is taken by inspection, and is 10^{-1} (the exponent, which is a logarithm, is divided by the root). The answer is therefore 2.472×10^{-1}, or 0.2472.

Negative Logarithms

Certain defined terms used in analytical chemistry involve the negative logarithm of a number. For instance, $pH = -\log [H^+]$ $pK_a = -\log K_a$; $A = -\log T$ (in spectrophotometry, absorbance $= -\log$ transmittance). The method of handling negative logs is illustrated in the following examples.

EXAMPLE 12

$$[H^+] = 2.5 \times 10^{-5} \qquad pH = ? \qquad\qquad (Ans.\ 4.60)$$

$$pH = -\log[H^+] = -\log 2.5 \times 10^{-5}$$

$$= -(0.40 - 5) = -(-4.60) = 4.60$$

The tabular mantissa for 2.5 is 0.3979, rounded to 0.40 according to the rule for significant figures in logarithms. Note that only the decimal part of a pH (and of similar terms) consists of significant figures. Numbers to the left of the decimal point are *not* significant figures—being characteristics of logs, they express magnitude only. For example, if $[H^+] = 2.5 \times 10^{-6}$, $pH = 5.60$.

EXAMPLE 13

$$K_a = 1.8 \times 10^{-5} \qquad pK_a = ? \qquad\qquad (Ans.\ 4.74)$$

$$pK_a = -\log K_a = -\log 1.8 \times 10^{-5}$$

$$= -(0.26 - 5) = -(-4.74) = 4.74$$

EXAMPLE 14 $pH = 6.30$ $[H^+] = ?$ (Ans.\ 5.0×10^{-7})

By definition, $pH = -\log [H^+]$. A pH is therefore a negative power of 10 that will give the $[H^+]$; that is, $[H^+] = 10^{-6.30}$. This exponent (log), consisting of a whole number and a decimal fraction, is entirely negative. The decimal part cannot be treated as a mantissa for location in a log table, because the mantissas in log tables are all *positive*. By the expedient of adding 1 to the decimal part, and subtracting 1 from the integral part, of the negative log, the decimal fraction becomes positive, and its antilog can be found by the use of a log table. In the example, $-0.30 + 1 = +0.70$, and $-6 - 1 = -7$. That is, $10^{-6.30} = 10^{\overline{7}.70}$; antilog $\overline{7}.70 = 5.0 \times 10^{-7} = [H^+]$.

EXAMPLE 15

$$pK_a = 4.18 \qquad K_a = ? \qquad\qquad (Ans.\ 6.6 \times 10^{-5})$$

$$K_a = 10^{-4.18} = 10^{\overline{5}.82} \qquad \text{antilog } \overline{5}.82 = 6.6 \times 10^{-5}.$$

LOGARITHMS

Natural numbers	0	1	2	3	4	5	6	7	8	9	Proportional Parts								
											1	2	3	4	5	6	7	8	9
10	0000	0043	0086	0128	0170	0212	0253	0294	0334	0374	4	8	12	17	21	25	29	33	37
11	0414	0453	0492	0531	0569	0607	0645	0682	0719	0755	4	8	11	15	19	23	26	30	34
12	0792	0828	0864	0899	0934	0969	1004	1038	1072	1106	3	7	10	14	17	21	24	28	31
13	1139	1173	1206	1239	1271	1303	1335	1367	1399	1430	3	6	10	13	16	19	23	26	29
14	1461	1492	1523	1553	1584	1614	1644	1673	1703	1732	3	6	9	12	15	18	21	24	27
15	1761	1790	1818	1847	1875	1903	1931	1959	1987	2014	3	6	8	11	14	17	20	22	25
16	2041	2068	2095	2122	2148	2175	2201	2227	2253	2279	3	5	8	11	13	16	18	21	24
17	2304	2330	2355	2380	2405	2430	2455	2480	2504	2529	2	5	7	10	12	15	17	20	22
18	2553	2577	2601	2625	2648	2672	2695	2718	2742	2765	2	5	7	9	12	14	16	19	21
19	2788	2810	2833	2856	2878	2900	2923	2945	2967	2989	2	4	7	9	11	13	16	18	20
20	3010	3032	3054	3075	3096	3118	3139	3160	3181	3201	2	4	6	8	11	13	15	17	19
21	3222	3243	3263	3284	3304	3324	3345	3365	3385	3404	2	4	6	8	10	12	14	16	18
22	3424	3444	3464	3483	3502	3522	3541	3560	3579	3598	2	4	6	8	10	12	14	15	17
23	3617	3636	3655	3674	3692	3711	3729	3747	3766	3784	2	4	6	7	9	11	13	15	17
24	3802	3820	3838	3856	3874	3892	3909	3927	3945	3962	2	4	5	7	9	11	12	14	16
25	3979	3997	4014	4031	4048	4065	4082	4099	4116	4133	2	3	5	7	9	10	12	14	15
26	4150	4166	4183	4200	4216	4232	4249	4265	4281	4298	2	3	5	7	8	10	11	13	15
27	4314	4330	4346	4362	4378	4393	4409	4425	4440	4456	2	3	5	6	8	9	11	13	14
28	4472	4487	4502	4518	4533	4548	4564	4579	4594	4609	2	3	5	6	8	9	11	12	14
29	4624	4639	4654	4669	4683	4698	4713	4728	4742	4757	1	3	4	6	7	9	10	12	13
30	4771	4786	4800	4814	4829	4843	4857	4871	4886	4900	1	3	4	6	7	9	10	11	13
31	4914	4928	4942	4955	4969	4983	4997	5011	5024	5038	1	3	4	6	7	8	10	11	12
32	5051	5065	5079	5092	5105	5119	5132	5145	5159	5172	1	3	4	5	7	8	9	11	12
33	5185	5198	5211	5224	5237	5250	5263	5276	5289	5302	1	3	4	5	6	8	9	10	12
34	5315	5328	5340	5353	5366	5378	5391	5403	5416	5428	1	3	4	5	6	8	9	10	11
35	5441	5453	5465	5478	5490	5502	5514	5527	5539	5551	1	2	4	5	6	7	9	10	11
36	5563	5575	5587	5599	5611	5623	5635	5647	5658	5670	1	2	4	5	6	7	8	10	11
37	5682	5694	5705	5717	5729	5740	5752	5763	5775	5786	1	2	3	5	6	7	8	9	10
38	5798	5809	5821	5832	5843	5855	5866	5877	5888	5899	1	2	3	5	6	7	8	9	10
39	5911	5922	5933	5944	5955	5966	5977	5988	5999	6010	1	2	3	4	5	7	8	9	10
40	6021	6031	6042	6053	6064	6075	6085	6096	6107	6117	1	2	3	4	5	6	8	9	10
41	6128	6138	6149	6160	6170	6180	6191	6201	6212	6222	1	2	3	4	5	6	7	8	9
42	6232	6243	6253	6263	6274	6284	6294	6304	6314	6325	1	2	3	4	5	6	7	8	9
43	6335	6345	6355	6365	6375	6385	6395	6405	6415	6425	1	2	3	4	5	6	7	8	9
44	6435	6444	6454	6464	6474	6484	6493	6503	6513	6522	1	2	3	4	5	6	7	8	9
45	6532	6542	6551	6561	6571	6580	6590	6599	6609	6618	1	2	3	4	5	6	7	8	9
46	6628	6637	6646	6656	6665	6675	6684	6693	6702	6712	1	2	3	4	5	6	7	7	8
47	6721	6730	6739	6749	6758	6767	6776	6785	6794	6803	1	2	3	4	5	5	6	7	8
48	6812	6821	6830	6839	6848	6857	6866	6875	6884	6893	1	2	3	4	4	5	6	7	8
49	6902	6911	6920	6928	6937	6946	6955	6964	6972	6981	1	2	3	4	4	5	6	7	8
50	6990	6998	7007	7016	7024	7033	7042	7050	7059	7067	1	2	3	3	4	5	6	7	8
51	7076	7084	7093	7101	7110	7118	7126	7135	7143	7152	1	2	3	3	4	5	6	7	8

Natural numbers	0	1	2	3	4	5	6	7	8	9	Proportional Parts								
												1	2	3	4	5	6	7	8	9
52	7160	7168	7177	7185	7193	7202	7210	7218	7226	7235	1	2	2	3	4	5	6	7	7
53	7243	7251	7259	7267	7275	7284	7292	7300	7308	7316	1	2	2	3	4	5	6	6	7
54	7324	7332	7340	7348	7356	7364	7372	7380	7388	7396	1	2	2	3	4	5	6	6	7
55	7404	7412	7419	7427	7435	7443	7451	7459	7466	7474	1	2	2	3	4	5	5	6	7
56	7482	7490	7497	7505	7513	7520	7528	7536	7543	7551	1	2	2	3	4	5	5	6	7
57	7559	7566	7574	7582	7589	7597	7604	7612	7619	7627	1	2	2	3	4	5	5	6	7
58	7634	7642	7649	7657	7664	7672	7679	7686	7694	7701	1	1	2	3	4	4	5	6	7
59	7709	7716	7723	7731	7738	7745	7752	7760	7767	7774	1	1	2	3	4	4	5	6	7
60	7782	7789	7796	7803	7810	7818	7825	7832	7839	7846	1	1	2	3	4	4	5	6	6
61	7853	7860	7868	7875	7882	7889	7896	7903	7910	7917	1	1	2	3	4	4	5	6	6
62	7924	7931	7938	7945	7952	7959	7966	7973	7980	7987	1	1	2	3	3	4	5	6	6
63	7993	8000	8007	8014	8021	8028	8035	8041	8048	8055	1	1	2	3	3	4	5	5	6
64	8062	8069	8075	8082	8089	8096	8102	8109	8116	8122	1	1	2	3	3	4	5	5	6
65	8129	8136	8142	8149	8156	8162	8169	8176	8182	8189	1	1	2	3	3	4	5	5	6
66	8195	8202	8209	8215	8222	8228	8235	8241	8248	8254	1	1	2	3	3	4	5	5	6
67	8261	8267	8274	8280	8287	8293	8299	8306	8312	8319	1	1	2	3	3	4	5	5	6
68	8325	8331	8338	8344	8351	8357	8363	8370	8376	8382	1	1	2	3	3	4	4	5	6
69	8388	8395	8401	8407	8414	8420	8426	8432	8439	8445	1	1	2	2	3	4	4	5	6
70	8451	8457	8463	8470	8476	8482	8488	8494	8500	8506	1	1	2	2	3	4	4	5	6
71	8513	8519	8525	8531	8537	8543	8549	8555	8561	8567	1	1	2	2	3	4	4	5	5
72	8573	8579	8585	8591	8597	8603	8609	8615	8621	8627	1	1	2	2	3	4	4	5	5
73	8633	8639	8645	8651	8657	8663	8669	8675	8681	8686	1	1	2	2	3	4	4	5	5
74	8692	8698	8704	8710	8716	8722	8727	8733	8739	8745	1	1	2	2	3	4	4	5	5
75	8751	8756	8762	8768	8774	8779	8785	8791	8797	8802	1	1	2	2	3	3	4	5	5
76	8808	8814	8820	8825	8831	8837	8842	8848	8854	8859	1	1	2	2	3	3	4	5	5
77	8865	8871	8876	8882	8887	8893	8899	8904	8910	8915	1	1	2	2	3	3	4	4	5
78	8921	8927	8932	8938	8943	8949	8954	8960	8965	8971	1	1	2	2	3	3	4	4	5
79	8976	8982	8987	8993	8998	9004	9009	9015	9020	9026	1	1	2	2	3	3	4	4	5
80	9031	9036	9042	9047	9053	9058	9063	9069	9074	9079	1	1	2	2	3	3	4	4	5
81	9085	9090	9096	9101	9106	9112	9117	9122	9128	9133	1	1	2	2	3	3	4	4	5
82	9138	9143	9149	9154	9159	9165	9170	9175	9180	9186	1	1	2	2	3	3	4	4	5
83	9191	9196	9201	9206	9212	9217	9222	9227	9232	9238	1	1	2	2	3	3	4	4	5
84	9243	9248	9253	9258	9263	9269	9274	9279	9284	9289	1	1	2	2	3	3	4	4	5
85	9294	9299	9304	9309	9315	9320	9325	9330	9335	9340	1	1	2	2	3	3	4	4	5
86	9345	9350	9355	9360	9365	9370	9375	9380	9385	9390	1	1	2	2	3	3	4	4	4
87	9395	9400	9405	9410	9415	9420	9425	9430	9435	9440	0	1	1	2	2	3	3	4	4
88	9445	9450	9455	9460	9465	9469	9474	9479	9484	9489	0	1	1	2	2	3	3	4	4
89	9494	9499	9504	9509	9513	9518	9523	9528	9533	9538	0	1	1	2	2	3	3	4	4
90	9542	9547	9552	9557	9562	9566	9571	9576	9581	9586	0	1	1	2	2	3	3	4	4
91	9590	9595	9600	9605	9609	9614	9619	9624	9628	9633	0	1	1	2	2	3	3	4	4
92	9638	9643	9647	9652	9657	9661	9666	9671	9675	9680	0	1	1	2	2	3	3	4	4
93	9685	9689	9694	9699	9703	9708	9713	9717	9722	9727	0	1	1	2	2	3	3	4	4
94	9731	9736	9741	9745	9750	9754	9759	9763	9768	9773	0	1	1	2	2	3	3	4	4
95	9777	9782	9786	9791	9795	9800	9805	9809	9814	9818	0	1	1	2	2	3	3	4	4
96	9823	9827	9832	9836	9841	9845	9850	9854	9859	9863	0	1	1	2	2	3	3	4	4
97	9868	9872	9877	9881	9886	9890	9894	9899	9903	9908	0	1	1	2	2	3	3	4	4
98	9912	9917	9921	9926	9930	9934	9939	9943	9948	9952	0	1	1	2	2	3	3	4	4
99	9956	9961	9965	9969	9974	9978	9983	9987	9991	9996	0	1	1	2	2	3	3	3	4

USE OF A SLIDE RULE

A slide rule, which is a mechanical form of logarithm table, is indispensable for making rapid calculations from analytical data and for checking the more exact calculations that have been made with a log table. All calculations from data taken in the laboratory should be checked with a slide rule as a means of quickly detecting any possible errors that may have been made in reading the log table.

Although many different types of calculation can be made with a slide rule, the student in analytical chemistry uses it most frequently for the operations of multiplication and division, and less frequently for taking logs, squares, and square roots. For these operations, an inexpensive 10-in. slide rule is adequate. It is not the intention to give here detailed instructions for the use of the slide rule; the operations of multiplication and division will be illustrated by simple examples. The student should consult the instruction manual, which is furnished when the slide rule is purchased, and practice on various examples, in order to learn to operate the slide rule proficiently.

It will be noticed that the C and D scales on the slide rule are logarithmic, that is, the divisions are not equal, but become smaller as the numbers become larger. The figures on the scale are *numbers*, and the spacings of the divisions correspond to their *logarithms*. The C and D scales are used for the operations of multiplication and division. The C scale is on a movable part that slides in grooves, so that a section of the C scale can be added to or subtracted from a section of the D scale, corresponding to the operations of multiplication and division by logarithms.

Multiplication. The process will be illustrated by simple examples. To multiply 2 by 3: set the 1, at the left end of the C scale, over the 2 on the D scale. (The 1 at the left and the right end of the C scale is called the *index*.) Then move the runner until the vertical hair line is on the 3 of the C scale, and under it, on the D scale, read the answer, 6. If the use of the left index, as just described, gives a product that is off the scale to the right, the scale must be reset, using the right index of the C scale. For example, if 3 is to be multiplied by 7, and the left index of the C scale is set over 3 and the runner moved to 7 on the C scale, the latter is off the right end of the D scale. Reset the slide with the *right* index (number 1) over the 3, and move the runner to 7 on the C scale, under which the answer, 21, is read on the D scale. In general, if the product of the first digits of the numbers to be multiplied is less than 10, use the left index on the C scale; otherwise, use the right index. The slide rule does not fix the position of the decimal point, just as the mantissa of a log table does not fix the position of the decimal point. Although there are methods of fixing the decimal point from the way in which the slide has to be moved, left or right, it is probably better to fix the decimal point by inspection; that is, round off the numbers so that a quick mental calculation will give the magnitude of the answer.

Division. In using logarithms, division is accomplished by subtraction of logs; the log of the divisor is subtracted from the log of the dividend, to give the log of the quotient. On a slide rule, division is accomplished by setting the divisor on the C scale over the dividend (number to be divided) on the D scale; the quotient is then read on the D scale under the index (number 1) at the end of the C scale. For example, to divide 75 by 3, set 3 on the C scale over the 75 on the D scale, and under the left index of the C scale read the quotient, 25, on the D scale. As in the case of multiplication, the position of the decimal point can be fixed by a quick mental calculation. Example: 5.4/0.24 = ? Set 24 on the C scale over 54 on the D scale; under the left index of the C scale read 225 on the D scale. Inspection shows that the quotient is of the order of magnitude of 20 (that is, in the "tens" rather than in the "units" or in the "hundreds" place), and the answer is therefore 22.5.

Time can be saved, when several multiplications and divisions are to be made for one calculation, by making the settings in such a way that divisions and multiplications follow each other alternately.

Logs, Roots, and Powers. The scales for carrying out these operations vary somewhat from one type of slide rule to another. Refer to the instruction manual accompanying the slide rule for these operations.

VIII

Suggestions to the Teacher

Samples for Analysis

Analyzed samples for student use can be purchased, and the cost is so moderate that the local preparation of samples is seldom warranted. The author has used samples from one supplier for more than 35 years, and has found them entirely reliable. Samples purchased in lots of a few to several pounds can be transferred to small vials for dispensing to the student the appropriate amount for the analysis according to the laboratory directions given. If desired, unknowns may be purchased (at somewhat higher cost) in sample vials for individual student analysis.

Certain samples specified in the laboratory work are issued as solutions. Given below are directions for their preparation that may be found useful by teachers and/or storeroom helpers.

Vinegar, for Acidity.   Heinz Distilled White Vinegar is the best product for this use; the acidity of this vinegar has been remarkably constant over a period of many years. In providing for large classes it is economical to buy the vinegar in gallon jugs. From the original vinegar (somewhat over 5% acidity), volumetric dilutions can be used to prepare a variety of samples (e.g., 4.5% and 4.0%, or any other desired content). Air-lift bottles are convenient for dispensing the solutions. Issue of 25 to 30 ml in a dry flask provides adequate volume for rinsing of pipet and for the required 5-ml portions to be titrated.

Hydrogen Peroxide.   A stock solution of appropriate concentration is made by diluting 1.3 liters of commercial 3 % hydrogen peroxide with 2 liters of water. The solution is dispensed as an accurately measured volume, 20 to 30 ml to provide a variety of samples, from an automatic buret fitted to the stock bottle. When student results are reported as directed in the experiment, the reported weight of peroxide divided by the number of milliliters of stock solution issued gives values to a common basis for grading the reports.

Chromium Solution. Accurately weighed amounts of primary standard potassium dichromate are made to known volume, to give an exactly known concentration. Concentrations appropriate to the directions given in the experiment are in the range of about 3.5 to 6 g of potassium dichromate per liter of solution. Each student should receive 90 to 100 ml of solution, in a dry flask. Air-lift bottles are convenient for dispensing the solutions.

Bleaching Solution. Commercial bleaching solution (such as Chlorox or Oxol) contains somewhat more than 5 % sodium hypochlorite. To 2 liters of the commercial bleaching solution add 1 liter of water, and mix well. Volumes of 20 to 30 ml, accurately measured from an automatic buret attached to the stock bottle, are issued in a 250-ml volumetric flask, for dilution to volume by the student. Grading of reports is done on the same basis as with hydrogen peroxide.

Solutions for Colorimetric *p*H, Gillespie Method. Harleco Water Soluble (WS) Indicators, and Parstains Buffer Powders (Hartman-Leddon Co., Philadelphia) are very convenient. Obviously, the unknown solution issued to the student must be within the range of the indicator issued. About 12 ml of unknown (buffer) solution and 12 ml of indicator solution (the latter identified to the student) are issued in dry test tubes.

Report Forms

In the author's course, the summary results of analysis are reported on forms appropriate to the type of determination involved. Uniform report blanks, for a given determination, for all students are a great convenience, not only in handling and in filing for reference, but also in checking, when necessary, the calculations from the data reported. Although details of weighing and of titrations are not shown on the report (these details are, of course, in the student's laboratory record book), sample weights, weights of precipitates, volumes of titrants used, etc., are shown, so that the calculated results can be checked by the laboratory assistant and/or by the person grading the reports.

Some sample report forms are shown herewith; other special forms (e.g., for Manganese in Steel and Colorimetric *p*H) can be designed by the teacher. Certain forms, such as for Gravimetric Analysis, Comparison and Standardization of Solutions, and Titrimetric Analysis, are required repeatedly. Either mimeographed or printed forms may be provided; the latter are neater, and in the quantities required for large classes they are moderate in cost.

QUANTITATIVE ANALYSIS REPORT. GRAVIMETRIC ANALYSIS

Name _____ Date _____ Chem. _____

Lab. Instr. _____ Lab. Sec. _____ Desk _____

Grav. anal. of _____ for (a) _____ content,

weighed as (b) _____ Grav. factor: _____

	I	II	III	Average
g. sample taken:. . . .	_____	_____	_____	
g. (b) obtained:	_____	_____	_____	
% (a) in sample: . . .	_____	_____	_____	_____
Deviation. %	_____	_____	_____	_____

Remarks:

D-90

Form 2

QUANTITATIVE ANALYSIS REPORT. TITRIMETRIC ANALYSIS

Name _____ Date _____ Chem. _____

Lab. Instr. _____ Lab. Sec. _____ Desk _____

Analysis of (a) _____ for (c) _____ content.

Method _____ G.m.e. wt. of (c): _____

Standard solution used (b) _____ Normality _____

If a single sample of (a) was aliquoted:

Wt. of sample: _____ g. Diluted to _____ ml.

	I	II	III	Average
g. sample or ml. aliquot of (a) taken: . .	_____	_____	_____	
ml. std. soln. (b) used:	_____	_____	_____	
% (or g.) of (c): . . .	_____	_____	_____	_____
Deviation. %	_____	_____	_____	_____

Remarks:

D-94

Form 5

Grading of Reports

For making an evaluation of the reliability of the student's analysis, a grading scale is set up on the basis of the certified analysis or the known content of the desired constituent, and on the performance record of students over a period of years in making the particular analysis. The grading scale starts at 10 points for an analysis in agreement with the true content, plus or minus a small allowable error, and goes down (9, 8, 7, etc.) as the student result is farther away from the true value, to a minimum score of 4 points; the latter merely recognizes that the laboratory work has been performed, but far from satisfactorily. Triplicate samples are analyzed, and each individual result is graded on the scale of 10 points. In this way, both the precision and the accuracy of the student results are expressed by a numerical score on the basis of 30 points possible. A score of 18 points or less is unsatisfactory, and the analysis should be repeated. (Other teachers, of course, may have different criteria for an unsatisfactory student analysis.) Reports of comparison and of standardization of titrimetric solutions are graded on the basis of the precision attained (since the "true" value is not known), for a total of 10 points on a triplicate comparison or a triplicate standardization. The accumulated point score, compared with the total possible point score, for the entire laboratory work of the course, gives a reliable measure of the student's performance.

INDEX

TABLE OF

FORMULA WEIGHTS

Based on 1961 Atomic Weights and Rounded to Two Decimal Places

$AgBr$	187.78	$CaSO_4$	136.14	$HC_7H_5O_2$ (benzoic)	122.12
$AgCNS$	165.95	$(C_2H_5)_3N$	101.19	$H_2C_2O_4 \cdot 2H_2O$ (oxalic)	126.07
$AgCl$	143.32	$C_6H_5NH_3Cl$	129.59	$H_2C_4H_4O_6$ (tartaric)	150.09
Ag_2CrO_4	331.74	$C_{12}H_{22}O_{11}$	342.30	$H_2C_8H_4O_4$ (phthalic)	166.14
AgI	234.77	$Ce(IO_3)_3$	664.82	HCl	36.46
$AgIO_3$	282.77	CeO_2	172.12	$HClO_4$	100.46
$AgNO_3$	169.88	$Ce(SO_4)_2$	332.25	HF	20.01
Ag_3PO_4	418.58	$(NH_4)_2Ce(NO_3)_6$	548.22	HNO_2	47.01
Ag_2S	247.80	$(NH_4)_2Ce(SO_4)_3 \cdot 2H_2O$	500.41	HNO_3	63.02
$Al(C_9H_6ON)_3$	459.45	CO	28.01	HSO_3NH_2 (sulfamic)	97.09
Al_2O_3	101.96	CO_2	44.01	H_2O_2	34.02
$Al(OH)_3$	78.00	$CO(NH_2)_2$ (urea)	60.05	H_3PO_4	97.99
$Al_2(SO_4)_3$	342.15	Co_3O_4	240.80	H_2S	34.08
As_2O_3	197.84	CrO_3	99.99	H_2SO_3	82.08
As_2O_5	229.84	Cr_2O_3	151.99	H_2SO_4	98.08
As_2S_3	246.03	$Cr(OH)_3$	103.01	H_2SiF_6	144.09
$BaBr_2$	197.16	$Cu(NO_3)_2$	187.54	HVO_3	99.95
$Ba(CNS)_2$	253.49	CuO	79.54	HgO	216.59
$BaCO_3$	197.35	Cu_2O	143.08	HgS	232.65
$BaCl_2$	208.24	$CuSO_4 \cdot 5H_2O$	249.68	Hg_2Br_2	561.00
$Ba(ClO_4)_2$	336.24	CuS	95.60	Hg_2Cl_2	472.08
$BaCrO_4$	253.34	Cu_2S	159.14	Hg_2I_2	654.99
BaF_2	175.34	EDTA, disodium $\cdot 2H_2O$	372.24	$KB(C_6H_5)_4$	358.34
BaO	153.34	$FeCO_3$	115.86	KBF_4	125.82
BaO_2	169.34	$Fe(CrO_2)_2$	223.84	KBr	119.01
$Ba(OH)_2$	171.36	FeO	71.85	$KBrO_3$	167.01
$Ba_3(PO_4)_2$	601.97	Fe_2O_3	159.69	KCN	65.12
$BaSO_4$	233.40	Fe_3O_4	231.54	$KCNS$	97.18
Bi_2S_3	514.16	$Fe(OH)_2$	89.87	K_2CO_3	138.22
BF_3	67.81	$Fe(OH)_3$	106.87	KCl	74.56
B_2O_3	69.62	FeS	87.91	$KClO_3$	122.55
$Ca_3(AsO_4)_2$	398.07	FeS_2	119.97	$KClO_4$	138.55
$CaBr_2$	199.90	$FeSO_4 \cdot 7H_2O$	278.02	K_2CrO_4	194.20
$CaCO_3$	100.09	$FeSO_4 \cdot (NH_4)_2SO_4 \cdot 6H_2O$	392.14	$K_2Cr_2O_7$	294.20
CaC_2O_4	128.10	$Fe_2(SO_4)_3$	399.89	$K_3Fe(CN)_6$	329.26
CaF_2	78.08	$Fe_2(SO_4)_3 \cdot (NH_4)_2SO_4$		$K_4Fe(CN)_6$	368.36
$Ca(IO_3)_2$	389.89	$24H_2O$	964.38	$KHCO_3$	100.12
CaO	56.08	HBO_2	43.82	KHC_2O_4	128.13
$Ca(OH)_2$	74.10	H_3BO_3	61.83	$KHC_2O_4 \cdot H_2C_2O_4 \cdot 2H_2O$	254.20
$Ca(NO_3)_2$	164.10	HBr	80.92	$KHC_4H_4O_6$ (tartrate)	188.19
$Ca_3(PO_4)_2$	310.19	$HCHO_2$ (formic)	46.03	$KHC_8H_4O_4$ (phthalate)	204.23
$CaSO_3$	120.14	$HC_2H_3O_2$ (acetic)	60.05	$KH(IO_3)_2$	389.92